THE MOTOR VEHICLE

THE
MOTOR VEHICLE

*A Text-book for Students,
Draughtsmen and Owner-drivers*

K. NEWTON

M.C., B.SC., A.C.G.I., A.M.INST.C.E., M.I.MECH.E.
*Sometime Assistant Professor, Mechanical and Electrical
Engineering Department, The Royal Military College of Science*

W. STEEDS

O.B.E., B.SC., A.C.G.I., M.I.MECH.E., MEMBER A.S.M.E.
*Sometime Professor of Mechanical Engineering,
The Royal Military College of Science*

LONDON   ILIFFE BOOKS LTD

Published for
AUTOMOBILE ENGINEER
by Iliffe Books Ltd., Dorset House,
*Stamford Street, London, S.E.*1

First Published 1929
Eighth Edition © *K. Newton and W. Steeds*, 1966

Printed and bound in England by
The Chapel River Press Ltd
Andover, Hants

Contents

CONTENTS

Preface to the Eighth Edition

The necessity for the preparation of an eighth edition of THE MOTOR VEHICLE confirms the belief of authors and publishers that readers have found the book of interest and help in the study of this important and rapidly expanding branch of industry, and it is hoped that this may continue.

The primary purpose of the authors remains the same, namely to present the fundamentals of engineering theory as applied to the automobile in a manner of service to the student and younger practitioner, and to lay a reliable foundation for more advanced study of the great wealth of technical literature now available.

Selection of appropriate illustrative examples is not an easy task, and in addition to the description of important current developments, the retention of certain earlier matter has seemed to be justified on historic and theoretical grounds. In this way the steady stream of technical progress may be studied against the ever-present background of commercial and financial considerations.

New matter includes the latest developments in carburettors and diesel injection pumps, and in engine construction, including the Wankel engine. Progress in petrol injection and turbines is reviewed, and new work on differential supercharging of the diesel engine. In engine cooling the development of wax element thermostats is mentioned.

In the transmission field recent refinements in clutches, gear boxes and automatic transmissions are described. Advances in steering and braking systems are covered. In the coverage of suspension systems considerable revision has been made necessary by the increasing use of independent suspension, and descriptions of the latest types, including the Rover 2000 front suspension, are given. Developments in air and liquid suspension systems are also mentioned and the B.M.C. Hydrolastic suspension is described.

Again it is desired to express the indebtedness of the authors to the Engineering Institutions and manufacturing firms for valuable information which is acknowledged in the text, and to the Editorial staff and Proprietors of *Automobile Engineer*, from which much authoritative matter has been culled.

Great care has been taken in detailed revision and correction of the text, and the authors would be grateful for intimation of any errors which may come to the notice of readers.

K. N.
W. S.

July 1965

Abbreviations Used

b.d.c.	bottom dead centre	i.m.e.p.	indicated mean effective pressure
b.h.p.	brake horse power	i.h.p.	indicated horse power
b.m.e.p.	brake mean effective pressure	l	litre
		lb	pound
B.Th.U.	British Thermal Unit	lb/b.h.p.-hr	pounds per brake horse power hour
°C	degree Centigrade	lb/cu. ft	pounds per cubic foot
c.c.	cubic centimetre		
C.H.U.	Centigrade heat unit (*or* pound calory)	lb/sq. in.	pounds per square inch
		l/min	litres per minute
C.H.U/cu. ft.	Centigrade heat units per cubic foot	m.e.p.	mean effective pressure
		mm	millimetre
C.H.U/lb	Centigrade heat units per pound	mm/sec	millimetres per second
		m.p.g.	miles per gallon
c.i.	compression ignition	pints/b.h.p.-hr	pints per brake horse power hour
cm	centimetre		
cu. in.	cubic inch	r.p.m.	revolutions per minute
cu. ft	cubic foot		
cu. mm	cubic millimetre	sec	second
ft	foot *or* feet	sq. mm	square millimetre
ft/min	feet per minute		
ft/sec	feet per second	t.d.c.	top dead centre
h.p.	horse power		

PART 1 : FUNDAMENTALS

CHAPTER 1

Engineering Drawings

The engineering viewpoint. Orthogonal projection. Relationship of views on paper. Sectional views.

A KNOWLEDGE of the principles of mechanical drawing, sufficient to enable simple engineering drawings to be understood, is of great use to all who have to deal with things mechanical. It is not practicable, perhaps not possible, to describe by means of a written description alone a piece of mechanism as intricate as the motor car. Drawings enable this to be done and, since they are used extensively in all engineering literature, it is thought advisable to begin this book with an outline of the principles of mechanical drawing and, by giving a number of examples, accompanied by photographs and descriptions of the objects they represent, to assist the reader to understand those that will be met later in the book.

There are several ways of depicting objects by means of drawings. One is by " perspective " views such as are seen in Figs. 1-15 and 1-16. These views are similar to photographic views and show the object as it appears to an observer, as far as this is possible on a flat paper. They can be made very lifelike by suitable shading, but are comparatively difficult to draw, and their field of usefulness, when engineering things are concerned, is somewhat limited. The best method of depicting engineering objects is by means of a number of " orthogonal projections " or " engineering views." We will therefore proceed to consider how such views are obtained.

1.1 " Engineering " View of An Object

An engineering view of an object along any " line of sight," that is, from any particular point of view, is obtained as follows: The plane paper on which the view is to be drawn is placed behind the object perpendicular to the line of sight. All the points in the outline of the object are then " projected " on to the paper by drawing lines from them perpendicular to the paper. If the points where these perpendiculars strike the paper are marked, the resulting figure is the orthogonal projection of the object along the line of sight chosen. The process is not confined to the outline of an object but is extended to any features on its face which it is desirable to show. The lines drawn from the points in the object perpendicular to the paper are known as " projection lines " and obviously are parallel lines. Now, since the rays of light that reach the eye from an object placed at a great distance are very nearly parallel, an engineering view of an object can be obtained by placing the object at a great distance. With small objects it

1

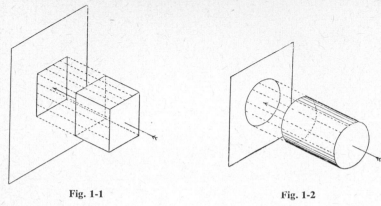

Fig. 1-1   Fig. 1-2

will be found sufficient to place them about six feet away and to close one eye.

1.2   Examples of Orthogonal Projection

The method of obtaining the orthogonal projection of a cube along a line of sight perpendicular to one of its faces is shown in Fig. 1-1, which is a perspective view of the operation.   The view obtained on the paper is in reality a square, but the perspective distorts it into a rhombus in the figure.   It should be noticed that the sides of the cube which are parallel to the line of sight appear in the projection simply as lines.

Fig. 1-2 shows the projection of a cylinder along a line of sight parallel to its axis.   The view obtained is a circle, but here again the perspective distorts it—into an ellipse.   When the line of sight is perpendicular to the axis of the cylinder the view obtained is a rectangle as shown in Fig. 1-3 where, owing to the perspective, it appears as a parallelogram.   The diameter of the circle representing the end view of the cylinder is equal to the breadth of the rectangle representing the side view of the cylinder.   The length of the rectangle is equal to the length of the cylinder.   The rectangle of Fig. 1-3 gives no indication that it is a view on the curved surface of a cylinder.   This may be done by shading the view.   Shading, however, is not much used in engineering drawings.

A little consideration will show that the orthogonal projection of a sphere along any line of sight is a circle.   The projection of a cone along a line of sight perpendicular to its axis is a triangle.   Consider now the projections of a circular disc.   When the line of sight is perpendicular to the disc the view is obviously a circle.   When it is parallel to the surface of the disc the view is simply a straight line.   In any intermediate position, when the line of sight is inclined to the disc, the view is an ellipse.   If any difficulty is experienced in realizing this the reader should cut out a disc of cardboard and test it for himself.   Having done this he should have no difficulty

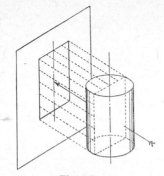

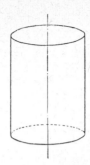

Fig. 1-3   Fig. 1-4

in realizing that the projection of a cylinder along a line of sight inclined to its axis is as shown in Fig. 1-4; the circular ends of the cylinder being seen as ellipses. Next consider a cylinder having one end cut at an angle to the axis. The actual shape of the slanting end is an ellipse. When such a cylinder is looked at along a line of sight as shown in Fig. 1-5, the elliptical end will appear less elliptical and may actually appear circular. Again if difficulty is experienced in realizing this it should be tested experimentally by cutting out an ellipse in cardboard. It will be found that from one particular point of view the ellipse will appear circular. When the line of sight is parallel to the slanting end the view will be as in Fig. 1-6.

A single perspective view often conveys a good idea of the general shape of an object, but a *single* engineering view fails in this respect. A rectangle, for example, might be a view of a cylinder, or of a square or triangular prism, or of a rectangular piece of tin-plate. It is therefore necessary in most cases to give more than one engineering view of an object. With simple objects two views may be sufficient, with most three are necessary, but in the case of

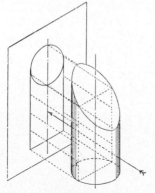

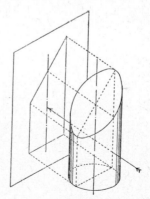

Fig. 1-5   Fig. 1-6

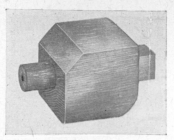

Fig. 1-7

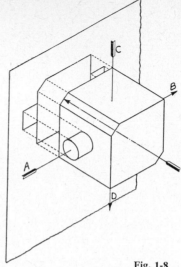

Fig. 1-8

complicated objects a number of views is required. Each one of these will be an engineering view obtained by projection as previously described.

The lines of sight along which the three views necessary with most objects are taken, are three mutually perpendicular lines. This may be illustrated by considering a simple house. A view of a house from the front, another from one end, and a third looking down on it from above, will give sufficient indication of the general shape of the house. These views are called the " front " view or " front elevation," the " end " or " side " view, and the " plan " respectively and, provided they were labelled so that the lines of sight along which they were taken could be recognized, they might be placed anywhere on the drawing paper. The relative positions of the views on the paper can, however, be used to indicate the lines of sight along which the views have been taken. The relative position of the views on the paper thus becomes a matter of importance, and there are three systems or conventions determining those positions. These systems will now be explained.

1.3   Relationship of the Views on the Paper

To explain how the various views come to occupy certain definite positions on the paper we will consider the object shown in the photograph Fig. 1-7. This object is a cubical block having two diagonally opposite corners bevelled off and having a cylindrical projection on one end and a square projection on the opposite end.

There is no difficulty in placing one view of this object on the paper; we have merely to place the paper behind the object perpendicular to the line of sight and to project the view as shown in Fig. 1-8. It will be observed that one face of the object has been placed parallel to the paper in obtaining this view, or in other words the line of sight chosen is perpendicular to one of the faces of the object. We now want to get a view of the object along a line of sight at right angles to the previous one. Such a line of sight

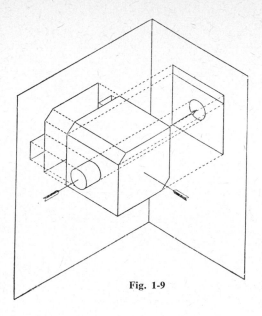

Fig. 1-9

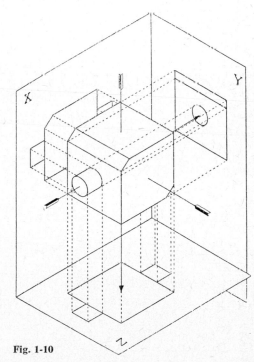

Fig. 1-10

is shown at AB, and in order to get the view along this line of sight on to the paper the latter must be placed behind the object perpendicular to the line of sight. To do this imagine the paper bent round at right angles as indicated in Fig. 1-9. The view can then be projected as seen. The third line of sight, perpendicular to the other two, is shown at CD, and in order to get this view on to the paper the latter must be bent round underneath the object (Fig. 1-10) until it is perpendicular to the line of sight. The view can then be projected as shown.

Now when the paper is bent in this manner the three portions on which the views have been projected occupy the same positions as the two walls and the floor of the corner of a square room. This should be clear from Fig. 1-10, where X is the " front " wall, Y the " side " wall and Z the floor. When the paper is folded back into the flat again it should be clear that the three views will occupy the positions shown in Fig. 1-11, where X is the front view, Y the side or end view and Z the " plan." The line yy is the fold by which the paper was got into position for the projection of the end view. This line, however, can also be considered as the view, on the wall X, of the wall Y as seen when looking along the first line of sight in obtaining the front view. Similarly the line zh represents the fold by which the plan view was obtained. This line also can be considered as the view, on the wall X, of the floor Z. Again the line jz represents the view, on the wall Y, of the floor Z and it should be clear that zh and jz form a continuous straight line so that zz can be taken as representing the floor line while yy represents the side wall Y.

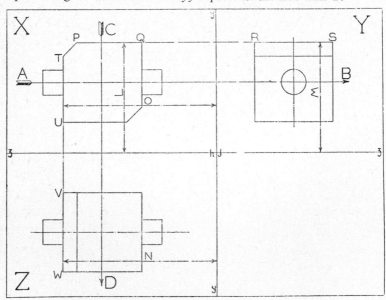

Fig. 1-11

Consider now the top surface of the object. This is represented in the front view by the line PQ and in the end view by the line RS. The distance between this surface and the floor is the distance L in the front view and the distance M in the end view.

Since the surface can only be at one distance from the floor the distances L and M must be equal, and therefore if PQ is prolonged as shown, it will coincide with RS. Similarly the end surface of the object is shown in the front view by the line TU and in the plan by the line VW. The distance of this surface from the side wall Y is given in the front view by the distance O and in the plan by the distance N and again, since the surface can be at one distance only from the side wall, those distances must be equal, and if TU is prolonged as shown it will coincide with VW. The lines PQ and RS are in projection and, in fact, the whole of the two views of which the lines PQ and RS are part are in projection. Similarly the lines TU and VW and the whole of the views to which they belong are also in projection. If the line of sight AB, along which the end view was obtained, is drawn in the front view as shown, then it should be clear that the projection lines connecting corresponding points in the front and end views are all parallel to that line of sight. Similarly the projection lines connecting the front view with the plan are parallel to the line of sight CD seen in the front view and along which the plan view was obtained.

When the front view, the end view and the plan are obtained in the manner described above, the relationship of the views is said to be according to the English convention or system. In that system, therefore, the view that appears *underneath* the front view is a view obtained by looking down on the *top* of the object, and the view that appears on the *right* hand of the front view is a view obtained by looking on the *left* hand end of the object. If a view appeared on the left hand of the front view, then that view would be a view obtained by looking on the right hand end of the object. These two end views would be identical as far as the outline of the object was concerned, but they would differ in the details seen. Thus, for the object considered above, one end view would show the cylindrical projection and the other end view would show the square projection.

The second method of relating the views is generally known as the " American " method, and is derived thus. The front view is obtained by placing the paper in *front* of the object, perpendicular to the line of sight. Then, imagining the paper to be transparent, the view is drawn on the side of the paper remote from the object. The view on the left hand end of the object is next obtained by bending the paper round in *front* of that end until it is perpendicular to the line of sight. The view is again drawn on the side of the paper remote from the object and again the paper has to be imagined to be transparent. Similarly with the plan, the paper is bent round over the top of the object and the view drawn on the side of the paper remote from the object.

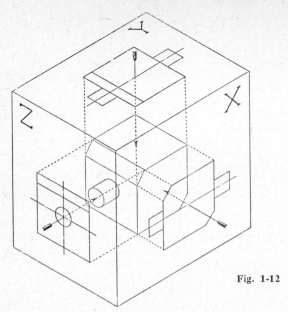

Fig. 1-12

The process is shown in perspective in Fig. 1-12. In this system the object is always behind the paper and one looks "through" the view on the paper to the object behind. This is the opposite to the procedure in the first system where the paper was always behind the object and one looked through the object on to the view.

When the paper is bent back into the flat the three views occupy the positions shown in Fig. 1-13. The view on the *left* hand end of the object here appears on the *left* of the front elevation, and the plan or view from *above* appears *above* the front elevation. Each pair of views, that is, the front elevation and end view, and the front elevation and plan, is in projection just as in the first system.

The third method of relating the views is a mixture of the two previous systems. Thus the English system is followed with regard to the plan, which therefore appears underneath the front elevation, but the American system is followed with regard to the end views.

Present day practice leans towards the use of the third system, which is sometimes known as the "mixed" system, but after a little practice no difficulty should be experienced in following drawings made on any one of the systems. In this book views are generally placed according to the mixed system.

1.4 Sectional Views

We have, so far, considered views on the outside of objects, but very often the internal shape has to be shown. This may be done

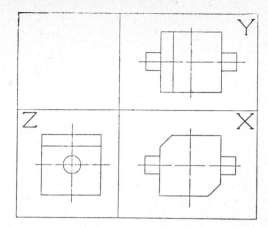

Fig. 1-13

in two ways: by means of dotted lines or by means of " sectional " views. Dotted lines are also used to show the shape of a part of an object when it is hidden by another part. Dotted lines are difficult to follow, however, and except with comparatively simple things their use leads to confusion.

A sectional view is obtained by cutting an object into two pieces and looking on the cut surface of either piece. It is sometimes necessary to cut an object in this way in order to find out its internal shape, but usually the process is an imaginary one carried out only in the mind of the draughtsman.

In the consideration of the components of a motor car the internal parts are, generally speaking, the more interesting ones, and the sectional view is of great use. A large number of examples will therefore be considered in order that the reader may become familiar with sectional views—

(1) Fig. 1-14 shows a " gudgeon " pin, a simple hollow cylindrical pin that acts as a pivot; *a* is a perspective sketch of a sectioned pin, and the corresponding engineering sectional view is seen at *b*; *c* is an ordinary side view in which the inside shape is shown in dotted lines. The pin is thickened at the middle to stiffen it. Observe that the straight line X represents the surface X seen at the back. Similarly the lines Y Y represent the ledges, Y Y, where the thickened part of the pin ends. The metal actually cut through is indicated by cross-hatching it.

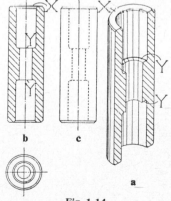

Fig. 1-14

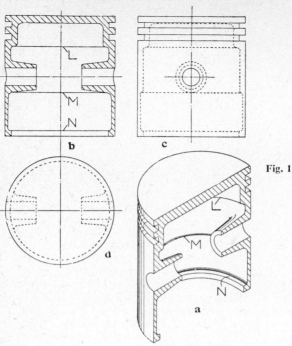

b

c

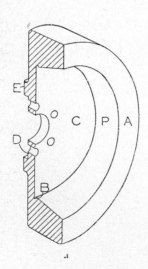

d

a

Fig. 1-15

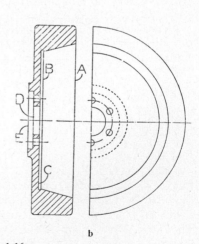

.a

b

Fig. 1-16

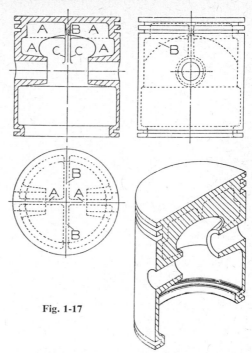

Fig. 1-17

(2) Fig. 1-15 shows a simple piston; *a* is a perspective view of the piston in section; *b* the corresponding engineering sectional view; *c* an outside end view and *d* a plan. Observe the lines L, M and N which represent the ledges, L, M and N, where the thickness of the wall or " skirt " of the piston changes.

(3) Fig. 1-16 shows a flywheel in section; *a* in perspective and *b* as an engineering view. The flywheel is formed into a hollow cone at P to form part of a clutch. Observe the lines A, B, C, D and E which represent the corresponding surfaces seen at the back. The end view of this flywheel is simply a number of concentric circles, since the whole thing is circular. When this is so an end view is not usually given but is left to the imagination.

(4) Fig. 1-17 shows another piston. The ceiling or " crown " of the piston appears in the perspective view to be very thick, actually it is not so, the apparent thickness being due to the fact that a third " rib " or " web " of metal runs across the middle of the piston to stiffen the crown, and this thin web has been cut right down the middle in making the section. In the engineering view the true thickness of the crown is emphasized by leaving the web AAAA blank. This is a recognized convention adopted by draughtsmen. There is a second web B (running at right angles to the web A) which is cut by the section. This web is cross-hatched, however, as no false impression is thereby given. The lines CC represent the

11

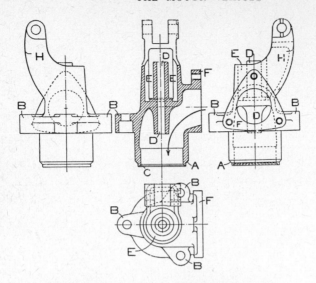

Fig. 1-18

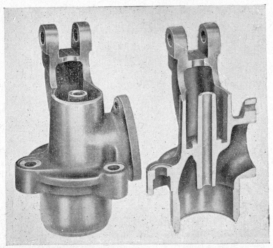

sides of this web where they run down into the skirt of the piston.

(5) Fig. 1-18 shows the inlet valve cage of a 150 h.p. Ricardo Tank engine, which had an overhead inlet valve and a side exhaust valve. The lower part of the cage is cylindrical and fits in a hole in the cylinder casting, a gas-tight joint being obtained by means of the conical seating A. The cage is held in place by studs and nuts which pass through three lugs integral with it; these lugs are seen at B and two can be seen in the photograph of the complete cage. There is a second conical seating C for the valve to seat upon. The stem of the valve is guided in the long guide D, and the coil springs

12

that close the valve are housed in the recess E. The cage is connected by the flange F with the induction pipe and the explosive mixture is drawn in, when the valve is depressed off its seat, through the space thus ⌠ shaped. It will be seen that a certain amount of obstruction to the flow of the gases is caused by the valve guide which projects into the gas passage. At the back of the cage is an arm H provided with a fulcrum pin upon which a rocker lever pivots.

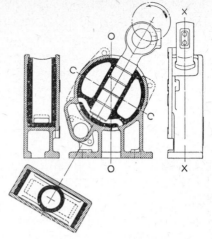

(6) Fig. 1-19 shows a plunger type oil pump used in the Ricardo engine. Its action is similar to that of the oscillating cylinder engines used on toys. The plunger is free to slide up and down in the cylinder which is formed in the member sectioned in black, and that motion is imparted to it by a crank pin which works in the hole in the end of the plunger. The cylinder is free to oscillate inside the casing, being cylindrical and a free fit therein. Suitable suction and delivery ports are provided in the casing as shown.

In the position shown in the drawing both ports are closed, but if the crank pin is turned in the direction of the arrow the cylinder will be oscillated clockwise, and the right-hand port will be put into

Fig. 1-19

communication with the cylinder. Since the plunger is moving up the cylinder oil will be drawn in through the port. As the plunger approaches the top of its stroke the cylinder is oscillated back to the central position and the suction port is closed. Continued motion of the crank pin causes the cylinder to oscillate further, thus opening the delivery port, and since the plunger is now moving downwards, oil is forced out of the cylinder. As the plunger approaches the

13

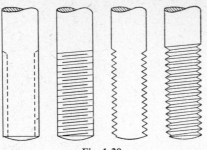

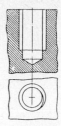

Fig. 1-20   Fig. 1-21

bottom end of its stroke the cylinder is oscillated back to the central
position and the delivery port is closed.   The cycle is then repeated,
if the crank pin continues to revolve.   The grooves in the plunger
serve to prevent the escape of oil.   Note that the plunger is shown
in outside view because nothing more would be shown if it were
sectioned.   This is frequently the case, and such things as shafts,
bolts, spindles, wheel spokes, etc., are, as a rule, shown in outside
view and not in section, although they would actually be cut through
if a section were made.

In the photograph two of the studs, by means of which the pump
is secured to the crank case of the engine, can be seen.   A stud is a
cylindrical piece of steel with a screw thread at each end.   One
end is screwed into one of two pieces that have to be secured
together, the stud projects through a hole in a flange of the other
piece which is then held in place by a nut which is screwed on the
other end of the stud.   Studs are meant to become a fixture in the
part into which they are screwed; if the two pieces are required to be
separated the nut is removed from the outer end of the stud and one
piece is lifted off.   Studs are used in preference to screws when
bolts and nuts cannot be used and when the parts may have to be
separated frequently.   If a screw were used the constant screwing up
and unscrewing would soon wear out the thread in the hole, and
this cannot be easily rectified.   When a stud is used it is the thread
on its end that will be worn, and this is easily remedied by fitting a
new stud.   Thus it is important that studs should remain fixed in
the part into which they are screwed, when their nuts are unscrewed;
if they do not steps should be
taken to secure them.   This is
especially important when studs are
screwed into soft metals such
as aluminium.

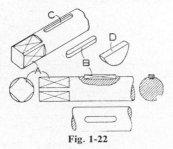

Fig. 1-22

1.5   Draughtsman's Conventions

Conventional methods of depicting certain things such as screw
threads, gear teeth, etc., are often

14

Fig. 1-23   Fig. 1-24

employed by draughtsmen and these, unless mentioned, may be puzzling when met with for the first time.

Four methods of showing a Vee screw thread on the end of a rod are shown in Fig. 1-20. Of these only the second and fourth indicate the " hand " of the thread, a right-handed thread being shown. These methods are also used for screwed holes, the lines being dotted unless the part is in section. In the latter case the method shown in Fig. 1-21 may be used.

Diagonal lines as shown at A in Fig. 1-22 are frequently used to indicate flats formed on cylindrical pieces. In the figure they are used to show two of the four flat faces of the squared end of a shaft, such as might be used when a handle had to be fixed to the shaft rotationally. A common method of securing a wheel is by a " key," which is a piece of metal as indicated at B. This is sunk for about half its depth in a recess C formed in the shaft, and then projects into a groove or keyway formed inside the boss of the pulley. An alternative form of key is shown at D; this is a " Woodruff " key. Keys are sometimes indicated by diagonal lines as shown. Another method of securing two pieces together rotationally is by means of a " splined shaft." This is in effect a shaft on which a number of keys are formed integrally, but the keys are then called " splines." The appearance of a splined shaft is shown in Fig. 1-23. They are sometimes indicated by diagonal lines also. (The curves at the ends of the recesses, as at A, are due to the use of a circular cutter in the manufacture.)

Diagonal lines are also used to indicate the teeth of gear wheels as shown in Fig. 1-24, and the teeth of " positive clutches " (see Section 21.1). The teeth of gear wheels are frequently not drawn fully but are indicated by dotted circles (Fig. 22-1).

CHAPTER 2

Bearings and Gearing

Various types of bearings and their uses. Care of ball bearings. Types and ratios of toothed gearing.

WHEN a shaft has to revolve it must be supported in " bearings " that will allow of the desired rotation. The simplest bearing is just a cylindrical hole formed in a piece of material and in which the shaft is a free fit. The hole is usually lined with a brass or bronze lining or " bush," which not only reduces the friction in the bearing but also enables an easy replacement to be made when wear occurs. Bushes are usually a tight fit in the hole in which they fit. To reduce the friction to the lowest amount, ball and roller bearings, in which " rolling " friction replaces the " sliding " friction that occurs in " plain " bearings, are used.

Considering the shaft shown in Fig. 2-1, it will be seen that two bearings are provided. This is almost universally done because otherwise the single bearing would have to be of an inordinate length. It will also be observed that the bearings shown are capable of withstanding only loads that are perpendicular to the axis of the shaft. Such loads are called " radial " loads, and the bearings that carry them are called " radial " or " journal " bearings. That part of a shaft that actually lies within a bearing is called a journal. To prevent the shaft from moving in the axial direction shoulders or collars may be formed on it or secured to it, as shown in Fig. 2-2, which shows the loose collar secured by a grub screw P. If both collars are made integral with the shaft then obviously in order that the shaft may be put into position the bearings must be split or made in halves, the top half or " cap " being put on and bolted in place after the shaft has been put in. The collars or shoulders withstand any end thrusts, and bearings that do this are termed " thrust " bearings.

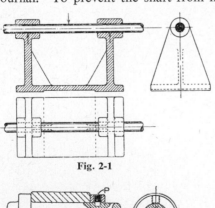

Fig. 2-1

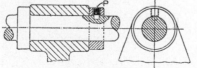

Fig. 2-2

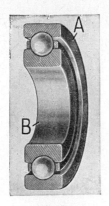  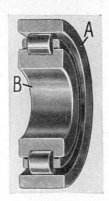

Fig. 2-3   Fig. 2-4   Fig. 2-5

Figs. 2-3 to 2-8 show various forms of ball and roller bearings, Fig. 2-3 shows a " single-row " journal or radial ball bearing. The inner race B is a ring of steel case-hardened (provided with a hardened surface layer but having a soft centre or core) with a groove or track formed on its outer circumference for a number of hardened steel balls to run upon. The outer race A is another ring but provided with a track on its inner circumference. The balls fit between the two tracks, thus enabling the outer race to turn relatively to the inner one, the balls meanwhile rolling round the tracks. The balls are kept from rubbing against each other by some form of cage. Such a bearing, as its name " radial " implies, is meant to withstand chiefly radial loads; they will usually, however, withstand a considerable amount of axial thrust and are often used as a combined journal and thrust bearing. Both the inner and the outer races are then secured in the end direction between nuts and shoulders or by other means. When the bearing is used simply to take radial loads one of the races is left free axially. Some journal-thrust ball bearings can take thrust loads only in one direction; care has therefore to be used in assembling these to ensure that they are properly placed to take the thrust load.

Fig. 2-4 shows an S. K. F. self-aligning ball bearing. The outer race is ground on the inside to form part of a sphere whose centre is on the axis of the shaft. Hence the axis of the inner race and shaft may be displaced out of parallel with that of the outer race without affecting the action of the bearing. Two rows of balls are used. Such bearings are desirable where the deflection of a shaft or frame cannot be limited to a negligible amount. They are often used in back axles.

An example of a parallel-roller journal bearing appears in Fig. 2-5. The tracks on the races A and B are now cylinders and cylindrical rollers take the place of the balls. Roller bearings can withstand heavier radial loads than equal sized ball bearings, but obviously

17

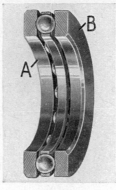

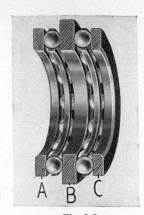

Fig. 2-6   Fig. 2-7   Fig. 2-8

the one shown cannot withstand any end thrust. By providing lips or shoulders on both inner and outer races a parallel-roller bearing can be made to withstand small end thrusts and this is sometimes done. If, however, the tracks and rollers are made conical, giving a taper-roller bearing, then large end thrusts can be taken in one direction. A taper-roller bearing is shown in Fig. 2-6. It may be pointed out that the angles of the cones forming the races and the rollers have to be such that when the bearing is assembled all the cones have a common apex lying on the axis of the shaft.

Roller bearings in which the length of the rollers is equal to several times their diameter are called " needle roller " bearings. Usually they have no cage, the rollers completely filling the space between the inner and outer races. An example is seen at H (Fig. 24-2).

Fig. 2-7 shows a " single thrust " bearing. The tracks are now formed on the faces of two discs, A and B, so that an end thrust can be carried. In Fig. 2-8 a " double " thrust race or bearing is seen, in which two sets of balls are provided so that thrusts in either direction can be taken; the races A and C abut against shoulders or nuts on the revolving shaft while the central race B is fixed in the stationary housing. The balls may be carried in a cage, but whereas this is almost universal with journal bearings, thrust bearings are often not provided with cages. Thrust bearings are not capable of taking radial loads; these, therefore, have to be taken by journal bearings.

From the point of view of the user the most important point concerning ball and roller bearings is the necessity for absolute cleanliness. Dirt, dust, particles of metal and water will quickly destroy them. In machining, the holes in which outer races fit should be truly cylindrical and the outer race should usually be a fairly free fit. The inner race, which is normally the revolving one, should, on the other hand, be a tight fit on its shaft.

18

Fig. 2-9

Fig. 2-10

Greases containing animal fats must not be used in ball bearings as the acids usually contained in these lubricants destroy the races and balls. Most oil companies put up greases which are suitable for ball bearings and their recommendations should be accepted.

In general, unless bearings are overloaded as a result of bad design or gross overloading of the vehicle, or are exposed to water or dust, they will give no trouble and may easily outlast the rest of the vehicle.

2.1   Types of Toothed Gearing

Toothed gearing, which is used to transmit motion of rotation from one shaft to another, assumes various forms according to the relative positions of the shafts. When the shafts are parallel the gears are called " spur " gears, and are cylinders with teeth cut on the outside or the inside according to whether they are external or internal gears. Examples of such gearing are shown in Figs. 2-9 and 2-10 respectively. In these cases the teeth are seen to be cut parallel to the axes of the gears. Such teeth are called " straight " to distinguish them from those shown in Fig. 2-11 which, being parts of helices, are called " helical teeth." Owing to the inclination of helical teeth there is an axial or end thrust on each gear tending to separate them axially. These end thrusts have to be resisted by suitable thrust bearings.

Fig. 2-11

19

Fig. 2-12

Fig. 2-13

The end thrust is avoided in "double helical" gearing (Fig. 2-12) where the thrust from one half of a tooth is counteracted by that from the other half. In all the forms of spur gearing the forces between the teeth in contact tend to separate the gears radially. These forces have to be taken by the journal bearings of the shafts.

When their axes intersect, shafts are connected by "bevel" gearing. Bevel gears are cones with teeth cut upon them. The teeth may be straight, giving straight toothed bevel gears as shown in Fig. 2-13 or "spiral," giving spiral bevel gears (Fig. 2-14). With straight toothed bevel gears since the forces between the teeth in contact tend to separate the gears both radially and axially, thrust bearings must be fitted behind each gear. When spiral teeth are used the axial forces on the gears may tend to separate them or to make them mesh more deeply; it depends upon the angle of the spiral, whether it is right or left handed, and upon the direction of rotation. With spiral bevel gears, therefore, it is usual to fit double thrust bearings.

Fig. 2-14

When the shafts are neither parallel nor intersect they may be connected by either "skew," "worm" or "hypoid" gearing. A pair of skew gears is illustrated in Fig. 2-15. These are usually cylindrical, being then identical with helical toothed spur gears, but one of them is sometimes hollowed out like a "worm wheel" so that it "embraces" the other, as this gives a better

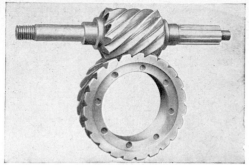

Fig. 2-16

Fig. 2-15

contact between the teeth and results in an increased efficiency.

The ordinary type of worm gearing is shown in Fig. 2-16. The " worm " (at the top) may be considered as part of a screw having a number of " threads." If the wheel is considered to represent a nut it will be seen that if the worm is prevented from moving in the axial direction then when it is rotated the worm-wheel will have to revolve also. This type is known as " parallel " worm gearing, the worm being a parallel screw. There is another type in which the worm is shaped to embrace the wheel, instead of being parallel. It is known in its general application as the " Hindley," " hour-glass " or " globoidal " type, but in its application to motor cars as the " Lanchester " worm, since Dr. Lanchester developed it for that application. In both types of worm gearing there are both radial and axial forces acting on the worm and the wheel tending to separate them. The directions of these forces change when the direction of the motion is reversed and, besides journal bearings, double thrust bearings have to be fitted to both worm and wheel. The efficiency of worm gearing depends to a very great extent on the quality of the materials used, the accuracy and degree of finish and on the lubrication. When these factors are right the efficiency is very high (commonly about 95-99 per cent).

The efficiency of good spur gearing is also very high, bevel gears are slightly less efficient and skew gears least efficient of all.

An example of hypoid gearing is shown in Fig. 2-17, from

Fig. 2-17

21

which it will be seen that the chief difference between it and spiral bevel gearing is that the axis of the pinion is placed lower than that of the crown wheel so that the axes of the gears do not intersect. If desirable the pinion axis may be placed above the crown wheel axis. There are two chief advantages claimed for the hypoid gear over the spiral bevel, greater quietness and greater strength; it is possible to make the pinion larger than that of spiral bevel gears having the same gear ratio and same size of crown wheel. If this increased strength is unnecessary then the hypoid gears can be made smaller than the corresponding spiral bevel gears. There is a sliding action in the direction of the length of the teeth of hypoid gears that is absent in bevel gearing and thus makes lubrication of the teeth a more difficult matter so that special lubricants frequently have to be used with hypoid gearing.

2.2 " Gear Ratio " of Toothed Gearing

When two shafts are connected by toothed gearing of any of the types described, the ratio between the speeds of those shafts will always be constant. This constant ratio is called the " gear ratio." In all the types of gearing considered when one wheel drives another the gear ratio between them will be the *inverse* ratio of the numbers of teeth in the wheels. Thus if a wheel A drives a wheel B then—

$$\frac{\text{Speed of A}}{\text{Speed of B}} = \frac{\text{Number of teeth in B}}{\text{Number of teeth in A}}$$

and the bigger wheel goes slower than the smaller one. This will be clear when it is realized that in any given time as many teeth of the wheel A as of the wheel B, pass the point (P) where the teeth mesh together. Now suppose the speeds of the wheels are S_a and S_b r.p.m. and the numbers of teeth N_a and N_b. Then the number of teeth of A that pass the point P in one minute is $N_a \times S_a$ while for B the number is $N_b \times S_b$ and these are equal, thus—

$$N_a \times S_a = N_b \times S_b \text{ or } S_a/S_b = N_b/N_a$$

The rule applies to worm gearing, the number of " teeth " in the worm being equal to the number of threads or " starts " it has. The number of starts is easily seen by looking at the worm from the end.

CHAPTER 3

Some Fundamental Principles of Mechanics

Mass, force and motion. Newton's laws of motion. Inertia forces. Couples.
Centrifugal forces. Friction. Work and energy.

THE subject of mechanics deals with the action of forces on bodies and with the motion that results from such action. A knowledge of the fundamental principles of mechanics is therefore necessary if the working of the various components of an internal combustion engined vehicle is to be properly understood, and if the reasons for the adoption of certain constructions are to be appreciated.

3.1 Mass, Force and Motion

A " body " in mechanics means a certain amount of " stuff " or " matter," and it is the quantity of matter in a body that we are principally concerned with in mechanics. This quantity is called the " mass " of the body, and it may conveniently be measured by means of weights and scales, the measurement being in reality a comparison with that of a standard body arbitrarily chosen.

Bodies are either at rest or in motion, both states being considered relatively to some body of reference, usually the earth. The motion of a body may be very complicated, but it can always be separated into two component motions of a simple character—Motion of Translation and Motion of Rotation. In the first every point of the body moves in a straight line. In the second all the points in the body move in concentric circles, that is, the body revolves about a fixed axis. It will be convenient to consider these motions separately.

3.2 Motion of Translation

Motion of translation is either uniform or variable. If it is uniform then the body will traverse equal distances in equal intervals of time, and the measure of the speed of the body is the distance covered divided by the time taken. If the motion is variable the speed changes from instant to instant, and dividing the distance covered by the time taken will only give the average speed during the interval. In mechanics speeds are usually measured in feet per second, and a speed of 20 feet per second is usually written 20 ft/sec.

When the speed of a body is changing, the rate at which it changes is called the acceleration of the body. Accelerations may be either uniform or variable. If uniform they may be measured by measuring the increase or decrease in the speed in a given time interval.

23

If the speed of a body increases by 1 ft/sec in one second, then the acceleration is one foot-per-second per second; this is usually written 1 ft/sec/sec or 1 ft/sec². Variable accelerations need not here be considered.

Forces, in mechanics, are any actions that tend to move a body from a state of rest or to alter the motion of a moving body. Altering the motion of a body means either increasing or decreasing its speed or changing the direction in which it moves. Forces are recognized as acting in definite directions or along definite " lines of action " and at definite " points of application."

The attraction between the earth and a body near it is a force, the magnitude of which varies with the quantity of matter in the body, that is, its mass. The unit by which forces are measured in engineering is the force of attraction between the earth and a standard mass of one pound. The engineering unit of force is thus a force equal to the weight of a 1 lb mass, and forces should be designated as being so many lb-weight. For shortness, however, the word weight is usually omitted and a force of say 10 lb-weight is written 10 lb.

3.3 Newton's Laws of Motion

The superstructure of mechanics has been raised upon three axioms first enunciated by Sir Isaac Newton and known as his Laws of Motion. They are—

(1) Every body continues in its state of rest, or of uniform motion in a straight line, except in so far as it is compelled, by external impressed forces, to alter that state.

(2) The acceleration produced by a force acting on a body is directly proportional to the magnitude of the force, inversely proportional to the mass of the body and takes place in the direction of the line of action of the force.

(3) To every action there is an equal and opposite reaction.

Certain corollaries follow from the first of these statements.

If a body at rest is caused to move, a force must have acted upon it; if a body in uniform motion in a straight line is caused to go faster or slower or to deviate from the straight line, a force must have acted upon it.

A body can move in a curved path only so long as a force acts upon it to deflect it from the straight path.

If a body is at rest or is moving uniformly in a straight line, then either there are no forces acting on it or the forces that act upon it are in " equilibrium," that is, they neutralize each other so as to have no net effect or " resultant."

From the second axiom it will be seen that if the force acting on a given body is doubled, then the acceleration will be doubled also, while if a given acceleration is to be produced in each of two bodies, and the mass of the first is twice that of the second, then the

force that must be applied to the first must
be twice that which must be applied to the
second.

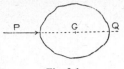

Fig. 3-1

The third statement will be made clear by
an example. If a body rests upon the ground
it acts downwards on the ground with a
force equal to its weight, but the ground
also acts upwards on the body with an equal force. Again, if a lorry is
hauling a trailer and pulls on the tow-rope with a force P, it is evident
that the rope tends to pull the lorry backwards with an equal force P.

3.4 Inertia Forces

Consider a body acted upon by a force P as shown in Fig. 3-1.
The force will accelerate the body in the direction PQ, and is spent
in overcoming the disinclination of the body to change its state of
motion, or briefly, in overcoming the " inertia " of the body. The
inertia of a body that is accelerated (or decelerated) by a force P,
may be expressed as a force P_1 equal to P and acting at the " mass
centre " of the body in a direction opposite to the force P, but
it must be observed that the force P_1 is an " internal " force and not
an external one.

The " mass centre " of a body is a point in the body such that if
the line of action of any force acting on the body passes through the
point, the force has no tendency to rotate the body. Or, it is that
point at which the whole of the matter in the body may be considered
to be concentrated. The more familiar phrase " centre of gravity "
should be used only in the case of gravitational forces.

It follows from the first definition that if a force acts on a body and
the line of action of the force does not pass through the mass
centre of the body then the force will have a tendency to rotate the
body. This may be seen as follows. In Fig. 3-2 the force P acting
on the body produces a linear acceleration in the direction PQ.
The internal inertia force expressing the disinclination of the body
to be accelerated is an equal and opposite force P_1 acting at the
mass centre G. Then clearly the two forces P and P_1 have a
tendency to turn the body in a clockwise direction. It must be
remembered that the force P_1 is an internal one. If it were an
external force the body would not be accelerated at all in the
direction PQ, since the two forces would produce equal accelerations in opposite directions which would cancel out. The tendency
to rotate, however, would remain.

3.5 Couples

Thus the only effect of two equal external
forces that act upon a body in opposite directions is to rotate the body. Such a pair of
forces is called a " twisting moment,"
" torque " or " couple." When motion of

Fig. 3-2

rotation alone is being considered we are concerned with couples rather than with forces.

The tendency of two forces, constituting a couple, to rotate the body upon which they act is proportional to the magnitude of the forces and to the perpendicular distance between their (parallel) lines of action. If the magnitude of the forces is P and the perpendicular distance between their lines of action is 1, then the magnitude of the couple is $P \times 1$. Since forces are measured in lb-weight and distances in feet or inches, couples are measured in lb-weight $\times$ feet, or lb-weight $\times$ inches, and these are usually written lb-ft and lb-in respectively.

It is now necessary to turn to motion of rotation.

3.6 Rotational Motion

The rotational motion of a body may be either uniform or variable. If it is uniform it may be measured by ascertaining the number of revolutions made in a given time. The speed would then be obtained as so many revolutions per minute or per second (r.p.m. or r.p.sec.) and this is the common method of measuring rotational speeds.

If the rotational speed is variable, then the measurement of the number of revolutions made in a given time will give only the average speed during the interval. When the rotational speed of a body is increasing or decreasing, the rate of increase or decrease, that is, the rotational or angular acceleration—may be measured, if it is uniform, by measuring the increase or decrease in the angular speed during a given time interval. The angular acceleration will then be obtained as so many r.p.m. per minute.

We may now consider Newton's three laws as they apply to rotational motion—

(1) Every body continues in its state of rest or of uniform rotation about an axis fixed in direction, except in so far as it is compelled by external impressed couples, or by a force whose line of action does not pass through the mass centre of the body, to alter that state.

(2) The angular acceleration produced by a couple acting on a body is directly proportional to the magnitude of the couple, inversely proportional to " the moment of inertia of the body about the axis about which the acceleration occurs," and takes place in the plane of the couple.

(3) To every couple there is an equal and opposite reactionary couple.

In considering the first of these it should be noted that the rotational motion of a body is not affected by any motion of translation the body may have and vice versa. Thus corresponding to uniform motion in a straight line when translatory motion is being considered we have, for rotational motion, uniform rotation about an axis that always remains parallel to its original position, that is, that is fixed in direction.

Certain corollaries follow from the first statement.

If a body at rest is caused to rotate a couple must have acted upon it.

If a body that is rotating uniformly about a fixed axis is caused to go faster or slower a couple must have acted upon it.

If a body is rotating about a certain axis and the direction of that axis is changed, a couple must have acted upon it.

If a body is at rest or is rotating uniformly about an axis fixed in direction, then either there is no couple acting on it or the couples that act upon it neutralize each other and have no net effect or resultant. The body is then in rotational equilibrium.

3.7 Moment of Inertia of a Body

If the second statement above is compared with the second statement in Section 3.3, it will be found that in place of the mass of the body there is now the " moment of inertia of the body about the axis about which the angular acceleration occurs." This quantity however, unlike the mass of a body, depends upon the shape of the body and on the position of the axis of rotation. This may perhaps be made clearer as follows.

Suppose a definite weight of steel is taken and is formed first into a long shaft of small diameter, and secondly into a flywheel as shown in Fig. 1-16. Then it should not be difficult to realize that while it will be comparatively easy to grasp the shaft and to twist it to and fro about its axis (an operation involving continual angular acceleration and deceleration of the shaft) it will be impossible to twist the flywheel to and fro at anything like the same rate. This is because the moment of inertia of the flywheel is very large compared with that of the shaft, although the weights (and masses) of the two are equal; this, in turn, is because the matter composing the shaft is disposed in such a way that it is all quite close to the axis of the shaft, whereas in the flywheel most of the matter is situated at a considerable distance from the axis. The effect, as regards rotational inertia, of each particle of matter in the bodies is dependent on the distance of that particle from the axis of rotation. (Actually the effect *varies* as the square of the distance, so that if the distance of one particle is twice that of another the effect of the first is four times that of the second.) It is possible to find an equivalent radius at which all the particles composing the body may be considered to act. This equivalent radius is called the " radius of gyration " of the body about the axis concerned, and the moment of inertia of the body is equal to the mass of the body multiplied by the *square* of the radius of gyration relative to that axis.

The " torque reaction " of a back axle is an example of the third axiom, and this is considered in Section 25.4.

3.8 Resolution of Forces

A force can be represented by a line drawn in the proper direction and of length proportional (on any convenient scale) to the magnitude of the force, but the representation is not complete until an arrowhead has been inserted to indicate the direction in which the force acts. Thus the line PQ in Fig. 3-3, being $\frac{1}{2}$ in long, represents a force of 15 lb to a scale of 1 in to 30 lb. If now a parallelogram PAQB is drawn upon PQ as diagonal it can be shown that if the lines PA and PB represent forces (to the same scale as for PQ) then the forces PA and PB acting together are equivalent to the force PQ and might replace that force without affecting the action in any way. The forces PA, PB are called the components of PQ, and the process of finding them is called the resolution of forces. Usually it is required to resolve a force in two directions which are at right angles; the parallelogram then becomes a rectangle.

3.9 Constrained Bodies

So far we have considered the action of forces upon bodies that are free and unconstrained; we pass on to the consideration of bodies that are constrained so that they can move only in definite paths determined by the constraining influence. An example of a constrained body is an axle carried in bearings; the body can have only rotational motion. Another example is a piston in a cylinder; which can have only motion in a straight line.

It will be found that the motions of the parts of mechanisms are all constrained motions. However, the motion of a constrained

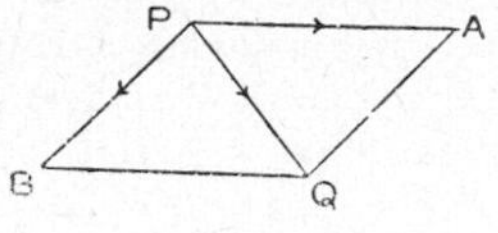

Fig. 3-3

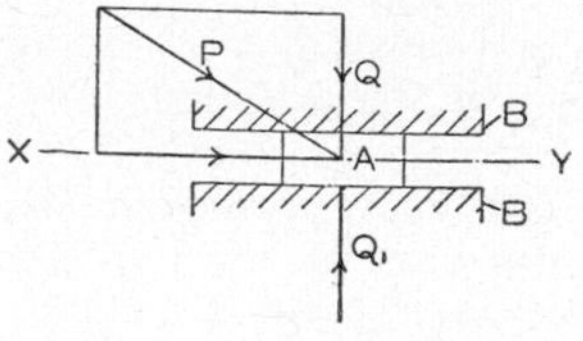

Fig. 3-4

body can be considered exactly as if the body were unconstrained, provided the forces introduced by the constraints are considered. These forces, however, can generally be found by considering the equilibrium of the body in the direction in which motion is prevented by the constraint. An example will make this clear.

Fig. 3-4 shows a body A constrained by guides BB so that it can only move along the straight line XY, while a force P acts upon it as shown. Then, since no motion is possible in the direction perpendicular to XY there can be no resultant force acting on the body in that direction. The force P, however, has a component Q in that direction; the constraint must therefore supply a force equal and

28

opposite to Q. This is supplied by the reaction Q_1 acting on the body, of the pressure between the body and the guide.

Since we know that there is equilibrium in the direction perpendicular to XY, when we are considering the motion of the body we need not consider the forces, or components of forces, that act in that direction, but can confine our attention to the forces, and the components of forces, that act parallel to XY.

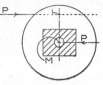

Fig. 3-5

As another example, consider a body pivoted on a fixed axis. The constraint is such that the body cannot have any motion of translation. There cannot, therefore, be any resultant force acting on the body. If a force P acts on the body as shown in Fig. 3-5, then the constraint (in this case the bearings in which the axle turns) will supply an equal force, acting parallel and in the opposite direction to P so that the only resultant action on the body is a couple, which can only produce rotational motion. (The force supplied by the bearings is an external force quite different from the internal inertia force shown in Fig. 3-2.) The magnitude of the couple is, of course, $P \times$ (distance LM). The force supplied by the bearings is often so much taken for granted that instead of speaking of the couple PP it is usual to speak of the product $P \times$ (LM) as the " moment of the force P about the axis M."

3.10 Centrifugal Force

A common form of constraint is that which compels a body to move in a circle. Since the direction of the motion is then continually changing (being always tangential to the circle), it follows that a force must be continually acting to produce the change. This force is supplied by the constraint; for example, if a cord attaches a body to a centre the force is the pull the cord applies to the body; it acts always towards the centre and is a centripetal force; its reaction is the pull applied by the body to the cord and acts away from the centre, being the centrifugal force. Its magnitude is directly proportional to the mass of the body and the square of the linear speed, and inversely proportional to the radius of the circle.

Centrifugal force $= Mv^2/r = M\omega^2 r$ where ω is the *angular* speed of rotation.

3.11 Friction

If a body is placed upon a flat horizontal table it will be found that in order to move the body over the surface of the table at a *uniform* speed a force must be applied to it. Since the speed is uniform the body is in equilibrium, and there is no resultant force acting on it. It follows, therefore, that acting somewhere on the

29

body there must be a force equal and opposite to the applied force, and the only place where such a force can exist is between the surfaces in contact. This force between the surfaces in contact is called the " Force of Friction." If the applied force is increased then the difference between it and the frictional force will go to accelerate the body. If the applied force is decreased, then the difference between it and the frictional force will go to decelerate the body and ultimately to bring it to rest.

The magnitude of the frictional force depends upon several factors. The first is the materials of which the surfaces are composed. The friction between two blocks of wood is greater than between two blocks of steel, other factors being the same. The second factor is the condition of the surfaces, whether rough, smooth or polished, clean or dirty, dry or oily. The third factor is the force acting between the surfaces in contact, but it is only the force perpendicular to the surfaces that affects the friction. This perpendicular force is called the " normal " force between the surfaces, the " normal " to a curve or surface being a line at right angles to the curve or surface.

The frictional force may be expressed in terms of the normal force, and a quantity that depends upon the kind and condition of the surfaces and which is known as the " coefficient of friction." Thus if—

F = force of friction
P = normal force
μ = coefficient of friction,
then $F = \mu \times P$.

In the consideration of any actual contact between two bodies, the kind of surface and the condition of the surfaces will not usually alter, so that the coefficient of friction in any particular case is usually a constant.

The above relation does not include any factor depending on the area of the contact or on the velocity of sliding. This is because those factors do not greatly affect the frictional force. If the force acting between two surfaces is kept constant, then altering the area of the contact will alter the *pressure* between the surfaces and the amount of wear in a given time, but it will not alter the frictional force. When the velocity of sliding is increased the frictional force will generally be decreased, but unless the increase in the velocity is large, the effect on the frictional force will be negligible. The value of the coefficient of friction varies from as low as 0·01 up to as much as 0·8 and more. Some values in particular cases are given in connection with " clutches." (See Section 19.7.)

It must be borne in mind that it is the *normal force* between the surfaces that determines the magnitude of the frictional force. If, therefore, a force acts upon a body at an angle to the contact surfaces it is the component of that force perpendicular to the surfaces that has to be considered.

When the above relation between the normal and the frictional force holds, the friction is called " solid " friction to distinguish it from the friction that occurs in liquids, which is known as " fluid " friction. If two bodies are separated by a complete film of oil or other fluid the frictional force between them depends on the laws of fluid friction. These are quite different from those of solid friction and are dealt with in Chapter 15.

Although, as already mentioned, an increase in the velocity of sliding has very little effect on the frictional force, yet if that velocity becomes zero, so that the bodies are at rest relatively, an appreciable change occurs in the frictional force between them, the change being an increase. This fact is allowed for by using a slightly higher coefficient when the bodies are at rest than when they are sliding. The coefficient that applies to the state of rest is generally called the " static " coefficient, and that applying to the state of motion the " kinetic " coefficient.

3.12 Work and Energy

To lift a weight from the ground on to a table requires the expenditure of energy. In lifting the weight work is done against the force of gravity. The amount of work done depends on the weight lifted and the height through which it is raised, and so the unit by which work is measured is defined as the amount of work done when a weight of 1 lb is lifted a vertical height of 1 ft. This unit is called the foot-pound and is written ft-lb. When a force moves one body over the surface of another against the force of friction, work is done. If a force of P lb acts upon a body and the point of application of the force moves a distance of L feet *in the direction of the force*, then the force does $P \times L$ ft-lb of work. *No* work is done by a force unless the point of application of the force moves in the direction of the force. Thus, if there is no friction, no work is done in moving a body over a horizontal surface, since the motion is perpendicular to the only force acting, that is, the weight of the body. If a force acts on a body along a line of action making an angle with the direction in which the body moves, then it is only the component of the force in the direction of the motion which does work. When a force acts to assist the motion of a body the force is said to do work on the body. When a force opposes the motion of a body the phrase " work is done against the force " is used.

The energy expended in lifting a weight is not lost, but is stored as " potential " energy, and may be obtained again. By means of suitable apparatus the weight in falling to its original level could be made to drive a dynamo and generate electric current or to raise the temperature of a quantity of water. When a force does work on a body by accelerating the body, the work done is stored as energy of motion or " kinetic " energy, which may be obtained again by bringing the body to rest. Energy may thus exist under many different forms. We have, for example, potential energy, kinetic energy, heat energy, electrical energy, the energy of light and sound, chemical energy and strain energy (the energy stored in a compressed spring is stored by virtue of the " strain " or deformation of the material of the spring). Energy existing in one form can generally be changed into energy in another form, but there are limitations to these processes of which more will be heard when we come to the consideration of heat engines.

3.13 Power

Although the same amount of work is done when a weight is lifted through a height, whether the process occupies one second, one minute, or one year, the *rate* at which the work is done varies with the time taken. When we say that one engine is more powerful than another we mean that it can do a greater quantity of work in a given time, that is, that it can work at a greater rate. The " power " of an engine thus expresses the " rate at which it can work." The unit of work being the ft-lb and the unit of time the second, the unit rate of working should logically be a rate of 1 ft-lb per second. This unit, however, is too small to be used conveniently by engineers, who therefore use a unit called the " horse power." One horse power is a rate of working of 550 ft-lb per second or 33,000 ft-lb per minute. It was introduced by James Watt and was meant to represent the rate at which a good horse could work continuously.

3.14 Principle of the Conservation of Energy

This principle states that although energy may be changed from one form to another, yet it cannot be destroyed or lost; it may pass out of control and be unusable yet it still exists. For our purposes the principle can be stated in the following way—

$$
\left\{\begin{array}{l}\text{Rate at which}\\\text{work is done on}\\\text{a machine at one}\\\text{end}\end{array}\right\} = \left\{\begin{array}{l}\text{Rate at which}\\\text{work is performed}\\\text{by the machine at}\\\text{the other end}\end{array}\right\} + \left\{\begin{array}{l}\text{Rate at which}\\\text{energy is stored}\\\text{within the machine}\end{array}\right\} + \left\{\begin{array}{l}\text{Rate at which}\\\text{energy is used in}\\\text{overcoming fric-}\\\text{tion within the}\\\text{machine}\end{array}\right\}
$$

PART 2: THE ENGINE

CHAPTER 4

General Principles of Heat Engines

Heat and work. Rotary and reciprocating engines. The four-stroke cycle. Power, speed and rating. Characteristic performance curves. Number and diameter of cylinders.

THE petrol or oil engine, which is the source of power with which we are immediately concerned, is a form of internal combustion " heat engine," the function of which is to convert potential heat energy contained in the fuel into mechanical work.

It is outside the scope of the present volume to go deeply into the physical laws governing this conversion, for a full study of which a work such as A. C. Walshaw's *Thermodynamics for Engineers* (Longmans-Green), should be consulted. It will not be out of place, however, to give a brief outline of the general principles.

4.1 Heat and Work

A quantity of heat is conveniently measured by applying it to raise the temperature of a known quantity of pure water.

The unit of heat is defined as that quantity of heat required to raise the temperature of unit weight of water through one degree, this quantity depending, of course, on the particular unit of weight and the temperature scale employed.

The Continental and scientific temperature scale is the Centigrade scale, dividing the interval between the temperatures of melting ice and boiling water (at normal pressure) into one hundred divisions, but unfortunately the unsatisfactory Fahrenheit scale is the commercial standard in Britain and U.S.A. This scale divides the foregoing interval into one hundred and eighty divisions.

It is thus necessary to define by name three different units of heat as follows—

The British Thermal Unit (B.Th.U.). The heat required to raise the temperature of one pound of water through one degree Fahrenheit.

The Pound Calorie or Centigrade Heat Unit (C.H.U.). The heat required to raise the temperature of one pound of water through one degree Centigrade.

The Kilogram Calorie. The heat required to raise the temperature of one kilogram of water through one degree Centigrade.

The first and second of these units are clearly in the ratio of the Fahrenheit degree to the Centigrade degree, or 5 to 9, while the second and third are in the ratio of the pound to the kilogram or 1 to 2·204. Thus the three units in the order given are in the ratio 5, 9, 19·84 or 1, 1·8, 3·97.

35

The " therm " used by the Gas Boards is 100,000 British Thermal Units.

In the notes that follow, the Centigrade scale and the Centigrade Unit (C.H.U.) will be used.

To recapitulate briefly some definitions already given—

4.2 Work

Mechanical work is done when a force is exerted a definite distance in the direction of that force. The quantity of work done is the product of the force and the distance, and is measured, in Britain and America, in foot-pound units.

If work is done by rotating a shaft, the quantity of work is the product of the torque or turning moment applied to the shaft in pound-feet, multiplied by the angle turned through measured in radians. One revolution equals 2π radians.

4.3 Joule's Equivalent

Dr. Joule was the first to show, in the middle of the last century, that heat and work were mutually convertible one to the other, being, in fact, different forms of energy, and that when a definite quantity of work is expended wholly in producing heat by friction or similar means, a definite quantity of heat is produced. His experiments, confirmed and corrected by others, showed that 778 foot-pounds produce one British Thermal Unit, or 1,400 foot-pounds produce one C.H.U.

This figure is called " the mechanical equivalent of heat," though it would perhaps be better to speak of the " thermal equivalent of work." For though the same equivalent or rate of exchange holds for conversion in either direction, while it is comparatively simple to convert to heat by friction the whole of a quantity of work supplied, it is not possible, in a heat engine, to convert to mechanical work more than a comparatively small percentage of the total *heat* supplied. There are definite physical laws which limit this per-centage—or " thermal efficiency " as it is called—to about 50 per cent or less in the best heat engines that it is practicable to construct.

4.4 Thermal Efficiency

The thermal efficiency is governed chiefly by the range of tempera-ture through which the working fluid, be it gas or steam, passes on its way through the engine.

This range of temperature is greater in internal combustion engines than in steam engines, hence the former are inherently capable of higher thermal efficiencies, that is to say, they are capable of converting into work a higher percentage of the total heat of the fuel with which they are supplied than the latter. Even so, the physical limitations are such that the thermal efficiency of a good petrol engine is only about 25 per cent. The remaining 75 per cent of the heat supplied, which is *not* converted into work,

36

is unavoidably lost in the exhaust gases and cooling water, and in radiation.

4.5 Calorific Value

When unit weight of any fuel is completely burnt with oxygen (pure or diluted with nitrogen as in the air), a certain definite quantity of heat is liberated, depending on the chemical composition, that is, on the quantities of the fundamental fuels, carbon and hydrogen, which one pound of the fuel contains.

To determine how much potential heat energy is being supplied to an engine in a given time, it is necessary to know the weight of fuel supplied and its calorific value, which is the total quantity of heat liberated, when unit weight of the fuel is completely burnt.

The calorific values of carbon and hydrogen have been experimentally determined with considerable accuracy, and are usually given as—

Carbon   8,080 C.H.U/lb
Hydrogen   34,500 C.H.U/lb

The calorific value of any fuel, consisting, as all important fuels do, of a known proportion of carbon, hydrogen and incombustible impurities or diluents, may be estimated approximately on the assumption that it consists simply of a mixture of carbon, hydrogen and incombustible matter, but the state of chemical combination in the actual fuel leads to error by this method, and the only accurate and satisfactory means of determination is experimentally by the use of a suitable calorimeter.

Average petrol consists approximately of 85 per cent carbon and 15 per cent hydrogen by weight, the lighter fractions containing a higher percentage of hydrogen than the heavier. Refined petrol contains no measurable impurities or diluents. Its gross calorific value is about 11,000 C.H.U/lb.

Liquid fuels are usually measured by volume, and therefore it is necessary to know the density before the potential heat supplied in any given case can be determined. An example will make this clear.

A sample of petrol has a calorific value of 11,000 C.H.U/lb; its specific gravity being 0·72. How much potential heat energy is contained in 14 pints? (One gallon of water weighs 10 lb.)

$$\text{Weight of 14 pints} = 10 \text{ lb} \times 0\cdot72 \times \frac{14}{8} = 12\cdot6 \text{ lb.}$$

Thus potential heat in 14 pints $= 12\cdot6 \times 11,000 = 138,600$ C.H.U.

4.6 Power

Power is the *rate* at which work is done, one " horse power " being defined (by James Watt) as a rate of working of 33,000 foot-pounds per minute.

Problem: What is the thermal efficiency in the following case?

A petrol engine develops 30 horse power and consumes 18 pints of petrol per hour, the calorific value being 11,000 C.H.U/lb and the specific gravity 0·72.

Potential heat supplied per hour

$$= 10 \times 0.72 \times \frac{18}{8} \times 11,000 = 178,200 \text{ C.H.U.}$$

Work done per hour

$$= 30 \times 33,000 \times 60 = 59,400,000 \text{ ft-lb} = \frac{59,400,000}{1,400} \text{ C.H.U.}$$
$$= 42,428 \text{ C.H.U.}$$

Therefore thermal efficiency is,

$$\frac{42,428}{178,200} = 23.8 \text{ per cent.}$$

4.7 General Method of Conversion of Heat to Work

All heat engines convert heat into work by the expansion or increase in volume of a working fluid into which heat has been introduced by combustion of a fuel either external to the engine, as in a steam engine, or internally by the burning of a combustible mixture in the engine itself, a process giving rise to the phrase "internal combustion engine."

Thus, in all so-called "static pressure" engines, as distinct from turbines, it is necessary to provide a working vessel, the volume of which is capable of variation, work being done on a moving portion of the wall by the static pressure of the working fluid as its volume increases.

In general both the pressure and temperature fall with the increase of volume.

4.8 Practical Form of Working Vessel

In practice it has been found that for mechanical and manufacturing reasons the only satisfactory form of working chamber is a straight cylinder closed at one end and provided with a closely fitting movable plug or "piston" on which the work is done by the pressure of the steam or gases.

This arrangement is common to steam, gas, oil and petrol engines, and to rifles and guns, all of which are forms of heat engine.

4.9 Rotary and Reciprocating Engines

The motion of the piston in the cylinder of the above arrangement is, of course, in a straight line, whereas in the majority of applications the final motion required is a rotative one.

Very many attempts have been made to devise a form of chamber and piston to give rotary motion directly, but practically all have been mechanical failures, the chief weaknesses being excessive friction and difficulty in maintaining pressure tightness. A recent design which shows good promise of success is the N.S.U. Wankel engine, described on page 166. The universally established " direct acting engine mechanism " with connecting rod and crank is, however, unlikely to be generally replaced in the near future. Thus in most applications the reciprocating motion of the piston must be converted to rotation of the crank by a suitable mechanism. The most important of these mechanisms are—

(1) The crank and connecting rod.
(2) The crank and cross slide as used in the donkey pump and small steam launch engines.
(3) The " swash-plate " or " slant " mechanism.
(4) The " wobble plate " or Z crank (see page 316).

The second of these is not used in the applications with which we are concerned, owing to its undue weight and friction loss, and the third is, in general, confined to pumps and compressors for the conversion of rotary into reciprocating motion.

The Michell crankless engine, though not produced commercially, used the swash-plate in conjunction with the Michell thrust bearing which has eliminated the chief objection to the swash-plate, namely, excessive friction and low mechanical efficiency.

The first-mentioned mechanism is practically universal in internal combustion engines owing to its simplicity and high mechanical efficiency. We thus arrive at the fundamental parts common to all reciprocating engines which use the crank and connecting rod.

4.10 Cylinder, Piston, Connecting Rod and Crankshaft

These fundamental parts are shown in simple diagrammatic form in Fig. 4-1.

In this figure the crank is of the single web or " overhung " type, as used in many steam engines, and certain motor cycle engines,

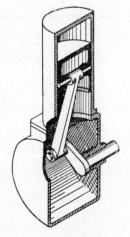

Fig. 4-1

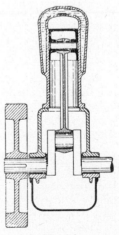

Fig. 4-2

but the double-web type, with a bearing on either side of the crank, is practically universal for internal combustion engines. This is illustrated in Fig. 4-2, which shows a cross-section through the cylinder, piston and connecting rod of the engine. A flywheel is mounted on the end of the crankshaft. The form and construction of the parts are considered later, only sufficient description being given here to enable their functions to be understood.

Cylinder. The ideal form consists of a plain cylindrical barrel in which the piston slides, the movement of the piston or " stroke " being, in most cases, somewhat longer than the bore, but tending to equality or even less since the abandonment of the R.A.C. rating for taxation purposes. This is known as the "stroke-bore ratio."

The upper end consists of a combustion or " clearance " space in which the ignition and combustion of the charge take place. In practice it is necessary to depart from the ideal hemispherical shape in order to accommodate the valves, sparking plug, etc., and to control the process of combustion.

Piston. The usual form of piston for internal combustion engines is an inverted bucket-shape, machined to a close (but free sliding) fit in the cylinder barrel. Gas tightness is secured by means of flexible " piston rings " fitting closely in grooves turned in the upper part of the piston.

The pressure of the gases is transmitted to the upper end of the connecting rod through the " gudgeon pin " on which the " small end " of the connecting rod is free to swing.

Connecting Rod. The connecting rod transmits the piston load to the crank, causing the latter to turn, thus converting the reciprocating motion of the piston into a rotary motion of the crankshaft. The lower or " big end " of the connecting rod turns on the " crank pin."

Crankshaft. In the great majority of internal combustion engines this is of the double-web type, the crank pin, webs and shaft being usually formed from a solid forging. The shaft turns in two or more main bearings (depending on the number and arrangement of the cylinders) mounted in the main frame or " crank case " of the engine.

Flywheel. At one end the crankshaft carries a heavy flywheel, the function of which is to absorb the variations in impulse transmitted to the shaft by the gas and inertia loads and to drive the pistons over the dead points and idle strokes. In motor vehicles the flywheel usually forms one member of the clutch through which the power is transmitted to the road wheels.

The foregoing are the fundamental and essential parts by which the power developed by the explosion is caused to give rotation to the crankshaft, the mechanism described being that of the " single-acting " engine, because a useful impulse is transmitted to the crankshaft while the piston moves in one direction only.

Most steam engines and a few large gas engines work on the " double-acting " principle, in which the pressure of the steam or gaseous explosion acts alternately on each side of the piston. The cylinder is then double-ended and the piston takes the form of a symmetrical disc. The force acting on the piston is transmitted through a " piston rod " to an external " cross-head " which carries the gudgeon pin. The piston rod passes through one end of the cylinder in a " stuffing-box " which prevents the escape of steam or gas.

4.11 Method of Working

It is now necessary to descrite the sequence of operations by which the combustible charge is introduced, ignited and burned and finally discharged after it has completed its work.

There are two important " cycles " of operations in practical use, namely, the " four-stroke " or " Otto " cycle, as it is sometimes called (after the name of the German engineer who first applied it in practice), and the " two-stroke " or " Clerk " cycle, which has owed its development largely to the late Sir Dugald Clerk.

The cycles take their names from the number of single piston strokes which are necessary to complete a single sequence of operations, this sequence, or cycle, being repeated continuously so long as the engine works.

The first named is by far the most widely adopted except for small motor cycle and motor boat engines, and for large diesels, for though it leads to greater mechanical complication in the engine, it shows higher thermal efficiency, and therefore greater economy in fuel. This cycle will therefore be described first.

4.12 The Four-stroke Cycle

Fig. 4-3 shows in a diagrammatic manner a four-stroke engine cylinder provided with two valves of the " mushroom " or " poppet " type. The cylinder is shown horizontal for convenience.

The inlet valve I.V. communicates through a throttle valve with the carburettor or vaporizer, from which an explosive mixture of fuel and air is drawn. The exhaust valve E.V. communicates with the silencer through which the burnt gases are discharged to the atmosphere. These valves are opened and closed at suitable intervals by mechanism which will be described later.

The four strokes of the complete cycle are shown at A, B, C and D.

Below the diagrams of the cylinder are shown the corresponding portions of what is known as the " indicator " diagram, that is to say, a diagram which shows the variation of pressure of the gases in the cylinder throughout the cycle. In practice such diagrams can be automatically recorded when the engine is running by a piece of apparatus known as an " indicator," of which there are many types.

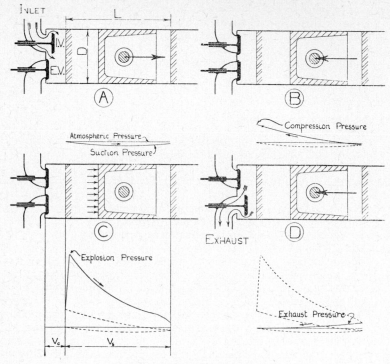

Fig. 4-3: The four-stroke cycle

The four strokes of the cycle are as follows:

(A) *Induction Stroke—Exhaust Valve Closed: Inlet Valve Open*

The momentum imparted to the flywheel by previous explosions, or rotation by hand or by starter motor, causes the connecting rod to draw the piston outwards, setting up a partial vacuum which sucks in a new charge of explosive mixture from the carburettor. The pressure will be below atmospheric pressure by an amount which depends upon the speed of the engine and the throttle opening.

(B) *Compression Stroke—Both Valves Closed*

The piston returns, still driven by the momentum of the flywheel, and compresses the charge into the combustion head of the cylinder. The pressure rises to an amount which depends on the " compression ratio," that is, the ratio of the full volume of the cylinder when the piston is at the outer end of its stroke to the volume of the clearance space when the piston is at the inner (or upper) end. In ordinary petrol engines this ratio is usually between 6 and 9 and the pressure at the end of compression is about 90 to 120 lb/sq. in., with full throttle opening.

$$\text{Compression ratio} = \frac{V_s + V_c}{V_c} \qquad\qquad V_s = \frac{\pi}{4} D^2 \times L$$

(C) *Explosion or Working Stroke—Both Valves Closed*

Just before the end of the compression stroke, ignition of the charge is effected by means of an electric spark, and a rapid rise of temperature and pressure occurs inside the cylinder. The explosion is completed while the piston is practically at rest, and is followed by the expansion of the hot gases as the piston moves outwards. The pressure of the gases drives the piston forward and turns the crankshaft thus propelling the car against the external resistances and restoring to the flywheel the momentum lost during the idle strokes. The pressure falls as the volume increases.

(D) *Exhaust Stroke—Inlet Valve Closed: Exhaust Valve Open*

The piston returns, again driven by the momentum of the flywheel, and discharges the spent gases through the exhaust valve. The pressure will be slightly above atmospheric pressure by an amount depending on the resistance to flow offered by the exhaust valve and silencer.

It will thus be seen that there is only one working stroke for every four piston strokes, or every two revolutions of the crankshaft, the remaining three strokes being referred to as " idle " strokes, though they form an indispensable part of the cycle. This has led engineers to search for a cycle which shall reduce the proportion of idle strokes and correspondingly increase the number of useful strokes in a given time, and the various forms of the " two-stroke " engine are the result. These are dealt with in Chapter 10.

4.13 Power, Speed and Rating

The work done on a moving piston, from our foregoing definition, is the product of the force in pounds acting on the piston head, and the distance in feet through which the piston moves.

If the force on the piston is variable, which is the case in all internal combustion engines, then the total movement or stroke may be divided into a number of parts, each portion of the movement being then multiplied by the value of the force during that movement, and the total work obtained by summation. What amounts to the same thing is to determine the mean force on the piston throughout the stroke and then multiply it by the length of the stroke.

The mean force on the piston is the mean intensity of pressure or " mean effective pressure " (usually measured in pounds per square inch), multiplied by the piston area, that is the cross-sectional area of the cylinder, in square inches. This mean effective pressure is determined from the indicator diagram if available in the following manner.

Referring to Fig. 4-3, the four small pressure diagrams show the variation of gas pressure during the four strokes, the pressure on the induction and exhaust strokes being exaggerated for clarity.

Fig. 4-4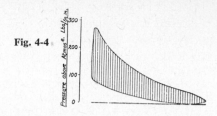

Approximate average figures for the *mean* pressures throughout each stroke are as follows—

(1) Induction   2 lb/sq. in. below atmosphere.
(2) Compression   30 lb/sq. in. above atmosphere.
(3) Explosion   150 lb/sq. in. above atmosphere.
(4) Exhaust   2 lb/sq. in. above atmosphere.

Now it must be remembered that the pressures are driving the engine, and are *positive*, only on the explosion stroke, being against the engine or negative on the three remaining strokes.

Thus the resultant mean *effective* pressure is

$$150 - (30 + 2 + 2) = 116 \text{ lb/sq. in.}$$

In practice the suction and exhaust pressures with full throttle are so small compared with those on the remaining strokes that they hardly show on a full-throttle indicator diagram, which reduces to the form shown in Fig. 4-4.

It will now be realized that the mean effective pressure can be obtained from the mean height of the shaded area (Fig. 4-4). If the area of the figure, obtained in any convenient manner, is divided by its length, the result will be its mean height in, say, inches. The height in inches is then multiplied by the scale of the spring used in the indicator, thus giving the mean effective pressure in pounds per square inch.

The " negative work " involved in the suction and exhaust strokes, which is usually too small to estimate from the indicator diagram, is regarded as part of the mechanical losses of the engine, and is known as the " pumping " work.

4.14   Factors Governing the Mean Effective Pressure

The mean effective pressure depends primarily on the number of potential heat units which can be introduced into the cylinder in each charge. When the volatile liquid fuels are mixed with air in the chemically correct proportions, the potential heat units per cubic foot of mixture are almost exactly the same in every case, being about 60 C.H.U/cu. ft. at standard temperature and pressure.

The " volumetric efficiency " represents the degree of completeness with which the cylinder is re-charged with fresh combustible and varies with different engines and also with the speed.

The " combustion efficiency " represents the degree of completeness with which the potential heat units in the charge are produced as actual heat in the cylinder. Its value depends on a variety of factors, among the more important of which are the quality of the explosive mixture, nature of fuel, quality of ignition, degree of turbulence, and temperature of cylinder walls.

Lastly, the " thermal efficiency " governs the percentage of the actual heat units present in the cylinder which are converted into mechanical work.

In engine tests the phrase " thermal efficiency " is taken comprehensively to include combustion efficiency as well as conversion efficiency, as in practice it is impossible to separate them.

They are further combined with the mechanical efficiency where this cannot be separately measured, as " brake thermal efficiency."

It can be shown theoretically that the conversion efficiency is increased with an increase in compression ratio, and this is borne out in practice, but a limit is reached owing to the liability of the high compression to lead to detonation of the charge, or " pinking " as it is popularly called. This tendency to detonation varies with different fuels, as does also the limiting compression ratio, which in most engines using ordinary fuel lies between 6 and $7\frac{1}{2}$. With special fuels a higher compression ratio (8 to 9) is possible, owing to the greater freedom from risk of detonation. (See Chapter 14.)

It thus follows that for the same volumetric efficiency, compression ratio and thermal efficiency the mean effective pressure will be practically the same for all liquid fuels. This is borne out in practice.

The thermal efficiency of an internal combustion engine of a given type does not depend very much on the *size* of the cylinders, though it is somewhat less with small cylinders owing to the greater proportional jacket loss.

The highest mean effective pressure obtained without supercharging, and using petrol as fuel, is about 160 lb/sq. in., but this is exceptional and very little below the theoretical maximum. A more normal figure to take in good conditions with full throttle is 120 to 130 lb/sq. in.

4.15 Work per Minute and Horse Power

Let the quantities be represented by the following symbols—

p = mean effective pressure (m.e.p.) in lb/sq. in. or p.s.i.

D = diameter of cylinder bore in inches.

A = area of piston in square inches = $\pi D^2/4$.

L = length of stroke in feet.

N = speed in revolutions per minute (r.p.m.).

f = number of effective strokes, or explosions per revolution of each cylinder.

n = number of cylinders.

Then—

Work per effective stroke of each cylinder = $p \times \pi D^2/4 \times L$

45

Work per minute per cylinder $= p \times \pi D^2/4 \times L \times f \times N$

Horse power per cylinder $= \dfrac{p \times \pi D^2 \times L \times f \times N}{4 \times 33,000}$.

Now for a single-acting four-stroke cylinder $f = \frac{1}{2}$ (that is, one explosion per two revolutions).

Hence—

Horse power per cylinder

$$= \frac{p \times \pi \times D^2 \times L \times N}{8 \times 33,000}$$

$$= \frac{p \times \pi \times D^2 \times L \times N \times 2}{16 \times 33,000}.$$

4.16 Piston Speed

Now $2 \times L \times N$ is the total distance in feet travelled by the piston per minute. This is called the " mean piston speed " and will be denoted by S.

Thus—

Horse power per cylinder

$$= \frac{p \times D^2 \times S}{168,067}.$$

4.17 Indicated and Brake Horse Power

The horse power obtained above from the indicator diagram (that is, using the m.e.p.) is known as the " indicated " horse power (i.h.p.), and is the power developed inside the engine cylinder by the explosion of the charge.

The useful power developed at the engine shaft or clutch is less than this by the amount of power expended in overcoming the frictional resistance of the engine itself. This useful power is known as the " brake " horse power (b.h.p.) because it can be absorbed and measured on the test bench by means of a friction or fan brake.*

4.18 Mechanical Efficiency

The ratio of the brake horse power to the indicated horse power is known as the " mechanical efficiency." Thus—

$$\text{Mechanical efficiency} = \frac{\text{b.h.p.}}{\text{i.h.p.}} = \eta$$

and b.h.p. = mechanical efficiency $\times$ i.h.p.

$$= \frac{\eta \times p \times D^2 \times S}{168,067} \text{ for one cylinder}$$

and b.h.p. $= \dfrac{\eta \times p \times D^2 \times S \times n}{168,067}$ for n cylinders.

* For further information on engine testing the reader is referred to " The Testing of Internal Combustion Engines " by Young and Pryer (Eng. University Press).

4.19 Limiting Factors

Let us see to what extent these factors may be varied to give increased power.

It has been shown that the value of p depends chiefly on the compression ratio and the volumetric efficiency, and has a definite limit which cannot be exceeded without supercharging.

The diameter of the cylinder D can be increased at will, but, as will be shown presently, as D increases so does the weight per horse power, which is a serious disadvantage in engines for traction purposes. There remain the piston speed and mechanical efficiency. The most important limitations to piston speed arise from the stresses and bearing loads due to the inertia of the reciprocating parts, and from losses due to increased velocity of the gases through the valve ports resulting in low volumetric efficiency.

If a large number of engines of different types and such widely varying length of stroke as occur in stationary, locomotive, marine and automobile types are examined, it will be found that where the stroke is long the revolutions per minute are low, and *vice versa*, but that the piston speed is sensibly constant for widely different types of engine, lying usually between 800 and 1,100 ft/min, if automobile and aircraft engines are excluded.

This limitation of piston speed represents the result of experience with all types of engines, the chief factors which determine the maximum desirable or permissible speed being the factors mentioned above. At the time when the Royal Automobile Club rating formula was established 1,000 ft/min was regarded as a normal piston speed, though at the present day this figure is more than doubled in most automobile engines.

4.20 R.A.C. Rating

The Royal Automobile Club, therefore, assumed a piston speed of 1,000 ft/min, and also made the further assumptions that the mean effective pressure could be taken as 90 lb/sq. in. and the mechanical efficiency as 75 per cent. When these several figures are put into the general formula derived, that formula reduces to—

$$\text{b.h.p.} = \frac{0 \cdot 75 \times 90 \times D^2 \times 1,000 \times n}{168,067} = \frac{D^2 n}{2 \cdot 5}.$$

This is the well-known formula for the power of an automobile engine which was formerly used by the Treasury for taxation purposes. It gives the brake horse power which an engine will develop on three specific assumptions, namely—

(1) A mean effective pressure of 90 lb/sq. in.

(2) A mechanical efficiency of 75 per cent.

(3) A piston speed of 1,000 ft/min.

At the time the formula was laid down the above figures represented fair average values, but in modern practice they are very greatly exceeded.

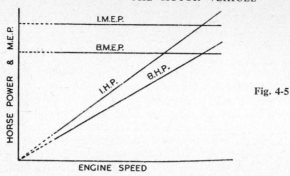

Fig. 4-5

Mean effective pressures of 140 to 160 lb/sq. in. are regularly obtained; improved design and efficient lubrication have brought the mechanical efficiency up to 85 per cent or more; and lastly, but most important of all, the reduction in the weight of reciprocating parts, and proper proportioning of valves and induction passages, and the use of materials of high quality, have made possible piston speeds of well over 2,000 ft/min.

It will thus be seen that a good modern engine may develop on a bench test as much as four or more times its R.A.C. rating. Hence the dual horse power figures sometimes quoted by makers in describing their engines, the first figure giving the R.A.C. rating and the second being usually the maximum brake horse power obtained on the test bench. The 12/50 Triumph " Herald " is a current example.

4.21 Characteristic Speed Power Curves

If the mean effective pressure and the mechanical efficiency of an engine remained constant as the speed increased, then both the indicated and brake horse power would increase in direct proportion to the speed, and the characteristic curves of the engine would be of the simple form shown in Fig. 4-5, in which the line marked b.m.e.p. is the product of " indicated m.e.p." and mechanical efficiency, and is known as " brake mean effective pressure " or shortly as " brake mean pressure." Theoretically there would be no limit to the horse power obtainable from the engine, as any required figure could be obtained by a proportional increase in speed. It is, of course, hardly necessary to point out that in practice a limit is imposed by the high stresses and bearing loads set up by the inertia of the reciprocating parts, which would ultimately lead to fracture or bearing seizure.

Apart from this question of mechanical failure, however, there are reasons which cause the characteristic curves to vary from the simple straight lines of Fig. 4-5, and which result in a point of maximum brake horse power being reached at a certain speed which depends on the individual characteristics of the engine.

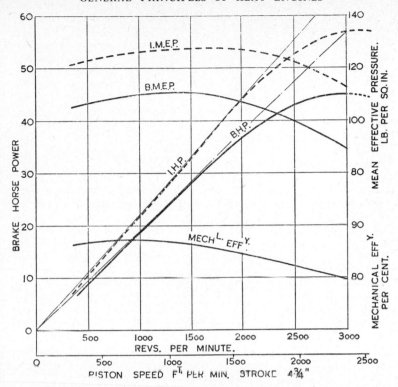

Fig. 4-6: Power curves of typical engine

Characteristic curves of an early four-cylinder engine of 3 in. bore and $4\frac{3}{4}$ in. stroke are given in Fig. 4-6. The straight radial lines tangential to the actual power curves correspond to the power lines in Fig. 4-5, but the indicated and brake mean pressures do not, as was previously assumed, remain constant as the speed increases.

On examining these curves it will be seen first of all that the mean effective pressure is not constant. It should be noted that full throttle conditions are assumed—that is, the state of affairs for maximum power at any given speed.

At low speeds the i.m.e.p. is less than its maximum value owing partly to carburation effects, and partly to the valve timing being designed for a moderately high speed; it reaches its maximum value at about 1,800 r.p.m., and thereafter decreases more and more rapidly as the speed rises. This falling off at high speeds is due almost entirely to the lower volumetric efficiency, or less complete filling of the cylinder consequent on the greater drop of pressure absorbed in forcing the gases at high speeds through the induction passages and valve ports.

49

When the m.e.p. falls at the same rate as the speed rises, the horse power remains constant, and when the m.e.p. falls still more rapidly the horse power will actually decrease as the speed rises. This falling off is even more marked when the b.m.e.p. is considered, for the mechanical efficiency decreases with increase of speed, owing to the greater friction losses. The net result is that the b.h.p. curve departs from the ideal straight line more rapidly than does the i.h.p. curve. The b.m.e.p. peaks at about 1,400 r.p.m., the indicated power at 3,200 and the brake power at 3,000 r.p.m., where 45 h.p. is developed.

4.22   Torque Curve

If a suitable scale is applied, the b.m.e.p. curve becomes a " torque " curve for the engine, that is, it represents the value, at different speeds, of the mean torque developed at the clutch under full throttle conditions—for there is a direct connection between the b.m.e.p. and the torque, which depends only on the number and dimensions of the cylinders, that is, on the total swept volume of the engine.   This relationship is arrived at as follows:

If there are n cylinders, the total work done in the cylinders per revolution is—

Work per revolution $= p \times \dfrac{\pi}{4} D^2 \times L \times n \times \frac{1}{2}$ inch-pounds (see

page 45), if L is here the stroke in *inches*.

Therefore the work at the clutch is—

Brake work $= \eta \times p \times \dfrac{\pi}{4} D^2 \times L \times n \times \frac{1}{2}$ inch-pounds.

But the work at the clutch is also equal to the mean torque multiplied by the angular distance moved through in radians, or $T \times 2\pi$ inch-pounds per revolution if T is measured in pound-inches.

Therefore—

$$T \times 2\pi = \eta \times p \times \frac{\pi}{4} D^2 \times L \times n \times \tfrac{1}{2}$$

$$\text{or} \qquad T = \eta\, p \times \frac{\left(\frac{\pi}{4} D^2 \times L \times n\right)}{4\pi}$$

Now $\dfrac{\pi}{4} D^2 \times L \times n$ is the total stroke volume or cubic capacity of the engine, which may be denoted by V.   Therefore we have—

$$T = \eta\, p \times \frac{V}{4\pi}$$

where $\eta\, p$ is the b.m.e.p. and $\dfrac{V}{4\pi}$ is a numerical constant for the

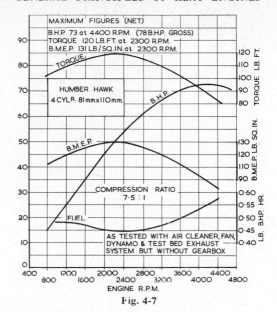

Fig. 4-7

engine, so that the b.m.e.p. curve is also the torque curve if a suitable scale is applied.

In the case of the engine of Fig. 4-6, the bore and stroke are 3 in and $4\frac{3}{4}$ in respectively, and V is 134 cu. in.

Thus $T = \eta\, p \times \dfrac{134}{4\,\pi}$

and the maximum brake torque is—

$T = 110 \cdot 5 \times 10 \cdot 7 = 1,182$ lb-in, or $98 \cdot 5$ lb-ft.

It is more usual to calculate the b.m.e.p. (which gives a readier means of comparison between different engines) from the measured value of the torque obtained from a bench test.

Indicated mean pressure and mechanical efficiency are difficult to measure, and are ascertained when necessary by laboratory researches.

Mean torque, on the other hand, can be measured accurately and easily by means of the various commercial dynamometers available. The necessary equipment and procedure are in general use for routine commercial tests. It is then a simple matter to calculate from the measured torque the corresponding brake mean pressure or b.m.e.p.—

$\eta\, p$ or b.m.e.p. $= T$ lb-in $\times \dfrac{4\,\pi}{V \text{ cu. in.}} = T$ lb-ft $\times \dfrac{48\,\pi}{V \text{ cu. in.}}$

The usual form in which these power or " performance " curves are supplied by the makers is illustrated in Figs. 4-7 and 4-8, which

51

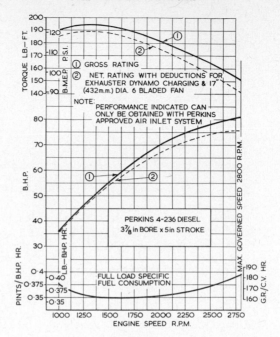

Fig. 4-8

show the torque and power curves for the Humber " Hawk " petrol engine and the Perkins 4/236 compression-ignition engine.

In both cases a curve of specific fuel consumption in pounds per b.h.p. hour is given, this in each case having a minimum value at a speed slightly greater than that for maximum torque. This fuel consumption is frequently shown in pints per b.h.p. hour, but this is not so satisfactory for comparative purposes, as fuels differ more in their calorific value per pint than per pound and it is necessary to know the specific gravity of the fuel before a satisfactory comparison can be made.

It will be seen that the specific fuel consumption of the oil engine is less than three-quarters of that of the petrol engine, an inherent advantage which is possessed by the former as a result of its higher compression ratio.

To the advantage of lower consumption is added that of lower cost per gallon, subject to tax discrimination.

A comparison of these two engines well illustrates the steady approach towards equality of the two basic types. Increase of compression ratio, improvement in fuels and carburation, and the possible future introduction of petrol injection, are means of lowering the consumption of the petrol engine, while advances in mechanical design, lighter injection equipment and the development of supercharging are contributing to the steady improvement in the speed and power/weight ratio of the compression ignition engine.

The consumption of the " Hawk " is exceptionally good, its weight rather on the high side, while the low weight, for a diesel, and high speed of the Perkins engine represent remarkable advances.

The fuel consumption ratio of about 4 to 3, and the torque ratio of about 1 to 1·6 for the same power, represent the basic contrast between the two types. The bare engine weights are about 500 lb and 670 lb, without gearbox.

The bearing of the shape of these curves on the choice of gear ratios is dealt with in Chapter 20, but an important difference between the petrol engine and the steam locomotive and the electric traction motor must here be pointed out.

An internal combustion engine cannot develop a maximum torque greatly in excess of that corresponding to maximum power, and at low speeds the torque fails altogether or becomes too irregular, while both the alternative prime movers are capable of giving at low speeds, or for short periods, a torque many times greater than the normal, thus enabling them to deal with gradients and high acceleration without the necessity for a gear box to multiply the torque. This comparison is again referred to on pages 321 and 447.

4.23 Commercial Rating

The performance curves discussed so far represent gross test-bed performance without the loss involved in driving auxiliaries such as water-pump, fan and dynamo. For commercial contract work corrected figures are supplied by manufacturers as, for example, the " continuous " ratings given for stationary industrial engines.

Gross test-bed figures, as used in the U.S.A., are sometimes referred to as the S.A.E. performance, while Continental makers usually quote performance as installed in the vehicle and this figure may be 10% to 15% less. See also page 146.

4.24 Number and Diameter of Cylinders

Referring again to the R.A.C. formula, it will be seen that the power of an engine varies as the square of the cylinder diameter and directly as the number of cylinders.

If it is assumed that all dimensions increase in proportion to the cylinder diameter, which is approximately true, then we may say that, for a given piston speed and mean effective pressure, the power is proportional to the square of the linear dimensions. The weight will, however, vary as the cube of the linear dimensions (that is, proportionally to the volume of metal), and thus the weight increases more rapidly than the horse power. This is an important objection to increase of cylinder size for automobile engines.

If, on the other hand, the *number* of cylinders is increased, both the power and weight (approximately) go up in the same proportion, and there is no increase of weight per horse power. This is one reason for multi-cylinder engines where limitation of weight is important, though other considerations of equal importance are the subdivision of the energy of the explosions, giving more even turning effort, with consequent saving in weight of the flywheel,

VARIABLE	A	B	C	ENGINE
PISTON SPEED	1	1	1	
STROKE	1	2	1	
R.P.M.	1	$\frac{1}{2}$	1	
BORE	1	2	1	
TOTAL PISTON AREA	1	4	4	
POWER	1	4	4	
MEAN TORQUE	1	8	4	
VOLUMETRIC CAPACITY	1	8	4	
WEIGHT	1	8	4	
$\frac{POWER}{WEIGHT}$	1	$\frac{1}{2}$	1	
MAX. INERTIA STRESS	1	1	1	
MEAN GAS VELOCITY	1	1	1	

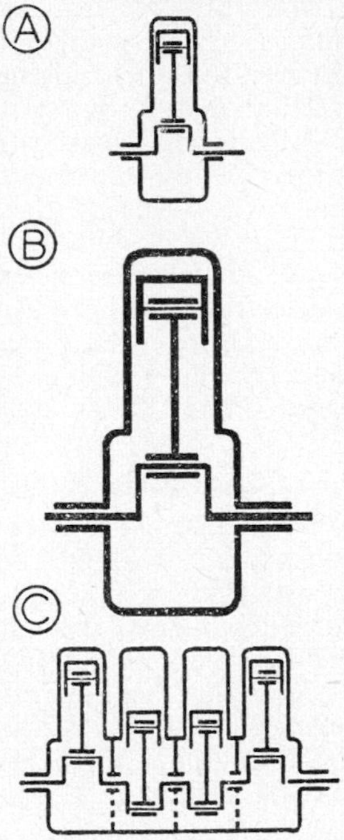

RELATIVE VALUE OF VARIABLES IN SIMILAR ENGINES [FOR SAME INDICATOR DIAGRAM]

Fig. 4-9

and the improved balancing of the inertia effects which is obtainable.

The relationship of these variables is shown in tabular form in Fig. 4-9, in which geometrically similar engine units are assumed, all operating with the same indicator diagram. Geometrical similarity implies that the same materials are used and that all dimensions vary in exactly the same proportion with increase or decrease of cylinder size. All areas will vary as the square of the linear dimensions, and all volumes and therefore weights, as the cube of the linear dimensions. These conditions do not hold exactly in practice, as such dimensions as crank case, cylinder wall and water jacket thicknesses do not go up in direct proportion to the cylinder bore, while a multi-cylinder engine requires a smaller flywheel than a single-cylinder engine of the same power. The simplified fundamental relationships shown are, however, of basic importance.

It can be shown on the above assumptions that in engines of different size the maximum stresses and intensity of bearing loads due to inertia forces will be the same if the piston speeds are the same, and therefore if the same factor of safety against the risk of mechanical failure is to be adopted in similar engines of different size, all sizes of engine must run at the same piston speed. This leads to the relationships shown between rotational speed, torque, power and weight, and gas velocities through the valves.

4.25 Horse Power per Litre

This basis of comparison is sometimes used in connection with the inherent improvement in performance of engines, but such improvement arises from increase in compression ratio giving higher brake mean pressures, the use of materials of improved quality, or by tolerating lower factors of safety or endurance. The comparison ceases to be a comparison of similar engines, for with similar engines the horse power per litre (or other convenient volume unit) may be increased merely by making the cylinder smaller in dimensions, and, if the same total power is required, by increasing the number of the cylinders. Thus in Fig. 4-9 all the three engines shown develop the same power per unit of piston area at the same piston speed and for the same indicator diagram, but the horse power per litre of the small-cylindered engines is double that of the large cylinder, not because they are intrinsically more efficient engines but because the smaller volume is swept through more frequently.

Thus, high horse power per litre may not be an indication of inherently superior performance, whereas high horse power per unit of piston area is, since it involves high mean pressures or high piston speed or both, which are definite virtues provided the gain is not at the expense of safety or endurance.

4.26 Considerations of Balance and Uniformity of Torque

In the next chapter consideration is given to the best disposition of cylinders to give dynamic balance and uniformity of torque, which are factors of vital importance in ensuring smooth running.

CHAPTER 5

Engine Balance

Forces set up when motion is changed. **Balance of revolving parts.** **Balance of reciprocating parts.** **Various twin-cylinder engines.** **The four-cylinder engine. Harmonic balancer.**

A NY moving mass when left to itself will continue to move in a straight line with uniform speed. If a heavy mass is attached to a cord and swung round in a circle a pull, known as centrifugal force, will be felt in the cord. This force represents the tendency of the mass to move in a straight line. Owing to the presence of the cord the mass is compelled to move round in a circle, its tendency to move in a straight line being overcome by the pull of the cord, as explained in Chapter 3.

Thus any mass revolving in a circle sets up an outward pull acting in the radial line through the centre of rotation and the centre of the mass. For example, the crank pin of a motor engine revolves in a circle round the centre of the main bearings, and sets up a force on those bearings acting always in the direction of the crank pin. If this force is not *balanced* a vibration of the whole engine will be set up, in time with the rotation of the crank pin. This vibration will be more or less apparent according to the rigidity with which the engine is bolted to the frame.

The mathematical expression for centripetal acceleration (see page 29) is $\omega^2 r$, where ω is the angular speed of the mass about the centre of rotation at a radius r. If ω is expressed in radians per second (there are 2π radians in one revolution) and r is measured in feet, then the acceleration is given in feet per second per second.

The corresponding force in pounds weight, inwards on the mass, outwards as a reaction on the bearing, is given by—

$$F = \frac{W}{g} \omega^2 r$$

where W is the revolving mass in pounds and g the numerical value of the acceleration of gravity, 32 approximately.

This may be conveniently expressed by means of the engineer's formula—

$$F = \frac{Wr\,N^2}{35,000}$$

where r must now be expressed in inches and N in revolutions per minute.

For example, suppose the crank pin and big end of an engine of 5 in stroke weigh together 4 lb and the engine is turning at 3,000 r.p.m., then, if there were no provision for balance, the reaction on the main bearings would be—

56

$$F = \frac{Wr\,N^2}{35,000}$$

$$= \frac{4 \times 2 \cdot 5 \times (3,000)^2}{35,000}$$

$=2,570$ lb, or well over a ton, due to revolving masses only.

It is, however, possible to balance the disturbing force by means of a balance " weight "* or mass, placed diametrically opposite the crank pin. In engines it is not possible actually to place this balance mass in the same plane as the crank pin, and it must therefore be divided into halves placed symmetrically on either side. If the balance mass is placed at the same distance as the crank pin from the crankshaft axis then it must be of the same amount; if the distance is twice as great the weight must be halved. Thus, in Fig. 5-1, $B \times r_1$, must equal $W \times r$.

Actually this force, with that due to the crank webs, would be balanced either against an opposed crank and big end, or by balance extensions to the crank webs. That part of it due to the big end of the connecting rod would represent part of the total inertia load on the big end bearing.

5.1 Practical Balancing

There is no mathematical difficulty in balancing revolving masses, and with simple disc forms or short crankshafts a static test is often sufficient. The part to be balanced is mounted on a true spindle (or its own journals) and placed on straight and carefully levelled knife edges or slips.

It will then roll until the heaviest side comes to the bottom. By attaching small counterweights until it remains indifferently in any position the error may be ascertained, and correction made by adding balance masses or removing excess metal as may be most convenient.

If the part has considerable axial length, there may be unbalanced couples which a static test will not reveal—it is not possible to ensure that Br_1 of Fig. 5-1 is in the same plane as Wr, though by a static test they may have been made equal. Such couples can be revealed and corrected only by means of a dynamic test during which the shaft or rotor is run up to speed and the couple or moment is shown by rocking or " pitching." Many ingenious dynamic balancing machines have been produced and are in use to measure and locate the plane of the unbalance in order that it may be corrected.

The degree of accuracy with which the correction is made is a question of the time and cost that may be expended.

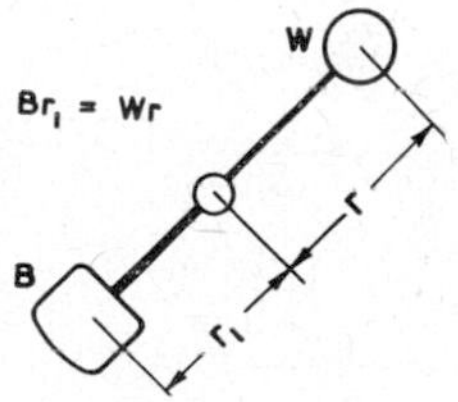

$Br_1 = Wr$

Fig. 5-1

---

* It is more correct to speak of "mass" in connection with running or dynamic balance, since the forces are not due to " weight " which is the attractive force of gravity.

57

The dynamic balance of complete rotational assemblies is usually carried out with great care, and may be dependent on the selected positioning of nuts and bolts.

In reassembling or refilling a fluid flywheel, for instance, care should be taken to replace plugs in the same holes from which they were removed.

5.2 Balance of Reciprocating Parts

The movement of the piston backwards and forwards in the cylinder is known as a reciprocating movement as opposed to the rotative movement of the crankshaft, flywheel, etc. The reciprocating parts of a motor engine are the piston, gudgeon pin and as much of the connecting rod as may be considered to move in a straight line with the piston (usually about one-third of the connecting rod is regarded as reciprocating, the remainder, including the big end, being considered as a revolving mass).

Now the reciprocating parts, which we will refer to simply as the " piston," have not a uniform motion. The piston travels in one direction during the first half of a revolution and in the opposite direction during the second half. Its speed of movement in the cylinder increases during the first half of *each* stroke (that is, twice every revolution) and decreases during the second half of each stroke, the speed being greatest and *most uniform* about the middle of each stroke. To change the speed of a body requires a force whose magnitude depends on the mass of the body and the rate at which the speed is changed, that is, the acceleration. This may be realized by holding an object in the hand and moving it rapidly backwards and forwards in front of the body. (See also page 25.)

The speed of the piston is *changing* most rapidly (that is, the acceleration is greatest) at the ends of the stroke, and it follows that the force required to change the motion is greatest there also. At the middle of the stroke the speed is not changing at all, so no force is required.

The necessary force is supplied by a tension or compression in the connecting rod. If the connecting rod were to break when the piston was approaching the top of the cylinder, the engine running at a high speed, the piston would tend to fly through the top of the cylinder just as, if the cord broke, the mass referred to earlier would fly off at a tangent. Now the reaction of this force, which is required to slow the piston at the top of its stroke and to start it on its downward stroke, is transmitted through the connecting rod, big end bearing, crankshaft and main bearings to the engine frame, and sets up a vibration.

At the two ends of the stroke the piston produces the same effect, that is, the same force, on the crank pin as if it were simply a revolving mass concentrated at the crank pin and, consequently, it may be balanced at these points by a revolving balance mass placed opposite the crank pin as in Fig. 5-2. Supposing that such a

58

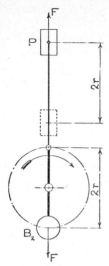

Fig. 5-2

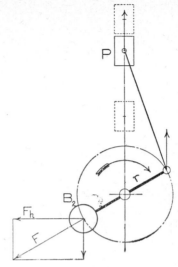

Fig. 5-3

balance mass B_2 is placed on the extended crankshaft webs, of sufficient mass to balance completely the reciprocating parts. The forces set up by the movement of the piston act in a vertical direction only, that is, in the line of the stroke. They will have their greatest value at the ends of the stroke, in opposite directions, and become nothing in the middle of the stroke. Referring to Fig. 5-3, as the crankshaft revolves the centrifugal force F of the balance mass, acting always radially outwards from the shaft centre, has a decreasing effect or " component " in the direction of the line of stroke, but an increasing one in a horizontal direction at right angles to the line of stroke. The decrease in the vertical component corresponds exactly to the decrease in the force set up by the piston. At the centre of the stroke the piston exerts no inertia force since its speed is momentarily steady, and the balance mass exerts no force in a vertical direction, since its " crank " is horizontal. The addition of this rotating balance mass then balances the engine completely in the vertical direction. Consider, however, the horizontal effect produced. The balance mass introduces a horizontal component force F_h (Fig. 5-3), which varies from zero when the piston is at either end of the stroke to a maximum when the piston is in the middle of the stroke when, as the crank is horizontal $F_h = F$. This is dealt with more fully in Section 5.12.

This horizontal effect is exactly equal to the original vertical effect due to the piston which it was sought to balance, and thus the only result of attempting to balance the reciprocating parts completely, by means of a revolving mass, is to transfer the disturbance from the vertical to the horizontal direction without

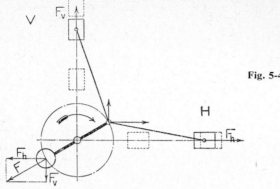

Fig. 5-4: 90° twin engine

altering its amount. In some cases this may be an advantage, but the engine is in no sense properly balanced.

In a single-cylinder engine a compromise is arrived at by adding a balance mass equivalent to a portion (usually half) of the reciprocating parts. This leaves the remainder unbalanced in a vertical direction, but the horizontal effect is only that due to the smaller balance mass. If half the piston is balanced the result is a vertical and a horizontal effect, each equal in amount to half the original unbalanced effect. If a greater balance mass is used the vertical unbalance is less, but the horizontal greater.

It is quite impossible to balance an ordinary single-cylinder engine completely by the addition of balance masses to the revolving crankshaft.

Consider a 90° twin engine, that is, one which is provided with two equal cylinders having their centre lines at right angles to each other in the same plane and both connecting rods driving on to a common crank pin. Suppose that the engine is placed with the centre line of cylinder V vertical as in Fig. 5-4. The centre line of cylinder H will then be horizontal.

We will assume that the revolving parts (that is, the crank pin, etc.) are already completely balanced by the addition of a suitable balance mass opposite the crank pin, incorporated in the extended crank webs.

A further balance mass is now required for the reciprocating parts. This is placed opposite to the crank pin and is of sufficient mass to balance the *whole* of the reciprocating parts of *one* cylinder. As already explained, this will secure complete balance in the vertical direction and further, as the mass turns into the horizontal position, it will supply the increasing horizontal balancing force F_h required by the cylinder H. In other words, when one set of reciprocating parts requires the full balance mass the other requires nothing, and in intermediate positions the resultant effect of the two sets of

60

reciprocating parts is always exactly counteracted by this single balance mass.

An engine of this type can therefore be balanced completely for what are known as the primary forces. The effect of a short connecting rod is to introduce the additional complication of what are known as secondary forces, which are dealt with in the latter portion of this chapter for the benefit of those readers with a mathematical turn of mind who may wish to study the matter further.

5.3 Other Vee Twin Engines

Vee twin engines in which the angle between the cylinders is not 90° but some smaller angle occupy a position intermediate between the 90° twin and the single-cylinder engine, primary balance being approached more nearly as the angle between the cylinders approaches 90°.

5.4 Horizontally-opposed Twin

In engines of the flat twin cylinder type, the reciprocating parts are not balanced by means of revolving masses, but one set of reciprocating parts is made to balance the other set by making them operate on two diametrically-opposed crank pins. The pistons at any instant are moving in opposite directions and the inertia forces oppose and balance each other.

Owing to it being impracticable to arrange the cylinder centre lines in the same vertical plane, there is a small unbalanced twist or couple. This is indicated in Fig. 5-5, which is a plan view of the engine. The inertia forces F F, being equal, have no resultant force, but since they do not act along the same line they constitute a couple. The magnitude of this couple, which tends to oscillate the engine in a horizontal plane, increases as the distance d increases.

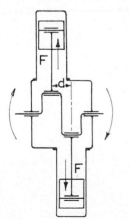

Fig. 5-5: Opposed twin engine

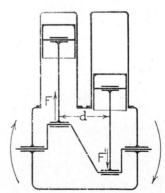

Fig. 5-6: Side-by-side twin engine

5.5   Side-by-side Twin with Cranks at 180°

Fig 5-6 shows a side-by-side twin engine with cranks at 180°. The motion of the pistons is still opposed, but in addition to the fact that the couple is increased owing to the greater distance d between the cylinder centre lines, this arrangement is not so good as the opposed twin because the secondary forces due to the shortness of the connecting rod do not balance.   This will be understood after a study of the effects of the secondary forces which are dealt with in Section 5.12.   The inertia force F, due to the piston which is on its inner dead point, is greater than the inertia force F^1, due to the other piston which is at its outer dead point.   With the usual ratio of connecting rod length to crank length F is about 60 per cent greater than F^1, the difference being twice the secondary force due to one piston.   Balance is, in fact, obtained only for primary forces and not for secondary forces or for primary couples.

5.6   Four-cylinder In-line Engine

Suppose, however, a second side-by-side twin, which is a " reflection " of the first, is arranged alongside in the same plane and driving the same crankshaft as in Fig. 5-7.   The couples due to the two pairs are now clearly acting in opposite directions, and their effects will be opposed so that there will be no resultant couple on the engine as a whole.   The engine is then balanced for everything except secondary forces, which in a four-cylinder engine can be dealt with only by some device such as the Lanchester harmonic balancer, illustrated in Fig. 5-11.

It should be clearly realized that it is only the engine as a whole that is balanced, and that the opposition of the two couples is effective only in virtue of stresses set up in either the crankshaft or crank case or both.

5.7   General Method of Balancing

This method of balancing by opposing forces and couples represents the general method of balancing multi-cylinder engines, the

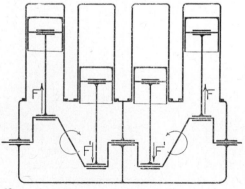

Fig. 5-7: Four-cylinder in-line engine

cylinders and cranks being so disposed that as far as possible or expedient the various forces and couples, both primary and secondary, may be made to neutralize each other throughout the engine as a whole. The best dynamic balance is not, however, always consistent with the best distribution of the power impulses and a compromise must therefore sometimes be made, as will be seen later. Another consideration is that of bearing loads due to the dynamic forces, and here again it may be desirable—as in high-speed racing cars—to tolerate some degree of dynamic unbalance in order to reduce the load factor on a particular bearing.

5.8 Couples Due to Revolving Masses

Referring again to Fig. 5-7, it will be appreciated that the *revolving* masses at each crank pin give rise to couples in just the same way as the reciprocating masses, except that here it is an " all-round" effect instead of acting only in the vertical plane. The revolving couple is unbalanced in Fig. 5-6, while in Fig. 5-7 the two opposite couples are opposed exactly as indicated by the arrows for the reciprocating effects, and the shaft-crank case structure must be so stiff as to avoid whip under the combination of the two independent disturbances.

5.9 Balanced Throws

The stresses and whip due to the revolving masses may be reduced by adding counterweights to the individual throws, as shown in the crankshaft illustrated in Fig. 6-13, thus eliminating the couples.

Cases have occurred where serious crankshaft whip has been eliminated only by the subsequent addition of these balance masses. They may be incorporated in the forging or be separately attached. Clearly their employment makes the crankshaft construction more expensive and in " straight " six- and eight-cylinder engines they may give rise to another trouble, namely " torsional vibration " of the crankshaft.

5.10 Torsional Vibration

Under the explosion impulses the shaft alternately winds and unwinds to a small extent, and as with all types of strain and vibration there is a certain " natural frequency " of this action. The longer and more slender the shaft and the larger the crank masses incorporated in it, the lower will this natural frequency be, and it may be so low as to equal the frequency of the explosion impulses at some particular engine speed. Resonance will then occur between the " forced " impulses and the " natural " frequency of the shaft vibration giving rise to dangerous torsional strain.

Such vibrations may be damped out by the use of a vibration damper as shown in Fig. 7-4 (page 141).

5.11 Secondary Forces and Couples

It was indicated on page 59 that the motion of the piston could be regarded as the vertical component of the motion of the crank pin, and this is known as " simple harmonic motion." If the connecting rod were " infinitely long " or remained always parallel to the engine centre line, or if the slipper and cross-slide mechanism referred to on page 39 were used, the piston, moving in its straight line of stroke, would have this simple harmonic motion.

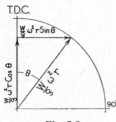

T.D.C.

Fig. 5-8

At any position of the piston measured by the crank angle θ from its top dead centre as shown in Fig. 5-8, the accelerating force required for the piston would be $\dfrac{W}{g}\,\omega^2 r \cos\theta$, while the horizontal force $\dfrac{W}{g}\,\omega^2 r \sin\theta$, which would represent the horizontal component of the centrifugal force of a *revolving* mass, has no existence for the reciprocating mass, since the piston has no displacement, velocity or acceleration at right angles to the engine centre line. This " primary " disturbing force is drawn in Fig. 5-9 as a full line having its maximum value when $\theta = 0°$ and 180°. Its direction must be considered in relation to the forces on the bearings of the connecting rod, which provides the necessary accelerating force and transmits the reactions to the crank pin and main bearings.

5.12 Effect of Short Connecting Rod

In an actual engine, owing to the shortness of the connecting rod, the motion of the piston is *not* simple harmonic, and its acceleration and the corresponding accelerating force require for their calculation other terms in the expression, of which only the " second harmonic " is of importance in the present connection.

The total accelerating force is then—

$$F = F_1 + F_2$$

$$= \frac{W}{g}\,\omega^2 r \cos\theta + \frac{W}{g}\,\omega^2 r \cdot \frac{r}{l}\cos 2\theta$$

$$= \frac{W}{g}\,\omega^2 r \left(\cos\theta + \frac{r}{l}\cos 2\theta\right),\text{ where } l \text{ is the length of the}$$

connecting rod between centres.

The ratio r/l is usually about $\frac{1}{4}$, and this value has been assumed in Fig. 5-9, the lower full line representing the " secondary " disturbing force which, it will be seen, has twice the " frequency " of the primary.

At the inner dead centre the secondary is in the same direction as the primary, while at the outer dead centre they act in opposite directions.

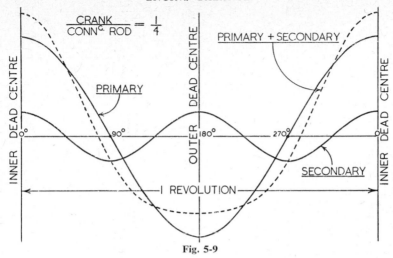

Fig. 5-9

To use a familiar phrase, the " dwell " of the piston is longer at the outer dead centre than it is at the inner (or " top " of the stroke), owing to the fact that the swing of the connecting rod neutralizes to some extent the swing of the crank.

To obtain the total disturbing force on the bearings the primary and secondary forces must be added, as shown by the broken line, but it is convenient and in many ways more enlightening to consider them separately, so that the conditions of balance in respect of primary and secondary forces, and primary and secondary couples may be assessed.

Thus, if the four-cylinder engine of Fig. 5-7 is considered, it will be seen that when pistons 1 and 4 are at their inner dead points, 2 and 3 are at the outer position, the corresponding values of θ being 0 and 180. The primary forces and couples are balanced as indicated in Fig. 5-7, while if the direction of the " secondaries " is examined with the help of Fig. 5-9, it will be found that all four act together, outwards at both dead centres and inwards at mid-stroke. They thus give rise to a total unbalanced force equal in magnitude—with a 4 to 1 connecting rod ratio—to a single primary force, and vibrating with twice the frequency.

In Fig. 5-10 are shown in diagrammatic form the conditions of balance for various arrangements of a four-cylinder engine with " flat " crankshaft. The reader should have no difficulty in checking the conditions of balance with the help of the curves in Fig. 5-9, if care is taken to avoid confusion as to the directions in which the primary and secondary disturbing forces act. The longer arrows represent the primary forces and the shorter the secondary.

They are drawn side by side for clarity, but actually both act along the cylinder centre line. The double coupling lines indicate

65

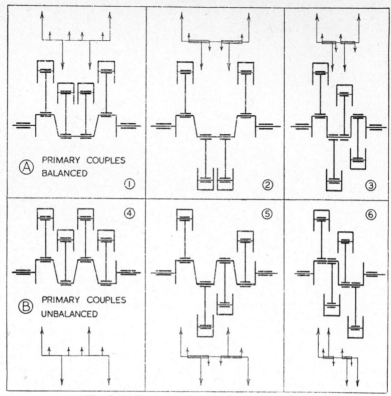

Fig. 5-10: Balancing diagrams for four cylinders

the " arms " of the secondary couples, while the primary couples will be clear.

The following points should be noted :

The balance of primary forces and couples depends on the crankshaft arrangement. Primary forces are balanced in all the six cases, while primary couples are balanced with the " looking-glass " crankshafts A but not with the zigzag shafts B. With the arrangements B the tendency to bend or whip the shaft due to inertia forces is less, and if a third bearing is provided, the inertia loading on this bearing is less than with the arrangements A.

The balance of secondary forces and couples depends on cylinder disposition. No. 2 is the only arrangement with complete dynamic balance for primary and secondary forces and couples.

5.13 Firing Intervals

It will be seen that it is also the only arrangement in which all four pistons are at their inner dead centres simultaneously. This makes it impossible to distribute the firing impulses at intervals of half a revolution, as is proper, because at least two pistons would be at the end of their compression strokes together, and this would result in the cylinders firing in pairs at intervals of one revolution. The smoothness of torque would then be no better than that of the 180° twin of Fig. 5-5. For this reason, arrangement No. 2 is not used in practice in spite of its perfect balance.

Arrangement No. 3 takes its place. Among recent examples the Jowett Javelin may be mentioned. It will be found that all the arrangements except No. 2 permit of half-revolution firing intervals, and the reader may find it instructive to write down the alternative firing orders for which the camshafts might be designed.

5.14 Compactness of Engine

Arrangements Nos. 1 and 4 provide the most compact engine transversely to the crankshaft, while No. 6 forms the shortest engine with the simplest shaft, but has large unbalanced couples. No. 3 is a compact and favourable arrangement with perfect balance except for secondary couples, which are not a serious objection.

With suitable form of crank webs, arrangements 2 and 5 can be made more compact in the axial direction than 1 and 4.

Nos. 4 and 5 would be the most expensive crankshafts to manufacture, and would normally be provided with three bearings, while 3 and 6 are particularly favourable to the two-bearing construction.

The most widely adopted form of the four-cylinder engine is No. 1 of Fig. 5-10 in virtue of its general compactness, symmetrical manifolding, possibilities of economic manufacture and convenience of installation in the chassis, combined with accessibility. The secondary forces remain unbalanced, however, and it is natural that engineers should have turned their attention to the problem of balancing these.

5.15 Harmonic Balancer

A most ingenious device for accomplishing this object is the Lanchester harmonic balancer, which was used in early days in Lanchester, Vauxhall and Willys four-cylinder engines, and has

Fig. 5-11: Lanchester harmonic balancer

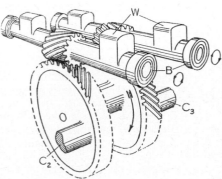

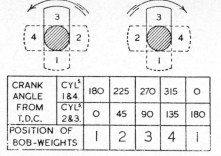

Fig. 5-12

CRANK ANGLE FROM T.D.C.	CYL^s 1 & 4.	180	225	270	315	O
	CYL^s 2 & 3.	O	45	90	135	180
POSITION OF BOB-WEIGHTS		1	2	3	4	1

been employed in numerous instances to cure vibration troubles in stationary and marine engines.

If suitable bob-weights are mounted on two shafts geared together to turn at the same speed in opposite directions, it is possible to produce the effect of a reciprocating mass having simple harmonic motion.

If the device is arranged to run at twice crankshaft speed, and is suitably proportioned, it may be made to balance the sum of the secondaries due to the four pistons.

One form of the device is shown in Fig. 5-11. C_2 and C_3 are the two inner crank pins of an ordinary four-throw shaft with three bearings.

The crank webs on each side of the centre bearing are circular in form and provided with helical gear rings which drive at double crankshaft speed the two cross shafts carried in bearings B.

Each of these shafts carries for symmetry two bob-weights W, each of which is proportioned to develop a centrifugal force equal to the secondary inertia force of one piston, so that the four bob-weights together neutralize the combined secondary forces due to the four pistons. Since the cross shafts revolve in opposite directions, it will be seen on referring to Fig. 5-12 that in the horizontal direction the two pairs of bob-weights neutralize each other, while they combine in the direction of the piston movement to give a reciprocating effect in opposite phase to the secondary piston disturbance. Thus complete dynamic balance of the engine is obtained.

5.16 Meadows' Harmonic Balancer

An interesting modern example of the harmonic balancer is that fitted by Messrs. Henry Meadows to certain of their four-cylinder c.i. engines.

This is designed as a unit assembly interposed between the bottom of the crank case and the lower sump, which may be fitted in applications where improved balance and freedom from transmitted vibration may be important considerations.

Two parallel longitudinal shafts are driven from the crankshaft by duplex roller chain and helical gearing, in opposite directions and at twice crankshaft speed.

There are four plain bushed bearings of the camshaft type to each shaft.

The necessary unbalance of the shafts is obtained partly by grinding one side of each shaft between the jumped-up bearing journals, and partly by the addition of small bob-weights to which correction can readily be made by grinding as necessary. The bob-weights just clear the bearing bores during assembly.

Fig. 5-13 shows the arrangement in a diagrammatic manner. The shafts are shown in the position at which the unbalances act outwards in opposition, producing no resultant horizontal force since none is required.

In the vertical direction the forces are added as in the Lanchester device described above.

The balance of six- and eight-cylinder engines is dealt with in Chapter 7.

5.17 Flexible Mountings

An engine which is perfectly balanced for forces and couples in the sense described above will have no tendency to move, or to transmit vibration to the frame or foundation to which it is attached, as a result of the sources of disturbance so far enumerated.

Small imperfections of actual balance may be troublesome in extreme circumstances, but the presence of the unbalanced secondary inertia forces in four-cylinder engines not provided with harmonic balancers may involve considerable vibration troubles.

This type of simple, inexpensive engine construction is increasingly popular for medium sized cars, at the expense of the admittedly superior mechanical properties of the six, which at one time appeared likely to oust the four from favour.

Resonant vibration of body panels, or " boom," arising from the unbalanced secondaries, intensified by frameless or unitary chassis

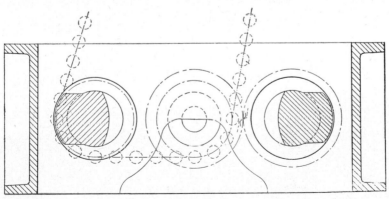

Fig. 5-13

construction, has forced designers to give urgent attention to methods of engine mounting to ensure that improved comfort in riding and silencing shall not be offset by fatiguing vibration effects.

5.18 Torsional Disturbances

Further disturbing effects, not capable of internal balance by the methods described above, are due to driving and inertia *torque* reactions.

Useful torque cannot be transmitted from the engine as a result of the internal gas pressures without a corresponding torsional reaction on the engine mass, arising through piston and bearing side-thrust.

This has a mean value determining the power at any instant, and a series of harmonics representing the fluctuations of torque on the crankshaft due to the variable gas pressures and their effective action.

These harmonics are a source of torsional vibration of the engine on its mounting, the frequencies ranging from the " $\frac{1}{2}$ order " or cycle frequency of the individual cylinders, to the higher orders. If the indicator diagrams of the several cylinders were precisely similar, there would be no " $\frac{1}{2}$ order " or half engine speed frequency, apart from camshaft effects.

" Inertia torque reaction " arising quite independently from gas pressures, may be visualized as the reaction of torque applied to the crankshaft by the flywheel to effect the piston accelerations. The connecting rod obliquities and piston side-thrusts develop the inertia torque and its reaction, which can be most noticeable under overrun conditions. Frequencies are the 1st, 2nd, 4th, 6th, etc., but only the 1st and 2nd are important.

5.19 Modes of Vibration, Natural Frequency, Forcing Frequency and Resonance

Any mass of finite dimensions, free to move in space, possesses six degrees of freedom, three of translation along, and three of rotation about, three mutually perpendicular axes. These axes may be arbitrarily chosen, in relation to the crankshaft axis, which has no significance while the engine is at rest, or may be the three " principal axes of inertia " of the engine mass, both sets passing through the mass centre of the unit.

The former may have no fundamental relation to the rotational inertias of the unit, but are convenient for calculations connected with static and transient loads due to dead weight, road shocks, cornering, braking and, if the crankshaft axis is chosen, driving thrust and torque reaction due to mean driving torque and impulsive clutch engagement from which clutch judder may arise.

Any " mode of motion " may be resolved into a number or all of these translations and rotations, the modes of motion becoming " modes of vibration " when regular periodic forces and torques are applied.

Engine mountings must be designed to completely constrain the power unit against these static and vibratory loads and dis-

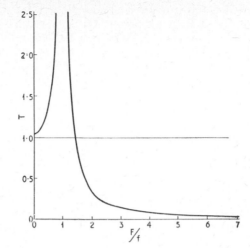

Fig. 5-14: Transmitted
vibration

turbances, with the maximum degree of insulation of the body structure from noise and transmitted vibrations of uncomfortable frequency.

The number of modes of vibration, each with its natural frequency, of the various parts and accessories of an automobile is practically infinite, and many of these modes have frequencies liable to resonant vibration with " forcing " vibrations emanating from the engine.

Natural frequency is determined by the mass or inertia and the stiffness (as of a spring) of the constraint. The stiffer the constraint in relation to the mass or its rotational inertia, the higher will be the frequency. Any component of the mounting may be called on to constrain two or more modes of motion, hence the value and simplicity of bonded rubber mountings.

Should the forcing frequency at some particular engine speed be equal to the natural frequency of the whole or part of the frame or body on which the engine is mounted, resonance will occur, and the amplitude of vibration, without damping, may theoretically become infinite.

Fig. 5-14 shows the theoretical proportion of the applied force or amplitude of movement which is transmitted from the " exciter " to the support for different ratios of forcing frequency to natural frequency F/f, the *frequency* of the transmitted vibration being the same as the forcing frequency.

It will be seen that when F/f is unity, the transmitted vibration amplitude T theoretically becomes infinite. In practice inherent damping always limits the amplitude, but it is in some instances necessary to incorporate positive stops to prevent excessive movement under certain conditions.

When F/f is increased to 3 by reducing f, only one-eighth of the forcing amplitude or force is transmitted.

Thus for insulation of vibration a low natural frequency, i.e., a soft mounting, is required, but a compromise may be necessary with the greater stiffness likely to be needed to take the various static and transient loads enumerated above. Road shock loads, for instance, may greatly exceed the dead weight.

5.20   Principal Axes of Inertia

If a long, fairly regular object, such as a potato or a lump of firm plasticine, is pierced with a knitting needle in the general direction of its greatest length, an axis of rotation may be obtained about which the moment of inertia is small compared with those about axes generally at right angles to it (see page 27).

There is a particular axis, passing through the mass centre, about which, owing to the general proximity of all the mass particles, the moment of inertia is a minimum for the solid. This is one of the principal axes. The two others, also passing through the mass centre, complete a trio of mutually perpendicular principal axes. Of the second and third axes, one will be the axis of maximum inertia and the other will have an intermediate value. These three principal axes, which may be described in reference to a power unit as the axes of natural roll, pitch and yaw, are the axes about which torsional oscillation can be initiated without introducing lateral or translational forces, and are the axes about which the mass, if supported in a homogeneous elastic medium (such as soft rubber or jelly) and with gravitational forces balanced, would take up component rotations when disturbed by any system of applied torques.

5.21   Importance in Design of Engine Mountings

These principal axes are important in the design of engine mountings, particularly the fore and aft " roll " axis, which ordinarily lies at an angle of 15° to 30° with the crankshaft axis, sloping downwards from front to rear as indicated in Fig. 5-15. Ideally, the mountings should be so disposed as to confine rotation to this axis, so that torsional vibrations may be constrained without introducing lateral

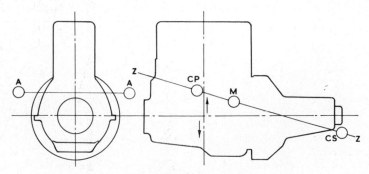

Fig. 5-15: Principal axes

forces. If rotation about any other axis is imposed by the mountings, such lateral forces will arise, and may require additional
constraints.

It will be noticed that, assuming lateral symmetry, the principal
axis intersects the crankshaft axis near the centre of the flywheel
housing, so that mountings placed on the sides of the housing could
deal with torsional vibrations about the principal axis as well as with
direct " bump " loads. The front mounting would be placed high,
as near to the principal axis as possible, and would take the balance
of the bump loads as determined by the position of the mass centre.

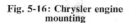
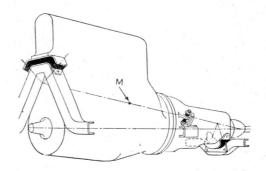

Fig. 5-16: Chrysler engine
mounting

In the Chrysler mounting shown in Fig. 5-16, all reactions are distributed between the front and rear mountings, snubbers only being
provided at the flywheel housing.

Fig. 5-15 also indicates the " centre of percussion," CP. The
position of the centre of percussion is determined by the distribution
of the mass relative to the rear suspension or pivot point, CS.
Usually it will lie near the central transverse plane of the engine,
which is the plane in which the resultant of the unbalanced secondaries in a four-cylinder engine acts. If CP can be located exactly
in this plane by suitable choice of CS and mass distribution, and if
the front mounting can also be so placed, there will be neither
pitching *moment* due to the secondary disturbing force nor reaction
at the centre of suspension, CS. The principle is similar to that
applicable to a door stop, which should be positioned at the centre
of percussion so that, if the door is suddenly blown open against it,
the hinges are not overloaded.

In practice, it is rarely possible to arrange for exact coincidence
as described above, but the central plane is a structurally desirable,
though not always convenient, location for the front mountings.
These are indicated at AA in Fig. 5-15, widely spaced to deal with
torsional vibrations about the axis ZZ.

This " percussion " system appears to be an ideal means of dealing
with pitching disturbances; road shocks and cornering loads would
be shared by the attachments at CS and AA in a ratio determined by
the position of the mass centre M.

A vee arrangement of links with rubber bonded bushes, with the link centre lines meeting on the principal axis and so utilizing the principle of the instantaneous centre may be used, or else a type of front vee mounting of " compression-shear " units.

The arrangement used for the mounting of the three-cylinder Perkins diesel engine in a light van chassis is shown in Fig. 5-17.

Both vertical and horizontal primary out-of-balance couples are present in this engine, and to obtain insulation against these as well as the $1\frac{1}{2}$ order torque harmonic it was necessary to use a suspension giving a high degree of rotational flexibility about all axes. This was achieved by using a vee arrangement of sandwich mountings very close to the centre of gravity (or mass centre) with the front rubber sandwich mounted so that its compression axis passes approximately through the centre of gravity. The degree of insulation obtained is excellent. Engine movement under shock, torque reaction, and when passing through resonance on starting and stopping, is quite large, but has not proved troublesome. A pair of circular sandwich units pitched to give greater torque control may be used at the front instead of the rectangular form.

A great variety of rubber-to-steel bonded units to provide the many different constraints required, has been produced by Metalastik Ltd. and a few of these are shown in Fig. 5-18. The illustration includes early unbonded cushions, bonded double shear and compression-shear mountings, bonded eccentric bush, rubber-steel compression spring, and others.

It is possible to design units capable of resisting various combinations of compression, shear and torsional loads, with appropriate variation in the elastic properties of the rubber obtained by a suitable mix.

Though no mathematical treatment has been attempted here, the reader will have realized that for quantitative analysis of inertias,

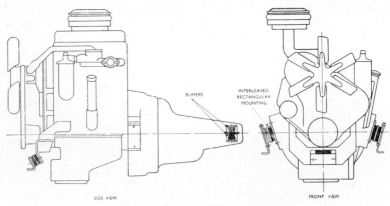

Fig. 5-17: Perkins P-3 mounting

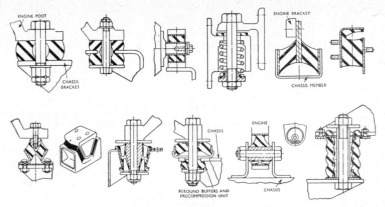

Fig. 5-18: Elastic engine mountings by Metalastik Ltd.

modes of motion and vibration frequencies, advanced and difficult mathematics are required, combined with experimental measurement.

Recourse must be had to trial and error in the development of actual mountings, which can only approximate to ideal arrangements.

Authoritative articles on the subject have been published in the Proceedings of the Engineering Societies and in *Automobile Engineer*, and the interested reader is referred to the comprehensive treatment given in an important paper by M. Horovitz read before the Automobile Division of the Institution of Mechanical Engineers in November, 1957. The present authors are much indebted to the author of the paper, to Metalastik Ltd. for technical information, and to the Council of the Institution for permission to abstract material from the Proceedings of the Institution.

This paper " The Suspension of Internal-combustion Engines in Vehicles " includes a full mathematical appendix and a useful bibliography.

Volume 43 of *Automobile Engineer* contains an article giving details of methods for determination of inertias and other authoritative matter, and " Engine Installation " by H. C. Harrison in Volume 46 of the same journal is of great interest.

CHAPTER 6

Constructional Details of the Engine

General arrangement of parts. Pistons, connecting rods and crankshaft. Poppet valves. Cylinders and crank case. Camshaft drives. Valve operating systems. Auxiliary component drives. The complete assembly.

IN Chapter 4 was described the conventional arrangement of cylinder, reciprocating piston, and connecting rod mechanism of the ordinary internal combustion engine. This construction is, with the exception of occasional isolated attempts to develop the swash plate or similar mechanisms, so generally adopted that it may be regarded as definitely established as the most satisfactory arrangement for all static pressure, as distinct from turbine engines. Many factors have contributed to this stabilizing of design, including mechanical success and reliability, suitability for economic production and standardization, and widespread familiarity and experience in maintenance requirements.

The requirements for continuous and economic production are stabilized and well-understood design features, and thus new ideas and inventions, however mechanically sound and desirable they may be, must conform with these powerful commercial considerations before widespread use becomes possible. Popular prejudice—in some countries more than others—is also a factor militating against revolutionary features. Many advanced designs have proved to be before their time from the point of view of the availability of suitable materials and manufacturing processes and after lapsing for a period have been revived as a result of advances in production technique.

The present chapter is confined to descriptions of the conventional and well-tried fundamental parts and the various assemblies of these which are used in current multi-cylinder four-stroke engines with notes on their comparative merits.

Since the poppet valve still remains a feature almost as general as the crank and connecting rod, its construction and operation are here included.

Sleeve and rotary valves and other special engine constructions, which represent the perennial search for engineering improvement and advance rather than current practice, are dealt with in Chapter 8, while Chapter 7 is devoted to types of engine having six or more cylinders.

6.1 General Engine Parts

What may be classified as " general " engine parts will first be described, followed by the poppet valve and its various possible

76

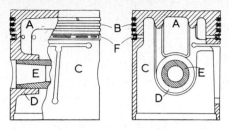

Fig. 6-1:
Typical light alloy piston

positions and methods of operation. General cylinder construction, which depends on the location of the valves, will follow and, finally, descriptions of typical four-cylinder engines will be given.

6.2 The Piston

The piston performs the following mechanical functions—
(1) It forms a movable gas-tight plug to confine the charge in the cylinder.
(2) It transmits the force of the explosion to the connecting rod.
(3) It forms a guide and bearing to the small end of the connecting rod and takes the side thrust due to the obliquity of that rod.

Its most usual form is shown in Fig. 6-1, which shows a typical aluminium alloy piston, with T slot skirt. A is the head or crown in which are turned grooves for the piston rings B. The skirt C provides a bearing and guiding surface in contact with the cylinder wall, and on the inside of the skirt are bosses D for the gudgeon pin E. An oil scraper ring F is provided to prevent excess oil reaching the combustion chamber.

In some designs this ring is placed below the gudgeon pin.

The material employed for pistons is cast iron, cast aluminium alloy or steel of cast or pressed composite construction.

In early years cast iron was almost universal owing to its excellent wearing qualities and general suitability in manufacture, etc. The reduction of weight sought in the reciprocating parts has led, however, to the use of a variety of aluminium alloys and light pressed steel constructions.

Aluminium is inferior to cast iron in strength and wearing qualities, and its greater coefficient of expansion necessitates greater clearance in the cylinder to avoid risk of seizure. To obtain equal strength a greater thickness of metal is necessary, thus some of the advantage of the light metal is lost. The heat conductivity of aluminium is about three times that of cast iron, and this, combined with the greater thickness necessary for strength, enables an aluminium alloy piston to run at much lower temperatures than a cast-iron one (200° to 250° C as compared with 400° to 450° C). As a result carbonized oil does not form on the under side of the piston, and the crank case therefore keeps cleaner. This cool-running property of aluminium is now recognized as being quite as valuable as its lightness; indeed, pistons are sometimes made thicker than necessary for strength in order to give improved cooling.

6.3 Special Forms of Piston

The greater allowance for expansion necessary with most light alloy pistons gives rise to what is known as piston " slap," that is, the noise caused by the movement of the piston, when cold, from one side of the cylinder to the other. As the piston warms up the clearance is reduced and the noise usually disappears. In order that finer clearances may be used without risk of seizure, special alloys have been introduced, and many proprietary designs of piston, aimed at limiting the changes of form which arise with changes of temperature, are in use. These special designs involve cam-grinding to non-circular forms, semi-flexible skirts incorporating oblique slits, controlled distortion and the like expedients.

6.4 " Lo-Ex " Alloy for Pistons

An interesting development in light alloys for pistons is known by the trade name of " Lo-Ex," signifying low expansion with temperature. It is an aluminium alloy containing 11 to 13 per cent of silicon, 0·7 to 2·5 per cent of nickel and about 1 per cent each of magnesium and copper. The coefficient of expansion is actually only about 20 per cent less than that of pure aluminium, but this improvement, combined with good wear- and heat-resisting qualities, makes the alloy a valuable one.

6.5 Birmingham Aluminium Casting Co. Ltd.

The above Company, in addition to a very large range of structural components in sand-cast and die-cast aluminium alloys, has produced interesting designs of piston. The principle of the Invar strut piston, which is not now in production, was based on the negligible coefficient of expansion of the alloy of nickel 36% and iron 64% known as " Invar ". Ties of plate form were completely embedded in struts connecting the gudgeon pin bosses to the slipper portions of the skirt, and on the gudgeon pin axis all metal was kept well clear of the cylinder wall, to allow for expansion along this axis, while clearances on the thrust axis could be kept small owing to the restraint of the Invar.

The Company, whose products bear the trade name " Birmal ", holds the sole rights in Britain for the manufacture of " Autothermic " and the currently produced " Autothermatic " pistons, patented by Mahle Kom-Gess in Germany.

In these, a bi-metallic distortion due to the different coefficients of expansion of the insert and the parent metal, transfers some of the generous initial clearance provided on the gudgeon pin axis to the thrust axis as the piston warms up. This action enables small clearances to be maintained on the thrust axis in both the cold and hot conditions, giving quieter running.

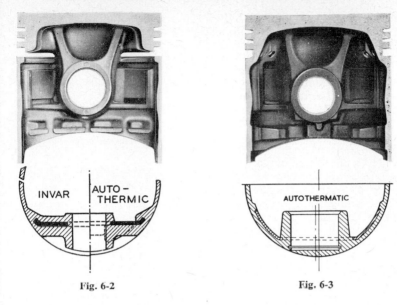

Fig. 6-2   Fig. 6-3

Fig. 6-2 shows a current Autothermic piston and Fig. 6-3 the later Autothermatic design, in both of which the insert is curved and extended towards the thrust axis to give improved control. A slit skirt and heat barrier slots are provided in the former, but neither in the latter, which is intended for the heavier duty demanded in modern engines and requiring more rigid pistons.

The line views illustrate both the obsolescent and current forms of the inserts, which are applied as indicated in the text.

The authors are indebted to the Company for information and photographs.

6.6 Flower Bi-metal Piston

An interesting example of the bi-metal construction is the Flower design, partial cross sections of which are shown in Fig. 6-4. A tubular steel shell S is formed with dished conical portions having inwardly extended short cylindrical portions incorporated in the gudgeon pin bosses, the bond being further assisted by means of holes drilled through these cylindrical portions of the shell. This steel shell, which forms the skirt of the piston, is accurately positioned in the mould, and the aluminium alloy forming the head, gudgeon pin bosses and frame of the piston is then cast within it. The aluminium, on cooling, shrinks away from the shell over the greater part of the surface, contact being maintained at the areas C and D in the gudgeon pin bosses, where a very firm and rigid bond is obtained. Additional contact at the bottom of the skirt, in order to obviate any danger of rocking, is provided for in the following manner. Before

79

insertion in the mould, the bottom of the shell is expanded slightly as indicated by the dotted lines. After casting and cooling, the enlarged diameter is closed in to make contact with the aluminium. The steel shell, owing to the light section of the aluminium at this point, and the moderate temperature, will easily control the amount of expansion. It will thus be seen that the steel shell, while functionally a part of the piston, will behave to a considerable extent thermally as part of the cylinder wall, relative expansion being very small and so permitting small clearances to be used.

Heat flow from the head will take place for the most part through the piston rings, as is normally the case in the opinion of many, though not all, experts.

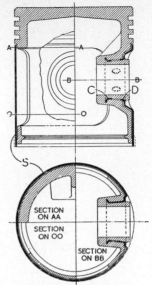

Fig. 6-4: Flower piston

A great variety of special designs of piston developed to meet the individual requirements of engine builders is produced by such well-known firms as Specialloid, Wellworthy, Hepworth & Grandage, Brico, etc.

The use of lead, tin or cadmium plating is extending, current practice favouring the latter.

Such a soft metal coating, extremely thin but most closely bonded, has a remarkable effect in protecting both piston and bore from scuffing, particularly in the running-in stages.

6.7 Specialloid Pistons

Specialloid production covers a wide range of pistons for aero, automobile petrol engines and diesel types as used for commercial vehicle, industrial stationary, rail traction, marine main propulsion and auxiliary purposes.

A design feature of the modern Specialloid diesel piston is the vertical ribbing on the internal surface of the skirt and the solid piers which take the load directly from the crown to the gudgeon pin bearing area. This makes possible the use of mechanized foundry apparatus having a single piece core which may be cooled by air, water, or low pressure steam, to equalize the freezing rate throughout the casting.

Extensive research has been devoted to the manner in which pistons of different designs respond to operating conditions, and the results have led to the adoption of the Thermoflow principle, where there are no abrupt changes in the sections which would form a heat flow barrier. The crown, ring-belt and skirt sections are proportioned to the thermal characteristics, which results in a substantial reduction in operating temperatures, thereby reducing the tendency for ring sticking and distortion or thermal cracking in the region of the valve pockets on the rim of the combustion bowl. The preferred material is a low expansion high tensile alloy having an 11–12% silicon content referred to as Specialloid S.132.

Fig. 6-5 shows a typical heavy duty Thermoflow piston as used in highly rated diesel engines.

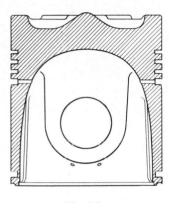

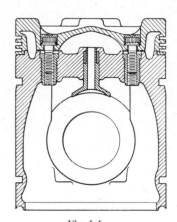

Fig. 6-5   Fig. 6-6

The multi-piece type of oil-cooled piston with either a forged steel or Nimonic iron crown, which in some cases incorporates the ring grooves, is becoming essential for highly rated engines. The crown is secured to the main body by bolts and cooling oil is fed either to the interspace or through channels and grooving between the two faces from the crankshaft, via a drilled connecting rod and a spring loaded pick-up pad which operates off the small end. Fig. 6-6 shows such a piston of medium size with forged steel combined crown and ring-belt, secured by set-bolts with heads in the crown. The crown can be removed for examination or replacement of the rings without withdrawing the main body of the piston from the cylinder bore, or disturbing either the big or small end bearing assemblies.

Noise reduction is effected in the case of medium rated petrol engines by using pistons incorporating T-slotting, which gives a combination of close clearances and skirt flexibility. For engines of the high performance type a flexible skirt is not favoured, instead thermal slotting is incorporated above the gudgeon pin, to form a heat barrier below the crown. This, in conjunction with low expansion alloys and machining to a barrelled form with a diminishing ovality, enables close clearances around the skirt to be used with safety.

Fig. 6-7

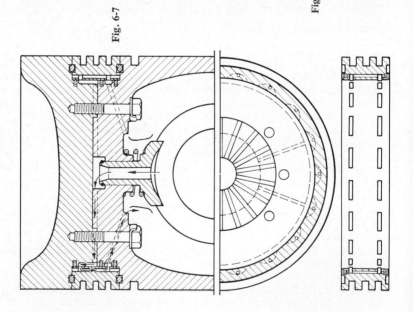

Fig. 6-8

A relatively large three-piece, oil-cooled piston for a marine type engine of 11½ in. cylinder bore is illustrated in Fig. 6-7

The construction permits of a wide choice of materials, especially for the ring-belt. Particular attention is paid to the oil ways and the flow path to obtain the maximum cooling effect at the ring grooves without over-cooling of the crown, with possible adverse effects on the combustion processes. In this design the heads of the set-bolts are inside the piston, but in these large engines access for removal can be obtained through the crankcase doors without disturbing the connecting rod assembly. The exploded view of Fig. 6-8 shows a three-part diesel piston arranged for four valves.

The authors are much indebted to Specialloid Limited for information and for drawings from which the figures were prepared.

6.8 Wellworthy Pistons

In the motor trade, the firm of Wellworthy Ltd. holds a high place in respect of the manufacture of pistons and rings for petrol and diesel engines.

They have the sole manufacturing rights in Great Britain of the " Al-Fin " molecular bonding process for cast iron inserted ring carriers for the top piston ring of high duty pistons. At one time applied to two or more rings, these inserted carriers are currently applied to only one ring as shown in the diesel piston of Fig. 6-9.

(a)   (b)

Fig. 6-9

The wear in the vulnerable top groove is thereby reduced to a minimum as compared with that which it would have been in the unprotected light alloy.

The Al-Fin metallurgical processes have overcome the great difficulties experienced through oxidation of the aluminium during casting and a close molecular bond is obtained which obviates any risk of the insert working loose.

In petrol engines where the severity of the working conditions does not justify the use of an insert, successful protection of the grooves has been obtained by the anodizing process.

The two pistons of Fig. 6-9 are typical of current Wellworthy construction. At (a) there is a petrol engine piston which has a slit skirt and heat barrier slots on *both* sides, but it may be noted that for severe conditions in modern engines of high compression ratio and high maximum speed there is a tendency to obtain greater rigidity by discarding slit skirts and other devices that increase flexibility. The diesel piston at (b) has neither slit skirt nor heat barrier slots. Metallurgical developments in cylinders, pistons and rings, careful control of manufacturing tolerances, attention to lubrication and in certain cases, slight off-set of the gudgeon pin axis, have mitigated " piston slap " in new engines.

The authors wish to thank the makers for information and illustrations.

6.9 Piston Rings

The metallurgy of piston rings has received intensive study, and their manufacture employs the most modern production technique, developed to meet the exacting conditions in modern high duty engines in performing the three functions of—

(1) Providing a pressure seal to prevent blow-by of the high temperature gases;

(2) Forming the main path for conduction of heat from the piston crown to the cylinder walls; and

(3) Controlling the flow of oil to the skirt and rings themselves in adequate quantity while preventing an excessive amount reaching the combustion chamber with consequent waste and carbonization.

Fine-grained alloy cast iron has proved superior to any other material for this purpose, having excellent heat- and wear-resisting qualities inherent in its graphitic structure. The ring is formed with a gap in the circumference to impart the property of radial expansion and compression which is necessary for assembly and removal of the ring, and particularly to enable it to exercise flexible pressure on the cylinder walls. The elasticity of the special cast iron is sufficient for these purposes if care is taken during assembly and removal. Many forms of cut have been devised and used, some of great elaboration, but the present tendency is towards simplification, and progress in this direction is indicated in Fig. 6-10 which shows the stepped and diagonal forms in wide general use in early years, and the current simple square cut which is superseding other forms.

Any tendency with this latter type to form a ridge in the cylinder bore, which might be expected, is mitigated by rotation of the rings.

The distribution of radial pressure around the circumference of the ring is important, and correct initial loading is obtained by means of various techniques. A ring which is initially circular will not fit the bore when closed in, but will bear only at the tips and back, and an early and still used method of correction is by " peening," or by imparting hammer blows to the back of the ring in a special machine which provides for accurate variation of both the energy and pitch of the successive blows.

More modern methods used by the leading specialists include hot forming of the ring by subjecting it to a medium temperature heat treatment while in contact with a precision former from which it takes up the correct shape.

6.10   Special Ring Sections

Sections other than the normal rectangular form of ring have been introduced and tried with varying degrees of success.   One of these is the L or " torsion " form, which when compressed into the groove tends to twist into a dished configuration owing to the absence of " compression " fibres above the central plane.   This brings the corners of the section into contact with the sides of the

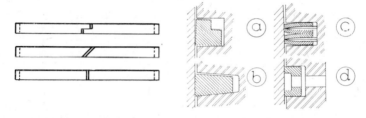

Fig. 6-10: Piston rings   Fig. 6-11

groove and cyliner wall in the manner indicated in Fig. 6-11 (*a*). Both the sealing and oil control of the ring should thereby be improved, though heat transfer may be worsened.

Fig. 6-11 (*b*) shows a wedge section groove and ring now advocated for compression-ignition engines as being less liable to sticking. The type is recommended for use in two-stroke engines.

When bottomed in the groove there is a minimum side clearance of one thousandth of an inch.

At (*c*) is shown a compound ring of special construction, the Cords ring, for which it is claimed that it will successfully seal tapered and worn bores.   Each ring consists of an assembly of four dished and gapped alloy steel washers providing flexible contact on both the cylinder wall and the sides of the ring grooves.

Fig. 6-11 (*d*) shows an oil scraper or control ring in which the desirable degree of specific pressure on the walls is obtained by suitable choice of width of the contact lands.   In the " delayed-action " type marketed by Messrs. Hepworth & Grandage, a series of flats are formed occupying about half the total perimeter.   These allow oil to pass freely during the early stages of bedding-in and wear, while providing for effective control in the later life of the engine as the ring becomes accurately bedded. This ring is intended for use as an additional scraper ring in a second groove.

6.11   Duaflex Oil Control Ring

Wellworthy Ltd. have devoted much research and ingenious design to the problem of oil control, and claim that their latest design, the Duaflex 61 assembly, has satisfactorily solved the difficulties associated with the provision of adequate lubrication of the piston skirt, while preventing excessive amounts reaching the combustion chamber, with consequent waste and carbonization.

The highly flexible assembly is shown in Fig. 6-12. The two rails A, with rounded and chromium plated edges are maintained

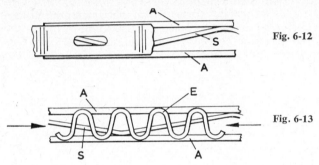

Fig. 6-12

Fig. 6-13

in close contact with the sides of the groove by a crimped spring spacer S. It is claimed that the rounded edges of the rails wipe, rather than scrape, the oil from the cylinder walls. The original form of expander is shown, bearing on the bottom of the groove.

In the new 61 assembly, Fig. 6-13, a backing expander E of stainless spring steel acts as a circumferential arch rotationally located by two tangs engaging in one of the oil return holes, and not touching the bottom of the groove. This arrangement prevents rotation of the whole assembly.

These new ring assemblies are currently supplied to several engine makers as original equipment, as well as being applied to worn bores.

The authors are indebted to the makers for details, and for illustrations from which the figures were prepared.

6.12   Cylinder Bore: Wear and Corrosion

The life of an engine between re-bores of the cylinders is determined by both abrasion and corrosion wear, the chief factors in the former being the nature of the prevailing atmospheric conditions and the efficiency of the air and oil filtration, while the latter is due to corrosive products of combustion formed during the warming-up period, and is most apparent in engines whose duty involves frequent starting from cold. Piston, piston rings and cylinder bore have to be considered together, and intensive metallurgical and engineering research is continuously devoted to the associated problems of blow-by, wear and corrosion of cylinder bores, and excessive oil consumption through pumping action due to lateral movement of the rings in their grooves.

Chromium plating of rings or bores, and provision of " dry " or " wet " liners of special irons centrifugally cast, are methods of attack which are used singly or in combination, with varying degrees of success and commercial justification.

Interest at present appears to be directed towards applying the benefits of hard chromium plating to rings rather than bore. This appears to be effective in protecting both ring and bore. In seeking to mitigate " lapping " effects, considerable difference in relative hardness of the moving parts should be sought, so that abrasive particles may be so deeply absorbed by the softer material that this fails to act as a lap for the harder.

Chromium plating of bores has produced remarkable results in reducing both abrasion and corrosion wear, so reducing bore wear that life between re-bores has been extended to four or five or even more times normal experience.

It is, however, costly, and running in a lengthy process, though assisted by the matt or slightly porous finishes used.

There seems little doubt that the exceptional hardness of chromium provides protection against the lapping effect of a soft piston on the theory indicated above, while a hard plated ring has much the same effect in the reverse direction on a moderately soft liner—it is too hard either to pick up abrasive particles and act as a lap, or to be lapped by a " loaded " bore, but has on the contrary a burnishing action on the bore.

Experience and user opinion appear to confirm the value of pre-finished chromium-plated liners in cases of heavy-duty engines in dusty atmospheres, the increased initial cost being more than balanced by reduced maintenance expenditure.

Centrifugally cast, pre-finished liners of alloy cast iron can be supplied to be specially resistant to corrosion wear for applications involving frequent starting from cold, or to give specially long life where abrasive conditions are adverse. These dry liners are finished to very close tolerances, and can be supplied if required to give a " slip " fit to aid easy renewal. They are sometimes copper-plated on their external diameter to aid both assembly and heat flow to the water jackets.

With the pre-finished type of liner the bores in the block must be finished to a very high degree of accuracy in order to avoid distortion of the liners on assembly, the thickness of these being of the order of $\frac{1}{10}$ in, and not providing for re-bore.

Wet liners are made much thicker, as their necessary stiffness, reinforced by joint flanges, must be self-contained. They are usually more easily renewable than the dry type, and for two-stroke engines the necessary scavenge air ports may be readily cast in. The

87

two types are illustrated in Figs. 6-32, 6-34 and 6-35, and may be seen in various illustrations of complete engine assemblies.

6.13 Gudgeon Pin

The gudgeon pin is of case-hardened steel; usually it is hollow and the conventional way of supporting it in two internal bosses on the piston walls is shown in Fig. 6-1. Many different ways of securing the gudgeon pin against end movement have been tried and abandoned, the device now most generally used being the spring " circlip." Sometimes tightness of fit is relied upon, and phosphor bronze or aluminium pads may be placed at the ends; these will not damage the cylinder should endways movement occur. An alternative arrangement is to secure the pin in the small end of the connecting rod and allow it to turn in long piston bosses, while in many cases a " floating " pin is used which is free to turn in both rod and piston, end pads being fitted.

The construction in which the gudgeon pin is secured in the connecting rod is popular with aluminium alloy pistons, in which case the hardened pin works directly in the piston bosses, no bushes being used. When the connecting rod is free on the gudgeon pin a phosphor bronze bush has to be provided; this bush is a tight fit in the " eye " of the rod. The small end bush develops very little wear and requires renewal only at long intervals.

In view of the very heavy alternate loading of the gudgeon pins of compression-ignition engines, special care is taken to avoid risk of fatigue cracks originating at the surface of the bore by broaching or honing or rapid-traverse grinding with the object of eliminating circumferential tool marks. The external bearing surface is finished to a very high degree of accuracy to ensure correct fit in the piston and connecting rod.

6.14 Connecting Rod

The connecting rod is usually a mild steel or duralumin stamping (except in aero-engine work, where it is machined all over from a steel forging). Its usual length between the bearing centres is about twice the stroke.

The small end is either a " solid " eye fitted with a phosphor bronze bush, or the gudgeon pin is secured in the connecting rod by a split eye and a " pinching " screw to close the eye round the pin.

The big end works on the crankshaft and, as pointed out previously, must be split, or provided with a separate cap, in order that it may be assembled on the crank pin. The cap is secured to the body of the rod by two or four big end bolts and nuts.

6.15 Bearing Bushes

The big end bearing must likewise be in halves. The older construction of a stiff steel or bronze shell lined with white babbitt

88

metal, in which tin or lead is the chief constituent, is being replaced by newer constructions in many applications.

Complete shells die-cast in white metal have been used, but for modern high-duty conditions these have been found deficient in strength to resist the high crushing loads arising in modern service. The thickness of white metal is now kept at the minimum amount consistent with production considerations, and at one period the practice in the case of the big end of white-metalling the rod direct by a centrifugal casting operation became popular.

6.16 Thin Wall Bearing

These types are now being widely superseded by the adoption of the " thin wall " bearing, in which a steel shell only about $\frac{1}{16}$ in thick is lined with white metal.

These thin shells are finished to extremely fine tolerances, and with the perfection of surface finish that may now be obtained by diamond turning and boring operations, and by precision lapping of crank pins and journals, it is possible to assemble or replace the shells without any process of hand fitting or scraping whatever, while the flexibility of the shell enables the truth of form to be maintained by the rigid and accurately machined rod-end or bearing housing. Continuous processes for the white metal lining of steel strip have been developed by various firms. The strip in coil form is uncoiled and passed continuously through a tinning bath and a white metal lining fixture, the white metal being cast on to the strip as it moves forward. The lined strip is then recoiled and subsequently blanked and formed by press operations into half bearings.

6.17 White Metals for Bearings

The term " babbitt " metal is used both in a general sense and also for the original alloy patented by Babbitt in 1839. A typical tin base alloy may be 88 per cent tin, 8 per cent antimony and 4 per cent copper. However, the composition may range from 90 per cent or more of tin, with no lead, to 80 per cent of lead and less than 5 per cent tin. Other constituents present, to make up the total of 100 per cent, include antimony and copper, which are usually added as hardening elements. Cadmium, nickel, arsenic and tellurium are occasionally included. The lead base babbitts are used in applications other than automobile engines.

Alloys giving somewhat greater life and load capacity consist of cadmium with small additions of other metals, such as silver, copper and nickel. These are readily bonded to steel shells but not to bronze. Straight mineral oils are recommended for use with them.

6.18 Copper-lead Bearings

For heavy duty and shock loads such as occur in high speed compression-ignition engines, lead-bronze or copper-lead bearings have been developed. The latter name is applied to the softer compositions containing from about 28 per cent to 40 per cent of lead, with a very small proportion of tin or silver, the remainder being copper.

The lining is bonded to the steel shell, either by casting processes or by the sintering processes of powder metallurgy, and has a thickness depending on the type of bearing. This thickness usually lies between 0·02 and 0·06 in.

The harder and stronger " bronzes " are sometimes supplied as solid half bushes, but are suitable for use only with specially hardened shafts. They contain up to about 25 per cent of lead with 5 to 10 per cent of tin.

For crankshaft big end and main bearings, a steel-backed copper-lead lined bearing is most commonly used, and in the most modern practice, the bearing surface is frequently plated with a thin layer of lead, lead-tin or lead-indium alloy.

The higher frictional properties of the copper-leads and lead-bronzes necessitate the provision of greater running clearances than are necessary with white metal lined bearings, in order to permit of adequate oil flow to carry away the frictional heat generated.

The sintering process is now applied to the production of thin steel-backed lead-bronze strip from which wrapped bushes as well

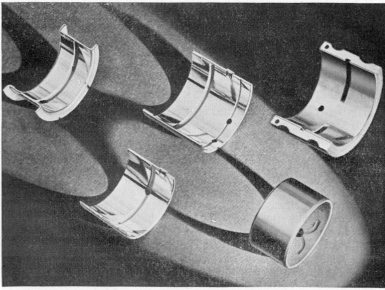

Fig. 6-14: Half shells and wrapped bush

as half shells are made. These wrapped bushes are finished to very close tolerances and, after insertion in their housing by pressing from a suitable arbor, are accurately finished to size by a burnishing tool.

They are made in a large range of standard sizes and for a wide field of application. They are capable of sustaining extremely high loadings.

6.19 P.T.F.E. Bearings

Polytetrafluoroethylene (p.t.f.e.) is an extremely inert plastics material with an unusually low dry coefficient of friction. It is extremely costly, and its use in the solid form as a bearing material is limited by its thermal properties. These disadvantages are overcome by its use as an impregnated bimetal material, but the resulting bearings cannot be machined in any way by the user.

At present available in the form of small wrapped bushes and thrust washers at low cost, it is claimed that the chemical inertness of the material makes it particularly suitable for applications where corrosive liquids would attack conventional bearing materials.

Where oil is difficult to retain, or its presence undesirable, as in food handling machinery and textile and chemical plant, there should be a wide range of applications. In automobile machinery there should be many uses in the less accessible auxiliaries.

Fig. 6-14 shows thin wall white-metalled shells, a heavy shell lined with copper-lead, and a standard wrapped bush made by the Glacier Metal Co., Ltd., to whom the authors are also much indebted for information on the p.t.f.e. bearings.

6.20 Reticular Aluminium–tin Steel Backed Bearings

One of the more recent developments is the use of reticular aluminium–tin on a steel backing. This is an aluminium alloy containing 20 per cent tin. The term " reticular " is used to describe the microstructure of the alloy. The Glacier Metal Co. Ltd., who, in conjunction with the Tin Research Institute, developed these bearings, liken the structure to a loofah impregnated with wax. In other words, all the material of the loofah (which represents the tin), is interconnected, and so also is that of the wax (which represents the aluminium). This structure occurs when the tin content exceeds about 9 per cent by weight and the alloy has been cast, worked and heat treated.

Data published by the above Company show that whereas a 70/30 copper–lead bearing gives 2·3 times the rate of wear of a white metal bearing on a shaft the hardness of which is about 200 B.H.N., that experienced with steel backed reticular aluminium–tin bearings is only 1·6 times that of white metal. The permissible fatigue stress at 100° C is 4,600 lb/sq. in. on the projected area, while at 150° C it is at least 3,500 lb/sq. in.

6.21 Typical Connecting Rods

A typical connecting rod of the bronze bush type for a medium-powered car or lorry engine is shown in Fig. 6-15. The castellated nuts are locked by split pins; or, alternatively, plain nuts may be secured by tab washers turned up against the flats. In some designs, with a view to saving in weight and reducing the number of loose parts, studs screwed into the body of the rod are used in place of

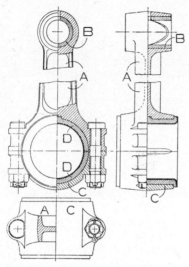

Fig. 6-15

Fig. 6-16

bolts. A is the forged steel body of the rod and C the cap. originally part of the same stamping. B is the bronze small-end bush and D the split big-end bush lined with white metal.

A big end of the floating-bush type is illustrated in Fig. 6-15. This type is sometimes employed with a built-up crankshaft, the floating bronze bush B and the case-hardened steel bush A being assembled on the crank pin during assembly of the crankshaft. The steel bush is then bolted firmly between the cap and body of the connecting rod in the usual way. The inner (bronze) bush rotates or " floats " relatively to both the steel bush or rod and the crank pin, there being thus two lubricated surfaces under relative motion resulting in distribution of wear and, under certain conditions, in decreased frictional resistance.

A modern piston and connecting rod assembly for a high-speed compression-ignition engine is illustrated in Fig. 6-16. This design is used in the Meadows 10·35 litre direct-injection engine, the rated power of which—namely, 130 b.h.p. at maximum governed speed of 1,900 r.p.m.—makes it one of the largest engines of its class produced in this country. The engine has been in extensive use in a variety of marine and portable applications, and the design may be regarded as well tried.

The piston runs in a dry alloy-iron centrifugally cast liner, and is provided with three pressure and two scraper rings, one above and one below the gudgeon pin.

The exploded details of the connecting rod, which is of patented design, show the construction clearly. The joint face of the cap is inclined to the axis of the rod at 35°, in order that the overall width of the dismantled big end may be small enough for withdrawal through the bore of the cylinder; and also, in marine and similar applications, that the big-end cap and bolts may be readily accessible through inspection covers on the side of the crank case.

The cap is secured by four big-end bolts, the two upper ones being screwed into cylindrical nuts housed in the transverse hole through the rod, this hole also serving the purpose of a locating hole on the machining jigs. The cap is accurately registered by the fitted centre portion of the bolt shanks, which also serve to take, in shear, a large portion of the load transmitted from the cap to the rod during the inertia tension loading of the rod on the exhaust and induction strokes. The robust ribbing of the cap, the twin tab washers, and the axial drilling of the rod for gudgeon pin lubrication may be noticed.

The two additional holes parallel to the bolt holes are for jig location and additional registering dowels, as may be found desirable. The authors are indebted to the makers for details.

6.22 The Crankshaft

This is usually a steel forging and, except in rare cases, is in one piece. However, cast crankshafts are gaining ground.

The number of bearings varies from two in a few small engines up to one between every pair of cranks. Thus in a four-cylinder engine there may be two, three or five bearings. The first gives a very compact arrangement and facilitates the use of ball or roller bearings, but a very stiff crankshaft is required, involving large diameter pins and greater frictional losses at the big ends. A larger

Fig. 6-17: Forged crankshaft with balanced webs

number of bearings enables the dimensions of the crankshaft to be cut down without danger of whip, but the cost is increased, and great care must be taken to ensure correct alignment of all the bearings. The most usual number with four cylinders is three but the five bearing layout is becoming increasingly popular.

The form of the bearing is very similar to the big end, the upper half of the bush being carried in a transverse web in the upper half of the crank case, while the cap carrying the lower half of the bush, which has to take the full force due to the explosion, is secured to this web by bolts or studs. Examples of solid forged

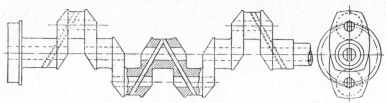

Fig. 6-18: Five bearing shaft for c.i. engine

crankshafts for four-cylinder engines are shown in Figs. 6-17 and 6-18.

Fig. 6-17 illustrates a precision finished, forged crankshaft as supplied by the Laystall Engineering Co. to various engine makers. The extended crank webs supply the opposing couple required in each half of the shaft to balance the revolving couple due to the pair of crank pins and big ends. The bearing loads are thereby reduced as compared with the expedient of relying on mirror symmetry of the whole shaft to balance these couples.

Fig. 6-18 illustrates a stiffly-designed shaft for a four-cylinder compression-ignition engine. Balance masses are omitted from the throws in this case, as reduction of weight is important, and the crank-case structure is made sufficiently stiff to resist the revolving couples which require to be mutually opposed.

6.23 Cast Crankshafts and Camshafts

The development of moulded crankshafts and camshafts, notably by such specialist automobile firms as the Ford Motor Company and the Midland Motor Cylinder Company, and by the Ealing Park Foundry for a wide range of industrial engines, has represented a great advance in metallurgical control and foundry technique.

The result is an application of special " cast irons " to components for which ordinary cast irons are quite unsuitable.

For highly-stressed shafts in power units of high performance or minimum weight, high tensile alloy steels will still have preference, but for ordinary " production " power units the casting process has outstanding advantages in producing complicated forms requiring the minimum of machining, apart from certain inherent merits in the material itself.

The chief of these are the resistance to fatigue and the excellent wearing properties of cast iron, and its capacity to withstand a given flexure with lower induced stress owing to the lower value of its elastic modulus.

Thus any misalignment of bearings due to crank-case distortion will cause a lower stress in a cast shaft than in a forged steel one of the same dimensions.

Internal damping properties under torsional oscillation are superior to those of a steel shaft, and appropriate heat treatment results in values of the ultimate strength comparable with medium alloy steels.

The material used by the Ford Company may be described in a general way as " copper-chromium-iron " with high carbon and some silicon, hence the descriptive name " high carbon, high copper, chrome silicon cast steel " used by some writers. The correctness of the designation " steel " is open to question, depending as it does on the amount and condition of the carbon present. The total percentage of alloys present is about $5\frac{1}{2}$ per cent, the remainder being iron.

An authoritative paper on nodular cast iron, with special reference to its suitability for crankshafts, was presented to the Institution of Mechanical Engineers in April 1954 by S. B. Bailey. (See *Proc. I. Mech. E.*, Vol. 168.)

An illustration of the moulded crankshaft for the Ford V-eight engine is given in Fig. 6-19, from which it will be realized that the casting process aids the economic production of a shaft of very complicated form. The purpose of the balance weights B_1 and B_2 is explained in Chapter 7, where the general arrangement of

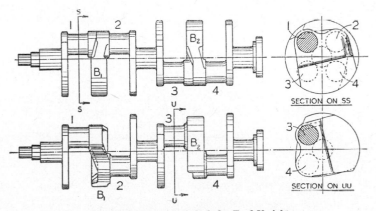

Fig. 6-19: Cast crankshaft for Ford V-eight

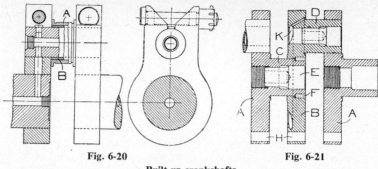

Fig. 6-20   Fig. 6-21

Built-up crankshafts

V8 engines is described. Machining is normally confined to the journals and crank pins and the drilling of the oil ways, the balance being corrected by the drilling of lightening holes and rough grinding of the webs as required.

The use of " chills " for local hardening of cam faces is referred to on page 97.

6.24   Built-up Crankshafts

Two examples of the built-up type of crankshaft are shown in Figs. 6-20 and 6-21.   In Fig. 6-20 is shown one throw of a crankshaft in which the crank webs are permanently shrunk on to the journals; the case-hardened crank pins being secured in the split webs by the clamping bolts shown.   The big-end bush is described on page 92.

The other example, Fig. 6-21, is the crankshaft of a special racing engine.   The webs of the shaft are formed of circular discs A and B, the A discs having as an integral portion the journals C while the crank pins D are integral with the B discs.   The B discs are a tight fit on the journals C and are secured thereon by means of plugs E.   The large ends of the latter are slightly tapered and are forced into the correspondingly tapered holes of the journals, thereby expanding the latter firmly inside the B discs.   Dowel pins F fitting in holes drilled half in the journals and half in the B discs give added security against relative motion of those parts. Similar tapered plugs are used to secure the crank pins in the A discs but no dowel pins are used.   When taking the shaft to pieces, plugs are screwed into the holes in the journals, thus forcing out the plugs E.   To ensure correct alignment of the journals an accurately ground rod is passed through holes H formed in the discs, during assembly of the shaft.

6.25   Surface-hardening of Shafts: Carburizing and Nitriding

The phrase " case-hardening," though also applicable to the nitriding and chill casting processes, is normally used for the time-honoured process of carburizing the surface layer of a suitable low carbon steel to obtain a high carbon case. The carburizing or carbon supplying agent may be solid, liquid, or gaseous. Subsequent quenching and heat treatment is applied with the object of producing a high degree of hardness in the case while maintaining strength and toughness in the core. Case-hardening steels are low carbon steels containing alloys which assist both the carburizing process and the requirements of the core.

The depth of case is dependent on time, temperature, and composition of the steel. The time required ranges from a minimum of about a quarter of an hour in the cyanide bath to several hours in box hardening with solid carburizing agents. In complicated forms such as crankshafts, though selective hardening of pins and journals is possible, the high temperatures involved and the subsequent quenching are liable to lead to quite unmanageable distortion, since the temperature of the whole component must be raised above the critical change point.

Nitriding, though developed comparatively recently, is a similar process in that the chemical composition of the surface layer is altered, but by the production of very hard *nitrides* of iron and certain alloying metals, of which aluminium and chromium are effective in producing extreme hardness in the case, while molybdenum increases the toughness and depth of penetration.

The nitriding agent is ammonia gas, which decomposes into hydrogen and nitrogen at the furnace temperature of about 500° C.

The process occupies from one to two days, and is thus a slow one compared with the rapid production methods described below. No quench is required.

The great advantage compared with carburizing is the exceptional degree of hardness obtainable and the relatively low temperature necessary, this being below the change point of the parent steel. This has the double merit of reducing or preventing distortion, and permitting the normal annealing and heat treatment processes of alloy steels to be carried out beforehand, without risk of subsequent interference.

Experience has indicated that nitrided shafts have high resistance to fatigue, this being attributed to the compressive stress set up in the surface layers by the slight increase in volume which occurs during the nitriding.

6.26 Chill Casting

The process of " chill casting " is a long-established one and is now being applied to the selective hardening of the cam surfaces of moulded camshafts.

By the insertion into the mould of suitably shaped iron " chills," rapid cooling of the necessary surfaces can be effected. This results in the formation of a high proportion of combined carbon, that is of very hard carbide of iron as distinct from the free

97

Fig. 6-22

graphitic form. The hard cam surfaces can then be ground in the usual way.

Fig. 6-22 illustrates such a camshaft made by the Midland Motor Cylinder Company in their Monikrom iron. The proprietary name indicates the three important alloying elements—molybdenum, nickel, and chromium.

A very valuable feature of this method of production is the incorporation of integral gear-wheel blanks, the finished gears showing, after prolonged tests, wear-resisting qualities fully comparable with the usual alternative materials.

6.27 High-frequency Induction Hardening: Flame Hardening

Heating by the induction effects of high-frequency alternating current, of parts possessing electrical conductivity, is now used in a great variety of applications.

In the surface hardening of steel automobile parts frequencies of 2,000 to 10,000 cycles per second are used for normal heavy work, and very much higher values of a " radio " order for specially light parts requiring small penetration.

The heating is followed immediately by a quench, and the process represents the physical hardening of a suitable medium or high carbon steel in contrast to the " casing " processes described above. The general mass of the material below the surface layers remains at normal temperature and is unaffected by the operation, owing to the extreme rapidity with which the heating and quenching are accomplished.

The process requires the installation of equipment constructed to deal with large numbers of particular components, the Tocco equipment, handled in this country by the Electric Furnace Company, having reached a very high degree of specialized, high-production development.

The authors are indebted to the above company for information.

The process consists in the application to the individual crank pin or journal, or whatever part is to be hardened, of a copper muff or inductor block—split as necessary—which forms part of a high-frequency, high-current electric circuit.

There is a clearance space between the muff and the shaft into which high-pressure jets of quenching water may be introduced. Frequencies of the order of 2,000 to 10,000 cycles per second, and currents up to 10,000 amperes are used, and the surface of the part

is heated to the hardening temperature in a period of only a few seconds by the induced eddy currents, the quenching water being then introduced over a period of seven to ten seconds, the time cycle depending on the depth of penetration required.

The equipment has been developed to handle every type of automobile component made of alloy steel requiring surface hardening, and the elaborate automatic controls enable the required depth and hardness of skin to be precisely controlled.

For rapid, precise and large-scale local hardening of suitable steels the process would seem to have no equal where the cost of equipment is justified by the large quantity of work to be dealt with.

The well-known firms of Birlec, Ltd., and Radio Heaters, Ltd., of Wokingham, are developing this class of apparatus in this country.

The Shorter process and equipment represent a successful attempt to introduce precision control into the use of the oxy-acetylene torch for local flame heating followed by rapid quenching.

The equipment varies in elaboration according to the nature and quantity of output, but various types of " push-button " apparatus have been introduced for the purpose providing the necessary relative motion of work and torch with the timed follow-up of the quenching sprays.

For some classes of work, particularly of the largest size where output is limited, the Shorter equipment is probably somewhat more flexible than the highly elaborated but very convenient and accurate Tocco apparatus. The Shorter process is now handled by the British Oxygen Company.

6.28 Engine Valves and Detail

General engine parts having now been described, the poppet valve will be dealt with before cylinder construction is considered.

The cone-seated poppet valve is still, in spite of its defects and its reputation as a source of weakness in the internal combustion engine, in practically universal use, and when in proper condition there is no better form of pressure seal to the cylinder. Once described as a " mechanical monstrosity and a metallurgical miracle," the poppet valve is increasingly being required to perform miracles and is succeeding as a result of metallurgical progress and improved heat treatment techniques.

Failure may arise from a variety of causes singly or in combination. Higher-lift cams and stronger springs, higher maximum engine speeds associated with spring surge, impose higher mechanical stresses on head and stem.

High temperature effects include general oxidation, serious distortion and the corrosive effects due to lead compounds from the highly " leaded " anti-knock fuels. Local cracking and flaking of carbonized deposits leads to " guttering " and rapid local failure of

99

valve seat and lip. Corrosion fatigue effects combined with high operating stresses produce ultimate failure of the head.

6.29 Protection of Valves by Special Coating Processes

Economic conditions of cost and supply that may arise in both peace- and war-time conditions have prompted much research and development in the direction of applying special coatings to valve steels of the less expensive and more readily obtained varieties.

The principal alloying elements are nickel, manganese, cobalt, chromium and silicon, but certain combinations of these, while giving excellent results, are expensive and may involve supply difficulties. Molybdenum, tungsten and titanium are less frequently used.

6.30 Brightray

The nickel base alloys, Nimonic 75 and 80, and B.A.C. Brightray, all containing 20 per cent chromium with 70 per cent to 80 per cent nickel as base, showed excellent resistance to the corrosive deposit effects of high lead content fuels during the last war, but cost and limitation of supply prohibited their general use.

Successful developments have taken place in the application by flame welding techniques of a Brightray coating to certain of the less expensive iron base alloys, such as Silchrome I and Silchrome XB.

It is reported that the deposition requires no flux, is not difficult, and if applied to the seat, lip and edge of crown gives high resistance to corrosion and cutting by high speed gases. Machinability is good.

6.31 Production Surfacing by Aldip Process

This is a large-scale highly mechanized process developed by General Motors.

The current method appears to involve the preliminary finish machining of the valve seats and the rough grinding of the stems followed by the application of the metal coating as a paste, by spraying, or by the placing of a ring or washer on the valve seat. Carried in an elaborate jig the batch of valves is then immersed for a few seconds in a molten flux bath at 1,400° F. Hence the jig is passed to an air blast fixture where surplus aluminium is blown off. The final result is a smooth, permanently adhering coating which does not require a further finishing process.

Photomicrographs of the coating show that an aluminium overlay covers a layer of iron-aluminium alloy, which appears to provide the resistant properties required to improve valve life. Production techniques and sequences of considerable elaboration have called for extensive experiment before large-scale economic development was achieved, but current experience shows improvement in life of coated relative to uncoated valves averaging 100 per cent.

6.32 Poppet Valve

Fig. 6-23 shows a typical general arrangement of a poppet valve in position in the cylinder casting.

The valve head A rests on a conical seating formed in the cylinder casting, the angle of the cone being usually 45°, though occasionally a flatter angle, of about 30°, is used. Flat-seated valves, though they have been tried in many instances, have not proved as satisfactory as the cone-seated type.

The stem passes through a guide G supported in the cylinder casting, the guide being usually cast iron or case-hardened steel and a push fit in the casting. In some cases the renewable guide is dispensed with, the stem passing through a plain hole in a suitable boss in the casting. This construction is inferior, however, since wear at the inlet valve guide causes leakage of air into the induction system and rectification is then troublesome.

The valve is closed and pressed on to its seating by a spring, usually helical, which abuts against a washer and bears on a washer resting on a split collar C, or on a cotter pin which passes through the lower end of the valve stem. Thus the gas pressure on the head of the valve assists the spring in pressing the valve firmly on its seating when closed, gas tightness being readily secured by careful grinding of the valve to its seating.

The valve is opened by positive mechanical means which will be

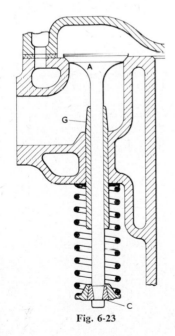

Fig. 6-23

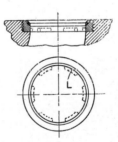

LUGS L REMOVED AFTER SEAT IS SCREWED IN

Fig. 6-24: Stellited seat

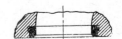

Fig. 6-25: Centri-lock seat

101

Objective	Requirements	Means of Provision
A POWER OUTPUT SMOOTH RUNNING	(1) High compression ratio. (2) High volumetric efficiency. (3) Rapid and efficient combustion. (4) Freedom from pinking (see page 330).	Small volume of combustion chamber. Early closing of inlet valve. Large inlet valve, suitable valve timing, limited pre-heating. Short flame travel, adequate turbulence, good plug scour. Short flame travel, well cooled " end-gas," suitable plug position.
B FUEL ECONOMY (low specific fuel consumption or high thermal efficiency).	(1) High compression ratio. (2) Low surface/vol. ratio. (3) Efficient use of weak fuel/air mixtures. (4) Adequate pre-heating.	Small volume of combustion chamber, etc. Hemispherical form of combustion chamber. Short flame travel, adequate turbulence, good plug scour. Hot jackets and induction manifold.
C ECONOMICAL MANUFACTURE	(1) Economy in machining. (2) Simple castings. (3) Simplified details. (4) Ease of assembly.	Elimination of unnecessary joints and attachments. May conflict with above. Simplified design. Standardization. Sub-, and main assemblies.
D EASE OF MAINTENANCE	(1) Accessibility. (2) Easy renewal of parts. (3) Ease of decarbonizing and valve grinding. (4) Limited weight of components.	Detachable head. Separate cylinder block. Renewable valve and tappet guides and cylinder liners. Unit assembly of head and valves. Sub-, and main assemblies.

Fig. 6-26 : Performance and construction

described later, the lift being usually about one-fifth of the diameter of the seating.

The description of sleeve valves and typical rotary valves is deferred until Chapter 8, as these types pass through periodical phases of popularity and inventive productivity without succeeding in establishing themselves in general use and production.

6.33 Special Valve Seat Inserts

The use of valve seat inserts is extending, and much research is being carried out to determine the most durable form in combination with various valve steels. These inserts are of phosphor bronze, special heat-resisting cast irons, or " stellited " steel. " Stellite " is a class of extremely hard alloys containing—according to the particular application—varying proportions of cobalt, chromium, tungsten and carbon, but without iron. It is applied by a flame-welding process as a facing to the contact portion of the steel valve seat ring. It may also be applied to the conical face of the valve.

The " centri-lock " insert is an under-cut stepped ring of special centrifugally cast iron. The machining tolerances are very closely controlled so that the " interference " on each diameter will hold the seat securely when it is pressed in. Figs. 6-24 and 6-25 illustrate these inserts.

6.34 Location of Valves and Form of Cylinder Head

The requirements to be met in the design of the cylinder head and location of valves are numerous and conflicting, and the search for the successful compromise has led to the designing, patenting and production of a very great number of different forms and arrangements, often with puzzling anomalies and inconsistencies in performance between different examples possessing apparently the same virtues.

The basic requirements to be met are indicated in tabular form in Fig. 6-26. They are stated very simply, but the four main requirements given under each lettered heading with the necessary means of provision cover the more important factors to be reconciled.

Fig. 6-27 illustrates four conventional arrangements which are in wide general use, and Fig. 6-28 and later illustrations give examples or variations of these which are in current production.

Fig. 6-27 (a) is the once popular side-valve construction with all valves in line, the detachable head being of the turbulence type providing for compression or " squish " turbulence, produced as the piston closely approaches the flat portion of the cylinder head. Valve diameter and adequate valve port cooling are in conflict, as with all valves in " single line " arrangements, unless the longitudinal pitch of the cylinders is increased; and volumetric efficiency is further limited by the changes in direction of the gas flow and

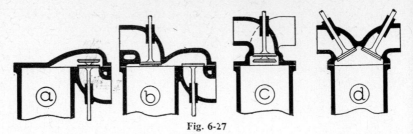

Fig. 6-27

restricted entry to the bore. Requirements A (3) and (4) are reasonably well met, though flame travel is long. Requirement B (2) is *not* met, and the high surface volume ratio of the head, if combined with undue turbulence and over-cooled jackets, militates against economy.

Requirements C and D are well met on the whole.

Fig. 6-27 (*b*) should give good volumetric efficiency as a large diameter inlet valve may be used, and the valve port gives direct access to the bore.

High compression ratio can be readily provided.

Other characteristics are similar to (*a*), though the construction is likely to be more expensive owing to the mixed direct and push-rod valve gear.

In both cases combustion is initiated in a hot region and the end gas is well cooled on a shallow flame front.

Diagram (*c*) illustrates the very widely used o.h.v. arrangement with vertical valves in single line, permitting the use of simple push-rod and rocker gear. The wider cylinder pitch at the main bearings sometimes permits of an increased length of combustion chamber, known as the " Bath-Tub " type, to accommodate larger valves.

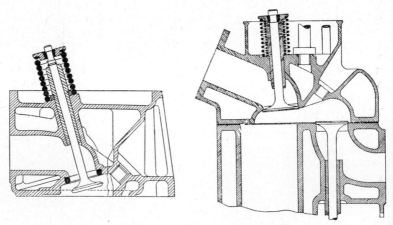

Fig. 6-28: Typical current cylinder heads

The width is usually less than the bore in modern designs to provide increased compression ratio and some compression turbulence.

At (d) is shown the classic approximation to the ideal hemispherical head which is used in many high performance designs. Large diameter inlet valves with free entry can readily be provided and with careful port design and possibly some degree of masking of the lower side of the inlet valve, there should be fair general turbulence though compression or squish turbulence is absent. Flame travel is short, and high compression ratio can be readily provided by means of a domed piston crown.

If four valves of smaller diameter are used the combustion

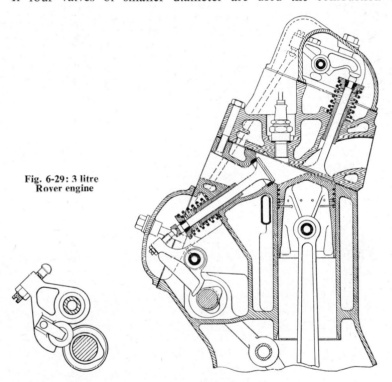

Fig. 6-29: 3 litre
Rover engine

chamber takes the " penthouse " form, and it is somewhat easier to accommodate the sparking plug on the cylinder centre line.

Valve gear is somewhat complicated and expensive, twin camshafts with push rods and rockers being probably the most satisfactory arrangement. The two diagrams of Fig. 6-28 may be taken to represent in each case one or more well-known makes.

Fig. 6-29 shows a detailed cross-section of an unconventional design introduced by the Rover Company which has shown high performance and excellent economy, the best value of the b.m.e.p.

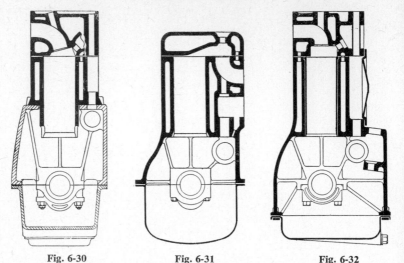

| Fig. 6-30 | Fig. 6-31 | Fig. 6-32 |

being about 130 lb/sq. in. at a compression ratio of 8·0 to 1 with 80-octane fuel. With 8·75 to 1 compression ratio, a maximum of 134 b.h.p. is obtained.

The lowest specific fuel consumption reported is about 0·438 pints/b.h.p.-hr, at a b.m.e.p. of 118 lb/sq. in.

The special features claimed are the approximately hemispherical form of the combustion chamber (though this does not give the low surface volume ratio of (*d*) above), large inlet valve with moderate lift, high degree of plug scour by compression turbulence, and short flame travel. The combustion chamber is machined all over.

The scrap view shows to an enlarged scale an interesting form of rocker introduced to combat some degree of wear experienced with the original design. Rotation of the disc roller in its recess will tend to maintain truth of circular form and thus avoid variation of tappet clearance. See also *Automobile Engineer* of March 1960.

Readers may care to compare these various arrangements on the basis of the table, and for a full discussion an interesting paper by Mr. J. Swaine will be found in *Proc., Automobile Division, Inst. Mech. E.* 1947–48, *Part II*.

6.35 Cylinder Block and Crankcase Arrangement

Typical arrangements of cylinder block and crankcase appear in Figs. 6-30 to 6-35. The black sectioning represents cast iron and the cross-hatching aluminium alloy. While the figures are simplified and to a great extent diagrammatic only, each is represented by one or more examples in past or present practice.

That shown in Fig. 6-30 is the conventional arrangement used in large engines of the highest quality, where it is not essential to economize in machining and fitting. Here a monobloc cylinder casting, with overhead valves in a detachable head, is bolted to a two-part aluminium alloy crankcase split on or below the crankshaft centre line. The maximum degree of accessibility is provided for valves, pistons and bearings.

Fig. 6-31 shows the side-valve arrangement of what has been the most widely used construction but which is now generally super-seded by the overhead valve arrangement shown in Figs. 6-32 and 6-33 with various camshaft arrangements. Modern designs simplify the cylinder block casting and improve accessibility of valves and rockers. A single monobloc casting in iron or in aluminium alloy—in which case wet cylinder liners are used—extends from the head joint face to usually well below the crank-shaft centre line, forming a rigid beam structure of great depth and stiffness. Well ribbed webs tie the crankcase walls together and carry the main and camshaft bearings. The bottom is closed by a light sump which is often ribbed for cooling purposes and may carry the main oil filters. For examination and overhaul, pistons and connecting rods must be withdrawn upwards through the bores unless removed bodily with the crankshaft.

The corresponding overhead-valve construction is illustrated in Fig. 6-32, which shows a low camshaft for push rod and rocker operation of the valves. A dry liner is indicated in this case. The valves all lie in the same longitudinal plane.

End assembly of the crankshaft is provided for in the construction of Fig. 6-33. When arranged for three bearings, the centre bearing is mounted in a circular housing of diameter exceeding the diameter of the crank webs. A popular Lea-Francis design used this con-struction, which provides a rigid and accurately aligned support

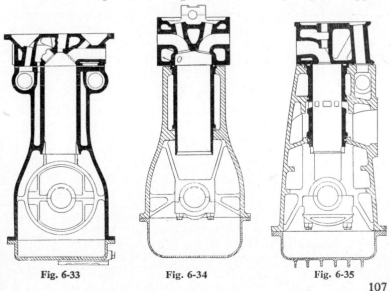

Fig. 6-33   Fig. 6-34   Fig. 6-35

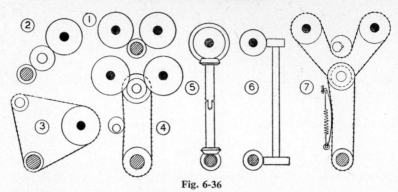

Fig. 6-36

for the crankshaft. Provision is made for twin camshafts to operate the inclined overhead valves which are pitched transversely.

Figs. 6-34 and 6-35 show two examples of wet liner construction, one for a medium-powered petrol engine and the other for a blower-charged, poppet-exhaust two-stroke c.i. engine. The air gallery and scavenge ports of the latter will be noticed. Water joints are made with synthetic rubber rings (as indicated) and gas pressure joints usually by separate gasket rings to each bore.

A light alloy main casting is indicated in these two cases.

6.36 Camshaft Drive

Whatever the type of valve used it is necessary in the four-stroke engine to drive it from a camshaft which runs at half the speed of the crankshaft, as each valve is required to function only once in two revolutions of the crankshaft. The necessary gearing for this purpose is placed, with few exceptions, at the front of the engine, that is, at the end remote from the flywheel and clutch. The camshaft or camshafts may be gear or chain driven, while in a few cases of overhead camshafts a " coupling rod " drive has been used. Fig. 6-36 shows some typical arrangements of two to one drive for both " low " and " high " camshafts, in diagram form.

No. 1 shows the simplest possible arrangement of direct gearing for either one or two camshafts. The wheel on the camshaft has twice as many teeth as the crankshaft wheel, and therefore revolves at half the speed of the latter. Where, as is often the case, the distance between the two shafts is considerable, this arrangement requires undesirably large gear wheels, and this has led to the adoption of the arrangement shown at 2. Here an intermediate idler wheel is interposed between the crankshaft wheel and the camshaft wheel. This idler wheel may be of any convenient size, as the number of teeth in it does not affect the gear ratio. The camshaft now revolves in the same direction as the crankshaft, whereas in the former arrangement it revolved in the opposite direction.

108

A chain drive is shown at 3. This is a very popular arrangement wherein the single chain drives the auxiliaries in addition to the camshaft, the drive thus being a triangular one.

At 4 is illustrated a combined chain and gear drive for twin " high " camshafts. The chain sprocket ratio is 1 to 1, and the 2 to 1 ratio is provided by the gearing.

An automatic chain tensioner of the " Coventry " eccentric type is indicated. The axis of rotation of the jockey chain wheel can swing eccentrically round the spindle on which it is mounted to take up slack in the chain, the desired pressure on the back of the chain being adjustable and automatically maintained by the clock-type spring, the inner end of which is secured to the mounting spindle and the outer end to the drum which carries the jockey-wheel bearing.

Various means of driving overhead camshafts are illustrated at 5, 6 and 7. Diagrams 5 and 6 show vertical shafts driven by bevel and skew gears respectively. In either case the two to one ratio may be obtained in one or two steps as may be most convenient.

In the latter case particularly, ratios of 3 to 2 and 4 to 3 are advantageous.

It will be noticed that in the case of the bevel gears a tongue and slot arrangement is provided so that expansion of the cylinder block will not affect the meshing of the gears. This provision is not strictly necessary with skew gears, though the slight axial movement of the vertical gear that may take place will result in a slight variation of timing between the hot and cold conditions.

No. 7 is the line diagram corresponding to the two-stage chain drive illustrated in Fig. 6-37. This arrangement divides the two to one ratio between the two stages, the tooth ratio of the four chain wheels being 21 to 28 × 20 to 30. This tends to distribute any slight wear that may take place and maintains uniformity of pitch, and also permits the use of smaller chain wheels.

Fig. 6-37 shows the general layout of the two-stage chain drive referred to above. This is the well designed arrangement used in the Jaguar 6-cylinder XK 120 engine of 83-mm bore and 106-mm stroke, which

Fig. 6-37

develops 160 b.h.p. at 5,400 r.p.m.   The construction should be clear from the illustration, and it may be noticed that the positive eccentric adjustment for the secondary chain is provided with two spring-loaded plungers half a tooth pitch out of phase to permit of finer adjustment.

A spring plate tensioner is provided on the non-driving side of the chain and a fibre damping block on the driving side.   This latter makes light contact with the chain plates in the event of any side thrash arising due to torsional oscillations, and so any incipient irregularity is at once checked.

The worm drive for the distributor direct from the crankshaft may just be seen.   This ensures the most precise possible timing of the ignition.

The slotted brackets are used for rotational control of the camshaft chain wheels during valve timing and maintenance operations.

The authors are indebted to Jaguar Cars, Ltd., and the Renold and Coventry Chain Company, Ltd., for photographs and information.

6.37   " PowerGrip " Timing Drive

A recent interesting development is the " PowerGrip " drive which has been used in many industrial applications for some years, and is now arousing the interest of designers as a camshaft drive. The drive is now manufactured by the North British Rubber Company under licence from the United States Rubber Company.

A continuous flexible belt comprises a stranded steel cable or braided core with a coating of synthetic rubber such as neoprene closely bonded to the core, and carrying shallow rubber teeth integral with its inner face.   The construction is described in British Patent No. 618,172.   The drive is transmitted through transversely grooved pulleys of cast iron or steel.

The steel core is built from high tensile steel wire about six thousandths of an inch diameter formed as either a stranded cable 36 thousandths diameter or a flat braid of about the same area but of half the thickness.   The latter has somewhat greater flexibility. The moulded rubber teeth are pitched half an inch apart and are $\frac{3}{32}$ in. deep.   The continuous part of the belt is about $\frac{1}{16}$ in. thick, and the width is determined by the particular duty.

Whichever form of core is used, it is wound spirally around the base of the vulcanizing mould, on a thin lining of wear resistant material which forms the skin of the teeth and inner face of the belt.   Clearance is left between adjacent convolutions to allow of penetration of the vulcanizing compound.   By this construction the steel core, forming the pitch line of the belt, can coincide closely with the pitch lines of the mating pulleys, the teeth of which have no addendum.   Thus change of pitch on engagement is avoided.

Descriptions of engines applying this drive will be found in *Automobile Engineer* for July 1963 and March 1965.

Improved silence and freedom from wear are reported, while

great flexibility and complete absence of stretch and slip are inherent in the design.

6.38 Camshaft Brakes and Compensating Cams

As each cam follower passes from the front to the back of the cam at the point of maximum lift, the effect of the valve spring changes from a resisting effort to a driving effort, and the direction of the torque in the camshaft (as far as that cam is concerned) is abruptly reversed. If the camshaft is long, this sudden reversal of torque results in considerable torsional whip, while if the torque on the camshaft as a whole (taking all the cams into consideration) reverses, then, if there is any backlash in the camshaft drive, noise will result from the blow as the backlash is suddenly taken up. This is avoided in some high-class engines by fitting a lightly loaded friction brake, as shown in Fig. 6-38, which exerts a continuous small resisting torque sufficient to prevent this torsional " flick " or whip. The small amount of friction necessary is often provided by

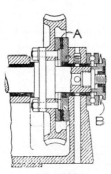

Fig 6-38

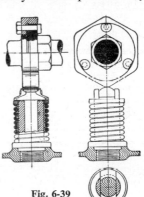

Fig. 6-39

the lubricated contact of a metal or fabric disc A against the rim face of the camshaft wheel, contact being maintained by a light compression spring or washer B.

Another means of avoiding the trouble is the use of a compensating cam operating a special spring-loaded tappet. The lobes of the cam are so designed in number, shape and spacing as to compensate the fluctuations of impulse of the main cams and thus ensure an approximately even torque on the camshaft. A design suitable for twin overhead camshafts for a six-cylinder engine, with spring-loaded " lag-tappet," is shown in Fig. 6-39, and a similar application to a four-cylinder engine has been used.

6.39 Camshaft Bearings

Camshaft bearings do not call for any special comment. In the majority of engines they consist of plain bushed or unbushed holes

111

in suitable bosses in the crank-case casting, the diameter being great enough to enable the shaft to be inserted bodily from one end. Such plain bearings stand up well to the impulsive loads which arise in the operation of the cams, they are inexpensive to manufacture, and are silent in operation. In the higher class of engine,

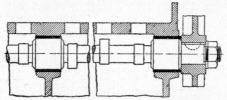

Fig. 6-40: Camshaft bearings

where it is desired to reduce the frictional torque to a minimum by reducing the diameter of the bearings, and also to provide adjustment for wear, the bearing bushes, usually white metal lined, are split, and provided with separate caps in a similar manner to the main bearings of crankshafts. The former arrangement is shown in Fig. 6-40, and the latter in Fig. 6-49.

6.40 Adjustment of Valve Timing

Since the camshaft is made in one piece, it will be clear that no relative variation of the inlet and exhaust valve timing or of individual cylinders is possible. The only alteration that can be effected is the advancing or retarding of all the events relative to the crankshaft, except in the more uncommon cases where two camshafts are used, when the exhaust and inlet valve timings can be varied independently.

The majority of makers key or spline the camshaft wheel to the shaft in such a position that when certain marked teeth are meshed

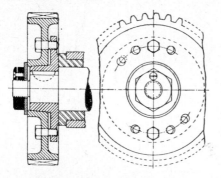

Fig. 6-41: Vernier timing adjustment
Fig. 6-42: Valve timing 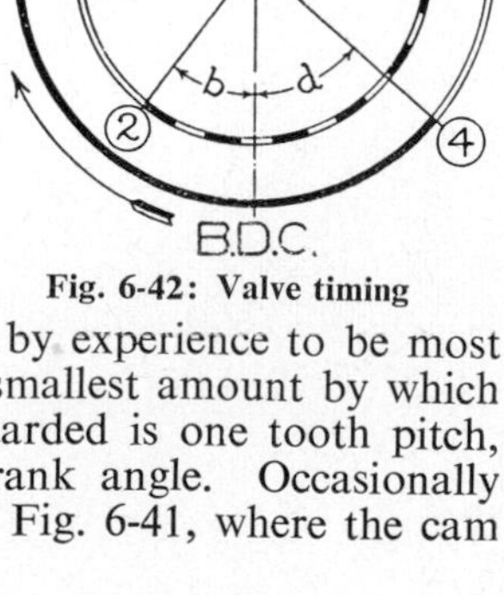

the timing is that which has been found by experience to be most suitable for the particular engine. The smallest amount by which the timing may then be advanced or retarded is one tooth pitch, corresponding to, say, 10° to 15° of crank angle. Occasionally finer adjustment is provided as shown in Fig. 6-41, where the cam

112

wheel rim is formed separately from its boss, and a series of " vernier " holes is drilled through the flanges of the two members so that they can be bolted up in relative angular positions which vary by a small fraction of a tooth pitch. While this adjustment is undoubtedly useful in some cases, and during development work, it is not necessary on the average engine, as the maker, having once found the proper timing, reproduces that timing in each engine.

A timing diagram forms the subject of Fig. 6-42. The five events shown are—

(1) Inlet valve opens.
(2) Inlet valve closes.
(3) Spark passes.
(4) Exhaust valve opens.
(5) Exhaust valve closes.

These events do not take place exactly at the dead centres, but rather " early " or " late " as the case may be. Thus, in order to get the exhaust gases clear of the cylinder as early as possible the angle d is, on the average, about $50°$, and as much as $70°$ in some racing engines. Very little of the useful pressure is lost since the piston is near the end of its stroke, while the total time available for the escape of the exhaust gases is very much increased.

The angle e is from $0°$ to $10°$ or $12°$, a from $10°$ early to $15°$ late, while b is from $20°$ to $40°$ late, in order to take advantage of the " ramming " or inertia effect of the rapidly moving gases in the induction pipe.

The spark occurs about $20°$ to $40°$ early when fully advanced, and approximately at top dead centre when fully retarded.

When the angle e is greater than the angle a there is said to be " overlap," that is, the exhaust valve closes after the inlet valve has opened. The purpose of this is to take advantage of the momentum of the high velocity exhaust gases in producing a scavenging vacuum after the piston has reached the top dead centre.

6.41 Operation of the Valves

The valves are operated from the camshaft in a variety of ways according to their disposition, but only in a few cases of overhead camshafts do the cam faces act directly on the valve stems. In the great majority of cases some form of cam " follower " or " tappet " is interposed between the cam and valve stem. In many cases, including practically all arrangements with overhead valves and a few with side valves, a rocker is introduced, the leverage of which usually increases the lift of the valve in relation to the cam eccentricity. This enables the overall diameter of the camshaft to be kept small, and reduces the frictional and inertia forces.

Four typical methods of operation are shown in outline in Figs. 6-43 and 6-44, namely, side valves, Fig. 6-43(a), overhead valves operated by push rods from a camshaft in the crank case

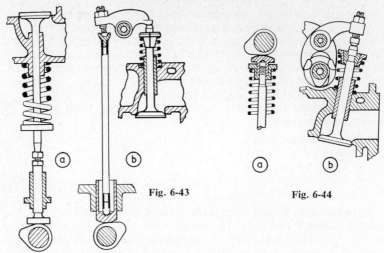

Fig. 6-43   Fig. 6-44

as in Fig. 6-4(*b*), while Fig. 6-44 shows two examples of the over-head camshaft. At (*a*) is shown direct operation of the cam on the valve stem, while (*b*) is an alternative method. The great majority of engines are fitted with one or other of the arrangements shown in Fig. 6-43, but Fig. 6-44(*b*) is popular with high-class sports and racing cars using a single overhead camshaft.

With side valves the interposition of a tappet only is required between the cam and the valve stem. The tappet slides vertically in its guide, which is sometimes of bronze or cast iron and renewable, while the foot engages with the face of the cam.

In modern simplified designs, as will be seen in later illustrations showing push-rod gear, the tappet is of simple bucket form, as shown in Figs. 6-43 and 6-45, moving in a plain reamed hole in the iron crankcase.

6.42 Forms of Cam Follower

There are three forms of tappet foot or cam follower in general use, namely—

(1) Solid curved foot (obsolescent).
(2) Mushroom or flat follower.
(3) Bucket type.

These are illustrated in Fig. 6-45. A is the tappet guide, B the adjustable tappet head by means of which a suitable small clearance is maintained between the tappet and valve to allow the latter to seat properly. C shows a curved foot follower operating a push rod enclosed in an oil-tight case. E shows a flat follower with its centre line offset from the centre of the cam. This offset causes the tappet to rotate and so reduces the amount of sliding between the

114

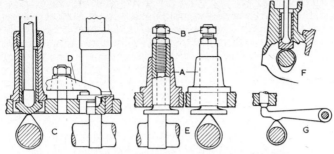

Fig. 6-45: Forms of cam follower

cam and tappet foot with consequent reduction of wear. At F is shown the " bucket " type of follower. This is very widely used in current designs, the material being cast iron.

The rocker type of follower G is sometimes introduced between the cam and tappet to reduce the side thrust on the latter and in some cases to increase the lift in relationship to the cam throw.

D is a clamping bridge employed to hold a pair of tappet guides in position. The roller type of follower, popular at one time because of reduced friction, was liable to become eccentric through wear, with consequent variation in tappet clearance. A modern example using needle roller bearings to correct this trouble may be seen in Fig. 10-10.

Except in the more simplified engines, means of adjusting the tappet clearance are provided, as shown in Figs. 6-45 and 6-47. Theoretically this clearance should be kept at the minimum possible

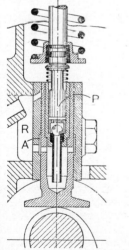

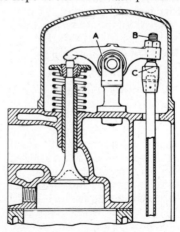

Fig. 6-47: Push rod and rocker

Fig. 6-46: Self-adjusting tappet

value that will allow the valve to seat under all conditions. As this clearance varies with engine temperature it is clearly necessary to adjust the tappets under conditions which make the clearance a minimum. With side valves this is usually when the engine is hot, as the downward expansion of the valve stem is greater than the upward expansion of the cylinder block. With overhead valves and push rods the clearance is usually a minimum with the engine cold, as the rods tend to keep relatively cool, while the upward expansion of the cylinder block has the effect of increasing the clearance, owing to the rise of the rocker pivot. With overhead camshafts the clearance will usually be a minimum when the engine is hot. A suitable clearance is 4 to 8 thousandths of an inch.

6.43 Hydraulic Self-adjusting Tappets

An interesting form of self-adjusting tappet manufactured by Automotive Products Company, Ltd., is illustrated in Fig. 6-46. Tappet clearance is automatically taken up during the idle period, the tappet head being raised by oil pressure from the ordinary pressure lubricating circuit. Oil is fed to the reservoir R behind the detachable tappet guide, provision being made for the release of any trapped air into the upper crank case. From this reservoir the oil has access through a port and annular recess A to a chamber formed in the hollow cam follower. The upper portion of the tappet comprises a cylinder into which the oil has access through a non-return ball valve, with a plunger P which forms the actual tappet head bearing on the valve stem.

The plunger is held in contact with the valve stem by a small compression spring of suitable stiffness, while oil under pressure follows up the plunger through the non-return valve during the idle period. During lift of the cam, the valve is raised on the oil trapped in the upper chamber, the slight leakage which takes place being followed up during the next idle period, and so allowing for slight changes in length of the valve stem with change of temperature.

6.44 Overhead Valves

The push rod and rocker method of operation is illustrated in Fig. 6-47. The upper end of the push rod which is usually of tubular section for lightness is provided with a cup C in which fits the ball end of the rod B, which is screwed and lock-nutted to the rocker for purposes of adjustment. The construction in which the rounded end of the push rod bears in an inverted cup formed in the rocker is somewhat less favourable for lubrication. The rockers may be mounted on ball or needle roller bearings, as here indicated at A, or they may be threaded on a tubular bearing bar running the whole length of the head and carried in suitable brackets. Light coil springs are usually threaded on in addition, in order to reduce noise by taking up end shake.

The interesting valve spring arrangement used in the Standard " Vanguard " engine is shown in Fig. 6-48. The main valve spring

116

is relieved of the duty of accelerating the rocker, push rod and tappet during closure of the valve, this action being performed by the auxiliary outer spring, the spring washers being so arranged that the clearance is always concentrated at the top of the valve stem. A slot S is provided for insertion of the feeler gauge during adjustment of the clearance.

The arrangement makes for reduction of noise as the clearance is taken up between only one pair of surfaces. The simple and effective provision for assembly by means of the " key-hole " drilling of the main spring washer may be noted.

Fig. 6-49 shows a well thought out and executed design, incorporating a single overhead camshaft with inclined valves and rockers. The camshaft is mounted above the rockers, which are of the third order of lever, thereby increasing the valve lift in relation to the cam throw. A further advantage of a long rocker is obtained, namely, that the " draw " or sliding of the rocker toe on the end of

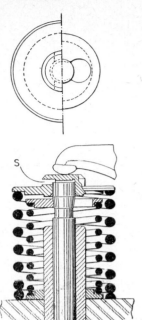

Fig. 6-48: Vanguard valve springs

the stem is less for a given valve lift, thus minimizing wear. The rockers A are machined from the solid to give maximum strength with lightness, and they incorporate an oil trough in which the cam roller runs, thus ensuring excellent lubrication. The rockers are mounted on bearing spindles B carried in independent forked brackets C. The portion of the pin B on which the rocker bears has a considerable eccentricity in relation to the end portions which are clamped in the brackets, so that by rotation of the spindles in the brackets the clearance between the roller and concentric portion of the cam, which represents tappet clearance, can be adjusted. Attention may be drawn to the arrangement of light steel sleeve and soft packing around the valve stem, which prevents excess oil reaching the stem and also avoids air leakage into the induction port, a source of trouble when adjusting the carburettor for idling.

6.45 Unconventional Rocker Arrangements

Two unconventional designs are illustrated in Figs. 6-50 and 6-51.

Fig. 6-50 shows an American construction of extreme simplicity suitable for large-scale economic manufacture. The rocker is a simple steel pressing of light weight and great strength, taking its bearing on a spherical spacer located by the self-locking nuts on

117

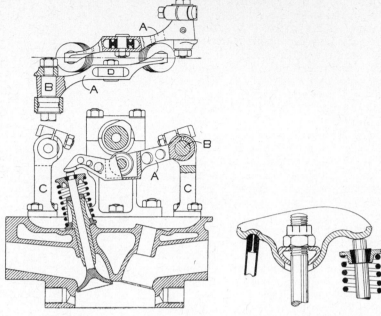

Fig. 6-49: Rocker gear of refined design for overhead camshaft

Fig. 6-50: Simplified rocker

individual mounting studs. The push rods are of light tubular construction working in close fitting guides formed by simple drillings in the upper deck of the head casting. The push rods are thus able to provide the necessary constraint to maintain transverse alignment of the rockers.

Tappet adjustment is effected by the above nuts on assemblies using bucket type cam followers, or may be provided by the employment of self-adjusting tappets of the type shown in Fig. 6-46. Selective assembly by push rod length may be used.

Lubrication may be through the support studs from a longitudinal gallery ,from the hydraulic tappets through the push rods, or by oil mist and splash.

Fig. 6-51 shows the typically original rocker arrangement used on the Lancia Aurelia, which facilitates the combination of hemispherical heads having longitudinally inclined valve stems, with a single camshaft in a V-type engine. The rocker axes are transverse, and individual bearing blocks are mounted longitudinally for each cylinder, for the pair of rockers.

The tendency to " off-set tilt " is thus greater than in conventional arrangements, but is catered for by the bearing surface and close fit of the large diameter rocker collars.

6.46 Auxiliary Drives

The following auxiliaries are common to both petrol and diesel engines, and provision for their drive must be made; oil pump, water pump, dynamo and fan. In petrol engines, the fan, impeller type water pump and dynamo, which do not call for an exact speed ratio, are usually driven by an all-round belt drive. Valve gear, ignition distributor and diesel injection pump require an exact ratio of 2/1 or 1/1 according to the cycle used. Such auxiliaries as exhauster and rotary blower are usually, though not necessarily, driven through longitudinal shafts by gearing or chain, while superchargers may be operated by either of these positive means or independently by engine exhaust.

In petrol engines, it is convenient to mount distributor and oil pump on a vertical or inclined shaft driven by 1 to 1 skew gearing from the camshaft, as shown in Fig. 6-56.

Magnetos are now rare, but were commonly driven with the water pump from a transverse shaft at a speed depending on the number of sparks provided per revolution by the magneto and required per revolution by the engine.

6.47 Typical All-round Chain Drive

A typical all-round drive employing duplex roller chain is illustrated in Fig. 6-52, which shows the auxiliary drive of an early A.E.C. compression-ignition engine. This type of drive is popular, and has the great advantages of adaptability to any convenient position of the auxiliaries and light weight, but for the larger diesel engines gearing is preferred.

The crankshaft carries a spur gear G for the 1 to 1 drive for the oil pump, while behind it is the twin sprocket for the chain. The 2 to 1 ratio for the injection pump drive is obtained by the large sprocket P while the 2 to 1 camshaft ratio is obtained by means of the spur gears C and C_1, of which the gear C is a twin gear having springs so disposed between the two parts as to impart relative rotational movement for the purpose of taking up backlash. The

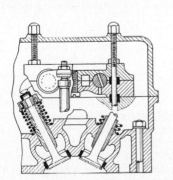
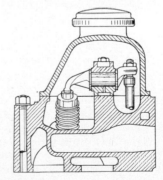

Fig. 6-51: Lancia Aurelia rocker

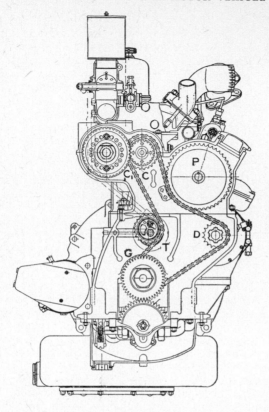

Fig. 6-52: A.E.C. chain drive. A typical "all round" chain drive for a high-speed diesel engine

slight increase in pressure on the driving side of the teeth is not detrimental, and quiet running is obtained.

The gear C_1 is coupled to the camshaft by a " vernier " coupling of the type illustrated and described on page 112. The sprocket D drives the dynamo at $\frac{7}{6}$ engine speed. The automatic tensioner T is of the eccentric type described on page 109.

6.48 All-gear Drive

An all-gear drive of high quality is shown in Fig. 6-53 which illustrates the rear end drive typical of Meadows diesel engines.

The crankshaft pinion is of generous diameter mounted detachably in the form of an open-ended thimble sleeve on the flywheel flange, and bolted up between the flywheel and the shaft flange, the centring spigot for the flywheel projecting through the bored end of the thimble. This forms a rigid and positive assembly in which a worn pinion could be readily replaced, and is not open to the objection that wear or damage to the pinion would involve scrapping of the crankshaft.

**Fig. 6-53: Typical Meadows
timing gears at rear of engine**

The 2 to 1 reduction is conveniently obtained by a compound train of ratios 4 to 3 and 3 to 2, without requiring unduly large gears for the camshaft and injection pump drives C and P respectively in Fig. 6-53. D is the dynamo shaft gear running at $1\frac{1}{2}$ times crankshaft speed, or higher if required.

If a blower or exhauster is provided, the shaft is driven by a suitable gear from the pump shaft gear.

All the gears have helically cut teeth and are robustly designed for their duty.

The camshaft and pump gears are mounted on shaft flanges with slotted bolt holes for purposes of timing adjustment.

Fig. 6-54 illustrates a somewhat unusual combination of chain and gear drive used on the Thornycroft KRN6 diesel engine. The Triplex roller chain drives an intermediate wheel and the dynamo drive sprocket, and is tensioned by a Renold spring-loaded eccentric unit.

Fig. 6-54: Thornycroft timing gears

121

The intermediate wheel is a compound wheel formed by bolting to the back of the driven sprocket a helical gear which meshes with the camshaft wheel on one side and on the other with the gear driving the injection pump and auxiliary compressor shaft. Provision is made in the construction for either right- or left-hand assemblies.

6.49   Complete Assembly

Some descriptions of the complete assembly will now be given in order that the relationship of the various components and the general arrangement of the engine may be clearly understood.

6.50   Vauxhall " Square " Engines

The abandonment by the Treasury of the R.A.C. formula for taxation purposes has influenced design, as was expected, in the direction of reduction of the stroke-bore ratio. Less weight is now attached to the power developed per square inch of piston area, though this remains a fundamental criterion of performance.

Piston speed for a given rotational speed is less, with the corresponding reduction in inertia stresses and friction losses.

Alternatively, rotational speed may be increased for a given limiting piston speed with a corresponding gain in horse-power per litre, the second commonly used criterion.

The removal of a penalty on bore has resulted in an improvement in breathing characteristics owing to the larger diameter valves which can be accommodated with an increase in bore.

It is therefore natural that Vauxhall Motors Ltd., with their American associations, have been among the early followers of this trend.

This introduction of the " softer " characteristics of American design is tending to replace the long-stroke, high piston speed proportions in engines designed for the popular market, though engines with a high stroke-bore ratio are still popular with the sporting and racing fraternity, by whom the tendency to harsher running may be tolerated or mitigated by the more expensive or exacting design expedients.

The Vauxhall $1\frac{1}{2}$ litre four, and $2\frac{1}{4}$ litre six, for the Wyvern and Velox respectively, have the same bore and stroke of 79 mm and 76 mm, being thus slightly " over-square." The compression ratio is 6·4 to 1 in both units.

As will be seen from the drawings of Fig. 6-55, many components and details are the same in the two engines. The longitudinal section (b) shows the general layout of the four-cylinder unit, while (a) is the cross-section of the six, of general application to both units.

The following information will serve to amplify the details of construction shown by the drawings.

Both the Vauxhall engines use forged crankshafts of generous proportions, all main journals being $2\frac{1}{8}$ in. diameter, with considerable overlap between the journal and pin diameters owing to the short crank throw.

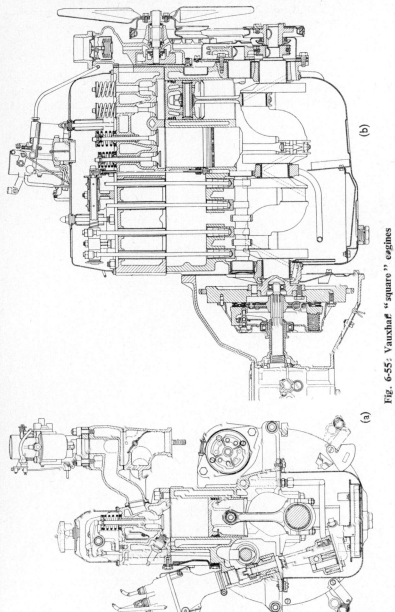

(b)

(a)

Fig. 6-55: Vauxhall "square" engines

The increase in the bore has made it possible to return to the usual square splitting of the big ends, as compared with the diagonal split of the earlier engines, of 69·5 mm bore, which is too small a dimension to permit of the withdrawal of the connecting rod— designed to suit a large diameter crankpin—through the block if split in the usual way.

Overhead valves, operated by push-rods seated in chilled cast-iron type tappets, serve a modified form of the controlled flame combustion chamber illustrated in Fig. 16-8. The flat piston crown

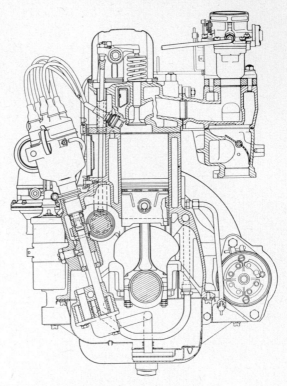

Fig. 6-56: New Vauxhall Victor engine

directs the squish turbulence to the plug and valves, giving good scour while at the same time ensuring adequate cooling of the end-gas in the " quench " area.

Directed cooling is here provided by the flattened distribution pipe in the cylinder head. Thermostatic control of the hot-spot manifold is shown to a larger scale in Fig. 11-24.

For a full description of both these engines the reader is referred to *Automobile Engineer*, Vol. 42, No. 9.

6.51 New Vauxhall Engines

The introduction of the Victor and the new Velox and Cresta models has been accompanied by the modification and development of the engines described above. The chief structural alteration is in the deepening of the crankcase skirt which is now extended well below the crankshaft centre line, giving improved stiffness in the longitudinal direction.

The cylinder head is of uniform depth transversely, so that all the holding-down bolts are of uniform length, and breathing character-istics have been improved by providing individual inlet ports leading to larger-diameter inlet valves. To improve the quietness of running, the gudgeon pins are now offset $\frac{1}{16}$ in towards the thrust side of the piston, thus reducing the tendency to piston tilt.

All these features are common to both the four and the six.

Performance of both models has greatly improved, especially the torque in the lower speed range. Alternative compression ratios are offered, and the Zenith 34VN carburettor, normally with 25 mm choke and automatic strangler is now standard.

The maximum gross horse-powers are given as 54·8 at 4,200 r.p.m. for the four, and 82·5 at 4,400 for the six, the compression ratio being 7·8 to 1 in both cases.

The sectional view of Fig. 6-56 may be compared with the general arrangement of Fig. 6-55, when the major alterations will be noted.

6.52 Standard Vanguard Four-cylinder Engine

An interesting medium-powered four-cylinder engine of con-ventional " production " layout is the 2,088 c.c. power unit fitted to the " Vanguard " chassis, illustrated in Fig. 6-57. While the general layout, apart from the wet cylinder liners, is on familiar lines, the details have been carefully worked out to produce a simple and reliable unit of excellent performance and suitable for quantity production at a price which has commanded a wide market.

A great merit on the wet-liner construction is the simplification of the foundry work on the cylinder block, with accompanying speed and accuracy of production. The increased machining required is largely confined to the specialized processes of sleeve manufacture, which in turn ensure that closely specified material of the most suitable type is used.

Replacement of liners is a simple operation.

The engine has a bore and stroke of 85 mm × 92 mm and a compression ratio of 6·8 to 1. The performance curves are given in Fig. 6-58 and the valve timing diagram in Fig. 6-59. The torque and b.m.e.p. curves fall somewhat steeply after the very good peak figure at 2,300 r.p.m., possibly reflecting the price to be paid for efficient air cleaning and silencing. The sealed crank-case breathing arrangements, with draw-off pipe (provided with a restriction orifice) to the inlet manifold, will be noted. These provide a through air-flow from the air cleaner, by means of an external pipe.

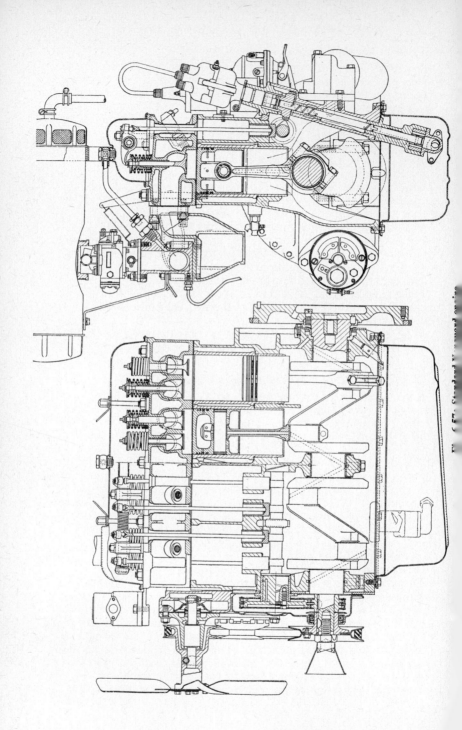

Fig. 57.—Standard V, 8-valved ae. engine

The general construction of deep cast-iron cylinder block with light pressed steel sump and detachable cylinder head will be noticed, while the stiff crankshaft and generous journal and crank-pin diameters should ensure freedom from troublesome vibration. The diagonally split big end, to facilitate withdrawal through the

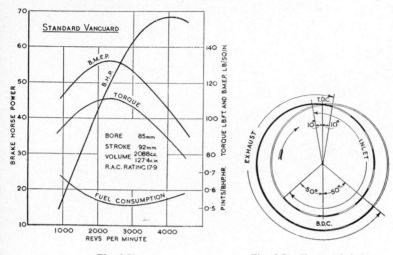

Fig. 6-58   Fig. 6-59: Vanguard timing

bore, is not yet common practice with petrol engines, though becoming general with diesels.

The interesting valve spring arrangement is shown in enlarged detail and described on page 117.

A Solex downdraught carburettor feeds an aluminium alloy inlet manifold, which makes hot-spot contact with the exhaust manifold.

Further interesting particulars will be found in *Automobile Engineer*, Vol. 48, No. 9.

6.53   Rover 2000 Engine

The engine of the new Rover 2000 model, known as the P6, is a modern development of considerable interest. This is a four-cylinder, overhead valve " square " engine of 85·7 cm bore and stroke, with a cubic capacity of 1,980 c.c. Its R.A.C. rating is 18·3, and its maximum net b.h.p. is 90 at 5,000 r.p.m. The maximum net b.m.e.p. is 144 lb/sq. in. at 2,500 r.p.m.

Major features of the design can be studied in Figs. 6-60 and 6-61.

The open-side cast iron cylinder block, with light closure covers, is reminiscent of the early 4-litre Bentley. This construction,

127

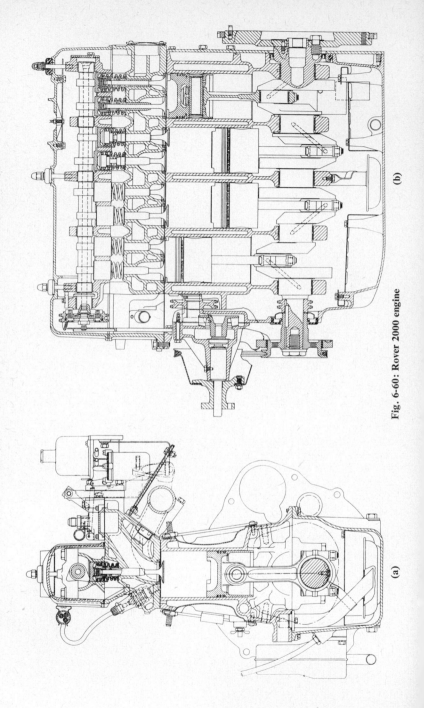

Fig. 6-60: Rover 2000 engine

(a)

(b)

owing to the excellent core support that can be provided, is conducive to economic and accurate moulding of the block, and the thickness of metal can be closely controlled.

A single overhead camshaft operating directly on inverted bucket type tappets is employed, the valves being longitudinally aligned. Correct tappet clearance is obtained by selected washers between the tappet and the valve stem. This arrangement may be seen in view (*a*) of Fig. 6-60.

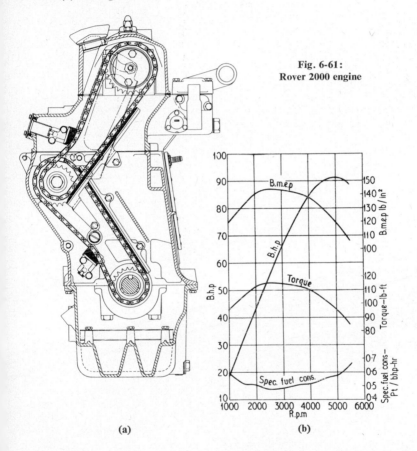

Fig. 6-61:
Rover 2000 engine

(a)   (b)

In the left-hand view of Fig. 6-61 the layout of the two-stage camshaft drive can be seen. Renold hydraulic type tensioners and neoprene rubbing pads maintain correct chain tension. Integral with the hollow jack-shaft to which the two intermediate chain sprockets are keyed, is a skew gear engaging a short vertical shaft on which is a cam to actuate the fuel pump; the usual tongue and slot arrangement on the end of this shaft drives the distributor.

129

The inlet valves have a throat diameter of 1·476 in. and the exhaust valves 1·189 in. Both bear on shrunk-in valve seats. All the valve ports are on the left-hand side of the aluminium alloy cylinder head, the underside of which is quite flat, since the combustion chamber recesses are formed in the tops of the pistons— an unusual construction for a petrol engine, but familiar with diesels. This construction has the great advantage that the surface of the combustion chamber can readily be machined all over. The compression ratio is 9 : 1.

Although the pistons are slightly heavier than the usual form, they are found to run cooler. They are " Bricomatic " solid skirt components supplied by the British Piston Ring Co. Ltd. Each has a steel cast-in restraint ring, which facilitates the use of fine clearances. Fully floating gudgeon pins, with circlips to locate them axially, are fitted.

The very sturdy crankshaft of forged steel has generous diametrical overlap of journals and crankpins, and is carried in five main bearings. Integral balance weights further ensure smooth running, and a torsional vibration damper of the Holset rubber bonded type is provided to control any torsional oscillations that might arise.

The " percussion " system of engine suspension described on page 73, is used. The front mounting arrangement consists of brackets attached to the sides of the crankcase at the rigid central web, and supported on Metalastik bonded rubber cushions. This location is at or near the centre of percussion in relation to the rear support, which comprises a helical spring and damping bush at the rear of the gearbox. The exact location of the front support may be adjusted if required, by the setting of the two brackets.

The performance curves shown in (b) of Fig. 6-61 have several points of interest. The maximum horse-power of just over 90 at 5,000 r.p.m. is five times the R.A.C. rating (see page 47). This shows the remarkable progress that has been made since the establishment of that out-dated formula. The mean piston speed at 5,000 r.p.m. is 2,800 feet per minute—nearly three times the R.A.C. assumption. The b.h.p. per square inch of piston area is 2·5 and per litre, 45.

The high-level, Hobourn Eaton oil pump is driven by a spline extension of the horizontal jack-shaft, and provision is made for keeping it primed when the engine is stopped. A belt-drive on the left-hand side of the engine drives the dynamo. A most informative fully illustrated series of articles in the *Automobile Engineer* describes the complete vehicle, the engine details being published in November 1963.

6.54 B.M.C. A.D.O. 15 Power Unit

The great success of the Morris Mini-Minor and new Austin Seven small car has naturally aroused great interest in the cleverly developed power unit and unconventional transverse installation in the frame combined with the front-wheel drive.

130

The exacting requirements of comfortable seating room and good luggage accommodation within restricted overall dimensions have thereby been successfully met.

The 848 c.c. four-cylinder engine may be regarded as a derivative of the Series A 948 c.c. unit (see *Automobile Engineer*, Vol. 50, No. 7); the following notes on the special features of the smaller engine are abstracted from a comprehensive description of the complete vehicle in *Automobile Engineer*, Vol. 51, Nos. 4 and 5.

The series A block and head are employed without alteration, a new crankshaft giving the reduced stroke of 68 mm. Thus with a bore of approximately 63 mm, the stroke-bore ratio is 1·08 to 1 which is nearly " square ".

To accommodate the larger bore in the limited length of block, siamesing of the cylinders in pairs and off-setting of the connecting rod big ends by ⅛ in is resorted to, with no detriment to the running. The big ends of the connecting rod are diagonally split, and the gudgeon pins are clamped in the small-end eye, a construction which, it is considered, contributes to silence as there is only one clearance to develop possible knock.

The sturdy forged crankshaft carries integral balance weights, and the short stroke results in considerable crankpin/journal overlap. All these features make a valuable contribution to smooth running and may be seen in Fig. 6-62.

The compression ratio is 8·3 to 1, achieved by using taller pistons to compensate for the shorter stroke.

The joint between cylinder block and sump is on the crankshaft centre line, as this affords free access to the big ends and provides a deep and rigid housing for the transmission.

The camshaft is of normal design, driven by a single roller chain of ¾ in pitch. To take the driving load and provide for wear, the front end bearing is a steel-backed white-metal lined shell, while the other two are of the plain type running in bores machined directly in the block. The Hobourn-Eaton oil pump is driven co-axially by a slot and peg mounted in a counter-bore.

The bucket type cam followers and cup-ended push rods are now common practice, but the rockers are of novel construction, being formed from a pair of light steel pressings by projection and spot welding. This results in a considerable saving in weight as compared with the usual stamping, and may be compared with the pressed form shown in Fig. 6-50. The rocker bearings are Clevite 8 wrapped copper-lead bushes.

Curves of engine performance, measured at the flywheel, are reproduced in Fig. 6-63.

Those shown by full lines are for the engine to B.M.C.'s standard specification. The gross performance, shown by dotted lines, is measured under conditions similar to standard, except that the air filter is removed and manual controls are employed for the carburettor and ignition.

Chain-dotted lines are used to indicate the performance as

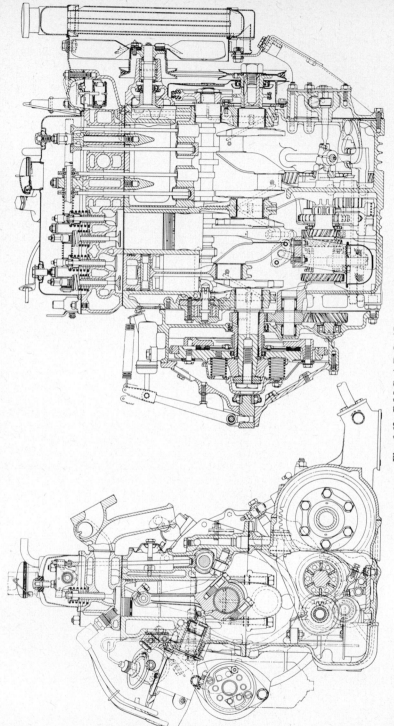

Fig. 6-62: B.M.C. A.D.O. 15 power unit

installed; the engine specification then differs from that for the standard curves in that the cooling fan is fitted, and the car's exhaust system replaces that of the test-bed installation. The results are obtained with an S.U. semi-downdraught carburettor.

It is of interest that the gross power output of 37 b.h.p. at 5,500 r.p.m. is slightly greater than that of the Austin A40, which has

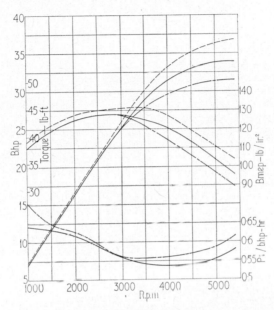

Fig. 6-63

a Zenith carburettor and produces 36 b.h.p. at 4,800 r.p.m., and less than that of the Morris Minor 1000, which is 40 b.h.p. at 5,000 r.p.m. The higher specific output of the A.D.O. 15 unit, 43·7 b.h.p./litre as against 38·0 for the A40 and 42·2 for the Minor, is mainly attributable to the proportionately larger valves, which have made possible an upward extension of the speed range. While the respective maximum piston speeds of the two 948 c.c. engines are 2,400 and 2,500 ft/min, that of the A.D.O. 15 unit is 2,460 ft/min. The A.D.O. 15 has a maximum gross b.m.e.p. of 132 lb/sq. in., about average for an engine of this type, and its b.h.p./sq. in. of piston area is 1·92.

6.55 Engine Position

Only in comparatively recent years has the long established placing of the power unit at the front of the chassis been seriously challenged. The success of some of the Continental designs of small popular car in which the rear position has been adopted may have tended to obscure certain objections to this arrangement.

Powerful influences on the sales success of these cars have been low price and good after-sales service combined with the design advantages of increased body space within a given chassis length, and good accessibility of the power unit. Traction on steep hills is good owing to the high proportion of the total weight on the rear wheels, which is as much as 60 per cent of the total with the chassis unladen.

The disparity of weight on the two axles may become excessive with a full passenger load.

Two important disadvantages of the rear engine position are a marked tendency to oversteer and cramped luggage space at the front of the body owing to the much smaller width between the wheel arches as compared with that at the rear, where it is more than adequate to accommodate the power unit.

Increasing the length of the bonnet to provide more luggage space, as in the Renault Dauphine, corrects this fault and improves the laden weight distribution, but to some extent neutralizes the important advantage claimed for the rear engine indicated above, namely, improved passenger space in a given body length.

The cleverly contrived Fiat Multipla utility body solves the difficulty by making the passenger and luggage space interchangeable.

Except on the score of the cost of construction, the front engine, front-wheel drive arrangement has nearly everything to recommend it. The weight distribution from the traction point of view is good, the body space is unencumbered by transmission, and the rear luggage space is fully available.

6.56 Under-floor Engines

For public service vehicles, heavy lorries, and for diesel multi-unit rail transport the under-floor engine is likely to become increasingly important. Horizontally opposed and Vee layouts have been developed by one or two makers, but the general tendency appears to be towards laying a normal vertical engine on its side, and making special provision for all parts and accessories affected by the changed gravitational conditions, such as the oil sump, lubrication layout and the carburation system, in the case of petrol engines.

Most of the well-known oil-engine builders have developed designs on these lines, and the arrangement would seem to have the merit that maintenance operations of any particular type can be confined to one or other side of the vehicle, with the additional facilities provided by access doors. An example is given in Fig. 6-64, which shows in cross section the 8-litre six-cylinder direct-injection diesel built and operated by the Birmingham and Midland Motor Omnibus Co. Ltd.

Only operational and commercial experience will show whether

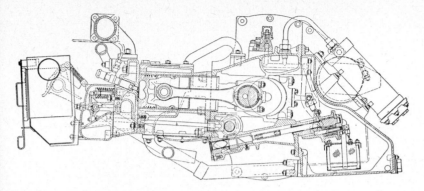

Fig. 6-64

there is any balance of advantages over the more conventional arrangement.

6.57 Panhard Dyna 55 Engine

Some years ago the Panhard Company developed a 12-cylinder horizontally opposed air-cooled petrol engine for aircraft purposes; an outside view of this is illustrated in *Automobile Engineer*, Vol. 43, No. 8.

The flat layout would have made this design eminently suitable for under-floor installation in heavy commercial vehicles, possibly in a shortened eight-cylinder version. The post-war competition of jet propulsion for aircraft, however, and of the diesel engine for heavy commercial vehicles, closed these avenues for commercial development, and it is of great interest to find that the basic conception of the design has survived in a twin-cylinder element for a totally different market.

Applied as a front-wheel drive installation to a platform type of chassis, the result is a body space completely unencumbered with transmission, shaft tunnel and live rear axle with gearing and possible source of noise. It will be recalled that a slightly smaller forerunner of the present engine was successful in its class in the 1953 Le Mans races.

A cross section of the engine is given in Fig. 6-65, which shows the horizontally opposed, air-cooled, overhead-valve construction which has been handed down from the 12-cylinder predecessor. Of 85 mm bore and 75 mm stroke, giving a swept volume of 851 c.c., the maximum power developed is 42 b.h.p. at 5,000 r.p.m. The maximum b.m.e.p. of 137 lb/sq. in. and torque of 47 lb-ft respectively are developed at 3,500 r.p.m.

The main features of construction are as follows. The cylinders are of aluminium alloy with integral heads, and the cooling fins are machined from solid, generously proportioned billets. Dry

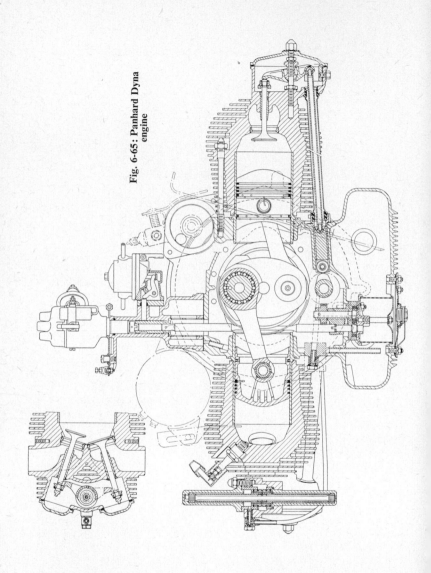

Fig. 6-65: Panhard Dyna engine

cylinder liners are provided and cylinder cooling is aided by the generous proportions of the cooling fins.

6.58   Crankshaft Assembly

The crankshaft is built up from three main components, the end units each comprising journal, web and crankpin, and a centre web. Expander plugs are pressed into the crankpin bores to complete the assembly (after the roller-bearing big ends are threaded on), and separate balance masses are added and secured by dowel pins and recessed cheese-head screws.   These masses balance the revolving couple due to the offset of the cylinder centre lines, and can be increased to balance partially the couple due to the reciprocating inertia of the pistons.

The whole crankshaft and connecting rod assembly can be assembled through the large oval aperture at the front end of the crankcase casting, thus dispensing with transverse or longitudinal joints in the latter.

6.59   Valve Gear

The valve gear is of interesting design and comprises torsion-bar springs and roller cam followers.   The valve rockers are of the same design as the simplified pressing illustrated in Fig. 6-50, but are of cast iron with somewhat more positively locked provision for tappet adjustment.

The general layout of the torsion bar springing may be noted from Fig. 6-65, but a fully detailed analysis of the constructional features, and also of the lubrication arrangement will be found in the April 1958 issue of *Automobile Engineer*.

CHAPTER 7

Six- and Eight-cylinder Engines

General considerations of six- and eight-cylinder engines. Dynamic balance. The straight eight. The V-eight.

THE desire for a more uniform turning moment and better dynamic balance has led to the production of six-, eight- and even twelve-cylinder engines where questions of first cost are not of primary importance. The effective driving effort of an ordinary four-stroke single-cylinder engine extends, when friction is taken into account, over only about 150° of crank movement, and, as in a four-cylinder engine the explosions occur at intervals of 180°, or half a revolution, it follows that there are appreciable periods when the shaft is receiving no useful torque whatever, and the stored energy of the flywheel is called on to supply the deficiency. At low speeds the flywheel does not contain sufficient energy to tide over the idle periods without undue variation of speed and hence jerky running and high transmission stresses are set up.

Remembering that the number of explosions per revolution is equal to half the number of cylinders, it will be seen that in a " six " the intervals between explosions, if the cylinders and cranks are so disposed as to make them equal, have a duration of 120° of crank angle, while in an " eight " the interval is 90°. There is thus an appreciable overlap in the former and a very considerable one in the latter. The result is great improvement in the smoothness of running and a lighter flywheel may be employed.

7.1 Six Cylinders

Fig. 7-1 illustrates the normal arrangement of cranks in a six-throw crankshaft, the full number of bearings, namely, seven, being here shown. The cranks are 120° apart in pairs, the halves being arranged to give " looking-glass " symmetry, in order to give opposition of the inertia couples as explained in Chapter 5. The

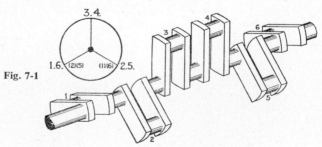

Fig. 7-1

circle diagram shows the two alternative crank arrangements consistent with the above symmetry.

In what may be called a " left-hand " shaft No. 1 crank is on the left when looking from the front of the engine, with 3 and 4 vertical. Cranks 1 and 6 may clearly be interchanged with 2 and 5 giving a shaft of the opposite hand. Both these arrangements are met with in practice.

7.2 Dynamic Balance

Just as three equal and symmetrically distributed revolving masses in one plane will be in dynamic balance, since their combined centre of gravity is clearly at the centre of rotation, so six equal and symmetrically distributed revolving masses which do not all lie in one plane will be in dynamic balance provided the couples due to the distances between the planes of revolution cancel out. This cancelling out is attained with the arrangement illustrated, provided the corresponding throw spacings are the same and the throws uniform. Dynamic balancing of crankshafts is carried out by the majority of makers to correct for slight errors in weights and size of the various throws.

In like manner the primary reciprocating effects balance, since these represent the vertical components of corresponding revolving effects. This will perhaps be realized better if *standing* balance is considered, where the only forces are vertical ones due to gravity. A six-cylinder engine, even if quite frictionless, will remain at rest in any position of the crank provided the moving parts of all cylinders are uniform in weight. Further, the secondary effects cancel out, as may be ascertained from Fig. 5-9, by a careful combination of the forces in correct phase. The six-cylinder engine is, in fact, capable of complete balance for both primary and secondary forces and couples, thus eliminating vibration from this cause.

7.3 Firing Order

To obtain good *distribution* of the fuel to all cylinders it is desirable and usual to arrange the inductions alternately in the front and rear halves of the engine. An examination of the circular diagram of Fig. 7-1 will make clear that the possible firing orders, to satisfy this condition, are 1 5 3 6 2 4 and 1 4 2 6 3 5 for the two arrangements of cranks. These are the most usual in practice, but others are sometimes met with. Thus, from the point of view of torsional oscillation, it may be desirable in some cases to have two cylinders in one half of the engine firing in succession in order to prevent the " unwinding " of the shaft between explosions. This problem is referred to later.

7.4 Eight Cylinders

Here the proper interval between explosions is 90°, and a " straight eight " may clearly be formed by placing two fours end to end with

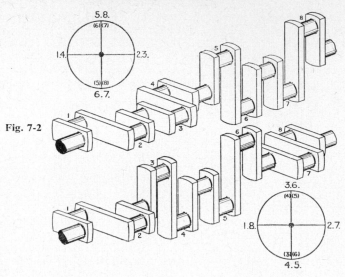

Fig. 7-2

their flat crankshafts at right angles, as in the upper diagram of Fig. 7-2. Each set of four cylinders is then in balance for primary forces and couples as explained in Chapter 5, but there remains the secondary effect. This secondary effect acts downwards when the cranks are horizontal and upwards when they are vertical; thus, while the downward secondary effect of one half of the engine opposes the upward effect of the other half there remains, with the " double four " arrangement, an unbalanced couple, tending to pitch the engine in the longitudinal plane.

This may be eliminated by adopting the " split four " arrangement shown in the lower diagram of Fig. 7-2. Here the downward secondary effect of two pistons at each end of the engine 1, 2 and 7, 8 opposes the upward effect of 3, 4, 5 and 6 without introducing a couple. This arrangement is in complete balance for primary and secondary forces and couples.

7.5 Firing Order

There are clearly many possible orders of firing with eight cylinders arranged as shown in Fig. 7-2, but the more usual are 1 7 3 8 4 6 2 5, 1 5 2 6 4 8 3 7 and 1 6 2 5 8 3 7 4. Other crank arrangements are met with in special cases, particularly for racing purposes, where considerations of bearing loads may be of greater importance than exact dynamic balance. With adjacent cranks in phase, as in the case of 4 and 5 in the lower diagram (Fig. 7-2), the centrifugal and inertia forces of the moving parts of both cylinders act always together, producing very heavy loads on the intermediate bearing. If adjacent cranks are placed 180° apart as far as uniformity of turning moment permits the mutual balance of opposing cranks is

140

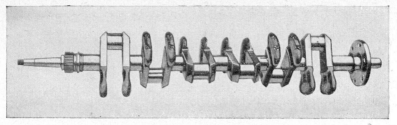

Fig. 7-3: Crankshaft with balanced throws

more direct, and bearing loads and crank case stresses are much reduced. Such arrangements result, however, in there being unbalanced couples.

7.6   Balanced Webs and Torsional Oscillation

Another method of reducing bearing loads and crank case stresses is to balance the individual throws for rotational effects by adding extended webs and balance weights, it being impossible, except in the 90° V engine, to deal with reciprocating effects in this way. But, as previously mentioned, while this expedient may cure shaft and crank case *whip*, it is very liable to increase the risk of torsional oscillation of the shaft, because heavy masses revolving with a slender shaft make the natural torsional or twisting vibration a relatively slow one; slow enough in some cases to give rise to dangerous and uncomfortable resonance with the torque variations. An aircraft shaft of relatively slender proportions, with such attached balanced weights, is shown in Fig. 7-3.

To reduce torsional vibration, a " vibration damper " may be mounted at the front end of the crankshaft. A damper of the Lanchester type is illustrated in Fig. 7-4 (a).   It consists essentially of

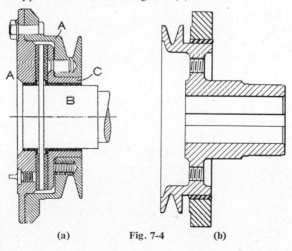

(a)   Fig. 7-4   (b)

141

a flywheel member A, of 8 to 12 in. diameter, according to the size of engine, driven through a friction disc clutch, the inner plate member B of which is keyed to the front end of the crankshaft. The friction is adjusted by the springs acting on the presser plate C so as to be insufficient to transmit to the heavy rim A the high torsional acceleration during the " winding up " and unwinding of the crankshaft as the torsional impulses are applied to the cranks. Thus the torsional wind and rebound are absorbed in friction in much the same way as in the case of a spring damper, and serious oscillations are not built up. Fig. 7-4(b) shows a simplified form of the bonded rubber insert type of damper which is now in general use. The illustration was prepared from a drawing kindly supplied by the Holset Engineering Co., among whose products are turbo-chargers and flexible couplings.

7.7 Difficulties Met in Design

" Sixes " and " straight eights " are liable to three important troubles in running and performance. These may be summarized as bad gas distribution, high fuel consumption and torsional oscillation. The second is partly a consequence of the first, and partly due to the rather lower thermal efficiency obtainable in cylinders of small size, owing to the relatively greater losses to the jackets and other causes. Bad distribution is one of the most elusive difficulties with which designers have to contend. Although a correct and homogeneous mixture may leave the carburettor, it is highly improbable that it will reach all the cylinders in exactly equal quantity or of similar composition. Thus it may be necessary to employ an unduly rich carburettor setting, with correspondingly high consumption, in order to prevent starvation of certain of the cylinders. This trouble is present even in four-cylinder engines, and is accentuated in sixes and eights, where the induction manifolds present far greater design difficulties. It is almost impossible for a designer to form a reliable forecast of the probable behaviour of any given arrangement of single or twin carburettor, and induction pipe arrangement, taken in conjunction with a particular firing order.

The third difficulty of torsional oscillation has already been referred to. These difficulties and the extra cost of manufacture of the six have enabled the reliable and economical, though less smooth-running, four-cylinder engine to maintain its popularity in the smaller powers, and for medium-sized commercial vehicles.

7.8 Humber Super Snipe Engine

To suit the requirements of the Humber Super Snipe range of vehicles which consists of saloon, touring limousine and estate car, three main considerations were demanded of the power unit in the initial design stage. These were high performance, refinement in operation and facility of production.

For this engine of 3 litres (2,965 c.c.) capacity, the " over square " bore/stroke arrangement was chosen to give a lower piston speed of 2,600 ft/min at maximum b.h.p. It also permits a crankshaft with overlapping pins and journals, thus ensuring a very rigid crank free from torsional weakness. Both these points contribute to the smooth running of the engine. The combustion chamber is of the hemispherical type, shallowed down to give a flat topped piston for the chosen compression ratio of 8·0 to 1. With the shallow type of head, smooth combustion is assured as the flame front build-up is quenched by the piston top before roughness is initiated.

Large valves (1·4 in inlet throat diameter, 1·2 in exhaust throat diameter) are possible, and with the uninterrupted gas flow characteristic of this hemispherical type of head, good filling is achieved. The low expansion aluminium alloy piston has two compression rings and a scraper, the top ring being chromium plated, the second ring stepped.

Both rings are 0·078 in thick and 0·16 in wide, giving the fairly high wall pressure necessary with over-square engines. The $\frac{15}{16}$ in. diameter gudgeon pin is fully floating and located with circlips.

A high camshaft position is a fundamental requirement of this type of engine. The design incorporates inclined valves placed transversely and push rod operated. A duplex chain with a Renolds S.C.D. type chain tensioner drives the camshaft.

Valve timing was selected to provide a good low-end torque with the power output necessary to maintain high cruising speeds. Details are shown in the table of engine data.

Details are shown in the table of engine data.

A water heated aluminium alloy inlet manifold is used to feed two separate galleries formed in the cast iron cylinder head. Each gallery feeds three cylinders.

The performance figures shown on page 146 are obtained with a single Zenith 42 W.I.A. down-draught carburettor.

Gross power output is 129·5 b.h.p. at 4,800 r.p.m. giving 43 b.h.p. per litre and a maximum torque of 161·6 lb/ft developed at 1,800 r.p.m.

The general arrangement drawings of Figs. 7-5 and 7-6, and the exploded diagram of Fig. 7-8 give a very clear picture of the construction, which may be amplified by the following notes.

The cylinder block is cast iron and the engine mounting point is rearward of the front face and therefore nearer to the centre of gravity of the unit. This, coupled with the deep section of the block, provides a rigid and vibration free unit when installed.

To reduce noise and wear, the camshaft and bucket type tappets run in an oil bath.

Particular attention has been paid to the valve gear to avoid unnecessary deflections. Short solid push rods operate cast iron rockers on induction hardened shafts.

The four-bearing forged crankshaft has integral balance weights and bearings of $2\frac{1}{2}$ in dia, the crank pins being 2 in dia, giving a valuable crankpin/journal overlap of $\frac{5}{8}$ in.

143

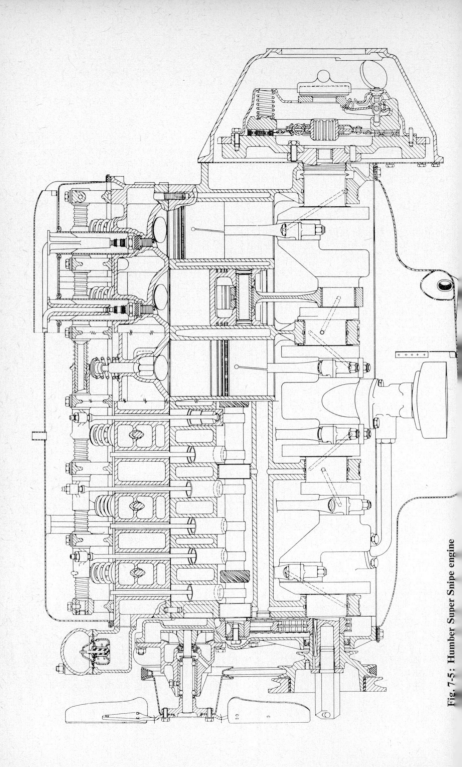

Fig. 7-5: Humber Super Snipe engine

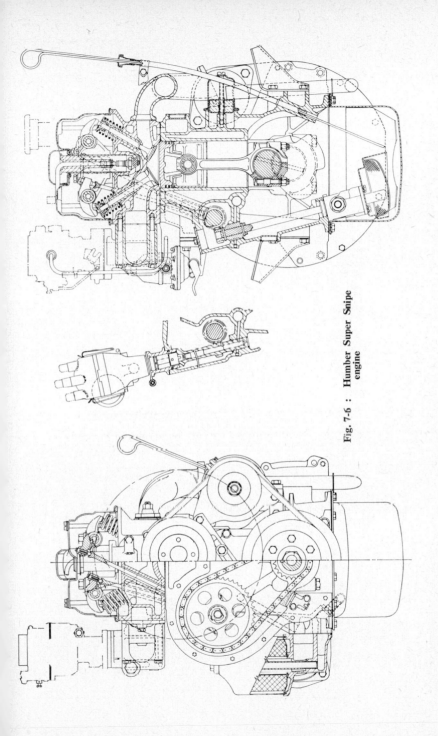

Fig. 7-6 : Humber Super Snipe engine

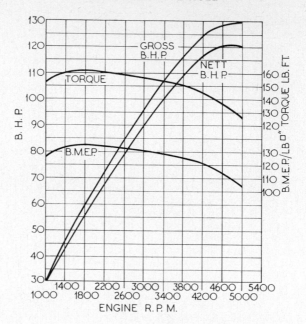

Fig. 7-7: Humber Super Snipe performance curves

HUMBER SUPER SNIPE SERIES III GENERAL DATA

General engine data

Number of cylinders	6
Bore (nominal)	3·4375 in (87·3 mm)
Stroke	3·25 in (82·6 mm)
Capacity	180·9 in³ (2,965 c.c.)
Compression ratio	8·0 to 1
Compression pressure	165-175 lb/in²
Firing order	1-5-3-6-2-4
Piston speed at max. b.h.p.	2,600 ft/min
R.A.C. rating	28·4

Engine performance

b.h.p. (nett)	121 at 4,800 r.p.m.
b.h.p. (gross)	129·5 at 4,800 r.p.m.
Max. torque	161 lb-ft at 1,800 r.p.m.
Max. b.m.e.p.	135 lb/in² at 1,800 r.p.m.

Valve timing

Inlet valve opens	20° B.T.D.C.
Inlet valve closes	46° A.B.D.C.
Exhaust valve opens	52° B.B.D.C.
Exhaust valve closes	14° A.T.D.C.

Tappet clearance

Inlet	0·014
Exhaust	0·014

A Metalastik torsional damper is fitted at the front end.

The following points may be noted in connection with the lubrication system.

The Hobourn-Eaton oil pump (see page 349) has a delivery of $2\frac{1}{2}$ gallons per 1,000 revolutions.

Oil is fed to the pump through a coarse mesh strainer and from the pump to a full flow filter and relief valve. From the valve, oil returns to the sump while the filtered oil passes to a gallery which feeds the main, big end and camshaft bearings. A feed is taken from the rear camshaft bearing to lubricate the rocker gear.

A separate positive feed is taken to both the oil pump drive gear and the distributor drive gear.

This drains back to the camshaft gallery together with the rocker surplus. Stand pipes and cast-in weirs maintain the level in the gallery and the overflow returns to the sump.

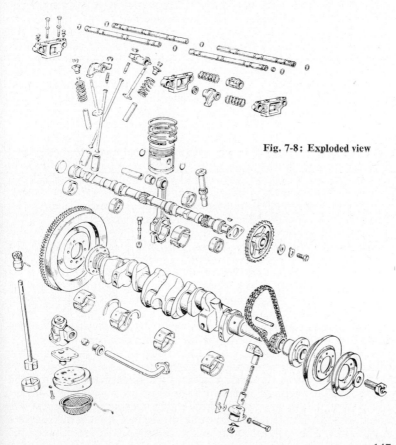

Fig. 7-8: Exploded view

The Renold S.C.D. type chain tensioner may be seen in the exploded view of Fig. 7-8. The plunger head, with special oil-proof rubber pad is urged forward by both spring and oil pressure, return movement being limited by an internal ratchet peg engaging with the notched helical slot in the " restraint cylinder," which is rotatably adjustable by means of an Allen key.

The authors are much indebted to Messrs. Humber Ltd. for drawings and information.

7.9 Jaguar 2·4 Litre Engine

In deciding on post-war policy, Jaguar Cars, Ltd., faced the problem of reconciling the conflicting claims of a variety of factors.

The great reputation built up by pre-war models for outstanding performance and elegant design at moderate selling price, suggested a continuance of the production of both six- and four-cylinder models to power the two sizes of vehicle. The six-cylinder XK engine of $3\frac{1}{2}$ litre capacity has been an outstanding success.

In deciding whether the smaller engine should be a six or a four many factors had to be weighed. Rationalization of manufacture, export markets, particularly the U.S.A., and considerations of balance and vibration problems likely to arise with the unitary body construction that it was intended to use, led to the final choice of the six. Cost and weight were at some slight disadvantage relatively to the four, but smoothness of torque and freedom from troublesome vibrations were regarded as over-riding considerations, particularly as it was possible to achieve a considerable degree of rationalization in manufacture and provision of spares by altering one principal dimension only, namely the stroke. The consequential modification to connecting rods, crankshaft, cylinder block and pistons have been satisfactorily achieved, and interchangeability of cylinder heads, valve gear and smaller components, such as bearing shells, will ensure economies in manufacture and maintenance.

The main features may be seen in elevation in Fig. 7-9 and in the cross-sectional views of Fig. 7-10. With the stroke reduced to 76·5 but with the same bore of 83 mm as the $3\frac{1}{2}$ litre engine, the cylinders are under square, the stroke/bore ratio being 0·92.

The cylinder block is a relatively simple chromidium iron casting extending to the crankshaft centre line, and closed by a deep pressed-steel sump. No liners are used, and the freedom from wear which has been Jaguar experience will no doubt be greatly helped by the chromium plated rings used in the top grooves (see page 86).

Features of the camshaft drive are referred to on page 109, and the direct skew-gear drive to the distributor shaft is of interest. The small number of teeth—only ten—and the large helix angle on the crankshaft gear will be noted, though not apparent in the conventional view of this gear in the longitudinal section, but the driving conditions at the teeth will be quite favourable for the two to one reduction. The driving gear is of case-hardened steel and the

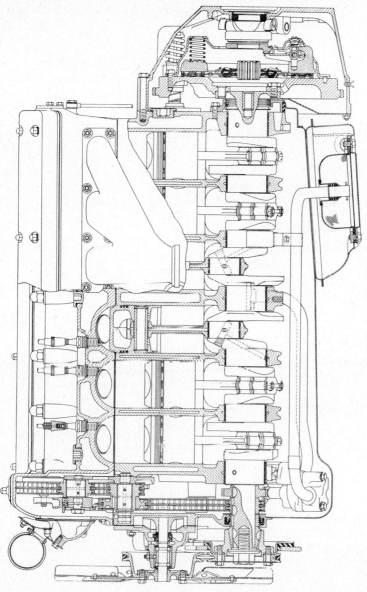

Fig. 7.9: Jaguar 2·4 litre engine

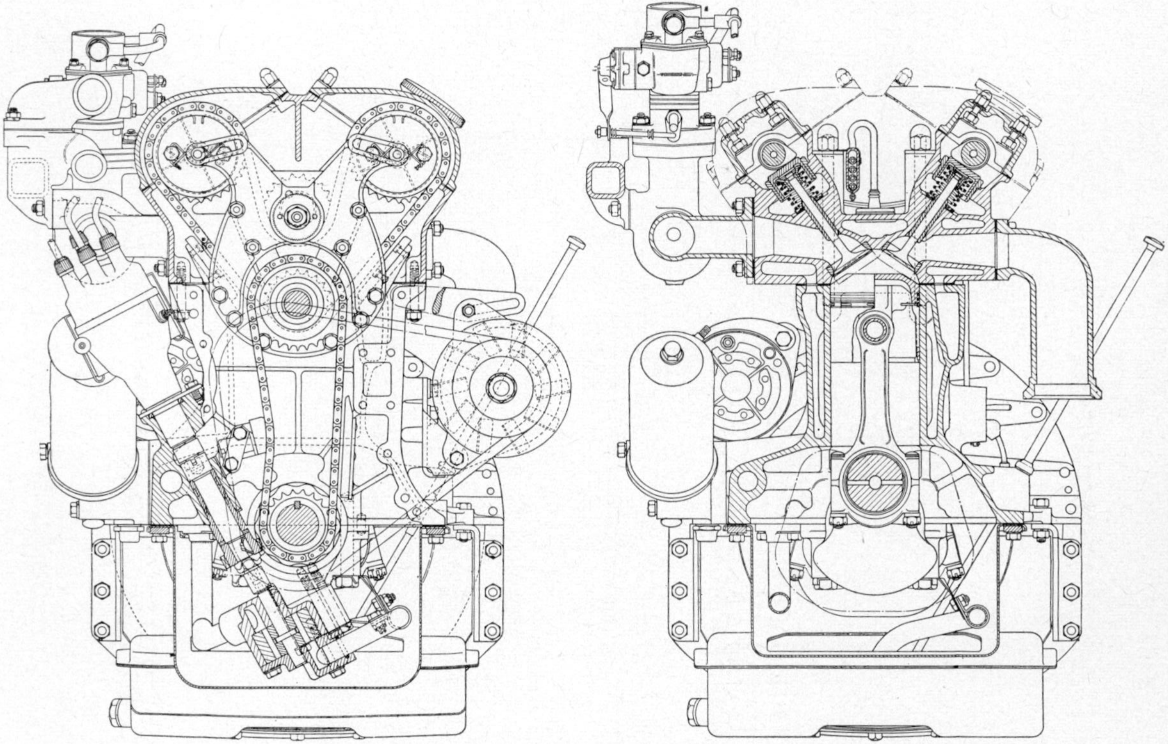

Fig. 7-10: Jaguar cross sections

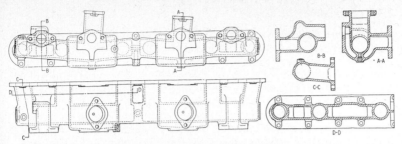

Fig. 7-11: Jaguar induction manifold

driven gear on the distributor-pump shaft of phosphor bronze.

The torsional vibration damper is a Metalastik rubber to metal bonded, inertia ring type.

Fig. 7-11 shows the design of the aluminium alloy induction manifold which is fed by two Solex B 32-PBI-5 downdraught carburettors, the main features of which are illustrated and described on pages 272-275.

With 24 mm chokes the performance curves shown in Fig. 7-12 are obtained. These represent a conservative tuning which could be considerably improved if desired. Fuel supply is by S.U. high pressure electric pump, and the air cleaner is a long cylindrical type of A.C. manufacture.

The lubrication system incorporates a Hobourn-Eaton pump of the type described on page 349 and a full-flow Tecalemit externally mounted filter. The somewhat unusual drilling of the crank pins, which has the effect of forming a useful sludge trap, may be noted.

A most informative and fully illustrated article will be found in *Automobile Engineer*, Vol. 46, No. 5.

Fig. 7-12: Jaguar performance curves

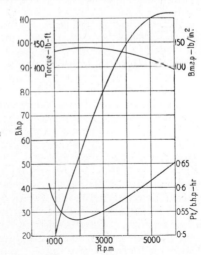

151

7.10 Straight-eight Engine

A large American straight eight of conventional design is illustrated in Fig. 7-13. This is the Packard 5,358 c.c. unit formerly fitted to their " Super-Eight " chassis.

With a bore and stroke of $3\frac{1}{2} \times 4\frac{1}{4}$ in, the engine develops 145 b.h.p. at 3,600 r.p.m., the maximum torque being about 265 lb-ft at 2,000 r.p.m., which corresponds to a b.m.e.p. of 122 lb/sq. in. This is a moderate figure typical of the larger American engines.

The monobloc cylinder casting and the detachable head are of alloy iron, the crank case being closed by a shallow pressed steel sump.

Autothermic aluminium alloy pistons, described on page 78, are used, and the large diameter hollow gudgeon pins, lubricated through a central drilling of the connecting rod, may be noted.

The crankshaft, of " split-four " arrangement, is of stiff proportions with integral balance weights, and fitted with a torsional vibration damper at the front end. The camshaft is driven by a chain of the inverted tooth silent type, and the fan–pump shaft and dynamo by a triangular belt drive. It will be noticed that the exhaust jacket to the induction manifold is controlled by a shutter thermostatically operated, the arrangement being similar to that described on page 271.

The engine is one of the last remaining side-valve designs in American practice, and is of a type that is being completely superseded by the high-powered V-eight.

7.11 The V-eight

An objection brought against the straight-eight engine, in addition to the liability to torsional oscillation of the crankshaft, is its great length, and an alternative arrangement of eight cylinders is the V-eight, employing two banks of four cylinders each, at right angles. This arrangement, long known and used in various applications, has recently established an overwhelming preponderance over alternative types in America for automobile purposes.

Following earlier pioneer designs, large-scale development was initiated by Cadillac in 1914, and aircraft and tank development produced air-cooled types. The flat or single plane crankshaft was used in these early constructions, but in 1926 Cadillac, and in 1932 Ford, introduced the 90° arrangement, the improved balance of which is described below. Side-valves gave place to overhead valves from 1949 onwards.

The early Ford 30 h.p. and 22 h.p. engines are well known in this country, but their power output proved rather higher than the general demand required, with the result that the popular Ford models in Britain, as indeed of all makes, are currently powered by in-line engines. The situation in America has been different. The insatiable demand for increased power, and the earlier availability of 100 octane fuels, has resulted in the production by all the big groups

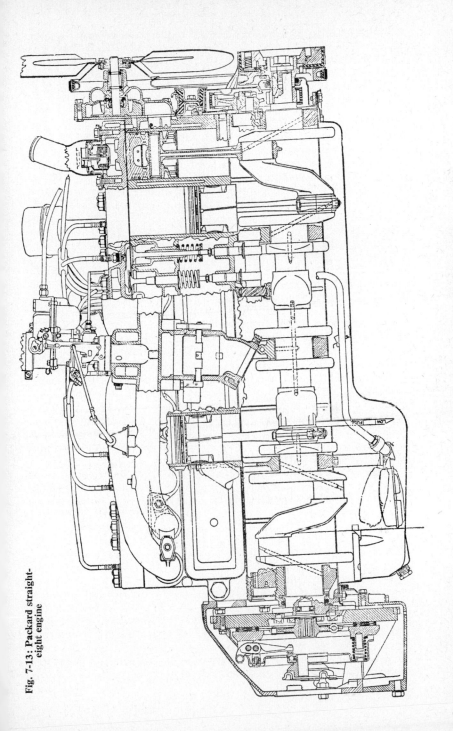

Fig. 7-13: Packard straight-eight engine

of overhead-valve V-eight engines of rated maximum outputs from 160 to 300 h.p., with compression ratios from 8 to 1 upwards, that of the Packard 300 h.p. being 10 to 1.

The cylinder dimensions are " under square," with few exceptions, averaging about $3\frac{3}{4}$ in bore and $3\frac{1}{4}$ in stroke, giving a piston displacement of about 290 cu. in.

7.12 Balance and Firing Intervals of V-eight

With the single plane crankshaft, the 90° firing intervals are obtained by the disposition of the cylinders in two banks at right angles, whereas with the two plane shaft, four of the intervals are due to cylinder disposition and four to crank arrangement.

The flat crankshaft is a simpler and, therefore, with comparable production methods, a less expensive form to make, but the dynamic balance of the engine is inferior to that obtained with the right angle disposition of cranks. The former arrangement is, for balancing purposes, treated as two ordinary four-cylinder engines sharing the same crankshaft, each set of four pistons being self-balanced for primary forces and couples, while the secondaries remain unbalanced in each bank. This gives a combined resultant secondary force for the whole engine which is zero in the " vertical " direction, but has, in the " horizontal " direction a value 40 per cent greater than that corresponding to one set of four pistons, since the horizontal components combine in the ratio $\sqrt{2}$ to 1, while the vertical components neutralize each other.

When the right-angle disposition of adjacent cranks is adopted, the engine is treated for balancing purposes as four 90° V twins, and the primary forces are counteracted by means of revolving masses in the manner described on page 60. The combined primary reciprocating effect of the two pistons, operating on the same crank pin and with their lines of stroke at right angles, is equivalent to the mass of one piston revolving at the crank pin, and the balancing problem is reduced to that of a revolving system.

In the V8 crankshaft illustrated in Fig. 6-15 the thinner webs adjacent to the journals may be regarded as circular disc webs each corrected to neutralize half of the actual revolving mass at each crank pin, that is, half the pin and one of the big ends.

The heavy masses B_1 and B_2 each incorporate in effect two of these corrected disc webs, together with further masses to balance both the adjacent *equivalent* revolving masses representing the effect of the two pistons on each pin.

If component couples in the plane of the paper for the lower view are considered, it will be realized that the arm of the couple due to cranks 1 and 4, which form a clockwise component couple, is greater than the arm of the component couple due to cranks 2 and 3, acting in the contrary sense. This is corrected by giving the masses B_1 and B_2, which act in intermediate planes, a bias to assist their opposition to cranks 1 and 4. This bias accounts for the unsymmetrical form of the masses.

Since the balance of the pistons involves masses incorporated in the crankshaft, it will be realized that not only should the piston masses be held to close tolerances among themselves, as in the four-cylinder engine, but also that their relation to the crankshaft must be carefully checked.

7.13 Secondary Balance with Two Plane Shaft

The secondary balance with the right-angle shaft is superior to that of the flat shaft.

It will be found that adjacent pairs of pistons in each bank, moving in the same longitudinal plane, operate on cranks at right angles. Thus when one piston is at the position corresponding to $\theta = 0$ (see Fig. 5-9) its neighbour in the same bank has $\theta = 90°$, and the corresponding secondary forces will be opposed.

Fig. 7-14 shows the disposition of the cylinders and cranks, the shaft being indicated with five main bearing journals in order to make clear the relative disposition of the throws. The arrows represent the secondary disturbing forces in the configuration shown, and it will be seen that these are self-balanced in each bank, for both forces and couples.

7.14 Construction of V-eight

A cross-section of the early Ford side-valve engine is given in Fig. 7-15, which shows the salient special features. The two banks of cylinders and the crank case are formed in a single monobloc casting, the sump which forms the lower half of the crank case being a light steel pressing.

Detachable heads with side valves operated from a single camshaft are conventional features, while the somewhat inaccessible position of the tappets and valve springs is mitigated by the special construction adopted. The tappets are non-adjustable, and the valve stems have a wide splayed foot which minimizes wear at this point. The valve stem guide is split along its centre line for assembly around the valve stem, and the whole assembly may be withdrawn

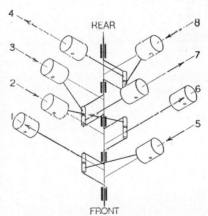

Fig. 7-14: Diagram of V-eight

upwards through the cylinder block after removal of a retainer of flat horseshoe form. Precision gauging during assembly is claimed to render adjustment between periodical regrindings unnecessary, and so enables a simpler construction to be adopted.

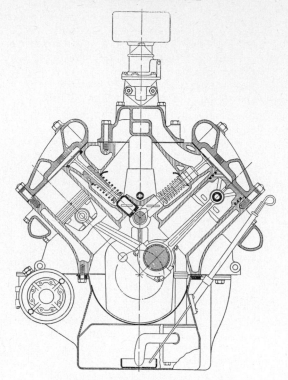

Fig. 7-15: Cross-section of early V-eight

A twin down-draught carburettor is fitted to a unit induction manifold and cover, rendering the whole assembly compact and of clean exterior form.   Numbering the off-side cylinders 1, 2, 3, 4 and the near-side 5, 6, 7, 8, as in Fig. 7-14, the near-side choke feeds numbers 1, 6, 7 and 4 while the off-side choke feeds 5, 2, 3 and 8 The firing order is 1 5 4 8 6 3 7 2, resulting in a regular interval of half a revolution between cylinders fed from the same choke. The induction tracts are symmetrically arranged, but are not equal in length for all cylinders.

Mounted at the rear of the induction manifold may be observed the crank-case breather and oil-filler, up which passes the push rod for operating the A.C. fuel pump.

7.15   British V-eight Engines

Notable V-eight engines of recent development are the Rolls-Royce, $6\frac{1}{4}$ litre engine having interesting features, and the two Daimler units of $4\frac{1}{2}$ and $2\frac{1}{2}$ litres respectively.   The smaller engine is used in both the SP 250 Sports model and the $2\frac{1}{2}$ litre saloon.

156

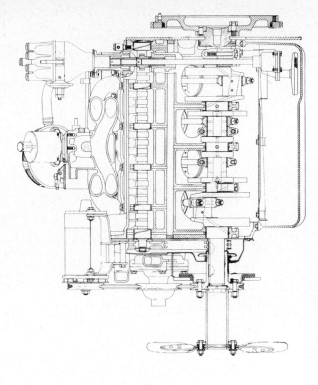

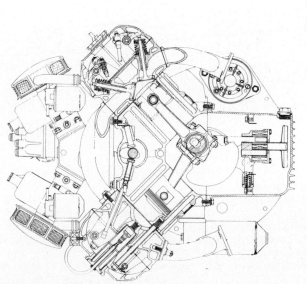

Fig. 7-16: Daimler V-eight engine

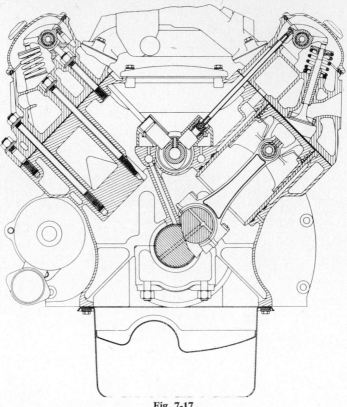

Fig. 7-17

The main features of the 2½ litre engine may be examined in Fig. 7-16. As is usual in this type of engine, an " over-square " ratio has been adopted—76·2 mm bore and 69·85 mm stroke. The cylinder block is of cast iron without liners, but all the other major structural components are of aluminium alloy.

Hemispherical combustion chambers with inclined overhead valves pitched transversely in a wide-angle V are used. The valves are operated by push rods and rockers from a single camshaft placed high in the V of the cylinder block, which extends down to the level of the crankshaft axis.

The camshaft drive is a simple duplex roller chain layout.

A forged steel, five bearing crankshaft with the fully balanced right-angle arrangement explained on pages 60 and 154 is used.

The addition of a light bonded rubber vibration damper should give the final assurance of smooth running.

Twin rocker shafts are necessary, with the push rods slightly splayed relative to the axes of the tappets. Since the operating

158

gear is light, however, the slight obliquity of thrust should not cause undue wear.

The securing of the rocker shaft pedestals by means of extended cylinder-head studs is of interest and should provide a simple and rigid assembly. Note the use of dowel tubes.

Over the rocker covers the width of the engine is somewhat large owing to the nearly horizontal disposition of the exhaust valves, but this is not accentuated by the exhaust manifolds, which are neatly tucked away under the cylinder heads.

In Fig. 7-17 is a sectional view of the cylinders and valve gear of the Rolls-Royce $6\frac{1}{4}$ litre engine. This unit has a bore of 104·1 and stroke 91·4 mm, and the compression ratio is 9 : 1. The inclined over-head valves, longitudinally pitched, serve tapered " bath-tub " type combustion chambers.

Interesting features are the design of the head to keep the width to a minimum, and the wet cylinder liners.

A comprehensive description of the Daimler engines will be found in *Automobile Engineer*, December 1961, and for details of recent American V-eights, Vol. 46, No. 5 of the same publication should be consulted.

CHAPTER 8

Sleeve Valve and Special Engines

Burt-McCullum single sleeve. Knight double sleeve. Cylindrical rotary valves. Aspin engine. N.S.U. Wankel engine.

INTEREST in the reciprocating sleeve valve has persisted throughout the history of the automobile engine, and though not now so widely used as in the early days of the Burt-McCullum and Knight patents, the single sleeve still has many strong adherents, and recent metallurgical advance has made possible such exacting and successful applications of the single sleeve as the Bristol " Perseus " and Napier " Sabre " aircraft engines.

The double sleeve has become obsolete owing to its greater cost of manufacture and greater viscous drag as compared with the single sleeve, and though the qualities of the Daimler-Knight, Minerva, and Panhard engines are proverbial, it does not appear likely that the double sleeve arrangement will experience revival.

The sleeve valve, as the name implies, is a tube or sleeve interposed between the cylinder wall and the piston; the inner surface of the sleeve actually forms the inner cylinder barrel in which the piston slides. The sleeve is in continuous motion and admits and exhausts the gases by virtue of the periodic coincidence of ports cut in the sleeve with ports formed through the main cylinder casting and communicating with the induction and exhaust systems.

8.1 Burt Single-sleeve Valve

The Burt-McCullum single-sleeve valve is given both rotational and axial movement, as it is impossible to obtain, with a single sleeve having only axial reciprocation, the necessary port opening for about one-quarter of the cycle and closure for the remaining three-quarters, if both inlet and exhaust are to be operated by the same sleeve. It will be found that a second opening occurs when the ports should be shut. The sleeve may be given its combined axial and rotational motion in a variety of ways, one of which is illustrated in Fig. 8-1. This shows an arrangement of ball and socket joint operated by short transverse shafts in a design due to Ricardo, and the same mechanism was used in the Napier " Sabre " engine. The ball B is mounted on a small crank pin integral with the cross-shaft A which is driven at half-engine speed through skew gears from the longitudinal shaft C. Clearly the sleeve receives a vertical movement corresponding to the full vertical throw of the ball B while the extent of the rotational movement produced by the horizontal throw of the ball depends upon the distance between the centre of that ball and the axis of the sleeve.

160

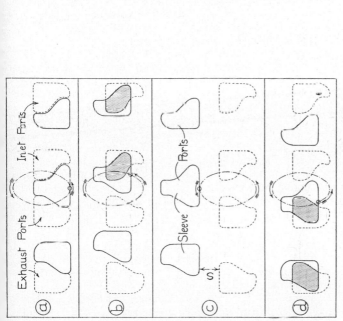

Exhaust Ports   Inlet Ports

Ports

Sleeve

S

(a)
(b)
(c)
(d)

Fig. 8-2: Single sleeve porting

(a) Shows the exhaust just closing and inlet about to open.
(b) Shows maximum port opening to induction.
(c) Shows the top of the compression stroke, S being the maximum "seal" or overlap of the ports and cylinder head.
(d) Shows maximum port opening to exhaust

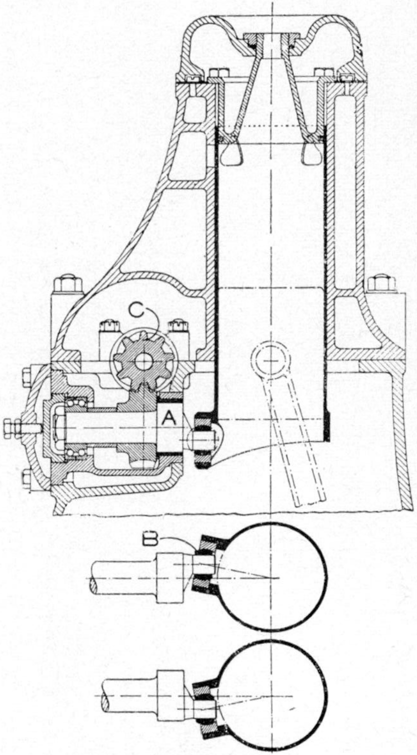

C
A
B

Fig. 8-1

8.2 Arrangement of Ports

The form and arrangement of the ports are arrived at as the result of considerable theoretical and experimental investigation in order that the maximum port openings may be obtained with the minimum sleeve travel. This is important, as the inertia forces due to the motion of the sleeve, and the work done against friction, are both directly proportional to the amount of travel. Fig. 8-2 shows an arrangement of ports wherein three sleeve ports move relatively to two inlet and two exhaust ports, the middle sleeve port registering in turn with an inlet and an exhaust port. The motion of the sleeve ports relatively to the fixed cylinder ports is the elliptical path shown. In the figure, the sleeve ports are shown in full lines in their positions relative to the cylinder ports (shown in broken lines) at various periods of the cycle. In practice it is usual to provide five sleeve ports and three inlet and exhaust ports.

8.3 Advantages and Disadvantages of Sleeve Valves

The great advantages of the sleeve valve are silence of operation and freedom from the necessity for the periodical attention which poppet valves require, if the engine is to be kept in tune. Hence sleeve valves have been used in cars of the luxury class where silence is of primary importance. The average sleeve valve engine has not shown quite such a good performance as its poppet valve rival in maintenance of torque at high speeds, owing chiefly to the somewhat restricted port openings obtainable with reasonable sleeve travel. Hence sleeve-valve engines have not figured prominently in racing, although some very good performances have been made from time to time. Sleeve valve engines share with rotary valve types reduced tendency to detonation owing to the simple symmetrical form of the combustion chamber with its freedom from hot spots, and shortness of flame travel. The construction also lends itself well to high compression ratios without interference between piston and valves. The disadvantages of gumming and high oil consumption experienced with early sleeve valve designs have been successfully overcome, but there is some element of risk of serious mechanical trouble in the event of piston seizure, which dangerously overloads the sleeve driving gear.

8.4 Rotary Valve

Many types of rotary valve have been invented, either to act as distribution valves only, or to perform the double function of distribution and sealing.

Their great mechanical merit is that their motion is rotative and uniform, and the stresses and vibration of the reciprocating poppet or sleeve valve are eliminated. They are suitable for the highest speeds, and the limitation in this direction is determined by the inertia stresses in the main piston, connecting rod and bearings. A high degree of mechanical silence is obtained.

The performance shown by the two proprietary makes described in the following paragraphs has proved conclusively that from thermodynamic and combustion points of view they have outstanding qualities as compared with the conventional poppet valve construction. In both the Cross and Aspin engines in the single-cylinder motor-cycle form, exceptionally high compression ratios with freedom from detonation with fuels of quite low octane value have been obtained. The corresponding b.m.e.p. reaches figures of the order 160 to 180 lb/sq. in. The quite exceptional outputs per litre arising from the combination of extreme rotational speeds with these pressures should be considered in the light of the remarks on page 55.

The remarkable freedom from detonation under a combination of high compression ratio and low octane fuel—a combination usually disastrous in a normal engine—is no doubt largely due to the general coolness of the combustion chamber, its smooth form and freedom from hot spots. Further, the high compression ratio probably results in complete evaporation of the fuel before ignition, and it is believed that this inhibits the formation of the peroxides referred to on page 331. This may be consistent with observation that tetra-ethyl lead, which is also regarded as an inhibitor of such formation, appears to have little effect in these cool engines.

To offset these remarkable characteristics there are, unfortunately, considerable mechanical difficulties in pressure sealing and providing adequate lubrication of the valves without excessive waste to the cylinder and exhaust ports. Very great progress has been made towards final success in these directions, and advances in metallurgy, and extended trials of different combinations of materials, may well result in the general supersession of the poppet valve—which has probably reached the peak of its development—by the rotary form.

8.5 Cross Rotary-valve Engine

The valve of the Cross engine normally runs at half engine speed, but by duplicating the inlet and exhaust ports through the valve it may be readily designed to operate at one-quarter engine speed.

The valve is cylindrical and rotates in a cylindrical housing, the gases entering and leaving the valve in an axial direction.

The valve housing is split about the centre-line of the valve, the halves being held in resilient contact with the valve. The bottom half of the valve housing is usually an integral part of the cylinder, which is not bolted to the crank case, but allowed to press upwards against the valve, such pressure being proportional to the gas pressure in the cylinder.

In cylinder sizes above 200 c.c. a controlled valve loading scheme is adopted so that the pressure on the valve by the housing is only just sufficient for adequate sealing.

The lubrication of the valve is brought about by pumping oil on to one side of the valve and removing it with a scraper blade on the other side, an essential part of the mechanism being a non-return valve which prevents oil being sucked into the induction side of the valve.

In cases where it is not possible to have a completely floating cylinder, the lower part of the valve housing is spigotted into the top part of the cylinder, suitable sealing rings being provided.

Cross engines usually use an aluminium cylinder without liner. The piston rings, being made from very hard steel, act not only as the means of pressure sealing, but as bearers to prevent the piston touching the bore. The cylinder bore wear with this construction is negligible.

Fig. 8-3 is a sectional view of an early type of valve for a 500 c.c. motor-cycle engine, having vertical shaft and bevel drive for the valve. V is the cylindrical valve operated by the dogs G on the half-time shaft. The induction port is indicated at I, and S is the tunnel

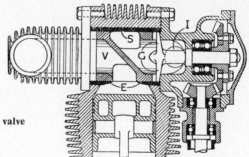

Fig. 8-3: Cross rotary valve

liner in which the valve rotates. In this design sealing is obtained by the resilient port edges E of the liner, which is so machined as to maintain an elastic pressure on the rotating valve.

This sealing pressure is transmitted through the valve body to the upper casting and back to the crank case through two long holding-down bolts.

Various materials have been tried for the valve and liner, a combination of nitri-cast iron valve running in a liner of bronze or nitralloy steel having given good results.

The makers report that this engine has developed a b.m.e.p. of 195 lb/sq. in. at 4,000 r.p.m. with a fuel consumption of 0·375 lb/b.h.p.-hr.

For further details of these interesting engines the reader should refer to a paper by R. C. Cross in Vol. XXX of the *Proceedings of the Institution of Automobile Engineers.*

8.6   Aspin Engine

Like the Cross engine, the Aspin engine has shown the most striking performance in the single-cylinder, air-cooled motor-cycle form, an engine of 67 mm bore and 70·5 mm stroke with a compression ratio of 14 to 1 having developed 31 b.h.p. at the remarkable speed of 11,000 r.p.m. When developing 21 b.h.p. at 6,000 r.p.m. the fuel consumption was recorded as 0·32 lb/b.h.p.-hr.

The general construction of this single-cylinder engine should be clear from Fig. 8-4. The valve consists of a nitrided alloy-steel shell partly filled with light alloy, within which a cell is formed to constitute the combustion chamber. As the valve rotates the cell is presented in turn to the inlet port I, the sparking plug P and the exhaust port E. During compression, ignition and combustion the cell is on the cool side of the cylinder, and after ignition the plug is shielded from the hot gases. These conditions play a great part in the thermodynamic properties of the engine. In this early engine a double-

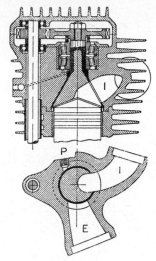

Fig. 8-4: Aspin engine

thrust Timken roller bearing was provided to take the bulk of the upward thrust due to the gas load, only a carefully regulated amount being carried direct on the conical surface.

A 4·6-litre four-cylinder Aspin engine has been developed for heavy duty, and in Fig. 8-5 are shown sectional views of the head construction. Water cooling has been adopted for the rotor, which

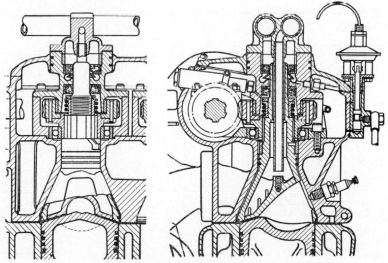

Fig. 8-5: Four-cylinder Aspin engine

is of fabricated steel construction, faced with a lead-bronze alloy, and running in a cast-iron cylinder head.

For full descriptions and analysis of performance of these engines, the reader should refer to articles by Louis Mantell and J. C. Costello in Volumes 34 and 35 of *Automobile Engineer*.

8.7 N.S.U. Wankel Rotary Engine

The information that follows is an abstracted summary of the comprehensive technical articles by R. F. Ansdale, A.M.I.Mech.E., in *Automobile Engineer*, Volume 50, No. 5 and Dr-Ing. Walter Froede in Volume 53, No. 8. An article by Felix Wankel on the performance criteria of this type of engine is in Volume 54, No. 10 of the same publication.

This latest enterprise in the search for a successful design of rotary pressure engine introduces no new principle or thermodynamic cycle. The four events of the " four-stroke " cycle take place in one rotation of the driving member.

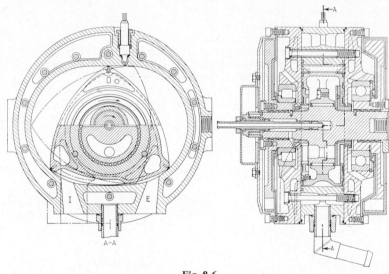

Fig. 8-6

The general profile of the straight working chamber is of epitrochoid form, a group of curves of the cycloid family, the geometry of which is fully discussed in the articles under notice.

The general construction of the current form, known as the KKM version, with three-lobed rotor, is shown in Fig. 8-6.

The rotor provides three equal working spaces, and clearly an exhaust release will occur each time an apex seal overruns the leading edge of the exhaust port E, that is, three times per revolution of the rotor, and this exhaust will continue until the following seal reaches the trailing edge of the port.

Induction will have commenced in the same space about 60° of rotor movement earlier.

There are thus three complete " four-stroke " cycles per revolution of the rotor in different working spaces, but all fired by the same sparking plug as maximum compression is reached.

The stationary shell pinion is fixed in the casing, and the annulus mounted at the centre of the rotor, and carried on needle rollers on the periphery of the shaft eccentric or " crank," engages and rolls around the fixed pinion. With 24 and 36 teeth on the pinion and annulus respectively, the main shaft will make 3 turns for 1 turn of the rotor, this giving a complete cycle for each revolution of the main shaft. The driving impulses transmitted to the shaft thus correspond to those of a normal two-cylinder four-stroke engine.

There is a rotating primary unbalance due to the eccentric path of the rotor, but this is readily dealt with by means of two symmetrically mounted flywheels, suitably drilled to provide the

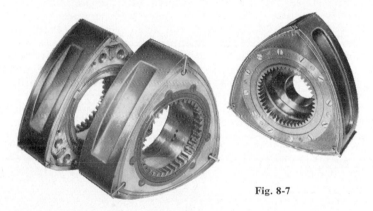

Fig. 8-7

countervailing unbalance. Suitable balancing provision for the cooling water and oil is incorporated.

The most interesting and informed articles on which these notes are based give an extensive description of the construction and related experience with the various sealing devices, and also performance curves and figures of the pioneer KKM unit in comparison with a normal piston engine.

Fig. 8-6 shows longitudinal and cross-sections of the current unit, and Fig. 8-7 gives views of three different forms of rotor. Recesses in the curved faces are provided to obviate strangling of the charge during passage from one zone to the next.

The form of these faces, subject to the necessary compression ratio being provided, is not limited to any particular profile.

Cooling has not presented many problems, because the complex movements of the rotor, and the resultant changing accelerations,

167

tend naturally to circulate the oil and so to cool the interior. The circulation thus set up contributes greatly to the cooling.

Most of the development problems have been associated with reducing the rates of wear of the apex seals and bore, and improving the efficiency of combustion.

As regards the wear, the problems are said to have been solved completely by suitable combination of materials for the seals and bores.

Although it is claimed that the burning is not as slow as the rather attenuated form of combustion chamber might lead one to suppose, the achievement of an acceptable brake specific fuel consumption must surely depend upon the perfection of the combustion process. A problem that seems inevitable is that, as the compression ratio is increased, so also must the degree of constriction through which the flame must pass—from one portion of the chamber to another—as the rotor sweeps past its top dead centre position. This will tend to interfere with the combustion process. Currently, the position is that the brake specific fuel consumption is low enough to compete with that of a two-stroke engine, but more work must be done before it can equal that of conventional engines operating on the four-stroke principle.

A survey of various types of rotary combustion engine, including brief comments on two-stroke and four-stroke versions under development by Renault, is given in a serial article by R. F. Ansdale, A.M.I.Mech.E., in *Automobile Engineer*, Volume 53, No. 11 and Volume 54, Nos. 1 and 2. The thermodynamics have been dealt with by D. Hodgetts, B.Sc., A.M.I.Mech.E., in Volume 55, No. 1 of the same journal.

CHAPTER 9

The Compression-ignition Engine

Comparison with large diesel engine. Air blast and mechanical injection. Form of combustion chamber. Injection pumps and sprayers. Comparison with petrol engine. Mechanical and hydraulic governors.

ONE of the most remarkable engineering developments of the last thirty years has been the rapid advance made in the application of the compression-ignition principle to engines for transport purposes, particularly on road and rail.

These engines are alternatively described as " Diesel " engines in honour of Dr. Rudolph Diesel, the German engineer, who was responsible for most of the pioneer invention and development work with large stationary units, and " heavy oil engines " from the higher specific gravity and less volatile—and therefore less inflammable—nature of the fuels which they are capable of using. The phrase " compression-ignition " is now generally preferred by authorities in this field, because the essential characteristic of the type, as compared with the volatile fuel spark ignition engine, is thereby clearly indicated.

This essential feature is the ignition of the fuel, when injected at or near the inner dead centre, by the high temperature of the air charge after compression through a volume ratio of not less than 12 to 1 or 13 to 1, and rising in some cases to as much as 20 to 1.

9.1 Temperature Produced by Compression

The resulting temperature depends on the temperature at the beginning of compression and the amount of heat loss during compression.

With an effective compression ratio of 14 from the point of closing of the inlet valve, an initial temperature of 60° C, and assuming no heat loss—true " adiabatic " compression—the resulting temperature at inner or top dead centre would be 675° C. These conditions would be approximately attained at full load and full speed, and a temperature of 675° C would be more than sufficient to ignite the fuels used, which have self-ignition temperatures in air at atmospheric pressure ranging from 350° C to 450° C, these temperatures of self-ignition being lower at the high pressure prevailing during injection.

Under light load and at starting, the conditions are less favourable. At starting from cold the prevailing temperature in the engine at the commencement of compression will be that of the atmosphere, say 15° C, and the heat loss during the relatively slow compression in a cold cylinder may prevent the temperature rising much above 400° C. This might prove insufficient to ignite certain fuels, and

169

in some engine designs arrangements are made to provide a higher compression ratio when starting than for normal running, in order to ensure that ignition will be obtained.

The temperature reached does not depend on the initial *pressure* of the charge, except to a slight degree indirectly, owing to the proportionately greater heat loss with a less dense charge. Thus, throttling the induction does not lower the compression temperature attained provided the initial temperature and volumetric compression ratio are the same. It is important to bear this in mind when studying the action of the pneumatic governor described later.

If the induction is unrestricted except by the normal throttling effect of the inlet valve, the pressure at commencement of compression will be from 13 to 15 lb/sq. in. absolute, depending on the speed and breathing characteristics of the engine. The pressure at the end of compression will depend on this initial pressure, the effective compression ratio and the amount of heat loss, its value ranging in different designs and according to the conditions from 450 to 550 lb/sq. in. or more.

Piston ring leakage will naturally reduce both the pressure and temperature at the end of compression. Thus far the cycle of operations differs from that in the petrol engine in that air only is compressed and a much higher compression ratio is used.

Shortly before top dead centre the liquid fuel is injected and ignites and burns in the heated air in the compression space. The combustion is not, as in the spark ignition engine, an explosion of a more or less homogeneous mixture of air and vaporized fuel, but rather a process in the early stages, of surface combustion of the liquid droplets which develops at a later stage, and to a varying degree in different designs, into a more or less rapid explosion. The variation of pressure during this process depends on the method of injection, whether it be by means of a high pressure air blast or simply by the agency of a mechanical pump, and on the form of the combustion chamber and conditions of turbulence.

9.2 Air Blast Injection

This method constituted the true Diesel method as originally used in large stationary and marine engines, and involved the following features. The compression pressure was about 500 lb/sq. in., and the fuel was measured and delivered by a mechanical pump to the annular space behind a small conical injection valve placed in the centre of the cylinder head and arranged to open outwards. To this space was applied an air pressure of 800 to 1,000 lb/sq. in. from air storage bottles charged by a compressor which was usually incorporated in the engine itself.

At the correct moment the injection valve was lifted off its seat and the high-pressure blast air drove the fuel in at a very great velocity, when it mingled with the combustion air in the cylinder and was ignited by the high temperature of this air caused by the

170

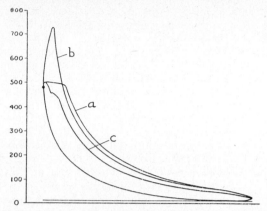

Fig. 9-1: Indicator diagrams of compression-ignition engine

high compression. It must be realized that the volume of liquid fuel delivered each cycle is an extremely small one, but the accompanying bulk of blast air, which was from 2 per cent to 3 per cent of the total air, lengthened the injection period with the result that the pressure did not rise during combustion, but was merely maintained at approximately the compression pressure as the piston moved outwards until combustion was completed.

The corresponding indicator diagram is shown at a in Fig. 9-1, the black dot indicating the approximate point of commencement of injection. The maximum pressure is about 500, and the mean pressure about 100 lb/sq. in., if the fuel injected corresponds to about three-quarters of the air present, representing about 30 per cent to 40 per cent excess air over that chemically necessary. The diagram marked c is obtained on part load with reduced fuel supply. The maximum pressure is the same, but the rate of combustion does not keep pace with the piston movement, and the pressure falls somewhat irregularly till combustion is complete.

These conditions represent approximately, combustion at constant pressure, and led to the adoption of that assumed condition of combustion in the hypothetical " Diesel cycle " in thermodynamic discussion.

9.3 Mechanical Injection

The high-pressure compressor required for the blast air was a costly and somewhat troublesome auxiliary, and absorbed considerable power, thus making the overall mechanical efficiency of the engine somewhat low. Further, storage bottles for the blast air were necessary, and the apparatus was far too cumbersome for motor vehicle use. Even with large land and marine diesel installations, mechanical injection by means of a jerk pump has almost wholly replaced the air blast method, which must be regarded as obsolete.

171

With mechanical injection the air blast is entirely dispensed with, and the oil is forced in from a pump through a sprayer or pulverizer, comprising one or more fine holes in a suitable nozzle. Very difficult conditions have to be met. The volume of liquid to be injected is very small and must be injected at a very high velocity in order that it may be thoroughly atomized and yet be capable of penetrating through the whole volume of air present. The jet must also be so disposed and directed that a stream of liquid is not likely to impinge on the cylinder wall or piston, where rapid carbonization would occur.

The injection of a small volume at high velocity implies a very short *period* of injection, and this results in the action approximating closely to an explosion with a more rapid rise in pressure and a much higher maximum pressure as shown at *b* in Fig. 9-1, which represents a typical full load diagram with mechanical injection. This higher maximum pressure makes the ratio of mean pressure to maximum pressure even less favourable than in diagram *a*, which already compares unfavourably in this respect with the petrol engine.

9.4 Power-weight Ratio

The above ratio of mean to maximum pressure is the determining factor in the value of the power-weight ratio, since the power depends on the mean pressure while the sturdiness and therefore weight of the parts will depend on the maximum pressure to be provided for. Thus, the compression-ignition engine is inherently heavier than its rival the petrol engine, owing to the very factor which results in its superior economy, namely, the higher compression and expansion ratio. As the petrol engine seeks to improve its fuel consumption by employing special fuels which permit of a higher compression ratio being used, so this difference will tend to disappear, and safety and cost of the fuel and general engine performance will become the determining factors. Metallurgical improvements and advance in manufacturing technique will be available equally to both types.

9.5 Injection and Combustion Processes

Extensive research has been and is being carried out to determine the best methods of injection and form of combustion chamber to give smooth and complete combustion of the injected fuel and suppression of the characteristic " diesel knock " which gives rough and noisy running of the high speed mechanical injection engine.

The problem is to inject into the cylinder an extremely small volume of liquid fuel in such a manner and into such an environment that every minute particle of oil shall be brought into immediate contact with its full complement of heated air, in order that combustion shall be rapid and complete without being so sudden as to give rise to rough running.

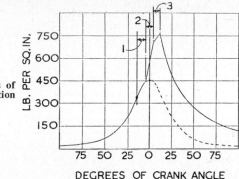

Fig. 9-2: Fundamental phases of combustion in mechanical injection diesel engine

DEGREES OF CRANK ANGLE

There are two general alternatives—either to cause the fuel to penetrate by its own velocity to all parts of the combustion chamber and find the air required, or to give the air itself such a degree of swirl or turbulence that it will seek out the fuel as it enters. The former represents the process of direct or open chamber injection in which any movement the air may possess is fortuitous or due to masking of the inlet valve, while the second covers the many designs of swirl or pre-combustion chamber arranged to give either ordered swirl or general turbulence to the air during injection of the fuel.

The merits and de-merits of the two general systems will be discussed when the details of the arrangements are described.

9.6 Three Phases of Combustion

Ricardo has recognized and described three phases of combustion which are illustrated in Fig. 9-2. This figure shows a form of indicator diagram which differs from the form in Figs. 4-4 and 9-1, in showing the pressures plotted on a continuous crank angle base instead of on a stroke base. With the crankshaft turning steadily at some measured speed, the crank angle base becomes also a *time* base and, as time is an important factor in combustion processes, very useful information can be obtained from such diagrams, though they cannot be used for the calculation of power output unless they are first reduced to a stroke base by a suitable graphical process. These crank angle diagrams can be obtained by means of indicators of the " Farnborough " and " cathode-ray " types.

9.7 Delay Period

Referring to the figure, the commencement of injection is indicated by the dot on the compression line about 15° before dead centre. The period 1 is the " delay " period during which ignition is being initiated, but without any measurable departure of the pressure from the air compression curve which is continued as a broken line in the diagram as it would be recorded if there were no injection and combustion.

173

9.8 Second Phase

This delay period occupies about 10° of crank angle and is followed by a second period of slightly less duration during which there is a sharp rise of pressure from 450 to over 700 lb/sq. in. This period represents a phase of rapid inflammation and combustion of the whole of the fuel present in the cylinder and approximates to the "constant volume" explosion of the vaporized fuel in the spark ignition engine. The steepness of this rise—here about 30 lb/sq. in. per degree of crank movement—is a determining factor in causing "diesel knock" or rough running. In general, though the form of the combustion chamber has an important influence, the longer the "delay" period the steeper will be phase 2 and the rougher the running, as a greater proportion of fuel is present. The nature of the fuel, the temperature and pressure of compression, and initial rate of fuel injection are all factors in deciding the length of the delay period apart from the form of the combustion chamber.

With the majority of engines the running is rougher at light loads and idling, as the lower compression temperature and smaller quantities of fuel injected increase the delay period, but this is not universal. Ricardo has shown that this period tends to be constant in time, thus occupying a greater crank angle at higher speeds and calling for injection advance, while the second phase covers more nearly a constant crank angle, as in a given engine it is dependent on turbulent displacement, the speed of which will increase with engine speed.

9.9 Final Phase of Combustion

The third phase involves combustion of the fuel as it issues from the sprayer holes, and represents the only phase over which direct control can be exercised by control of the rate of injection. With air blast injection this period could be largely determined by the blast pressure, and the characteristic flat top to the diagram could be obtained; but with mechanical injection most of the fuel is already in the cylinder before this stage is reached, and control is less certain.

It should be appreciated that the diagram in Fig. 9-2 is hypothetical, and that the three phases are not in general so sharply distinguishable one from the other.

9.10 Types of Combustion Chamber

Typical forms of combustion chamber are shown in Figs. 9-3 to 9-8. These illustrations are diagrammatic and are a selection from the many forms that have been invented and introduced with varying degrees of success. In Great Britain, the swirl or ante-chamber has very generally given place to direct or open chamber injection, and combustion chambers are now formed largely as a hemispherical or toroidal recess in the piston crown.

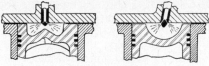

Fig. 9-3: Direct injection

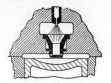

Fig. 9-4: Benz

9.11 Direct Injection

Fig. 9-3 illustrates the direct injection or open chamber type, in which the fuel is sprayed through two or three fine holes at a high velocity, and requiring injection pressures of 4,000 lb/sq. in. or more. The resulting " hard " jet enables the fuel to penetrate the dense air and find the necessary oxygen for combustion, aided in most cases by some residual swirl or turbulence set up during the induction stroke by the masking of the inlet valve, as is indicated in Fig. 9-7. The merits of this type are that a moderate compression ratio of 13 to 1 or 14 to 1 may be used, no auxiliary starting devices such as heater plugs or cartridges are necessary, and the smaller sizes of engine can be started by hand-cranking from cold, provision being made for releasing the compression until the engine is rotating at sufficient speed.

The form of the combustion chamber, with a moderate ratio of surface to volume is favourable to the reduction of heat loss, and engines of this type show good fuel economy and high mean pressure. Maximum pressures tend to be high, however, and there is a somewhat greater tendency to rough running. The indicator diagram approaches in form to " constant volume" rather than to " constant pressure " combustion. The injectors with their minute spraying holes—about eight-thousandths of an inch—and high pressures require highly skilled technique in production and most careful provision for filtering the fuel.

Direct injection engines have not generally been considered capable of quite such high speed or so tolerant of poor fuel as the pre-combustion or ante-chamber types, but their easy starting and high thermal efficiency have produced many converts as the more difficult injection technique has been mastered.

9.12 Pre-combustion Chamber

Fig. 9-4 shows the " pre-combustion " chamber type developed largely by the Benz firm and used in several Continental designs. The action gives an approximation to the characteristics of air blast injection and limits the maximum pressure. The pre-chamber represents about 40 per cent of the total clearance space, and the fuel is injected into this air and partly burned, the spread of ignition being helped by the turbulence arising from the passage of the air through the communicating " pepper castor " holes during compression.

175

The products of this partial combustion and the remaining fuel are then forced by the excess pressure in the pre-chamber back through the communicating holes at high velocity as the piston commences to descend. The high turbulence thus created aids the final inflammation and combustion in the main cylinder, while the piston is protected from the high initial pressure which would arise from too rapid combustion of the whole fuel charge. This system has the disadvantage that there is considerable cooling loss during passage of the air through the communicating holes, and due to the high surface-volume ratio of the combustion chamber.

The cooling effect is mitigated by partially isolating the inner lining of the chamber from the main body of metal as shown in the figure, but even so a higher compression pressure is necessary to obtain satisfactory starting with (in the majority of designs) the further help of heater plugs. Though engines employing this arrangement are in general free from rough running and high maximum pressures, and give a clean exhaust, they have not shown either such good economy or high output as more modern types.

9.13 Controlled Air Swirl

His investigations and experience with these and other types, and a realization of their defects, led Ricardo to develop the principle of ordered turbulence or swirl of the air. His initial work was carried out on a single sleeve valve engine, as this gave the greatest possible freedom in choice of form of the combustion chamber.

He quickly discovered that by arranging for the air to enter the inlet ports in a partly tangential direction, a rotational swirl or vortex about the cylinder axis could be formed, which persisted throughout the compression stroke and that, owing to the conservation of angular momentum in a free vortex, the rotational speed of the vortex became increased as the air entered the smaller diameter of the combustion chamber. If injection then took place in a direction at right angles to this ordered swirl, as shown in Fig. 9-5, a very complete and rapid distribution of fuel throughout the whole mass of air was obtained, it being possible to use a relatively soft and finely atomized jet with low injection pressure. This construction has been successfully applied to a range of medium speed stationary engines by Messrs. Brotherhood, and a fuel consumption as low as 0·36 lb/b.h.p.-hr has been obtained.

9.14 Comet Swirl Chamber

A fairly general prejudice against the sleeve valve led to the development by Ricardo in conjunction with the Associated Equipment Company and other firms of the " Comet " chamber, illustrated in Fig. 9-6, which shows a recent form and construction. Different designs vary in detail, and the twin turbulence recesses in the piston crown are a later development.

The usual shape of chamber is spherical with a single tangential

Fig. 9-5: Vortex

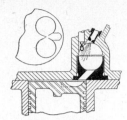

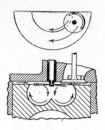

Fig. 9-6: Comet

Fig. 9-7: Saurer

entry passage, but in a modified form (described as the " whirlpool ") the chamber is flattened vertically and has two entry passages so disposed as to give swirl rotation about a vertical axis. It has been found possible to dispense with heater plugs in this design. An important feature of the Ricardo patents is the semi-isolated hot plug forming the lower part of the chamber, the purpose being the mitigation of the heat loss to the jackets, which loss gives rise to higher specific fuel consumption, as in the pre-chamber arrangement.

Comparative tests of A.E.C. transport engines with open and comet chambers showed lower fuel consumption and better low-speed torque with the former but better high-speed torque with the latter.

A new application to the Ricardo comet chamber, enabling easy starting to be obtained without a heater plug, is the " Pintaux " injector nozzle developed jointly by C.A.V. and Ricardo. This is illustrated and described on pages 182–183.

9.15 Saurer Dual-turbulence System

This system combines the effect of what has been aptly termed the " squish " of the air trapped between the piston crown and cylinder head, with rotational swirl produced by masking the inlet valve, as indicated in Fig. 9-7. In the actual construction there are two inlet and two exhaust valves, and the two directions of swirl are superimposed in the " doughnut " shaped recess in the piston head. The injector has four radially directed holes and only a moderate injection pressure is called for owing to the relatively large diameter of these. With a compression ratio of 15, no heater plug is required to obtain easy starting, and the delay period, owing to the good turbulence, is short.

9.16 Perkins Direct Injection Engines

The earlier " Aeroflow " design of Perkins P type engines is now being replaced by the direct injection system, though a limited number of the former is still produced by the Firm's Continental Associates, encouraged by successful performance.

The current somewhat simpler and more economical direct injection type is shown in Fig. 9-8. The general design follows familiar lines, a deep unit crankcase and cylinder block with dry cylinder liners being used. An interesting feature is the arrangement

177

of the drive for the C.A.V. distributor type injection pump, which incorporates a flange-mounting at the top of a nearly vertical shaft, in the manner familiar with the ignition distributor of the petrol engine: in fact, it takes little more room than the latter.

The performance curves of the 4/236 variant of this engine are shown in Fig. 4-8, from which the high speeds obtainable with modern design and materials can be seen. The smallest engine in the Perkins range, the 4/99 is capable of a maximum speed of 4,000 r.p.m.

Interesting developments of the Perkins 6/354 engine in connection with differential supercharging, are described on pages 321 and 509, and the Specialloid pistons are mentioned on page 80. The authors are indebted to the makers for drawings and information.

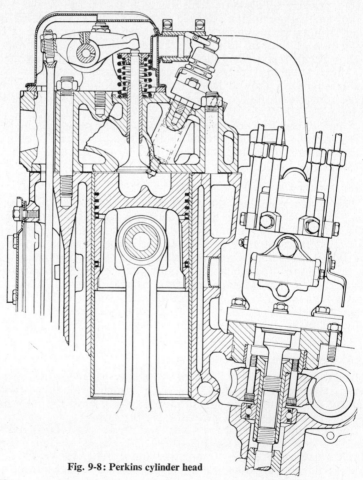

Fig. 9-8: Perkins cylinder head

9.17 Injection Equipment

In describing the two alternative injection methods, with or without air blast, some indication of the nature of the problem was given. A few simple calculations will serve to emphasize the extremely precise measurement and control that is actually required.

The weight of air contained in an engine cylinder of $4\frac{1}{4}$ in bore by 6 in stroke at the moment of closing the inlet valve and at normal load is about 0·003 lb. The corresponding weight of fuel, assuming " 100 per cent injection " would be about one-fifteenth of this, say 0·0002 lb. Actually the injection is considerably less than 100 per cent even at full load, but this weight will be assumed.

The volume of 0·0002 lb of gas oil is about $\frac{1}{10}$ cubic centimetre, or 100 cu. mm. With the smallest cylinders now in use, and at idling loads, the volume per injection may be less than one-tenth of this, say 8 to 10 cu. mm.

This minute quantity of liquid must be accurately metered and forced through the injector nozzle in such a manner that it will penetrate and mingle uniformly with the dense air in the cylinder. With direct injection the necessary injection velocity is of the order of 600 to 800 ft/sec through the sprayer holes. The hydrostatic head necessary to impart this velocity, if the effects of viscosity of fuel and length of sprayer hole are neglected, is given by the formula—

$$h = \frac{v^2}{2g},$$

that is, for 800 ft/sec,

$$h = \frac{(800)^2}{2 \times 32} = 10,000 \text{ ft}$$

The pressure corresponding to this head, assuming the oil to have a density of 53 lb/cu. ft, is—

$$\frac{10,000 \times 53}{144} = 3,700 \text{ lb/sq. in. approximately}$$

The diameter and number of the sprayer holes in combination with the available time for injection must be such as will give this velocity.

If the injection is assumed to extend over 24° of crank angle and the engine is rotating at 2,000 r.p.m., the available time is—

$$\frac{24°}{360°} \times \frac{60 \text{ sec}}{2,000} = 0·002 \text{ sec}$$

Reducing the calculation to millimetres—

$$800 \text{ ft/sec} = 244,000 \text{ mm/sec.}$$

The area of sprayer holes necessary to discharge 100 cu. mm in 0·002 sec at the above speed would be—

$$\frac{100}{244,000 \times 0·002} = 0·205 \text{ sq. mm}$$

179

9.18 Diameter of Sprayer Holes

The diameter of a single hole for this area is 0·51 mm, and of four separate holes 0·255 mm, or approximately ten thousandths of an inch. In multi-hole sprayers for direct injection combustion chambers, diameters of even less than this figure are in use, so the reader will appreciate the delicate technique required in the production of these nozzles, and the importance of meticulous care in filtering the fuel.

9.19 Pintle-type Nozzle

With the pre-chamber and swirl types of combustion head, it is possible to use " soft " jets giving finer atomization but less penetration, as the air will find the fuel. Injection velocities and pressures are correspondingly lower. Either a single hole may be used or a nozzle of the self-clearing pintle type. In this type the fuel issues as a hollow cylindrical or conical spray through the annular space between a central stem or pintle and the main bore of the nozzle. By giving the pintle a suitable shape, usually slightly conical, the jet may be given a form suited to its particular application. Many special forms of approach channel to the final orifice, both of the single hole and pintle type, have been devised and tried with a view to giving swirl or impact effects to the jet in order to obtain good atomization. In general, these forms increase the hydrostatic injection pressure.

9.20 Open and Closed Nozzles

With air blast injection it was seen that a mechanically operated valve is used to time and control the injection in conjunction with a suitable control of the blast pressure according to the load. The pump develops a pressure no greater than is necessary to deliver the fuel to the space behind the injection valve at the pressure of the blast air, namely about 1,000 lb/sq. in. The commencement and finish of injection is accurately controlled by the opening and closing of the injection valve, though the very small lift of this requires precise setting of the tappet clearance.

The opposite extreme to this mode of injection is by means of a jerk pump through an open nozzle, that is through a pipe and sprayer provided only with one or more ball-type non-return valves to prevent the compression pressure forcing the fuel back to the pump.

Injection will commence when the pressure in the fuel is sufficient to overcome the pressure in the combustion chamber and the resistances of the pipe and sprayer, and will cease when the pressure falls below this value and the non-return valves close.

The sprayer becomes of very simple form and is somewhat less liable to choke than the closed nozzle, but the timing of both commencement and finish of injection is less certain and very sensitive to the diameter and length of the delivery pipe. Dribble and secondary injection are liable to occur owing to pressure surges

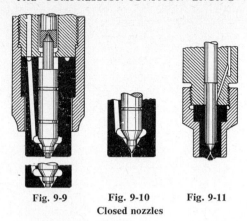

Fig. 9-9   Fig. 9-10   Fig. 9-11

Closed nozzles

in the pipe, unless these surges are directed and controlled to occur at favourable moments.

9.21 Closed Nozzle

The closed type of nozzle appears to be the only satisfactory type for high-speed engines, for though its construction is slightly more complicated than the open type, it is still possible to dispense completely with mechanical operation, and the spring-controlled delivery valve incorporated in the injector renders the timing more accurate and the cut-off more definite, while the behaviour is less sensitive to the length of the delivery pipe. This enables a multi-plunger unit pump to be placed in any convenient position on the engine with delivery pipes leading to the separate injectors. It is in general desirable to make the length of the delivery pipes equal in order to equalize the delivery characteristics for individual cylinders.

Typical closed nozzles are illustrated in Figs. 9-9 to 9-11, which show the C.A.V. pintle and hole types and the Gardner hole type. The latter has four equally spaced holes $\frac{8}{1000}$ in. in diameter. All the three nozzles shown are provided with a spring-loaded differential needle or delivery valve which is typical of this type of nozzle. Injection commences when the valve is lifted off its seating by the hydrostatic pressure acting on the annular area between two diameters of the valve stem. When this lifting takes place, the pressure is operative over the whole projected area of the valve stem, and the valve will not close until the pressure has fallen to somewhat below the opening pressure, depending on the ratio chosen for the two diameters. The mean value of these operating pressures can be adjusted by altering the strength or initial compression of the control spring. In the C.A.V. assembly provision is made for adjustment of this pressure by the user, as these injectors are employed in a wide variety of engines requiring different injection pressures. In the Gardner design the determination of

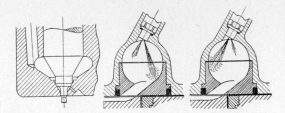

Fig. 9-12:
Pintaux nozzle

the operating pressure is regarded as a works adjustment and no provision is made for its modification by the user.

9.22 Pintaux Nozzle

The " Pintaux " nozzle has been developed jointly by Messrs. C.A.V. and Sir Harry Ricardo, and is applicable only to the Ricardo comet type cylinder head. The nozzle has been introduced primarily to enable easy cold starting to be obtained without the use of heater plugs.

With the normal type of pintle nozzle the spray is coaxial with the injector, and the direction of injection found most advantageous for all-round engine performance is that indicated in the diagrams of Fig. 9-12, which is down-stream on the opposite side of the swirl chamber from the throat entry.

Investigation has shown, however, that under starting conditions the hottest zone of the chamber is outside this spray path and nearer the centre of the chamber on the opposite side.   By directing

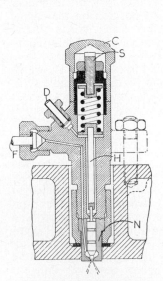

Fig. 9-13: C.A.V. injector

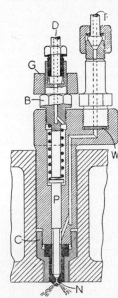

Fig. 9-14: Gardner injector

182

the spray into this zone considerably improved starting can be obtained without the use of heater plugs.

This direction does not, however, give the best all-round engine performance, and the construction of the nozzle has been so contrived that at the low speeds of starting, when the injector needle is only partly lifted, the main orifice is largely blanked by a cylindrical portion of the needle point, and the bulk of the delivery is discharged through the oblique hole shown in the enlarged view of the nozzle. At normal running speeds the cylindrical portion is lifted clear, and about 90 per cent of the delivery issues in the normal manner, but preceded by a small pilot charge which promotes quieter running.

9.23 Injector Assemblies

Diagrams of two typical injector assemblies are shown in Figs. 9-13 and 9-14. In both cases provision is made for collecting and returning to the supply pipe any fuel leakage that may take place between the differential valve and its guide.

This leakage is reduced to a minimum by the most precise and accurate lapped finish which is given to the stem and guide assembly, working tolerances of the order of $\frac{1}{10000}$ in being commonplace in this class of work. Assemblies of the valve and body must be maintained as a pair and never interchanged.

Referring to Fig. 9-13, the nozzle N shown is of the pintle type. H is the spindle which transmits the spring load to the differential valve, the spring load being adjustable by the screw S and locknut, on removal of the protecting cap C.

In the Gardner injector (Fig. 9-14) the spring acts directly on the differential valve or plunger P, the upper end of the spring butting on the breech plug B, on the top of which bears the holding down yoke G.

N is the nozzle and C the nozzle cap, while at W is provided a very fine gauze filter washer as a final safety precaution against choking of the fine sprayer holes. In both figures the fuel enters at F and leakage past the valve is led away at D, being returned to the main fuel intake.

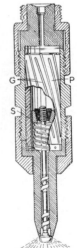

Fig. 9-15:
Morris injector

9.24 Morris Commercial Saurer Injector

This injector, which is illustrated in Fig. 9-15, incorporates final edge-filtration of the fuel with a nozzle of the poppet type.

The filtration is effected as the fuel passes from one set of the helical grooves G, formed on the surface of the hardened steel plug P, to the second set, through the fine radial clearance between the plug and body, both of which are finished to close tolerances.

183

The nozzle is of the outwardly opening poppet type, the opening pressure being adjusted by the stiff helical spring S.

On the stem of the valve are formed two sets of " swirl " grooves which make an important contribution to the fine atomization of the umbrella-shaped spray which enters the combustion chamber. This injector is no longer used but is of technical interest.

9.25 Injection Control

For the high-speed automobile engine, the " jerk " type of constant stroke plunger pump is now practically universal, the term " jerk " indicating the sudden impulse which it is sought to give to the fuel at the instant required for injection, followed at the appropriate moment by a sudden collapse of pressure which will result in the cessation of injection in an abrupt manner, preventing dribble.   Inertia and wave effects have been applied to this end. In railway and similar heavy applications, Messrs. Beardmore have been pioneers, and have developed a type of jerk pump in which the almost instantaneous development and collapse of the injection pressure is obtained as a result of the rapid opening and closing of by-pass ports by means of a cylindrical " flash " valve, while the pump plunger is itself in rapid motion near the middle of its stroke.

9.26 Volumetric Capacity of Injection System

The volumetric capacity of the injection system, including pump chamber, delivery line and injector may be one hundred or more times the volume of the fuel injected per stroke, while at light loads the elastic compression alone of this volume, during generation of the necessary injection pressure, may be greater than the volume to be injected.

Clearly there is ample scope for the very able and highly specialized research which is being carried out in this field, and as the conditions of wave transmission and flow in the injection system become more thoroughly understood, it is possible that suitable choice of diameter and length of delivery pipe and of pump cut-off characteristics will lead to further mechanical simplification of injectors.

9.27 C.A.V. Injection Pump

The C.A.V. injection pump, developed from original Bosch designs to a very high degree of precision and efficiency by C.A.V. Ltd., is by far the most widely used pump on the market.   The N type pump illustrated in Fig. 9-16 is a recent development of an extensive series of types and incorporates many ingenious improvements in ease of adjustment, accessibility, and provision for thorough filtration of the fuel.   When combined with the H type hydraulic governor, one of the mechanical (flyweight) governors, or the pneumatic governor described on pages 193–194, it forms a reasonably compact and self-contained control unit of great sensitiveness and accuracy.

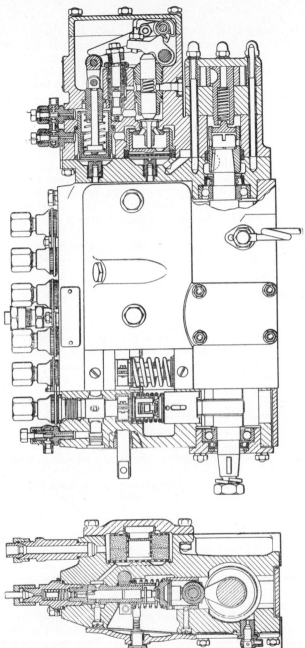

Fig. 9-16: C.A.V. N-type injection pump with hydraulic governor

Fig. 9-16 shows the six-element pump, but two-, three-, four- and five-element models to suit engines of the corresponding number of cylinders are available.

The stroke of the pump plunger is standardized at 9 mm, with bores ranging in eight sizes from 5 mm to 10 mm, giving maximum useful outputs per stroke of 22 to 200 cu. mm.

The plunger is positively driven by a cam during the delivery stroke and returned by a spring suitably proportioned to maintain contact of the tappet roller and cam at the highest speed at which the pump is intended to run, which is 1,300 r.p.m. for four-stroke engines, giving a maximum engine speed of 2,600 r.p.m.

This speed is considerably above the maximum permitted running speed of the majority of engines on the market, and for two-stroke engines of similar working speed special camshafts and tappet springs are provided. As the plunger descends, its upper edge uncovers, towards the end of the downward stroke, the fuel feed ports and fuel enters to fill the partial vacuum that has been produced. On the return stroke the plunger overrides the ports and the fuel is compressed and delivered.

9.28 Anti-dribble Device

To ensure sharply defined commencement and end of injection it is necessary to build up the pressure in the delivery pipe before pump delivery commences and ensure collapse immediately it ceases. To this end, the pump delivery valve is provided with a closely fitting cylindrical collar which must be raised clear of the edge of the seating before delivery can commence. The corresponding volumetric displacement is proportioned to the combined volumetric elasticities of the pipe and liquid due to the increase of pressure to the required value at commencement of injection. Thus the metered delivery takes place into a pipe and injector body pre-loaded to the required pressure, with the result that the volume of fuel injected corresponds accurately to the volume metered by the pump.

On completion of injection the reverse action takes place and the pressure collapses sharply. This constitutes the anti-dribble device.

9.29 Action of Spill Port and Helix

Control of injection to suit load requirements is accomplished by utilizing one of the feed ports as a spill port which is uncovered by the edge of the control helix at a suitable point in the delivery stroke.

The action of the anti-dribble device and of the control helix H with the axial channel C is shown in Fig. 9-17, in which relative dimensions are modified for diagrammatic clarity.

Diagram A shows the plunger descending and just uncovering the two ports through which the fresh charge of fuel flows from the feed gallery to fill the partial vacuum. The downward stroke continues, uncovering the whole area of the ports; the plunger returns and, having closed the ports, lifts, by its further travel, the

186

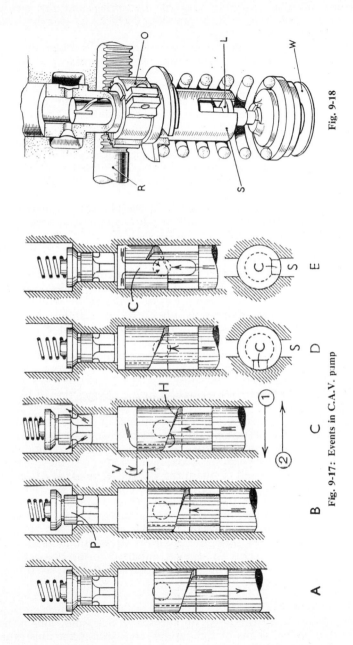

Fig. 9-18

Fig. 9-17: Events in C.A.V. pump

delivery valve against the load of the spring and the residual
" loading " pressure in the pipe-line, which is usually about
500 lb/sq. in.

Diagram B shows the instant at which flow through the valve
commences, the plunger now being near mid-stroke and moving
rapidly.

Diagram C shows the instant of spill when the edge of the helix H
overruns the spill port S, and the fuel is by-passed down the axial
channel C and spilled to the suction chamber. The pressure
collapses suddenly and the delivery valve returns to its seating.

The descent of the cylindrical " unloading collar " causes a
corresponding increase in the volumetric capacity of the delivery
system, and the accompanying collapse of pressure results in a
sharp cessation of discharge from the injector nozzle and prevents
dribble, as already indicated.

At D the delivery valve is shut and the plunger is still rising to
complete its stroke. Spill continues through the full area of the
spill port for the remainder of the stroke.

9.30   Variation of Spill Point

Variation of spill point to suit load requirements is obtained by
rotation of the plunger by means immediately to be described.
If the plunger is rotated in the direction indicated by arrow 1, later
spill and increased delivery is obtained. If rotation is in the
direction 2, the spill is earlier. The delivery volume is indicated
by V between diagrams B and C.

When the plunger is rotated to the position shown at E, the
channel C registers with the spill port and no delivery can take
place; this is the " stop " position.

The method of control by rotation of the plunger should be clear
from Fig. 9-18.

A sleeve S is a close sliding and rotational fit on the pump body,
and is provided at its lower end with a slot engaging a lug L formed
integral with the pump plunger, which must therefore rotate with
the sleeve while reciprocating in the pump body. At the upper end
of the sleeve is carried a quadrant O, the teeth of which engage
with corresponding rack teeth cut on the control rod R. This rack
runs the full length of the pump and carries a similar set of teeth
for each pump element; it is connected at one end to the accelerator
control linkage or the governor as the case may be. Endwise
movement of the rack thus rotates all the sleeves simultaneously by
an equal amount. This rotation is imparted to the plungers, and
the spill port is overrun by the helix earlier or later, as the case
may be.

9.31   Calibration

The quadrant O mounted on the sleeve S is split, and is held
from rotating by means of a clamping screw seen in the illustration.
It will be seen that for any setting of the control rod, the quadrants

will be held in position by the rack, but by slackening the clamping screws the relative rotational positions of the sleeves S, and hence of the plungers in their barrels, may be altered. This provides a means of adjusting the spill points of the separate elements, so that precisely the same delivery is obtained from each. This operation is referred to as calibration.

9.32 Phasing of Injection

In addition to the calibration adjustment, it is necessary to ensure that the commencement of injection from the several pump elements occurs at equally spaced angular intervals, corresponding to the crank intervals of the engine.

This requires that the delivery point indicated at B in Fig. 9-17 must be correctly phased for the several plungers, depending as it does on the height reached by the top of the plunger at the required instant. The necessary tappet adjustment is easily and quickly made by means of a selected hardened steel washer or shim W in Fig. 9-18, placed between the lower spring washer and the tappet, in a counterbore formed in the top of the latter. Shims of thickness ranging from 0·7 mm to 1·4 mm in steps of 0·1 mm are available, corresponding to half a degree of rotation of the pump camshaft. A simple, accurate and stable adjustment is thus provided.

9.33 Built-in Filter

The supreme importance of meticulous filtration of the fuel, in order to ensure trouble-free operation, cannot be over-emphasized.

Abrasive particles far finer than would normally choke the nozzle orifices—though this must be guarded against—will cause serious damage to the finely finished mating surfaces of the pump and injector and lead to inaccurate metering.

To provide an additional safeguard against ingress of dirt during the servicing of the outside filter or fuel pipe-line, the N type pump is provided with a built-in final filter located immediately before the fuel gallery. This will be seen in the sectional view of Fig. 9-16. The filtering elements consist of felt packs supported in non-corrodible containers carried on pressed spigots, mounted on the cover of the filter chamber. Each pack serves two pump elements through a communicating passage leading to paired inlet ports.

In this way uniform supply of fuel is secured, while the large entry periphery of the square packs ensures that there is no undue loss of pressure through the filter.

9.34 C.A.V. Paper Element Filter

Filter elements of cloth, felt and other materials have been used, but an extremely efficient filter for the purpose is the paper element filter produced by C.A.V. The element is in the form of a double spiral of vee-form, creped paper coils, wound on to a core and the whole contained in a "cartridge" or metal canister.

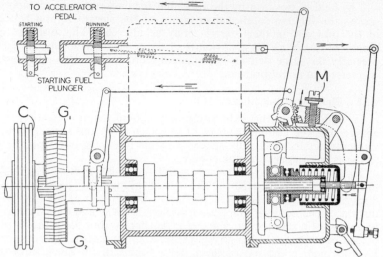

Fig. 9-19: Diagram of Gardner control

The filter paper is specially selected, and is treated with resin; it is of high strength when wet. The element has been shown to give over six times the life of fuel injection pump elements, by reducing abrasive wear. The spiral construction gives a large filtering area, and the life of the element before choking is comparable with the older cloth or felt types. The authors are indebted to Messrs. C.A.V. for information and drawings from which the various illustrations of their equipment were prepared.

9.35 Control of Engine Speed

The fitting of some form of governor to control both maximum and idling speeds is general with c.i. engines, as it is necessary to limit the inertia stresses that arise from the acceleration of the massive moving parts, and to guard against idling instability arising from the metering of very small quantities of fuel.

It will be realized that in the petrol engine a single " authority " —the carburettor—is responsible for delivering a correct mixture, and the air flow in effect controls the petrol flow. In the c.i. engine the situation is different. With ordinary methods of control the air drawn in is dependent on the breathing characteristics of the cylinders, and varies with speed and operating temperature in some manner which is characteristic of the engine. The quantity decreases with increase of speed in the same manner as in a petrol engine.

The fuel delivered is determined quite independently by the characteristics of the pump, which for a fixed control position may show a rising characteristic with speed, which would result in over-injection.

This problem of " matching " the characteristics of engine and pump is a difficult one, where it is necessary to provide for running

190

at varying speeds on a definite accelerator position; or where it is necessary to ensure that, without limiting maximum torque at any speed, there shall not be excessive injection with its attendant waste and smell at any combination of speed and accelerator position.

9.36   Mechanical or Centrifugal Governor

This may be designed merely to limit maximum speed, in which case movement of the governor sleeve takes place only when the centrifugal force developed by the revolving masses is sufficient to overcome the fixed initial load of the control spring.   The governor then operates to cut down the fuel supply only at the pre-determined maximum speed.

Below this maximum the accelerator pedal directly operates the pump control rack, suitable lost motion arrangements being provided to allow the governor to override the foot control at maximum speed.

Another arrangement, adopted in the Gardner control system, is to dispense with all direct connection between the accelerator pedal and pump control rod, and to provide that all actual movement of the rack is performed by the governor under the control of a governor spring, the compression of which is determined by the position of the accelerator pedal.

The pedal thus provides a movable reaction to the governor spring, and the speed of the engine and vehicle is fixed by the

Fig. 9-20: Gardner pump assembly

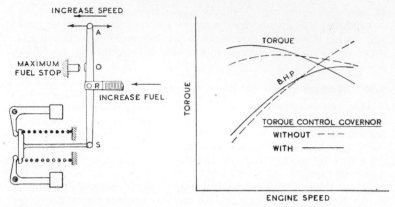

Fig. 9-21: Torque control governor   Fig. 9-22: Torque characteristics

position of the pedal, the governor operating spindle then moving the control rack to the position required to maintain, under the prevailing road conditions, the speed corresponding to the compression of the governor spring. This constitutes an " all-speed " governor. With the mechanism is linked an injection advance control which gives to one of a pair of helical driving gears a slight axial movement, which results in a corresponding change of phase between the pump shaft and the driving shaft.

The arrangement is shown diagrammatically in Fig. 9-19, in which the arrows indicate the movements which would result in increase of speed and injection advance. C is the chain sprocket on the engine camshaft, G_1 the wide camshaft gear and G_2 the sliding pump shaft gear. S is a stopping lever acting directly on the pump control rack and M is a speed screw operated by hand or remote control to maintain any steady speed desired. This is a convenience for stationary or marine applications or for test purposes.

Fig. 9-20 shows an external view of the injection control system of the 4 L.W. engine, and the reader will be able to compare this view with the diagram of the layout given in Fig. 9-19. The four special priming levers for operating the pump plungers, and the equalized delivery pipes to the injectors, are clearly seen. The finned cylinder on the left is the exhauster for servo brake operation, and the spherical air vessel on the pump suction may be noted.

9.37 Torque Control Governor

This is an all-speed mechanical governor provided with a modified arrangement of maximum fuel stop. This stop, instead of acting directly on the pump control rack, is offset as shown in Fig. 9-21, and bears on a floating lever at a point O above the line of the control rack. The floating lever AS is attached to the accelerator rod at A and to the governor sleeve at S. The point of attachment to the control rack is R.

At low speeds S will move to the left and A to the right, thus giving the floating lever an inclination which permits of a greater movement of the control rack in the " increase fuel " direction, before contact with the stop is made, than at higher speeds when the inclination will be in the opposite direction.   Thus a high degree of low-speed supercharge, characteristic of a reciprocating or positive displacement compressor may be utilized, while the amount of injection at higher speeds may be limited as desired.

This enables torque characteristics such as those shown in Fig. 9-22 to be obtained.   See also page 317.

9.38   C.A.V. Pneumatic Governor

An alternative to the mechanical governor described above is the pneumatic governor which is now being successfully applied to small engines by Messrs. C.A.V.

Previously, control has been exercised on the fuel only, the full charge of air being drawn in on the induction stroke.   With this method, control is by *quality* of the mixture, and there is very little reduction of maximum pressure at light loads, leading to the unfavourable comparison with the light load diagrams for the petrol engine illustrated in Fig. 9-24.   With pneumatic induction pipe control, the air supply at light loads is throttled by a butterfly valve placed in a choke C, Fig. 9-23, this valve being directly operated by the accelerator pedal.   The throttle unit is placed between the air cleaner and the entry to the inlet manifold, and the result is that at part load the pressure of the air at the end of induction, and therefore its weight, is reduced.

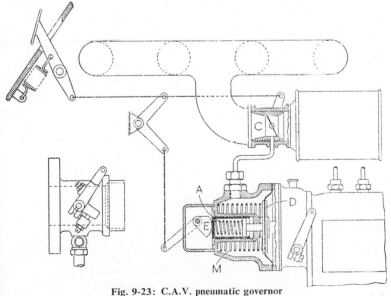

Fig. 9-23: C.A.V. pneumatic governor

Provided the initial temperature and the compression ratio are the same, however, the temperature at the end of compression will be practically the same as without throttling, though the pressure will be less. Injection then takes place into less dense air than with unrestricted induction, and the control thus becomes quantity rather than quality control.

The accompanying control of the fuel injection is obtained by communicating the depression at the choke to a diaphragm chamber mounted on the end of the injection pump. The diaphragm plate D is mounted on the end of the control rack of the pump, being pushed to the right, or full load position, by the main control spring M.

An increase of depression at the throttle, arising when the accelerator pedal is released, will pull the diaphragm and control rod to the left, thus reducing the supply of fuel.

An auxiliary spring A is found necessary to balance the high depression at idling speed, and to " match up " the breathing characteristics of the engine with the delivery characteristics of the pump. This auxiliary spring may be brought into action progressively by the action of a cam E which may be formed to suit the engine.

An external view of the throttle fitting showing the idling stop is given in the separate view. The connecting pipe is usually a stout rubber hose.

9.39 Bearing Load Factor

In Fig. 9-24 are shown two pairs of indicator diagrams on a crank angle base which bring out an unfavourable comparison of the c.i. engine with the petrol engine. The diagrams are due to Ricardo and show the actual cylinder pressures at full load and one-third load, the mean pressures being the same in each engine for the corresponding load. The favourable bearing load factor at reduced power of the petrol engine is at once apparent, while a reduction in load of the c.i. engine mitigates to only a very slight degree the

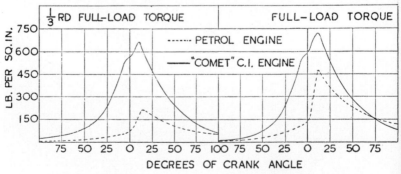

Fig. 9-24: Pressures in oil and petrol engines

high gas pressures and bearing loads, owing to the fact that in taking these diagrams there was no throttling of the air intake, and the compression ratio necessarily remained the same.

Were, however, the performance of the petrol engine to be improved by increasing the compression ratio to that of the c.i. engine, assuming suitable fuels to be available, the situation on full load would be reversed, as the maximum pressure in the petrol engine would then be very much greater than in the c.i. engine.

The light load conditions would still be favourable to the petrol engine owing to the throttled induction.

These considerations suggest the desirability of using throttled induction with the pneumatic control already described, and it is probable that the use of this system will extend.

There are, however, accompanying difficulties to be met in the injection control, for in the less dense air in the combustion chamber there is risk—particularly with the hard jets of direct injection systems—of getting too great penetration, resulting in the liquid fuel reaching the cylinder walls. This not only causes high consumption and carbonization, but results in pungent smell. Owing, too, to the lower compression pressure (the temperature is not very much affected) the delay period will be increased and rough running may ensue.

9.40 Hydraulic Servo Governor

An important and ingenious development in governing devices is the C.A.V. hydraulic governor which eliminates the very high mechanical forces, bearing loads and possible torsional vibrations in the drive which are a potential source of difficulty in the ordinary centrifugal governor if a large ratio of maximum to idling speed is to be provided for.

Like the Gardner governor, the C.A.V. hydraulic governor is an " all-speed " governor, that is, the governor is in control throughout the whole speed range from idling to maximum, the injection pump control rack being operated by the governor and not directly by the accelerator pedal. In both types the driver's pressure on, and movement of the accelerator pedal, merely adjust the compression and corresponding load of the main governor spring, thereby dictating the speed at which the engine—and, subject to gear ratio in use, the vehicle—shall run. The governor automatically makes the necessary adjustments to the fuel supply to maintain this speed, no matter what the power requirements may be from moment to moment.

In the mechanical governor, the operative agent is centrifugal force, varying as the square of the speed; in the hydraulic governor it is the pressure difference across an orifice required to pass the oil flow from a positive oil pump driven by the engine. Whatever the actual speed of the pump relative to the engine (normally it is driven from the injection pump camshaft) the volume flow per second will be dependent on engine speed, being directly proportional to this if volumetric slip is neglected. The actual characteristic speed-flow curve of the pump can readily be catered for in the design and adjustment of the governor.

The pressure difference required to pass this flow through a fixed orifice will thus vary as the square of the engine speed, just as does centrifugal force (see pages 29, 179 and 245).

The orifice in question is the accurately formed hole O in the piston P of the amplifier in the diagrammatic view of the governor

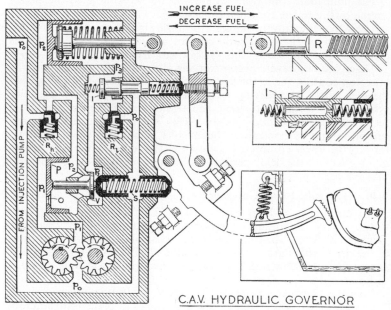

C.A.V. HYDRAULIC GOVERNOR

DIAGRAMMATIC ARRANGEMENT

Fig. 9-25

shown in Fig. 9-25, which should be compared with the sectional drawing of the governor in Fig. 9-16. This piston, the amplifier valve V and the main speeder spring S are, when equilibrium conditions are attained and the valve is sufficiently open to pass the pump delivery, in a condition of floating balance between the pressure of the driver's foot on the accelerator pedal (modified by any leverages and return springs in the linkage) and the hydrostatic pressure differences acting on the piston and valve of the amplifier. We have seen that the pressure difference across an orifice of fixed size is a measure of the oil flow and so of the engine speed, which therefore must be determined at equilibrium by the pressure of the driver's foot on the accelerator pedal.

The very small movement of the inner end of the speeder spring due to the opening and closing of the amplifier valve is without appreciable influence on these conditions.

196

In completing its circuit from the pump delivery to the pump suction, the oil flow passes through three controlling orifices in series. These are—

(1) Fixed orifice O already described.
(2) Variable opening of the amplifier delivery valve.
(3) Variable opening of the idling piston valve I, supplemented by the low pressure relief valve R_l at speeds above idling.

The corresponding pressures may be denoted by p_1, p_2, p_3 and p_o, which last is the closely constant pressure in the pump suction line, determined by the spring pressure of the diaphragm feed pump.

The relevant pressure differences are $(p_1 - p_2)$, $(p_2 - p_3)$ and $(p_3 - p_o)$, and, in addition to the high degree of mechanical skill applied to its design and construction, the governor owes its success to the ingenious manner in which these pressure differences are controlled and utilized in producing the movements required to effect control.

The minimum pressure in the system p_o, being the delivery pressure of the fuel feed pump, remains constant. The passage through the idling valve is so restricted that at speeds above an engine idling speed of about 250 r.p.m., the pressure difference $(p_3 - p_o)$ required to pass the flow becomes sufficient to open the low pressure relief valve R_l, which then provides an additional opening in parallel with the idling valve. The low pressure relief valve thus acts as a regulating valve to maintain p_3 at a constant value of about 20 lb/sq. in. throughout the speed range above idling. This constant value of p_3 assists the servo piston spring to move the pump control rack in the closing direction against the opening tendency of the pressure p_2. The pressure p_2 must thus be greater than p_3 by the amount necessary to compress the servo piston spring sufficiently to bring the control rack to the position called for by the engine load, while the speed is maintained at the driver's requirements.

For purposes of illustration it may be assumed that the value of $(p_2 - p_3)$ required to maintain the control rack in equilibrium varies from 5 lb/sq. in. at no load to 20 lb/sq. in. at full load, these figures representing the selected spring rate in relationship to the area of the servo piston.

This range of p_2 (since p_3 is constant above idling speed) must be obtainable with an acceptably small speed variation at any desired road speed throughout the range, that is, the governor must give reasonably sensitive control at the required speed through the full range of engine torque.

It will be noted that a rise of speed, resulting in an *increase* in $(p_1 - p_2)$ must produce a *fall* in p_2 if the control rack is to move in the required direction.

By applying the principle of the " inverted hydraulic amplifier," pressures of sufficient magnitude and having sufficiently steep rates of variation can be provided to meet the above conditions.

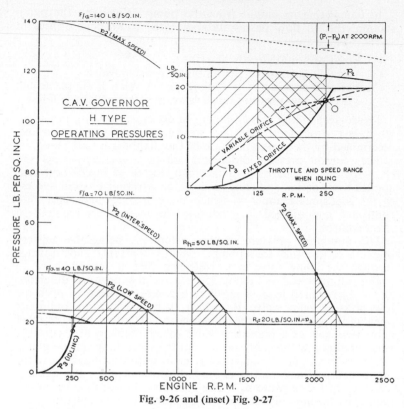

Fig. 9-26 and (inset) Fig. 9-27

If the areas of the amplifier piston and valve are A and a respectively, and the spring force produced by the driver at any moment is F pounds, then for equilibrium—

$$F = (p_1 - p_2)A + p_2a,$$

since the pressure p_3 acts on equal areas of valve and spring sleeve.

Thus
$$p_2 = \frac{F}{a} - \frac{A}{a}(p_1 - p_2).$$

$(p_1 - p_2)$ is the pressure difference required to pass the flow through the orifice in the amplifier piston, and will vary as the square of the speed, as has been seen. The size of orifice in relation to pump delivery is so chosen as to make the maximum value of this pressure difference only about 12 lb/sq. in., the values at lower speeds being much less than this, as shown by the fine dotted curve in Fig. 9-26.

The term $\dfrac{F}{a}$ in the above equation is the value of p_2 necessary to open the amplifier valve against the spring force if acting alone,

198

as would be the situation at very low pump speeds when $(p_1 - p_2)$ is negligible. When the accelerator pedal is giving maximum compression to the speeder spring the corresponding value of p_2 would be about 140 lb/sq. in. with normal settings, but the governor components are protected from any undesirable pressure by the high-pressure relief valve R_h, which is normally set at about 50 lb/sq. in. The action of the two relief valves is therefore to confine the operating pressures to the zone between the thick horizontal lines in Fig. 9-26 except during idling as described later.

To return to the amplifier equation, the comparatively small controlling pressure difference $(p_1 - p_2)$ is amplified in the ratio A/a of about 10 to 1 in order to produce a sharp reduction in p_2 with increase of speed, and so allow the servo piston and control rack to move in the closing direction.

It will be seen that the variation of p_2 is a parabolic reduction from whatever value of $\dfrac{F}{a}$ may be dictated by the driver, the steeper portions of the parabola being utilized at the higher speeds, and providing at all speeds above a no-load idle of about 800 r.p.m. the range of pressure necessary for the full control-rack movement.

As the speed decreases, the operative part of the parabolic curve becomes less steep, that is to say, the range of speed to produce the working range of p_2 between no load and full load becomes greater —the governor is less sensitive.

It would be impossible to obtain sensitive idling without danger of stall by variation of p_2 alone, but as the speed falls below about 260 r.p.m., p_3 drops rapidly below the relief valve pressure owing to the decreased oil flow. The required value of the operating pressure difference $(p_2 - p_3)$ on the servo piston is now obtained by the reduction of p_3, as p_2 has become too low in value to give the required range, and if the idling valve orifice were fixed in size, the curve of p_3 against speed would be the lower full-line curve of Fig. 9-27, which shows the pressure variations at idling on a larger scale.

It will thus be seen that the full operating range of $(p_2 - p_3)$ is now obtained in the speed range from 250 to 125 r.p.m. This makes the idling sensitivity rather too great, leading to risk of surge —though not of stall—as the rack moves between the extreme positions. There is risk of unduly large corrections to meet purely transient disturbances.

The construction of the idling valve meets the difficulty by a successful combination of several effects.

As will be seen from the enlarged section in Fig. 9-25, the assembly consists of a compression spring divided into two unequal parts by a piston valve interposed at one-third of its length. This valve controls the area of the orifice passing the oil flow under the pressure difference $(p_3 - p_0)$ or, simply, the pressure p_3. This area is reduced as the servo piston moves to the full-load position. The outer spring sleeve bears on an adjusting screw carried at about two-thirds the length of the link or lever L, with the result that the normal travel of the piston valve is one-third of two-thirds, or about one-fifth of the travel of the servo piston. This progressive closure of the port as the servo piston and rack move towards the full-load position causes p_3 to rise above the "fixed orifice" parabola, and to follow a curve of the form shown by the chain dotted line, coincidence being at some designed point O. This reduces the sensitivity, the full-load pressure difference of 20 lb/sq. in. being reached only when the speed has fallen to about 40 r.p.m.

Before this point is reached, however, the increased injection should have prevented stalling. In connection with the above figure of 20 lb/sq. in. it will be appreciated that since the idling spring is opposing the servo spring, its effect is to decrease the initial effective spring load on the piston and increase the effective spring rate, and they must be designed as a combination.

It is now necessary to consider the stabilizing provision against over-control during transient disturbances. The longer portion of the divided spring is enclosed in what constitutes a dashpot, into and out of which oil flows through the small central drilling through the piston valve.

For rapid movements the restricted access to the dashpot renders the enclosed spring inoperative, and the piston valve moves with the outer spring sleeve at about two-thirds of the rate of the servo piston. This results in much more rapid variation of the valve orifice with consequent further flattening of the p_3 curve as indicated by the short broken line branching from the "free spring" curve, indicating the effect of a transient disturbance during idling. Thus the dashpot further reduces the sensitivity for sudden changes, but subject to a time lag during which the piston valve and springs take up their equilibrium configuration, the normal sensitive control corresponding to the chain dotted curve is restored.

The result of this ingenious arrangement is that over the whole speed range sensitive yet stable control is maintained, with accurately set idling free from risk of surge or stalling.

The governor is provided with a positive fuel cut-off, and a newly designed maximum fuel stop and excess fuel device.

The authors are indebted to C.A.V. Ltd., for diagrams and information, and the reader will find further information in a descriptive analysis published in *Engineering* of 18 March, 1949.

9.41   C.A.V. " D.P.A." Pump

In the development of the smaller diesel engines, manufacturers soon realized that the cost of multi-line fuel injection pumps of the classic type was becoming a prohibitive proportion of the total engine cost, and that progress depended on the development of smaller, simpler and less costly equipment.

These, and other advantages, were offered by the distributor type of pump on which much development work had already been done.

Late in 1956, C.A.V. Ltd. introduced their D.P.A. pump, based on Hartford designs, and developed to meet British and European requirements.

The distributor type of pump has a single pumping element which serves all cylinders, distribution to the individual injectors being through a rotary distributor having the required number of outlet branches. This ensures both uniformity of delivery to all injectors

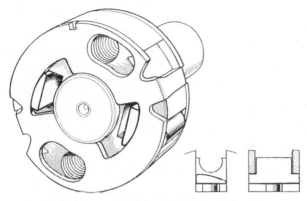

Fig. 9-28: The adjusting unit assembled for fitting

and in-built and exact uniformity of interval between successive injections. There are no adjustments to be made or maintained, these being inherent in the precision of manufacture.

In the pump under notice the pumping element consists of two simple opposed transverse cylindrical plungers in a rotating cylindrical body of which an extension forms the rotary distributor; this is provided with drillings which register in turn with an inlet port and delivery ports of the required number in the outer steel " hydraulic head ", which is mounted in the aluminium-alloy body. The pumping plungers are forced apart by the pressure and volume of the metered supply of fuel (see below) delivered by the transfer pump through the metering valve and inlet port. They are returned

A — cam-shape slot
B — lug on roller shoe
C — roller shoe
D — roller
E — plunger
F — adjusting plate
G — locking screw hole in
shoe carrier

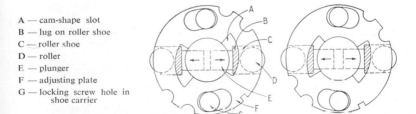

Fig. 9-29: The method used to adjust the maximum travel of the plungers

to effect the injection by lobes on the internal periphery of an external cam ring, which is stationary except for a small angular movement provided within the pump body to give automatic advance to the injection timing when required.

Hardened rollers carried in sliding shoes are interposed between the pumping plungers and cam ring. Cam-shaped lugs on the sides of the shoes engage with corresponding slots in two rotatable side plates, thus providing the adjustable " maximum fuel " stop by limiting the outward movement of the pumping plungers (see Figs. 9-28 and 9-29).

No ball or roller bearings, or return springs are required for the location or control of the moving parts, which are lubricated by the fuel oil delivered under sealed pressure by the transfer pump.

These features of construction result in important reductions in cost and gains in performance. The small mass of the pumping elements and elimination of spring return of the pumping plungers enable higher speeds to be attained; the present limit is about 12,000 deliveries per minute, the controlling factor being the ability to recharge the pump between successive injections.

The only adjustment to be made by the engine builder is that of the maximum delivery stop described above.

Fig. 9-30 represents diagrammatically the general lay-out of the pump; this should make clear the basic method of operation.

Variation of delivery with load is effected by the metering valve

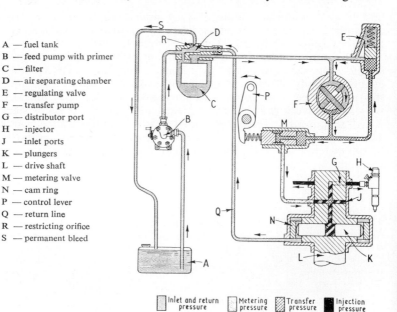

A — fuel tank
B — feed pump with primer
C — filter
D — air separating chamber
E — regulating valve
F — transfer pump
G — distributor port
H — injector
J — inlet ports
K — plungers
L — drive shaft
M — metering valve
N — cam ring
P — control lever
Q — return line
R — restricting orifice
S — permanent bleed

Inlet and return pressure | Metering pressure | Transfer pressure | Injection pressure

Fig. 9-30: Circuit diagram for a D.P.A. pump fitted with a hydraulic governor

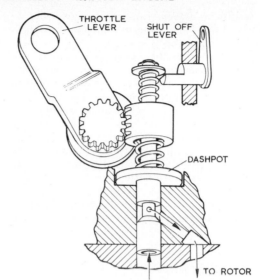

Fig. 9-31: Hydraulic governor

under the control of an "all-speed" governor of either the mechanical or hydraulic type, the former having important merits of precision and flexibility of control, while the latter is more compact, simpler and less costly, being of very simple form.

Both types apply the principle referred to on pages 191, 192 and 195. The accelerator pedal movement does not control the amount of injection directly, but only the *position* at which spring load balances centrifugal force or hydraulic pressure. The required speed of the engine is then maintained automatically, no matter what the load, gradient or gear ratio of the transmission may be.

In Fig. 9-30 the simple hydraulic type of governor is indicated; a more detailed illustration is shown in Fig. 9-31.

The control lever pinion engages a rack of cylindrical form, which through the combined action of opposing helical springs balancing the fuel transfer pressure, locates the metering valve in the position required.

The method of metering is by opening communication through a variable orifice between the transfer pump (under regulated pressure) and the injection plungers for an interval of time determined by the period of registration of the rotor inlet ports.

This period varies with rotor speed, but the governor will automatically adjust the variable orifice so that within the period the required *volume* of fuel is delivered. The automatic movement required to correct transient variations of speed arises from the change of transfer pressure with change of speed, and the change of *time* available for filling.

For a given position of the accelerator pedal, a fall in speed

203

results in lower transfer pressure, which in turn results in wider opening of the metering valve; thus the volume injected increases and equilibrium is restored.

Considering the metering system in a general way, that is, with either mechanical or hydraulic governor, the pump is basically stable in the fixed metering valve condition (equivalent to " fixed rack " of the in-line pump). For the volume of fuel metered, during the fixed angle of registration of the filling ports, is inversely proportional to speed; thus, for example, as speed is reduced, the time period for filling or metering is increased, more fuel is metered and the equilibrium tends to be restored.

As mentioned earlier, this pump can have a simple but effective device for automatic injection timing advance, dependent on speed. The device consists of a piston, subjected to transfer pressure, moving in a housing mounted under the pump body. The transverse piston movement, applied through a ball-ended

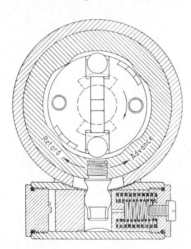

Fig. 9-32: The injection timing is controlled automatically by moving the cam ring

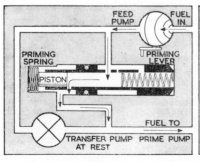

(a)

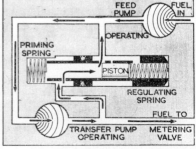

(b)

Fig. 9-33: Regulating valve

ASSEMBLED HEAD

BARREL

SLEEVE

ROTOR

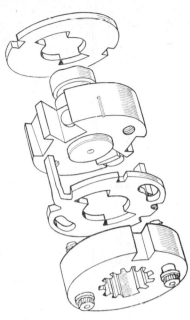

HYDRAULIC GOVERNOR

METERING VALVE

HYDRAULIC HEAD

ROTOR

FUEL INLET

NYLON FILTER

REGULATING VALVE SLEEVE

REGULATING PISTON

TRANSFER PUMP

TO INJECTOR

ADVANCE DEVICE

CAM RING

PLUNGERS

DRIVE SHAFT

Fig. 9-34: C.A.V. D.P.A. injection pump

screw, causes the cam ring to rotate; piston equilibrium is maintained by springs opposing the force of transfer pressure. Thus any desired relation between speed and injection timing can be obtained very simply; the timing device shown in Fig. 9-32 can be fitted to both the hydraulic- and mechanical-governor versions.

Fig. 9-33 (a) and (b) shows diagrammatically the operation of the regulating valve during priming, when the transfer pump is at rest, and during normal running. The fuel-feed pump, which is a separate unit, is operated by hand for priming and the free plunger piston is under the control of the low pressure feed and the light priming spring.

When the high pressure feed of the transfer pump becomes operative, the stiffer regulating spring is in control.

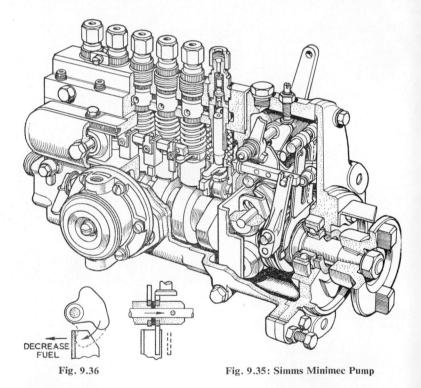

DECREASE FUEL

Fig. 9.36   Fig. 9.35: Simms Minimec Pump

The spring characteristics and orifice arrangement determine the final torque/speed characteristics of the engine, and can be varied to suit the application. For diagrammatic convenience the valve is shown in the horizontal position. The actual setting in current models may be seen in Fig. 9-34.

Fig. 9-34 is a grouped illustration of the components. On the left is seen the striking comparison in size between six-cylinder units of the two types of pump, both with mechanical governor.

Readers are referred to a comprehensive article in *Automobile Engineer* of January 1959 in which characteristic performance diagrams are included.

The present authors are much indebted to C.A.V., Ltd., for further information about this important and successful development, and for assistance in proof reading.

9.42   Simms Minimec Injection Pump

Simms Motor Units have an early association with the motor vehicle industry and were pioneers in the development of diesel equipment in Britain.

The now generally accepted principles of the original fuel injection system are utilized in their latest pumps but, at an early stage, Simms introduced certain modifications to the upper end of the plunger and the helical spill groove for which important advantages are claimed.

In the Minimec pump, a new arrangement for rotating the plungers has been adopted, for control of delivery, in place of the more familiar rack and pinion device. This is shown in the enlarged scrap view of Fig. 9-37. Horizontal arms secured to the lower ends of the plungers engage control forks clamped to the square section control rod. Calibration of delivery is carried out by sliding the forks along the rod and re-clamping. It is claimed that the large radius of the arms compared with the rack pinion of the older arrangement provides a more sensitive and accurate adjustment.

Fig. 9-36 shows both the maximum fuel cam seen in Fig. 9-35 and the stop cam, omitted there to avoid masking the former. Both operate through the same

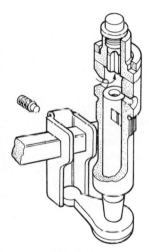

Fig. 9.37

L shaped fork rivetted to the control rod, the stop cam by rotation of the stop lever seen on the left, and the maximum fuel cam by linear movement along the same axis. This spring controlled axial movement provides for enrichment by hand control at starting. The cam moves clear of the fork, but remains in contact with the head of the adjusting screw, so that when the engine speeds up and the control is released, the cam returns to its normal position.

The general mechanical arrangement of the pump follows familiar lines, but a valuable constructional feature is the splitting of the

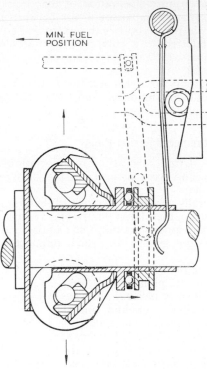

Fig. 9.38

body on a horizontal plane in order that the complete assembly of the pumping elements may be removed without disturbing the cambox and drive. This is clearly a most useful feature during maintenance operations, and enables the more rigid steel material to be used for the upper body while retaining light aluminium alloy for the cambox. The delivery valve holders have serrated heads, instead of the earlier hexagonal form, thereby enabling the pitch between the pumping elements to be reduced and so shortening the overall length of the pump.

The new mechanical " all-speed " governor may be seen in the pictorial view of Fig. 9-35 and in the sectional view of Fig. 9-38.

The revolving weights are not carried on bell-crank levers as in more conventional designs. The weights consist of two assemblies like dumb-bells, closely but freely confined between a U-shaped backplate bolted to the camshaft, and a reacting sleeve described as the weight carrier assembly on which the control spring acts through a ball thrust pad. The control spring, formerly of torsional form but now a leaf spring, is loaded by the accelerator pedal to maintain the speed required.

In the weight carrier assembly, each pair of weights is mounted on a pin which is located in an inclined slot as shown in Fig. 9-38. Each pin supports a slipper which is free to slide along a ramp in the centre of the weight carrier. The slope of the two ramps causes the weight carrier to move against the control spring as the weights move outwards, and operate the control rod through a rocking lever. These details may be seen in the figures. Thus the fuel is continuously adjusted to the load while the required steady speed is maintained.

In the latest version of the Minimec pump, replacement of the torsional control spring by a leaf spring has enabled a variable rate to be obtained. The governor functions in the same manner as described previously. The load on the leaf spring is controlled by the position of a roller on a ramp mounted on the governor cover, as shown in Fig. 9-38. The movement of the roller is caused by a fork operated by the accelerator pedal.

The movement of this roller fulcrum varies not only the load on the spring and sleeve but also the spring rate. The arrangement assists in preserving the stability of the governor and preventing " hunting " at high spring loads, as compared with the less favourable conditions in which only the initial load on a constant rate spring is altered.

The authors are much indebted to the makers, Simms Motor Units Ltd., for drawings and information.

9.43 Representative Designs of C.I. engine

An outstandingly successful example of the direct injection type is the Gardner L.W. engine, built in three-, four-, five- and six-cylinder forms, all of $4\frac{1}{4}$ in bore and 6 in stroke to develop about 17 b.h.p. per cylinder at a maximum governed speed of 1,700 r.p.m., with a best b.m.e.p. of about 102 lb/sq. in.

The meticulous care and skill devoted to the manufacture of the engines and injectors have resulted in an engine of proved reliability which has been adopted as the power unit by a large number of commercial vehicle manufacturers. To meet the challenge of the demand for a still lighter and higher speed engine, the makers, Messrs. Norris Henty and Gardners Ltd., later produced the 4 L.K. engine of $3\frac{3}{4}$ in bore and $5\frac{1}{4}$ in stroke, which develops 53 b.h.p. on a rising curve at 2,000 r.p.m. governed speed.

At the bare engine weight (without electrical equipment) of 575 lb, the specific weight is 11 lb/b.h.p. This engine is in successful use in the lighter types of commercial vehicles, replacing the 3 L.W. unit which develops about the same power but at a lower speed. The fuel pump used on all Gardner engines is of the C.A.V. type, modified to incorporate special priming levers. The method of control is described on page 191, and the arrangements for altering the compression at starting are as follows:

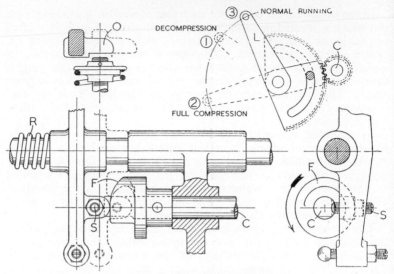

Fig. 9-39: Gardner compression control

A compression control lever is provided for each pair of cylinders as shown at L in Fig. 9-39. This operates a gear quadrant meshing with a gear pinion mounted on the end of a control shaft C lying under the push rod end of the valve rockers.

The shaft C carries radial cams for lifting each inlet valve rocker through the adjusting studs S and a face cam F, which in one position of the lever L moves the rocker of No. 1 inlet valve to the left against the coil spring R, thus bringing the offset portion O of the rocker end over the valve stem. This offset end is stepped so as to increase the tappet clearance to about $\frac{1}{16}$ in. There is a further slight increase due to the tilting of the push rod as its cupped upper end moves over with the rocker.

The effect of this increase of tappet clearance is to make the closing of the inlet valve earlier, and thus give an effective compression ratio corresponding to the full swept volume of the cylinder.

The accompanying later opening and reduced lift of the valve do not, at the low speed of cranking, have any appreciable strangling effect on the induction.

The radial cams are provided for all cylinders, and consist simply of clearance flats on the control shaft C, rotation of which causes the adjusting studs S to ride on to the cylindrical portion and so raise the rockers. The corresponding positions of the control levers are shown in the diagram in Fig. 9-39.

The first position (1) gives complete decompression by holding the inlet valves off their seats during initial cranking. Position (3) is the normal running position with the starting control cut out.

The face cam is ordinarily provided for No. 1 cylinder only,

210

Fig. 9-40: Gardner 5 L.W. engine

and is brought into action in position (2) of the lever to give higher compression in that cylinder in order to obtain the first impulse. The control levers may be operated by a common grouped control or independently, as may be most suitable for the particular installation. It may be found convenient to keep a pair of cylinders decompressed until the starting cylinders have got well away.

Fig. 9-40 shows an exterior view of the near side of the 5 L.W. engine. A feature which should be noted is the deep and rigid crankcase structure extending well below the crankshaft centre line. The sump is an electron casting. The cylinder block is in two separate portions of three and two cylinders, and the special C.A.V. injection pump is assembled from corresponding units.

9.44 Perkins P3 Diesel Engine

The application of the compression ignition engine to lighter types of vehicle has been delayed by the fact that injection and combustion difficulties increase greatly with diminution in size of cylinder. This has stimulated interest in the use of a reduced number of cylinders for the lower powers.

The Perkins P3 engine has been developed as a substitute or conversion unit for certain tractors and light commercial vehicles where the flat torque characteristics and operational economy of

211

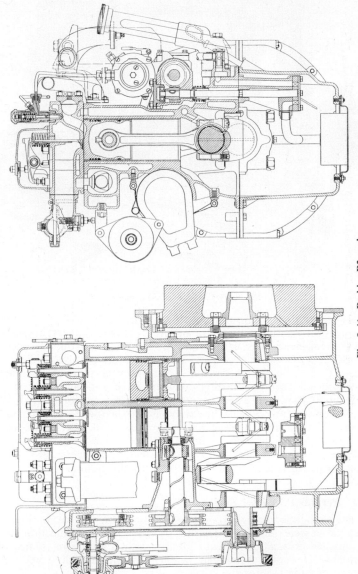

Fig. 9-41 : Perkins P3 engine

the diesel engine are decisive factors in the choice of the power unit. Suitably limited power is obtained without the difficulties that are experienced with small cylinder and injection equipment, and a simplified servicing system and rationalized manufacture are made possible by the use of standardized general engine parts in the P3, P4 and P6 engines.

The P3 is half the P6 engine, the special parts required being confined to those depending on the length of the engine, such as crankshaft, cylinder block and sump.

The overall dimensions have proved very convenient for installation in the space occupied by the alternative petrol engine, and the high reputation of the engine has led to a considerable demand for the P3 as a conversion unit both at home and abroad.

Longitudinal and cross-sectional views of the engine are shown in Fig. 9-41, from which the sturdy and yet compact design will be noted. Dry cylinder liners are fitted into a nickel or chromium cast iron block which extends from the head face to the crankshaft centre-line in the conventional manner.

The bore and stroke are 3·5 in and 5·0 in respectively and the connecting rods are 9 in. long between centres.

The sturdy four bearing crankshaft is of forged steel, the four main journals being Tocco hardened.

With three cranks at 120° pitch there are no primary or secondary unbalanced reciprocating forces, and the rotating couple is balanced by the two attached balance weights on the end crank webs. Primary and secondary reciprocating couples remain to be absorbed by the engine mounting, and this disadvantage and the massive flywheel required to absorb the variations in turning moment are the penalties to be paid for the convenience of the three cylinder lay-out.

9.45 Thornycroft 11·33 Litre Diesel

This engine is the largest produced by the makers and is intended for the heaviest commercial applications, particularly in undeveloped areas.

Designed robustly with the view of its installation in the naturally aspired form (KRN6) or turbo-blower supercharged (KRN6/S), the design follows well established principles in the construction of British direct injection engines.

The general construction follows that shown in Fig. 6-30 adapted to diesel requirements with dry cylinder liners and crankcase extended well below the crankshaft centre line. This construction, while involving more, but readily accessible, machining processes, is also well adapted to variations of assembly, handing and mounting for special requirements; the separate components are lighter and more easily handled.

The crankshaft is without integral balance weights in order to save weight, but at the moderate speeds involved, mirror symmetry, combined with the generous proportions of the shaft and crankcase

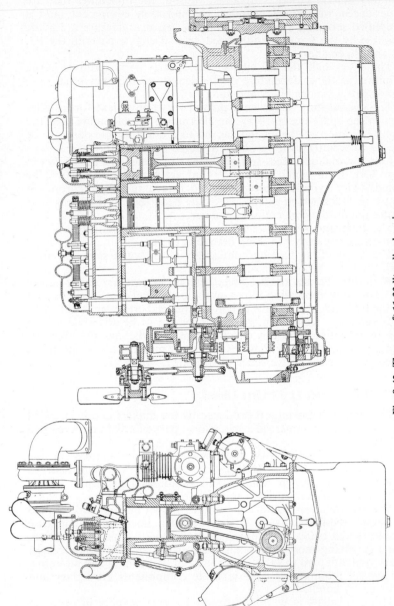

Fig. 9-42: Thornycroft 11·33-litre diesel engine

ensures vibration-free running. A torsional vibration damper of the Holset steel-rubber bonded type is bolted to the first crank web as will be seen from Fig. 9-42. The crankshaft is nitride hardened on journals and pins.

Steel-backed, prefinished, copper lead lined bearings are used throughout, with the exception of the small end of the connecting rod, where a phosphor bronze bush is fitted. A floating gudgeon pin is end-located by Seeger circlips. The camshaft bearings are of aluminium alloy.

The Wellworthy pistons are of tin-plated Lo-Ex aluminium alloy, and are of the solid skirt type, with an offset toroidal cavity in the crown. The valve gear follows conventional design, the valve stems working in phosphor bronze guides in the cast-iron cylinder head.

The timing gear, which is of mixed chain and gear design, is described on pages 121–122. The case is separate from the main crankcase casting, to facilitate the provision of right- or left-hand assemblies—referred to above.

Performance curves and further particulars are given in Chapter 13 on Supercharging, and the reader will find a comprehensive description in *Automobile Engineer*, Vol. 47, No. 2.

9.46 Comparative Merits of Spark Ignition and C.I. Engines

In spite of the inherent disadvantages of greater weight and bulk per horse power and rougher running, the c.i. engine has fully consolidated its position. Greater economy, greater security from risk of fire, and with modern bearing materials and methods of manufacture a degree of general reliability which is not less than that of the petrol engine, are definitely attained.

The injection equipment, provided proper care is taken with filtration of the fuel, is proving itself more reliable than the electrical equipment of the spark-ignition engine. Overheating troubles are less, for owing to the higher thermal efficiency the heat losses, both to the jackets and to the exhaust, are smaller than with the petrol engine. Flexibility, silence and smooth running still leave something to be desired, but as knowledge of the injection and combustion processes increases, so will the smoothness of performance improve.

First cost of both engines and injection equipment remain high, owing to the meticulous care required in manufacture, but for the commercial user whose vehicles cover a high annual mileage, particularly on long runs, saving in fuel costs results in a rapid recovery of initial expenditure.

In special cases it may be possible to approach, by raising the compression ratio of the petrol engine, the efficiency of the c.i. engine, but this is only possible by the use of very expensive and special fuels, as the requirements of the vapour compression (spark-ignition) engine become increasingly exacting with increase of compression ratio, though rotary valve engines appear to be exceptions to this generalization.

215

For equal thermal efficiency the spark-ignition engine does not require quite such a high compression ratio as the c.i. engine, and maximum pressures would be about the same. Thus weight per unit of cylinder volume would tend to be the same.

If the lower fuel-air ratio of the c.i. engine were compensated by supercharging, there would be little to choose between the two types in power-weight ratio, and under these somewhat hypothetical conditions the relative cost and safety of the fuels would become the deciding factor.

The question of fuels for compression-ignition engines is dealt with in Chapter 14.

CHAPTER 10

The Two-stroke Engine

General considerations. The three-port engine. Limitations of the type. Special designs. Two-stroke c.i. engine. Torque and bearing load factor.

THE limitations of power output given by the four-stroke cycle for a cylinder of given size running at a given speed have led designers to seek an alternative cycle which should eliminate the idle exhaust and charging strokes which occupy one complete revolution of the crankshaft. These two strokes and the corresponding crankshaft revolution may be regarded as interpolated between the active explosion stroke and the idle though necessary compression stroke of the following cycle.

If the exhaust of the old charge and the introduction of the new could be accomplished while the piston is passing the outer or bottom dead centre without sacrificing any great portion of the explosion or compression strokes, then a useful working stroke would be obtained for every revolution of the crankshaft instead of every alternate revolution, and the engine would develop twice the power of the four-stroke cycle engine provided the speed, mean effective pressure, and mechanical efficiency remained the same. In most cases very much less than this doubled power is obtained, for it is quite impossible with the ordinary two-stroke engine to obtain such high mean effective pressures as with the four-stroke cycle for reasons which will be explained presently. Nor is the mechanical efficiency of the two-stroke engine so high when the pumping losses are included with the mechanical friction losses. The net result is that most two-stroke engines give only from 10 per cent to 40 per cent more power than four-stroke types of the same piston displacement running at the same speed, while fuel economy is in most cases greatly inferior to that of the four-stroke engine.

However, greater mechanical simplicity and consequent cheapness of manufacture, more uniform turning moment arising from the smaller interval of time between the explosion impulses, leading to a reduction in the necessary weight of the flywheel, and greater mechanical silence, have made the two-stroke engine popular in cases where moderate power is required and where high fuel economy is not essential. Its widest fields of application at present, apart from certain large stationary and marine types, are to the small motor cycle and to the small motor boat, in which latter application it is usually made in the twin-cylinder water-cooled form.

To return to the means of obtaining a complete cycle of operations in two strokes or one revolution of the crankshaft it will be found

217

that as the crankshaft turns from 45° before the outer or bottom dead centre to 45° after it, that is to say, through one-quarter of a revolution, the piston " dwells " within less than one-eighth of its stroke from the bottom dead point. This quarter revolution, or in some cases considerably more, is devoted in two-stroke engines to the exhaust of the old charge, usually through a port or ports cut through the cylinder wall and communicating with the exhaust pipe or silencer, when the port or ports are uncovered by the top of the piston towards the bottom end of its stroke.

The exhaust gases escape for the most part in virtue of the excess of their own pressure over that in the silencer or atmosphere, but the final clearing or " scavenging " of the cylinder, since it cannot be done by the return of the piston, as in the four-stroke engine, must be accomplished by the introduction under a slight pressure of " scavenge " air. This scavenge air may or may not carry with it the necessary fuel for the succeeding explosion, the variations between the many designs of two-strokes in use consisting in the means employed for the introduction of the scavenge air and fuel. In all cases, however, the whole or major part of the scavenge air is introduced while the exhaust ports are open, and if this air carries with it the fuel vapour, as is the case with volatile liquid or gaseous fuels, there is a serious risk of loss of some portion of the fuel charge through the exhaust ports. In cases of bad design the proportion becomes excessive and is one of the main reasons for the high fuel consumption of the two-stroke engine.

The introduction of the scavenge air (with or without fuel) requires some form of scavenge pump which may consist of a separate pump cylinder with its piston operated from the crankshaft and usually of somewhat greater capacity than the working cylinder, or the main crank case may be made air-tight and the displacement of the under side of the main piston be used to form a pump of the same displacement capacity. A third system is to use a rotary blower of the displacer type or a high-speed centrifugal fan, just as in supercharging a four-stroke engine. Examples of these types will be described.

10.1 Three-port Two-stroke Engine

Fig. 10-1 shows in simple diagram-form the Day three-port engine. The exhaust port is shown at E, this being uncovered by the piston after completion of about 80 per cent of its stroke. The " transfer " port T, through which the charge is pumped from the crank case opens slightly *later* than the exhaust port, as shown in 1, to reduce the risk of hot exhaust gas passing into the crank case and igniting the new charge. It follows that the transfer port is closed by the rising piston slightly before the exhaust port, so that the final pressure in the cylinder, and therefore the total quantity of charge (consisting of a mixture of burnt gases, air and

218

fuel vapour) is determined not by the pump delivery pressure but only by the extent to which the throttling and " pulse " effects of the exhaust pipe, silencer, etc., raise the cylinder pressure above that of the atmosphere. The piston head is specially shaped to

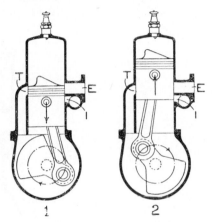

Fig. 10-1: Three-port two-stroke engine

deflect the entering gases to the top of the cylinder. This is known as " cross-flow " scavenge.

The piston rises and compresses the charge, after which it is ignited and expands in the usual way. The indicator diagram takes the form shown at *a* in Fig. 10-2, which differs from that of the four-stroke cycle only in the rather more sudden drop of pressure as the exhaust ports are uncovered and the elimination of the " bottom loop " showing the exhaust and suction strokes. This bottom loop is replaced, of course, by the indicator diagram, shown at *b*, obtained from the crank case or scavenge pump cylinder. There is no possibility of eliminating this pump work from either the four-stroke or the two-stroke cycle—in one case it is done in alternate revolutions in the main working cylinder, and in the other in every revolution in the scavenge pump cylinder. Indeed, the " phased pump " type of two-stroke engine, of which a modern example is the new Trojan design shown in Fig. 10-5, may be regarded as a V-twin four-stroke engine in which the positive work is concentrated in one cylinder and the negative pumping work is done in the other, instead of each cylinder doing half of both.

To return to the Day type of engine, it is necessary now to describe how the charge is drawn into the crank case from the carburettor.

As the piston rises a partial vacuum is formed in the crank case, the pressure becoming steadily lower until, near the top of its stroke, the rising piston uncovers the induction port I (which communicates with the carburettor), as shown in 2. Air rushes

219

in to fill the vacuum and carries with it the petrol from the jet necessary to form the explosive mixture. It will be realized that the suction impulse on the jet is a violent one of short duration—the very worst from the point of view of obtaining a correct and homogeneous mixture--while the time interval during which the induction port is open is also unduly short from the point of view of

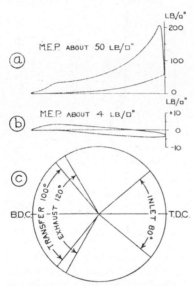

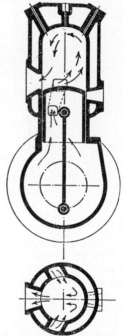

Fig. 10-2: Two-stroke indicator diagram

the inspiration of a full charge of air. Fig. 10-2c shows a typical timing diagram of the various port openings and closings expressed in degrees of crank angle.

Fig. 10-3: D.K.W. engine

An alternative to the piston-controlled induction port which is used in many two-stroke heavy-oil engines is the light spring-controlled automatic air valve. This valve remains open for practically the whole of the upward or suction stroke of the piston, ensuring higher volumetric efficiency though at the cost of an additional moving part. The American Gray motor, extensively used for marine work in the water-cooled form, employs both port and automatic valve.

10.2 Reverse Flow Scavenge. D.K.W. Engine

An interesting and successful example of the three-port engine using "reverse flow" or "inverted" scavenge is the German D.K.W. small car engine. This is a twin cylinder unit of 76 mm bore and 76 mm stroke, using crank case displacement, but having

220

twin transfer ports on either side of the exhaust port, and imparting a tangential and upward flow to the entering charge.

The piston deflector is dispensed with, thus eliminating pressure and inertia tilt due to lack of symmetry—a source of two-stroke rattle—and the direction of scavenge flow becomes somewhat as indicated in Fig. 10-3. By the provision of ports through the piston skirt the transfer passages are kept short, but as an additional change of direction is involved it is doubtful if the transfer resistance is appreciably reduced as compared with the arrangement of Figs. 10-1 and 10-4.

The makers have carried out comparative tests of the two methods of scavenge, and at 3,000 r.p.m. have improved the b.m.e.p. from 43 to 57 lb/sq. in., by converting to the reverse flow system.

The Villiers Company has successfully applied this principle in a modified form, using two pairs of transfer ports and two exhaust ports in their well-known air-cooled motorcycle engines. From their 249 c.c. engine 12 b.h.p. has been obtained at 5,000 r.p.m., which represents a b.m.e.p. of 62 lb/sq. in.

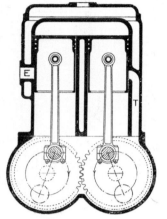

Fig. 10-4: Lucas engine

10.3 Special Constructions of Two-stroke Engine

The loss of efficiency arising from the loss of new charge through the exhaust ports, which occurs in these simple port constructions, has led to the use of a double-piston form of engine in which two pistons working in twin barrels side by side share a common combustion chamber and sparking plug. There is, of course, only one impulse or explosion per revolution, no matter what particular arrangement of connecting rods and cranks is employed. The Lucas engine (Fig. 10-4) is now no longer made but has interesting and ingenious features.

The two pistons drive independent connecting rods operating on separate cranks, which are arranged to run together by means of gear teeth cut in the periphery of the circular crank webs. The flywheel and clutch are connected to one of these cranks only, so that half the power necessarily passes through the gear teeth. The cranks clearly revolve in opposite directions, and use is made of this fact to obtain complete primary balance. Each crank assembly is provided with revolving balance weights corresponding to the whole of the revolving and reciprocating parts for one line. This ensures primary balance in the vertical plane as explained in Chapter 5, while the unwanted horizontal effects of the two revolving

221

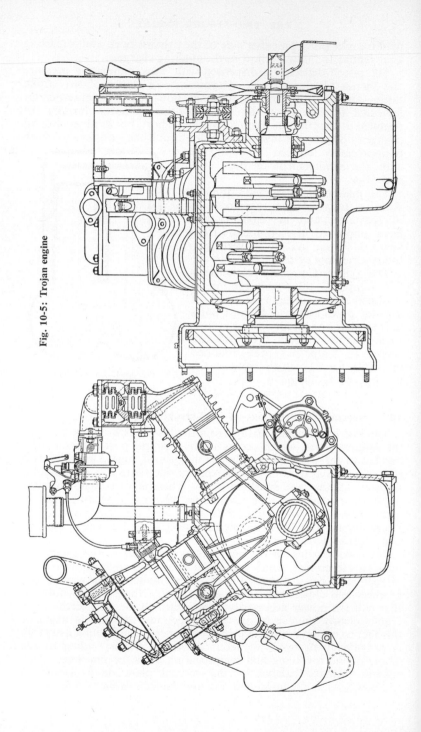

Fig. 10-5: Trojan engine

balance weights neutralize each other, exactly as in the Lanchester harmonic balancer, which, however, deals with secondary unbalanced forces.

With the twin cylinder-barrel in this arrangement one piston may be used to control the transfer port T while the other uncovers the exhaust E, and in this way the new charge has to traverse the full length of both barrels before there is any possibility of its escaping out of the exhaust port. Further, it is possible, by suitably meshing the gear wheels, to arrange that the exhaust port is given a " lead " which results in its opening *and* closing somewhat ahead of the corresponding events of the transfer port, thus tending to give a more complete cylinder charge. If this is done, however, the advantage of exact primary balance will be affected.

10.4 Separate Phased Pump

The reader will have realized, in considering the characteristics of simple crank case displacement, that the swept volume available for induction is the same as that of the main cylinder, namely, the piston area multiplied by the stroke, and, moreover, that the charge is not transferred to the cylinder simultaneously with the pump displacement, but in a rush after pre-compression. This causes the indicated pumping work to be high, and though some of this energy is no doubt usefully applied to producing a warmed and homogeneous mixture as a result of the turbulence, there is risk of admixture with the old charge and loss of fuel through the exhaust port.

Both the quantity and, especially at light loads, the quality of the mixture suffer, leading to limited power output and high specific fuel consumption.

These considerations have led many designers to have recourse to the separate charging pump, which is driven usually by a separate crank placed in appropriate phase relationship with the main crank.

10.5 Trojan Engine

The redesigned Trojan engine retains the twin-barrel construction successfully used in the original model, but, instead of crank case compression scavenge, the phased charging pump is now adopted, in combination with piston-controlled transfer and exhaust ports.

As a result of this change, a normal lubrication system can be used, and the necessity for pressure sealing of the crank case is obviated.

In early development of the new engine, a mechanically-driven, cylindrical distribution valve was used, but this has now been replaced by light, spring-blade automatic valves.

The general construction should be clear from the two sectional views given in Fig. 10-5, while Fig. 10-6 shows about three-quarters full size the details of the interesting automatic valves.

223

The bore of the working barrels is 65·5 mm and of the charger cylinders 96·8 mm, the stroke of all being nominally 88 mm, but owing to the off-set cylinder axes, the actual stroke is fractionally greater than twice the crank throw in each case, different off-sets being used for the three bores.

The nominal swept volume of the power cylinders is therefore 1,186 c.c., or the equivalent of two cylinders of 92·6 mm bore, while that of the pump cylinders is 1,293 c.c., thus providing a 9 per cent displacement margin.

The effect of the cylinder off-sets, combined with the relative position of the leading edges of the ports, is to give the exhaust period, with a duration of 106°, a lead over the 104° inlet period, of about 22°, the overlap being about 83°.

The off-set of the pump axis not only reduces the obliquity of thrust on the delivery stroke, but advances the stroke timing by about 8° relatively to the 90° at which the cylinders are set. By the use of a single transfer pipe and twinned inlet ports for the two sets, No. 1 charging cylinder delivers to No. 2 pair of working bores and *vice versa*.

All the six connecting rods are identical, and each pair of aluminium alloy main pistons with their small ends are made identical in weight with the corresponding cast-iron piston of the charging cylinder. Dynamic balance is thus secured on the

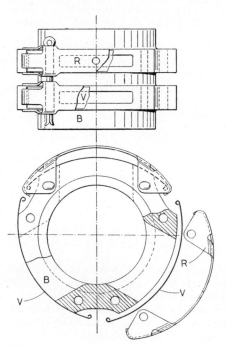

Fig. 10-6: Trojan automatic valves and cage

224

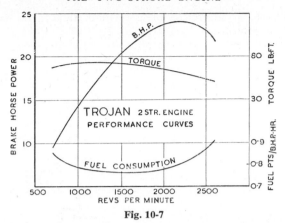

Fig. 10-7

principle described on page 60, the necessary balance masses being incorporated in the cast crankshaft of Mehanite iron. There is a slight discrepancy due to the off-set bores, and the secondaries remain unbalanced, but neither of these gives rise to serious vibration.

One cage of the automatic valve assembly is shown partly "exploded" in Fig. 10-6. The upper inlet cage is identical with the lower delivery cage, the "arc-flow" being radially outwards in both cases.

Two tiers each of three spring blades V form the valves, which bear on faces machined to an eccentric radius on the outside of the aluminium alloy body B. The pressed steel retainers R exercise a minimum constraint for the location of the spring blades, which have less free curvature than have the retainers, with the result that when blown open by the air flow the blades are strained against the retainers, and spring back sharply to the closed position on reversal of the flow. The rolled ends of the blades minimize friction under the relative motion. The total area of the six ports is about one square inch.

The flame trap, consisting of four thicknesses of gauze, may be noticed at the junction of the transfer pipe and transfer port, with a petrol priming pipe to aid starting.

A representative set of performance curves is shown in Fig. 10-7, a most valuable feature being the excellent maintenance of torque at low speeds. This results in very good top gear performance, reflected in satisfactory m.p.g. consumption figures, though the specific fuel consumption on the bench is higher than normal four-stroke figures.

10.6 Kadenacy and Schnuerle Systems

The scavenging systems of large two-stroke diesel engines, essentially of the stationary constant speed type, have in the last

225

ten years been the subject of intensive theoretical investigation and practical experiment.

An authoritative work by P. H. Schweitzer, *Scavenging of Two-stroke Cycle Diesel Engines*, and published by The Macmillan Company of New York, deals exhaustively with the mathematical and practical aspects of design involved in the efficient utilization of exhaust gas energy in scavening and charging engines with and without blowers.

The phrase " Kadenacy effect " has been extensively and somewhat loosely used to describe pulse phenomena that have been utilized

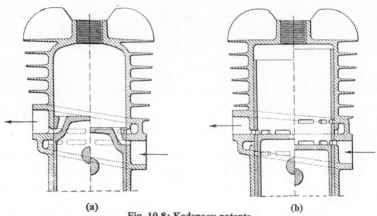

(a)   (b)

Fig. 10-8: Kadenacy patents

with varying degrees of success in different designs, often showing little similarity with the patent specifications.

In Schweitzer's work the Kadenacy system is described as basically the development of a high degree of vacuum in the cylinder by the sudden and very rapid release of the charge through sharp-edged exhaust ports of large area, this depression being sufficient to aspire the new charge without the necessity of a positive blower or pump.

Kadenacy British Patents Nos. 308,593 and 308,594, which relate to small engines of the automobile type, cover a variety of claims relating to cylinder porting, a somewhat elaborately ported piston working in a cylinder provided with inlet and exhaust belts each ported round the full circumference of the cylinder as shown in Fig. 10-8(a) and several claims of a different nature involving the use of light automatic non-return valves in both inlet and exhaust ports, a mechanically operated sleeve valve as shown in Fig. 10-8(b) and a mechanically operated inlet valve.

An opposed piston design is also covered.

The early type of deflector piston, liable to distortion and to cause " two-stroke rattle " is replaced by flat-topped pistons in all cases.

The possibility of dispensing with a scavenge blower is suggested in the valve operated designs, but not with the simple ported constructions, except under favourable conditions of steady speed and load.

Poppet exhaust-valve engines such as the General Motors and Foden designs can hardly be said to use the above fundamental Kadenacy principle, the Kadenacy effect in these instances being rather a sustained extractor effect due to the moving column in the exhaust, as in the four-stroke engine with valve timing overlap.

10.7 Loop Scavenge

The term " loop scavenge " is associated with Schnuerle and other patents, and is usually indicated diagrammatically as shown in Fig. 10-3, applied to the D.K.W. engine, in which case the less common designation " reverse flow " is used.

Schnuerle patents cover also a variety of exhaust pipe systems in which the extractor and non-return effects of a volute form initiating vortex flow are described.

These ideas are being developed and exploited in the small two-stroke engines used on the Continent for the popular family car of small cost.

10.8 Exhaust Pulse Charging

Though not fully applicable to the variable speeds and loads of automobile engines, this important development by Crossley Bros. and H. D. Carter, described in Vol. 154, *Proc. Inst. Mech. E.*, should be mentioned.

In multi-cylinder stationary diesel engines, by providing a " tuned " exhaust system, the high-pressure pulse from the initial exhaust of each cylinder is utilized to " pack up " the fresh charge in an adjacent cylinder which has reached the last portion of the exhaust port opening period.

Thus the first portion of a new, relatively low-pressure charge may be caught as it is entering the exhaust pipe, where the mean pressure again may be low, and be forced back into the cylinder to raise the density of the charge finally trapped. In a single cylinder engine it may be possible to produce a suitable wave pulse by reflection from an appropriate face of the exhaust manifold.

10.9 Uniflow Scavenging. Opposed Piston Engines

Uniflow scavenging occurs in any design in which the inlet and exhaust ports or valves are situated at opposite ends of the cylinder bore, as in the poppet exhaust and sleeve valve constructions, but more particularly, and with simpler cylinder construction, in the opposed piston engine.

10.10 Compression-ignition Two-stroke Engine

Since in the compression-ignition engine no fuel enters the cylinder until all ports and valves are closed, and cannot therefore

227

be lost through the exhaust ports, one of the greatest objections to the two-stroke cycle is eliminated, and it is probably with this type of engine that the cycle is likely to make its greatest progress in the future. There is another important merit of the high-compression c.i. engine in its application to the two-stroke form. The high expansion ratio results in lower exhaust temperature and reduced waste heat, and thus the inherent cooling difficulties of the cycle arising from doubled heat flow are less than with the petrol engine.

This factor, combined with the unidirectional scavenge with cool air over piston head and valves, appears to have justified the development work that had been devoted in recent years to the port scavenge, poppet valve exhaust two-stroke engine, which has attained a considerable degree of success.

At first sight the type appears to perpetuate one of the chief weaknesses of the four-stroke engine, the highly stressed and heated exhaust valve, in addition to the mechanical complication of camshaft and valve operating gear. Experience seems to show that, owing to the favourable conditions described above, the valves give remarkably little trouble.

10.11   Rotary Blower and Poppet Exhaust Valves

An interesting example of this construction is the three-cylinder General Motors engine shown in Fig. 10-9. In the six-cylinder form this engine was used during the 1939–45 war in a variety of military applications, including the Sherman tanks.

The engine illustrated has a bore and stroke of $4\frac{1}{4}$ in. and 5 in., and a compression ratio of 16 to 1. The continuous rated output is 64 b.h.p. at 1,600 r.p.m. with a fuel consumption of 0·45 lb/b.h.p.-hr, while the maximum output is given as 80 b.h.p. at 1,800 r.p.m.

The corresponding values of the b.m.e.p. are 70 and 83 lb/sq. in. respectively. These ratings would be applicable to marine propulsion or similar duties.

The high camshaft and the three-lobed Roots blower are driven by gearing at the flywheel end of the engine, damping and cushioning devices being incorporated. The camshaft is duplicated by a balancing shaft, both carrying bob-weights which produce a reciprocating effect in a similar manner to that of the Lanchester harmonic balancer, but in this case arranged to produce a couple to balance the primary reciprocating couple due to the three pistons. In the figure the bob-weights are shown in false phase for convenience of illustration.

The direct injection system is employed, a combined pump and sprayer unit of special construction being mounted between the two exhaust valves and operated by a rocker from the camshaft.

Very complete information on this engine is given in the work by Schweitzer, referred to under " Kadenacy and Schnuerle Systems ".

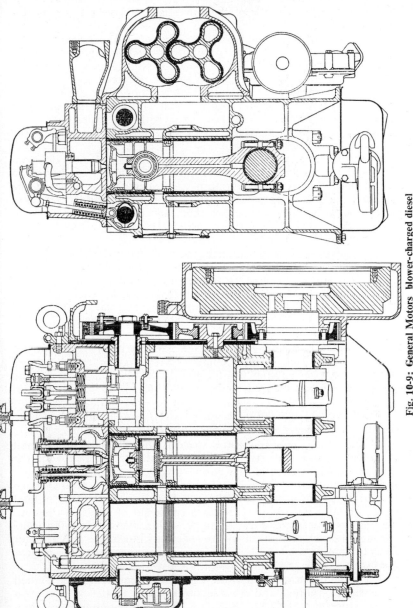

Fig. 10-9: General Motors blower-charged diesel

10.12   Foden Six-cylinder Two-stroke C.I. Engine

An interesting example of the same general system is the Foden engine.

A full description of the FD.6 Mk. I engine, with an account of its behaviour on the road will be found in *Automobile Engineer*, Vol. 39, No. 4 and in *Bus and Coach*, Vol. 20, No. 238. Later reports have been published from time to time in the technical press, but the reports mentioned give detailed descriptions of the engine.

The injection pump and control unit consists of a high-speed model of the C.A.V. pump, combined with the hydraulic H-type governor described on page 195 *et seq.*, which gives remarkably sensitive and accurate control.

The most recent engines are straightforward and logical developments of the earlier Marks. The bore has been increased from 85 to 92 mm, thin shell Aluminium–tin bearings have replaced the original thick shell white-metal bearings and the cylinder head and liner design has been altered so that each cylinder has a separate head. Also, the Mark VII six-cylinder engine is exhaust turbocharged and intercooled.

As a measure of the advance in design of this particular engine, a comparison of up-to-date performance figures with those obtained from the Mark I engine is interesting. Although the physical dimensions of the engine have remained practically unchanged, the b.h.p. has increased by 79%, the torque by 82%, the specific weight has decreased by 40% and the specific fuel consumption has improved by 10·7%.

An output of 46·9 b.h.p. per litre at 2,200 r.p.m., a specific weight of 6·3 lb/b.h.p., an overall length of less than 4 ft and weight, without electrical equipment of 1,400 lb, compare most favourably with the most advanced designs of four-stroke diesel engines available.

The maximum value of the b.m.e.p. is 155 lb/sq. in. at 1,300 r.p.m. and the best specific fuel consumption is 0·36 lb/b.h.p. hr.

At maximum r.p.m. the piston speed is about 6 per cent less than in corresponding four-stroke types, and this, combined with the unidirectional loading of the connecting rod, makes the rod and bearing load-factors more favourable. Since every upward stroke is a compression stroke, and the gas load exceeds the inertia load up to about 3,500 r.p.m., there is no reversal of stress in the connecting rod, or big-end cap loading. The fluctuations of torque throughout each revolution are consequently much less, and a lighter flywheel can be used, with direct gain in liveliness and ease in gear changing.

The general construction of the FD.6 Mk. I engine may be studied from the longitudinal and cross sections of Fig. 10-10.

Centrifugally cast wet liners are used in an aliminium alloy monobloc casting, with two cast-iron heads, each covering three bores.

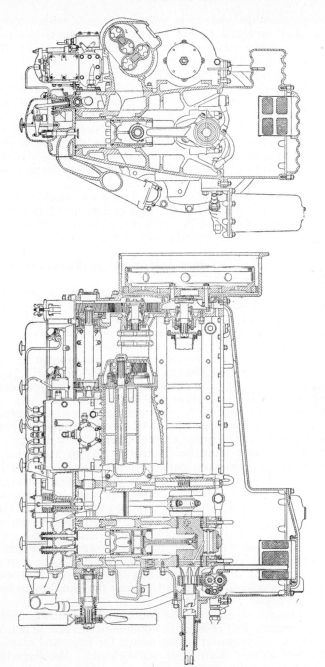

Fig. 10-10 : Foden two-stroke diesel engine

The various pressure and water joints are made with copper gasket rings and synthetic rubber sealing rings respectively, the joint faces of the liners standing proud of the block to ensure the proper degree of nip on the various washers.

The air delivery gallery supplies air to each bore through a series of ports formed to impart tangential swirl in a clockwise direction, seen from above, the injector delivering fuel from a single-hole nozzle " downstream " into the air. The toroidal recess in the piston crown has the effect of increasing the rotational swirl when the piston reaches the top of the stroke, on the principle of the conservation of angular momentum in a space of reduced diameter, as utilized by Ricardo in the cylindrical head of sleeve-valve engines.

Tin-plated cast-iron pistons are fitted, and the great length of these above the gudgeon pin will be noted. This makes them admirably fitted to perform the crosshead function of the piston without risk of tilt, and provides generous bearing area with an excellent wearing material.

The arrangement of piston rings is of interest as illustrating two-stroke requirements.

The top ring is a composite " flame " ring designed to give gas sealing for the full depth of the top land and incorporating the ring groove for the first normal pressure ring, which is provided with a snug to prevent relative rotation. The flame ring serves to prevent the top edges of the scavenge ports being exposed to the cylinder gases earlier than the nominal instant when they are overrun by the top of the piston and the gas pressure is sufficiently reduced. Two further pressure rings—they are all of taper section—are provided above the gudgeon pin, and below are the air-chest seal ring to prevent blow-by of scavenge air to the crank chamber as the piston rises, and a normal oil scraper ring. All the rings have integral cast snugs or dowel pegs to prevent circumferential movement and ensure that the joints ride along one or other of the port bars.

The continuous compression loading of the connecting rod is reflected in the arrangement of the gudgeon pin and piston bosses, the latter being stepped in order to give the maximum bearing area on the underside combined with the fullest possible support of the pin against bending. Provision is made for pressure lubrication of the pin through a central drilling of the rod, to ensure continuous maintenance of an oil film under the somewhat more difficult conditions when no reversal of load occurs. An oil-jet for piston cooling is incorporated, and in view of this provision, the thickness of the piston crown is limited in order to reduce the heat flow to the piston rings and lands.

The diagonally split big ends may be noticed. This is now general practice in c.i. engines, and reflects the continuous increase in crank pin and main journal diameter in the search for improved crank-shaft stiffness and reduced intensity of bearing loads. The diagonal split enables the lateral width of the big end to be made small enough for upward withdrawal through the bore.

10.13 Blower and Scavenging

The blower is of the Roots type with two-lobe rotors and runs at twice engine speed, average boost pressure is about 5 lb/sq. in, sufficient with the " Kadenacy extraction effect " to give thorough scavenge and exhaust valve cooling, followed by a degree of supercharge which enables " four-stroke " values of the b.m.e.p. to be maintained.

The twin exhaust valves, of moderate diameter, are driven by push rod and rocker gear of the normal type, but roller cam followers, running on needle roller bearers, are employed.

Fig. 10-11 shows the interesting timing of the valves and cylinder ports, the early opening of the exhaust valves aiding the thorough scavenge without unduly delaying the commencement of compression. The effective expansion ratio is appreciably less than in the average four-stroke compression-ignition engine, but some of the remaining energy is usefully employed in the wave extraction due to the carefully designed exhaust ducts, which extend independently for about 6 in. from the ports.

The camshaft and auxiliary driving gear is at the rear of the engine and, having helical gears, is of similar construction to that described on page 121, though with a 1 to 1 ratio for the camshaft and injection pump shaft. To conform with the best practice, ball and roller races are housed in spigotted bronze castings fitted on studs, instead of being carried directly in the aluminium alloy casting. The whole timing gear is robust and well designed.

Careful arrangements are made for vigorous circulation of the cooling water, with jets directed to the potential hot spots around exhaust valves and injectors. The direct cooling of the valve guides will be noticed.

An indication of the remarkable coolness of the exhaust is the successful use of an aluminium alloy exhaust manifold.

10.14 Crankshaft Balance and Firing Order

The crank throws are phased 120° apart in two sets of three, the two sets being out of phase by 60° to give 60° firing intervals, six in each revolution. This sets the opposing primary and secondary

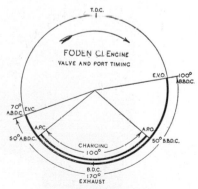

Fig. 10-11: Foden c.i. engine valve and port timing

233

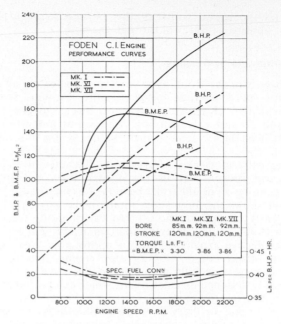

Fig. 10-12: Foden diesel engine performance

Fig. 10-13: External view of Foden two-stroke diesel engine

couples slightly out of phase, as the shaft is not in exact mirror symmetry. However, the resulting slight tendency to pitch and yaw is of negligible effect, though of some technical interest. The engine is quite free from critical vibration within the normal speed range.

The firing order is 1 5 3 4 2 6, repeated each revolution. Performance curves for the FD.6 Mk I, Mk. VI and Mk. VII engines are given in Fig. 10-12. They show exceptionally good maintenance of torque at high speed, and the improvement in b.m.e.p. and power of the late Marks is an outstanding achievement.

As stated earlier, all marks of engines after the Mark I were fitted with individual heads. Mark III and all later engines have thin shell bearings and a larger diameter crankshaft. At this point the fuel injection pump was also modified for engine oil lubrication in place of the fuel oil lubrication which had been used hitherto. The lubricating oil pump and water circulating pump speeds were also increased at this stage. Mark VI and VII engines had the cylinder bore increased to 92 mm, these two engines being similar in all mechanical details except that the Mark VII was fitted with a C.A.V. turbocharger and intercooler.

An external view of the FD.6 Mk. VII engine is given in Fig. 10-13.

The intercooler and the connecting trunk between the supercharger and the Roots blower have been removed so as not to mask the engine detils.

The authors are much indebted to the makers of the engine for information and for drawings from which the figures were prepared.

10.15 Opposed Piston Engine

The Lucas and Trojan engines, with parallel cylinder barrels, may be described as uniflow opposed piston engines since the scavenge air flows continuously from the inlet ports uncovered by one piston to the exhaust ports uncovered by the other, the two pistons moving towards each other for compression and away from each other for expansion.

More usually, however, the description is confined to the construction incorporating a single straight cylinder barrel in which the two pistons move in opposite phase towards and away from each other.

This involves either two crankshafts phased by gearing or equivalent means, or a single crankshaft to which the power of one piston is transmitted directly, and that of the other by means of return side and connecting rods, or alternatively by means of a symmetrical reversing rocker system for each piston.

Side return rods involve either a three-throw crankshaft, a crank and two eccentrics with smaller throws (Harland and Wolff), or the special arrangement used in the successful Fullagar marine diesel, in which, in each unit pair of cylinders, oblique tie rods connect the

235

pairs of pistons which move in phase, suitable crossheads and slides being provided to take the side thrusts. Thus two cranks and two connecting rods serve four pistons. In the return rocker arrangement a two-throw shaft with offset rockers is sufficient for each cylinder.

These have been exemplified in (1) the Junkers Jumo aircraft engine, (2) the Oechelhauser horizontal gas engine of sixty years ago and the more recent Peugeot-Lilloise single-line stationary type made under Junkers licence and (3) a number of recent designs and proposals of which the Commer T.S.3 is in production. The return connecting-rod method, if applied to a multi-line design, would clearly involve a crankshaft of prohibitive complexity and flexibility, with a lack of symmetry leading to balancing difficulties.

When first installed for electric generating purposes in Johannesburg, the Oechelhauser gas engines gave considerable trouble through the distortion of crankshafts and side rods arising from pre-ignition due to dirty gas.

The large gas engine, though important in its day in the utilization of blast-furnace gas, is obsolete as a prime-mover.

The third of the constructions listed above, namely the return rocker arrangement with a single crankshaft, has been the subject of many patents and designs.

Two of these, which are of special importance and interest, are illustrated in Figs. 10-14 to 10-16.

Fig. 10-14 shows the Sultzer engine, which, produced thirty or more years ago, has features of historic interest as representing a design by an experienced firm of repute, in which the opposed-piston rocker arrangement is combined with a phased reciprocating scavenge pump, in a manner that will be clear from the illustration.

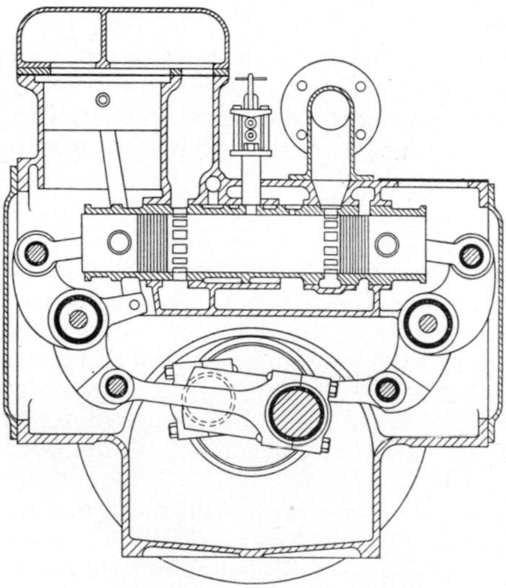

The admission and discharge of air to the scavenge pump, the capacity of which is considerably in excess of the displaced volume of the main cylinders, is by automatic valves of the reed type.

The bore and combined stroke are 90 mm and 240 mm respectively, giving a volume of 1,527 c.c. per cylinder, the maximum rating under intermittent full load

Fig. 10-14: Sultzer opposed piston engine

conditions being 30 b.h.p. per cylinder at 1,500 r.p.m. This corresponds to a b.m.e.p. of 85 lb/sq. in.

Phasing of the pistons, to give a lead to the exhaust, is accomplished by the disposition of the rocker pins and their arc of movement. With clockwise rotation of the crankshaft, it will be noticed that the right-hand rocker has passed its dead point while the left-hand one is just on it, the 180° disposition of the cranks being maintained for balancing purposes.

The new Commer T.S.3 compression-ignition engine is a current example of the opposed-piston and rocker construction which is in production and successful use.

Instead of the phased pump, a Roots blower is used for scavenging, this being more in line with present two-stroke practice. The engine has three cylinders of 3·25 in bore and a combined stroke of 8 in, giving a swept volume of 199 cu. in.

At 2,400 r.p.m. the maximum output of 105 b.h.p. is obtained, corresponding to a b.m.e.p. of 60 lb/sq. in.

The maximum value of the b.m.e.p. is 105 lb/sq. in., attained at 1,350 r.p.m. The minimum specific fuel consumption claimed is 0·38 lb/b.h.p.hr, an excellent result.

The forged crankshaft has four main bearings and six crank pins in pairs opposed at 180°, and for each crank pin there is a normal connecting rod, a rocker, and a short swinging piston link, and piston. Except for the couple arising from the distance between the planes of the two connecting rods of each pair, and the corresponding offset of the two arms of the rocker, the two sets of reciprocating masses are in dynamic balance (see page 61), but heavy pin loading in each set of reciprocating parts is involved in all examples of this construction because of the large masses.

Reversal of loading due to inertia forces is less likely to occur than in a four-stroke engine, as compression is met on each inward stroke. Thus running should be quiet at some sacrifice of the benefit to lubrication of thrust reversal. It will be noticed that the rockers in the Commer design are longer than the centre distance between cylinder and crankshaft, but owing to the reversal of the porting relative to the direction of rotation,

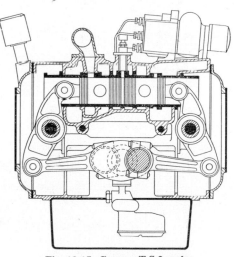

Fig. 10-15: Commer T.S.3 engine

237

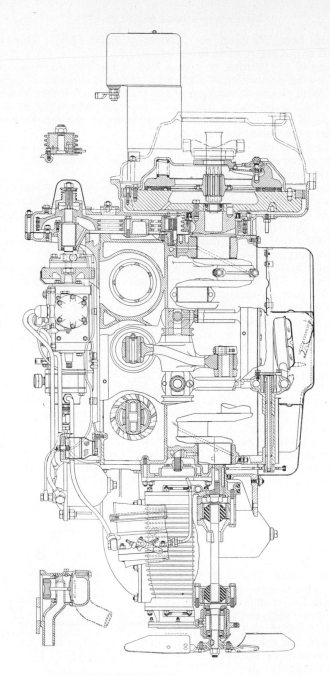

Fig. 10-16: Commer T.S.3 opposed piston engine

lead of the exhaust piston is again provided. Figs. 10-15 and 10-16 show the general lay-out of this engine arranged in such a manner as to make it very suitable for under-floor installation. Full details will be found in *Automobile Engineer*, Vol. 44, No. 8. There is also an interesting article by R. Waring-Brown in Vol. 47 of the same journal.

10.16 Comparison of Advantages

From the foregoing descriptions it will be realized that the high performance two-stroke engine cannot claim greater mechanical simplicity than its four-stroke competitor, and it is still doubtful whether it will ever achieve equally favourable specific fuel consumption.

Higher output for a given space and weight approaching 100 per cent appear to be achieved, though progress in supercharging of the four-stroke engine may reduce the advantage once more. Waste heat difficulties may well be the ultimate determining factor with both types.

Smoother torque and more favourable bearing load factors are inherent advantages which the two-stroke cycle will always be able to claim, and these should react favourably on maintenance and operational acceptability. Higher rotational speeds and smoother torque will react favourably on transmission design and endurance, and the advantages of a lighter flywheel in facilitating gear changing and aiding rapid acceleration have already been mentioned.

Developments over the next few years should be of great interest.

CHAPTER 11

Carburation and Carburettors

The process of carburation. Engine suction. Volumetric efficiency. Throttling. Determination of air and petrol flow. Fixed choke and other classes. Carburettor characteristic. Automatic speed governor.

THE term "carburation" may conveniently be applied to the whole process of supplying to the engine continuously a suitable combustible mixture of vaporized fuel and air. A mixture carrying just the necessary air for complete combustion, in accordance with the chemical composition of the fuel, is not by any means the best in all circumstances, as will be seen later, but the study of the main principles involved is simplified if constant mixture strength in the chemically correct proportions is assumed to be the object sought.

The complete process of carburation in modern jet carburettors may be divided broadly into three stages as follows—

(1) Continuous measuring out in correct proportions of liquid fuel and air for combustion.
(2) "Atomization" or breaking up into very fine spray of the liquid stream and its intimate and uniform mixture with the air current.
(3) Provision of the necessary "latent heat of vaporization" to the liquid fuel so that the mixture may form a homogeneous vapour preparatory to ignition.

The perfect carburettor would fulfil all these requirements under varied climatic conditions and at all speeds and throttle openings, that is, no matter what the demand and its rate of fluctuation for fuel by the engine. Great difficulties arise from the different nature of the two fluids, one a mixture of permanent gases, oxygen and nitrogen, and the other a more or less volatile liquid. The mechanical characteristics of the engine (valve setting, induction pipe arrangement, etc.), the great and rapid fluctuations in demand for fuel and the variations of temperature and humidity of the atmosphere introduce further serious difficulties and it is therefore small wonder that the perfect carburation system does not exist, each design having its good features and its limitations.

Before entering on the consideration of the chemical and physical properties of the various fuels suitable for the ordinary internal combustion car or lorry engine, the mechanical process of measuring out and atomizing the fuel will be dealt with, as it is in this first process that the greatest difficulties arise.

240

11.1 Engine Suction

When an internal combustion engine is revolving, either under its own power or by the agency of the starting motor or handle, the displacement of the piston on the induction stroke represents potential ability for forming a vacuum in the cylinder, the degree of vacuum produced depending on the speed of the engine and the size of the apertures admitting air and vapour to the cylinders (these apertures being the throttle opening and any leakage openings into the induction pipe), and to some extent also on the ratio of clearance volume to swept volume.

The opening through the inlet valve is " in series " with the above openings, but it becomes a determining factor only at high speed and full throttle openings, for under average conditions the smallness of the throttle opening, in relationship to the valve opening, results in the former being, as the name implies, the chief factor in controlling the flow of " gas "—using the term to denote the combustible mixture of air and petrol vapour—to the cylinders.

The suction displacement of the piston in a four-stroke engine takes place only once every two revolutions, thus a cylinder of 1 litre swept volume at 2,000 r.p.m. represents a suction capacity of 1,000 l/min. If the cylinder had no clearance volume, remained at atmospheric temperature, and if there were no restriction to the flow at the throttle or the valves, 1,000 litres of gas would be drawn in per minute, the pressure in the cylinder during induction being equal to that of the atmosphere. Except by " supercharging," no greater *quantity* of gas could be introduced into the cylinder, and provided the mixture were correct, the explosive force or mean effective pressure would have its greatest possible value. If at the same time the engine were running at its maximum permissible speed, then the power developed would be a maximum, it being here assumed that the limit of speed is determined from purely mechanical considerations.

11.2 Volumetric Efficiency

In an actual engine the effect of clearance volume and the high temperature of that portion of the previous charge left in the clearance space reduce both the volume and density of the fresh charge drawn in, and the effect of restricted openings at the valve and throttle, which increases as the speed increases, reduces the pressure and therefore the density of the charge still further. The ratio of the weight of fresh charge actually drawn in, to that which would fill the swept volume at atmospheric temperature and pressure is known as the " volumetric efficiency." Even in the best modern engines this ratio seldom exceeds about 80 per cent, and the actual value fluctuates with the speed and throttle opening. It is also very dependent on valve timing, and it is not possible with fixed timing (which is universal in normal engines) to maintain the highest volumetric efficiency at all speeds.

11.3 Throttling

From what has been said it will be apparent that should a reduced explosion be required, as for instance when after climbing a hill on top gear it is desired to maintain the same speed on a subsequent level stretch of road, it is necessary to reduce the *quantity* of the charge by restricting the throttle opening.

The smaller opening results in a greater degree of vacuum being produced in the cylinders and induction pipe by the movement of the pistons. The weight quantity of the charge—which determines the force of the explosion—is thus decreased by the lower density resulting from the decreased *pressure* in the cylinders. Under these conditions the flow through the carburettor is reduced and there is less vacuum or " depression " at the choke than under full throttle conditions.

The throttle may therefore be regarded as a means of preventing the full suction of the engine from acting on the carburettor when less than the maximum explosion or torque is required. This may occur at low or high speed, and therefore at low or high power.

The diagrams in Fig. 11-1 show the pressure differences arising in the induction system under different conditions of engine speed and throttle opening, but for the sake of clarity the degree of suction, vacuum or depression through the carburettor has been exaggerated in relation to the perfect vacuum or zero pressure line. The carburettor indicated is of the " fixed choke " type with a properly formed " venturi," which results in a recovery of pressure after the relatively low value reached at the choke.

In constructing these diagrams it has been assumed that the flow is steady and that the amount of depression at any point is constant for any given values of engine speed and throttle opening. This is an ideal condition which is only approximately realized in actual practice. Clearly in a single-cylinder engine the suction impulse occupies approximately only one quarter of each cycle or 25 per cent of the total time, thus giving rise to a pulsating flow. This is damped out to some extent by the capacity of the induction pipe and the restricted throttle opening, and in a multi-cylinder engine with four or six cylinders fed from the same carburettor an approximately uniform flow is realized through the carburettor, but these pulsations of depression still remain a source of difficulty owing to the different inertia effects arising in the two fluids. The heavy liquid petrol is far more subject to lag than the relatively light and elastic air, particularly if the passages to the jet are long and restricted. This results in the flow of petrol in relation to the air being too small at some moments and too great at others. Thus a patchy mixture results and an uneven supply of fuel to the various cylinders, or bad " distribution " as it is called.

This problem is intimately concerned with the shape and size of the induction pipe, with the valve timing and with the position of the carburettor. Its solution is largely a question of patient experiment on the part of the manufacturer, and can be touched on

242

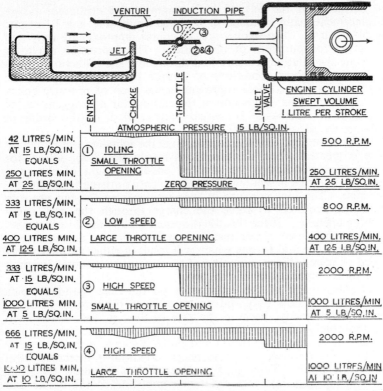

Fig. 11-1: Pressures in induction system

only briefly in a work such as this. For our purposes we will assume that for any given engine speed and throttle opening the depression and consequently the flow are steady.

Four sets of conditions are indicated in Fig. 11-1:—

(1) Low speed, small throttle opening. As when the engine is idling.
(2) Low speed, large throttle opening. As at the commencement of acceleration, or when labouring on top gear.
(3) High speed, small throttle opening. As when running down hill.
(4) High speed, large throttle opening. As when developing maximum power.

Since the air forms almost the whole of the flow (with a chemically correct mixture only about 2·2 per cent of the volume consists of petrol vapour), we may assume without serious error that the amount of fluid passing each constriction or orifice is the same. The flow of air in litres per minute, reduced to atmospheric pressure,

243

is indicated on the left of each diagram, the maximum piston displacement being assumed to be 1,000 l/min, that is a 1-l engine at 2,000 r.p.m. The figures are, of course, approximate only and are given for purposes of illustration. The depression diagrams illustrate the relative pressure loss throughout the induction system under the different conditions of throttle opening and speed, the depth of the shaded area representing the drop of pressure below atmospheric. The depression at the carburettor is exaggerated for the sake of clearness. In actual practice it is of the order of one-quarter to one-half of 1 lb/sq. in.

It will be noticed that the depression in the cylinders and induction pipe is greatest when the throttle is nearly closed for idling, for under these conditions the smallest possible weight of charge is required and this is secured by the low density arising from the low pressure. The low pressure in turn results from the big pressure difference required to force the charge through the very small throttle opening. If the throttle is opened slightly the flow increases and an increase of power results, appearing first as an increase in explosion force and torque which will result in either an increase of speed or merely the overcoming of an increased resistance (as on a hill) or a combination of the two.

The depression at the carburettor on the other hand depends on the rate of flow only and not directly on the throttle opening, but only indirectly, because the rate of flow is itself determined by the combination of throttle opening and engine speed. The suction or depression at the jet and choke is seen to increase steadily as the flow (reduced to atmospheric conditions) increases from 42 to 666 l/min. Thus, in Fig. 11-1, (2) and (4) show the same throttle opening, but very different depressions at the choke and jet, while (2) and (3) show the same flow and carburettor depression, but very different speeds and throttle openings.

11.4 Factors Which Determine Air and Petrol Flow

To force a given quantity of fluid per minute through an orifice of given size requires a certain difference of pressure between the two sides of the orifice.

The pressure difference which causes the flow of petrol may arise from the hydrostatic head of the liquid petrol—if the jet is below the petrol level in the float chamber—from the difference of air pressure between the float chamber and jet outlet, due to the depression at the choke, or to a combination of these two, while the flow of air through the choke is due to the excess of atmospheric pressure or supercharger pressure at the entry to the carburettor over the pressure on the engine side of the choke. In studying carburettor action it will be found helpful to realize that flow takes place as a result of excess pressure *behind* the fluid, whether the general pressure be above or below atmospheric—there is no such thing as suction in the sense of lifting or pulling a fluid,

PRESSURE		WATER D = 62·4 LB./CU.FT.			PETROL D = 47 LB./CU.FT.			AIR D=0·081 LB./CU.FT.	
LB./SQ. IN.	INCHES OF MERCURY	HEAD FEET	INCHES	$\sqrt{2gh}$	HEAD FEET	INCHES	$\sqrt{2gh}$	HEAD, FEET	$\sqrt{2gh}$
0·01	0·02	0·023	0·277	1·21	0·031	0·37	1·41	18	3·4
0·027	0·055	0·063	0·754	2·01	0·083	1·00	2·31	48	5·5
0·100	0·204	0·231	2·77	3·84	0·306	3·67	4·43	178	107
0·136	0·277	0·314	3·77	4·48	0·417	5·00	5·17	240	124
0·272	0·554	0·628	7·54	6·34	0·833	10·00	7·30	480	175
0·500	1·02	1·15	13·8	8·59	1·53	18·4	9·92	890	240
1·00	2·04	2·31	27·7	12·16	3·06	36·7	14·0	1780	340
14·7	30·0	33·9	407	46·6	45·0	540	53·6	26,000	1290

Fig. 11-2: Pressure, head and velocity

but only in the sense of reducing the pressure which opposes the flow, by the application of a vacuum pump effect, whether due to the human lungs or the piston displacement of an engine.

In order to maintain, or artificially increase, the final density of the charge in the cylinder, a supercharger may be employed to raise the pressure behind the flow in place of relying on the reduction of pressure opposing it.

No matter how the pressure difference may be caused or measured, for purposes of calculating the flow it must be expressed in terms of head of the fluid which is flowing, in order that the fundamental fluid flow formula $v = \sqrt{(2gh)}$ may be used.

This formula gives not only the velocity acquired by a body falling freely *in vacuo* under the acceleration of gravity, but also the velocity of efflux from an orifice or jet as the result of a pressure difference corresponding to a head h of the fluid which is flowing.

Any convenient units may be used (say, feet and seconds, or centimetres and seconds), provided they are consistent throughout.

The table (Fig. 11-2) shows pressures and the corresponding heads and velocities for water, petrol and air, the density for air being taken as that corresponding to 14·7 lb/sq. in. and 0° C. The velocities are calculated from the formula quoted above and represent the conversion, without loss, of potential energy of head or pressure into kinetic energy of velocity. Just as when a body falls through the atmosphere it meets with air resistance which prevents its velocity from attaining the full amount given by the formula, so the viscosity of liquid petrols causes their velocity of flow through carburettor jets to follow a slightly different equation from the one above, which, however, serves with reasonable accuracy for the air flow, as air approaches more closely to the ideal of a perfect fluid.

The depression in fixed choke carburettors ranges, during normal running, from approximately 4 in. to 20 in. of water column, corresponding to air speeds of 130 to 280 ft/sec. The corresponding petrol speeds are, of course, much less.

245

11.5 Volume Flow and Mass Flow

The volume flow through an orifice in cubic feet per second or in cubic centimetres or millimetres per second, according to whatever units may be convenient, is obtained by multiplying the velocity by the cross-sectional area of the jet—

$$\text{Volume flow} = A \times \sqrt{(2gh)}$$

It is now the general practice to test all carburettor jets for flow, and to stamp them with the flow in millilitres—that is, cubic centimetres—per minute under a standard head of 500 mm. This flow testing is carried still further by certain firms who submit each complete carburettor to a flow test before assembly on the engine. Such tests give valuable information and ensure consistency in setting, though it is naturally impossible to reproduce exactly all the final running conditions.

In combustion calculations it is often desirable to determine the mass or weight flow per second or per minute, so that in the above formula the volume must be multiplied by the density D to give—

$$\text{Mass flow} = A \times \sqrt{(2gh)} \times D$$

Further, the head h may be expressed in terms of the effective pressure difference by the relationship $h = \dfrac{(p_1 - p_2) \times 144}{D}$ in which, using English units, p_1 and p_2 are the absolute pressures in pounds per square inch on the two sides of the orifice and D is the density of the fluid (air or petrol) measured in pounds per cubic foot.

The formula for mass flow thus becomes—

$$\text{Mass flow} = A\sqrt{(2g)}\ 12\sqrt{(p_1 - p_2)}\sqrt{D}$$
$$= \text{Constant} \times A\sqrt{(p_1 - p_2)}\sqrt{D}$$

where the constant in addition to the quantity $12\sqrt{2g}$ may be taken to include a coefficient to correct for the discrepancy between the actual flow and the " no friction " flow. This discrepancy depends on the viscosity coefficient of the fluid and the form and proportions of the jet, the " coefficient of discharge " being from 0·6 to 0·8 for ordinary carburettor jets.

For a given form of jet the coefficient does not vary very much with the size of the jet, nor does the density of a given petrol change appreciably with change of temperature. Changes in density of the air are, of course, important, and result in enrichment of the mixture on a warm day or at high altitudes owing to the reduced weight of air consequent on its lower density. If changes of density are disregarded, there remain two variable quantities in the above formula, namely pressure difference and orifice area, which control the rate of mass flow.

11.6 Two Main Classes of Carburettor

Carburettors may therefore be divided broadly, though not rigidly, into two classes in one of which, the " constant choke "

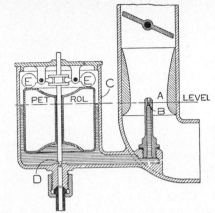

Fig. 11-3: Simple jet carburettor

class, the orifice area is constant and the pressure difference or depression is varied, while in the other, the " constant vacuum " class, the area of the orifice is varied to meet the changing demand, the depression being kept constant or approximately so.

11.7 Fixed or Open Choke Type

Fig. 11-3 shows in simple diagrammatic form the essentials of a constant choke carburettor of the vertical type. The choke A is the air orifice and the jet B, placed at the narrow waist of the choke, forms the fixed petrol orifice. The float chamber C, of the now obsolescent bottom feed type, is shown on the left, the float acting on the needle valve D through the levers E so as to close the former when the petrol level reaches the proper height. This level is thereby maintained slightly below the level of the jet orifice. A small vent-hole is provided in the lid of the float chamber to ensure that the surface of the petrol is subject to atmospheric pressure.

It will now be realized that when the engine is running, the air and petrol orifices, namely, the choke and jet, will be subject to the same depression, or lowering of pressure below that of the atmosphere, and if the relative areas are suitably chosen, having regard to the density of the two fluids, air and petrol will flow into the choke in suitable fixed proportions.

The density of average petrol is about 47 lb/cu. ft, while that of air at normal temperature and pressure is about 0·08 lb/cu.ft. Thus the ratio of the densities of petrol to air is 587 to 1. The ratio by weight of air to petrol in a chemically correct combustible mixture is about 15 to 1. Hence, it follows that for a given suction or depression acting on both air and petrol orifices, the relative areas should be—

$$\frac{\text{Area of choke}}{\text{Area of jet}} = \frac{15}{1} \times \sqrt{\frac{587}{1}} = 363.$$

247

$$\frac{\text{Diameter of choke}}{\text{Diameter of jet}} = \sqrt{363} = 19.$$

If air and petrol were ideally perfect fluids, and if friction, etc., could be eliminated, this simple carburettor would give a constant ratio of air and petrol liquid by weight, and would therefore fulfil the first function of a carburettor quite satisfactorily.

Unfortunately these conditions do not hold. Air is a mixture of permanent gases and, as already mentioned, approximates closely in behaviour to the perfect fluid, while the viscosity, surface tension and inertia of the liquid petrol cause its behaviour to follow a somewhat different and more complex equation than that given for perfect fluids. With steady flow, inertia effects do not arise, and the curve shown by a full line in Fig. 11-4 gives the relationship between the depression acting on the jet and the experimentally determined mass flow for a Zenith jet No. 110, the specific gravity of the petrol being 0·75 and temperature 0° C.

The depression is shown in centimetres of water column, and the corresponding scales of petrol and air column are added. For simplification of these scales, slightly different densities from those in the table, Fig. 11-2, have been assumed, but the comparison will be found very close if the centimetres are converted to inches by dividing by 2·54.

Three other parabolic or " square root " curves have been added

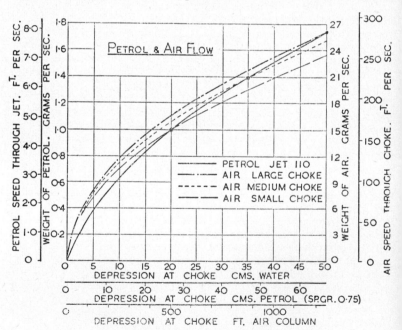

Fig. 11-4: Petrol and air flow

to represent the air flow through three alternative choke tubes suitable for the jet. Scales of air and petrol speed through choke and jet have been added, the former to be read from the uppermost air flow curve which may be taken to represent the theoretical relationship $v = \sqrt{(2gh)}$.

The petrol speed is calculated direct from the experimentally determined mass flow, and will be found to be about 65 to 70 per cent of the speed given by the formula above. The scale for mass flow of the air is so chosen that coincidence of the air and petrol curves would represent chemically correct mixture in the ratio of 15 to 1. It will at once be noticed that owing to the distorted shape of the petrol curve coincidence with the parabolic curves (which may be taken to represent the air flow very closely) cannot be obtained, the best that can be done being an intersection representing correct mixture at some one value of the depression depending on the size of the choke selected. It should be realized that the same general effect would be obtained if—as would be the usual procedure—the jet were altered instead of the choke. There is an inherent tendency towards enrichment of the mixture with increase of depression, owing to the flattened form of the petrol flow curve. With the large choke the mixture is weak throughout the whole range up to 50 cm depression, at which it becomes chemically correct. With the small choke, the chemically correct proportions are reached at a depression of 20 cm, the mixture being weak below that point and rich above it. The correct mixture may be obtained at any point desired by a suitable choice of the ratio of choke to jet, but the curves cannot be made to coincide. To obtain a constant air-fuel ratio throughout the range, whether in the correct chemical proportions or not, requires some form of " compensation " in order to correct the natural tendency to enrichment described above.

11.8 Compensation in Fixed-choke Carburettors

Compensation is the process of adjusting the mixture strength either by weakening it at large depressions or by enriching it at small, so that throughout the whole range sensibly constant proportions are maintained. Many devices have been introduced with varying degrees of success and the following list is representative—

(1) Extra air valve, hand or automatic.
(2) Hydraulic devices incorporating compensating jets.
(3) Air " bleeder " arrangements whereby the jet is partially relieved of the choke tube depression at the upper part of the range.

The third of these is now superseding all others, as in addition to enabling a great range of automatic correction to be realized, the air entering the bleed holes leads to a high degree of atomization of the petrol stream and so aids distribution and vaporization.

11.9 Extra Air Valve

Carburettors of the motor-cycle type are still fitted with a hand-operated extra air valve or slide which can be opened at large depressions to prevent excessive enrichment of the mixture. Here the correction or compensation is entirely experimental, and though, if the driver is willing to take the trouble, better results can usually be obtained by this means than with any automatic device, the extra complication and manipulation involved is regarded by many as a serious objection.

In America the automatic spring-loaded extra air valve obtained great popularity, but is now superseded by more modern devices coming under (2) and (3).

11.10 Hydraulic Means. The Submerged Jet

A very ingenious and successful method of compensation is that known as the Baverey compound jet arrangement, employed in the popular Zenith carburettor. The petrol supply is drawn through two orifices, ultimately mixing in the choke with the air stream which may be regarded as consisting of two parts, one fed with petrol from the main jet and the other from the " compensating " jet.

In Fig. 11-5, which is a purely diagrammatic illustration, A is the main jet and B the compensating jet, which is submerged, while C is the compensating jet delivery tube. It will be seen that the main jet is fed directly from the float chamber in the ordinary way, with the result that in respect of its own portion of the air stream it gives an increasingly rich mixture as the suction increases for the reasons already explained. The compensating jet, on the other hand, discharges into a well D which is in direct communication with the atmosphere.

When the petrol in the well is level with that in the float chamber, there is no flow through the compensating jet since the surfaces of the petrol on both sides of it are level and subject to the same pressure (atmospheric). As the throttle is opened the resulting

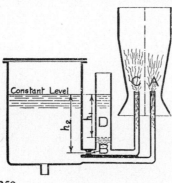

Fig. 11-5: Diagram of Zenith jets

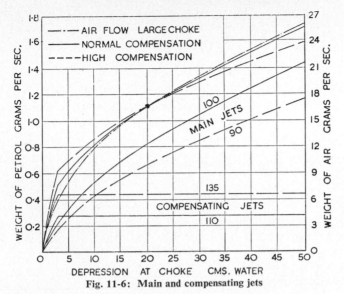

Fig. 11-6: Main and compensating jets

depression in the choke causes petrol to flow from the well through the delivery tube and consequently the petrol level in the well falls. The rate of flow through the compensating jet depends on its size and the difference of level h of the petrol in the well below that in the float chamber. An intermediate condition as the well empties is shown by h_1 while h_2 is the maximum head which can act on the compensating jet.

Thus when the well is emptied at quite a small depression, the compensating jet flow reaches a maximum and thereafter remains constant, no matter how great the depression at the choke may become, owing to the fact that atmospheric pressure is maintained in the well.

The further increase in the depression in the choke will, however, increase the air flow and hence it follows that the portion of mixture formed by the petrol which passes through the compensating jet will become progressively *weaker*. This balances the increase in richness of the mixture from the main jet, and the total mixture remains of appreciably constant strength provided a suitable combination of main and compensating jet sizes is chosen.

Since this Baverey method of compensation is still incorporated in Zenith carburettors, though in combination with the air-bleed principle, it will be instructive to study the flow curves in more detail by graphical plotting, particularly as other curves of fundamental importance may be readily derived therefrom.

In Fig. 11-6 are drawn mass or weight flow curves for main jets 90 and 100 and for compensating jets 110 and 135 and also the air flow curve for the large choke of Fig. 11-4.

251

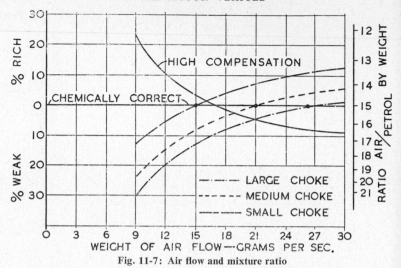

Fig. 11-7: Air flow and mixture ratio

It will be noticed that the compensating jet flow lies above that of the main jets in both cases as the head increases from zero up to 3 cm of water, that is 4 cm of petrol, which is the limiting value of h_2 in Fig. 11-5. After this point the flow remains constant. On combining the flow through the main jet 100 with compensator 110, and main jet 90 with compensator 135, it will be found that in each case the totals coincide with the air curve, indicating chemically correct mixture, at 20 cm depression. The jets were chosen to give this result, but it will be found that at other parts of the range the two combinations give different mixtures. The larger main jet with small compensator gives reasonably correct mixture throughout, though with definite slight over-compensation.

The other combination gives considerable over-compensation, which we shall see presently is a desirable result. To the left of the point of " correct " mixture there is considerable enrichment, while to the right is a progressive weakening, thus reversing the conditions in the simple carburettor.

In Fig. 11-7 these same curves are plotted in another way, showing quality of mixture (both as a percentage and a ratio) plotted against weight of air flow. The three curves from Fig. 11-4 and the high compensation curve from Fig. 11-6 may thus be compared on an important and helpful basis. The reader should appreciate that these curves represent hypothetical rather than wholly experimental results, though they are based on actual behaviour.

11.11 Air Bleed Compensation

Before proceeding to discuss whether, by a high degree of compensation, all requirements are met, the process of compensation by air bleed devices will be described.

The earlier Solex carburettors, the main jet assembly of which is shown in Fig. 11-8, provide a simple example.

The jet orifice O is submerged, the jet tube G being inserted in a well forming part of the carrier *t* and secured by the cap A which makes metallic contact with the flange at the top of the jet tube. The petrol level is at *m n* at the neck of the choke K. Air bleeder holes are drilled at *a* and for " high compensation " also at higher points in the jet tube. As the jet tube becomes emptied by the suction these bleeder holes become uncovered and are then in direct communication with the atmosphere through holes *s* drilled in the cap. The result is that the jet orifice is subject to less than the full

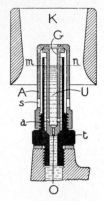

Fig. 11-8

depression in the choke, the amount of relief depending on the size of the bleeder holes in relation to the internal diameter and length of the jet tube body U.

In Figs. 11-9 to 11-12, which are diagrammatic, are shown the air bleed arrangements in the now obsolete Claudel-Hobson, and the most widely used constant-choke carburettors, namely the Solex, Stromberg and Zenith. In each case V is the choke or venturi, M the main jet and A the air metering plug for the bleed. There is also in most types of all makes an additional bleed resulting from reverse air flow through the idling jet when the well or feed passage becomes emptied. For the Solex the arrangement shown is known as " assembly 20," and it will be noticed that the single calibrated air plug A replaces the bleed holes in the jet tube of the older type shown in Fig. 11-8.

This enables the bleed to be altered without changing the jet,

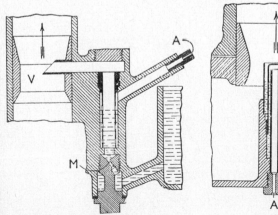

Fig. 11-9: Claudel-Hobson air bleed

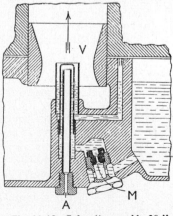

Fig. 11-10: Solex " assembly 20 "

253

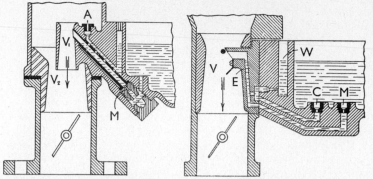

Fig. 11-11: Stromberg air bleed   Fig. 11-12: Zenith air bleed

and so makes tuning more flexible and definite. The down-draught form of this assembly is shown in Fig. 11-25.

It will be noticed that in the up-draught form the petrol on its way to the choke must pass through the holes in the emulsion tube, owing to the necessity for supporting this from the bottom. This makes no difference to the principle of the bleed action, for the lowest row of holes is quite sufficient to pass this petrol, as the upper holes become uncovered to pass the bleed air when the depression increases. There should be no difficulty in visualizing this action if the atmospheric pressure is regarded as a positive pressure forcing air through A and petrol through M, the two fluids sharing the holes in the emulsion tube and meeting to form an emulsion in the stand pipe on the way to the choke. In the Claudel-Hobson and Stromberg arrangements the petrol and air meet *inside* the emulsion tube, but there is no fundamental difference in the action. In each case a series of air jets penetrates the rising column of petrol producing an atomized emulsion, and by their " atmospheric leak " effect relieve the main jet of some portion of the choke depression.

The action is progressive and the degree of compensation can be modified by changing the size of the air bleed plug.

11.12 Double Diffuser

In the Stromberg down-draught arrangement illustrated, the two chokes V_1 and V_2 represent a device for intensifying the de-pression and therefore the air velocity at the outlet from the emulsion tube. In a smooth and gradually enlarging venturi tube, the absolute pressure at the outlet is higher than at the throat, as indicated in Fig. 11-1, so that with the outlet from V_1 placed at the throat of V_2 it is possible to obtain the highest local depression and velocity just at the point where the emulsion meets the first main air stream, which results in the formation of a rich and homogeneous mixture ready to join the final air stream through the main choke.

11.13 Zenith V-type Emulsion Block

In the down-draught Zenith diagram, Fig. 11-12, which represents generally the special features of the V type, C is the compensating jet, placed with the main jet in the bottom of the bowl and delivering, not as formerly directly to the well W, but to an intermediate chamber formed in the emulsion block E. The depression in this chamber will be intermediate between the atmospheric pressure in the well and the depression in the choke, depending on the size and characteristics of the communicating holes and the resistance of the main passage in the emulsion block. This principle of the intermediate chamber is discussed somewhat more generally on page 259. It will thus be seen that the flow through the compensating jet is controlled partly by choke depression, and not solely by hydrostatic head as formerly.

The air bleed or leak effect is clearly also communicated to the main jet petrol, at a point intermediate between the main jet and the outlet from the emulsion block to the choke, and it becomes impossible to forecast with any certainty the flow curves for any particular jet sizes. The flow characteristics of the mixed petrol-air fluid, and the form of the passages are too complicated for any quantitative estimate to be made, and recourse must be had by designer and tuner to experiment.

As a well-known research engineer has remarked, every carburettor man has his own pet bleed holes and drillings, and development involves much drilling and plugging alternately before the desired flow characteristics are obtained.

11.14 Secondary Suction Effects

It is sometimes stated that the petrol flow through the jet is due to the velocity of the air past the jet. This is not fundamentally true. It is possible to interrupt the petrol flow entirely by applying the necessary degree of " suction " to the float chamber vent hole, though the air flow through the choke may be uninterrupted. This principle of modifying the pressure behind the petrol to reduce the net depression which causes its flow is applied in altitude controls for aircraft.

There are, however, certain secondary suction effects due to the aspect of the jet outlet or the obstruction that it causes, arising from the partial vacuum ordinarily formed on the down-stream side of such an obstruction. The chamfered emulsion outlets of the Claudel-Hobson and Zenith arrangements, and the " distributor bar " shown in black circular section in the Zenith diagram, are examples of such obstructions. They introduce modifications to the flow which must be determined experimentally.

11.15 Mixture Requirements for Economy and Power

The results of physical theory and research have shown that the chemically correct mixture is not the best for either economy (high thermal efficiency) or for power (high b.m.e.p. and torque). For the former, weak mixtures down to 20 or more to 1 are desirable, provided such weak mixtures can be properly distributed, ignited and burned, while for high b.m.e.p. mixtures 12 per cent to 15 per cent rich are required.

The physical and thermal properties of the products of combustion are such that high thermal efficiency is aided if, combustion being complete, there remains in the mixture a minimum of carbon dioxide and water vapour in proportion to nitrogen and residual oxygen. This enables the best use to be made of the *fuel*.

High b.m.e.p. and torque, on the other hand, require that the best possible use be made of the *air* that is aspired, and this necessitates the burning of the air to produce carbon monoxide

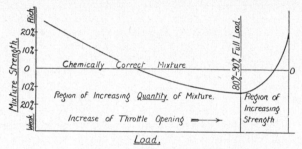

Fig. 11-13: Ideal carburettor characteristic

rather than carbon dioxide, though the latter is always present in considerable quantity and represents the final product of combustion of carbon. Thus incomplete combustion of the fuel, but complete combustion of the air, results in high b.m.e.p. and torque, while combustion of a weak mixture leads to high thermal efficiency, except at small throttle openings, when a richer mixture is required to compensate for greater dilution by exhaust gas. To summarize, a weak mixture is required for economy, and a rich mixture for power and acceleration.

11.16 Carburettor Characteristic

Fig. 11-13 is an " ideal " carburettor characteristic suggested by D. Finlayson (see *Proc. Inst. Aut. Eng.*, Vol. XIX). The mixture becomes progressively weaker for the sake of economy up to say, 80 per cent or 90 per cent of full load, at which point the throttle opening should give the maximum weight charge in the cylinder. Further movement of the throttle should enrich the mixture without decreasing its quantity in order that maximum torque shall be obtained. It is thus seen that mixture strength should depend on throttle opening no matter what the speed, depression or flow may be.

If reference is again made to Fig. 11-1 it will be seen that under the conditions of (2) and (3) there is the same rate of flow through the carburettor and, therefore, the same carburettor depression, with widely different engine speeds and throttle openings. The mixture required in (2) is a rich one in order that the utmost values for the mean effective pressure and engine torque may be obtained so that full throttle opening may result in rapid acceleration, while in (3) a weak mixture is desirable in order that economy at moderate loads may be realized. Condition (4) again requires a rich mixture in order that maximum power at full throttle may be attained. With the carburettor of Fig. 11-4 the same mixture would be delivered for both (2) and (3), since the flow and choke depression are the same, and there is moreover no recovery to a rich mixture at maximum delivery.

Thus a carburettor in which the mixture strength depends on the choke depression or flow only cannot meet all requirements, and the mixture ratio must be controlled by other factors.

11.17 Mechanically-controlled Power Jet

Apart from the enrichment at low speeds and part throttle which is required by most engines to prevent stalling, and for which special provision is sometimes made, enrichment for maximum torque and power is required only at the larger throttle openings, and may therefore be effected by bringing into action an additional " power jet " by the last few degrees of movement of the throttle lever.

Fig. 11-14 illustrates three arrangements for providing this enrichment mechanically. At (a) is shown the power enrichment valve added to the Claudel-Hobson carburettor of Fig. 11-9, at (b) the scrap view is taken from Fig. 11-31 of the Zenith W type carburettor and shows a modification of the pump operating lever

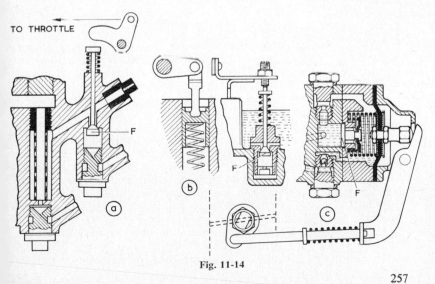

Fig. 11-14

257

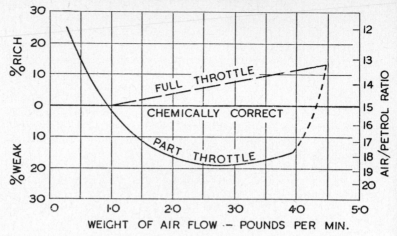

Fig. 11-15: Dual carburettor characteristic

which was introduced, though not widely used, to open the power enrichment valve by the last few degrees of throttle movement. Fig. 11-14 (c) shows the mechanical arrangement used in the Solex carburettor illustrated in Fig. 11-26, which is functionally the same as in the Zenith W type, except that the mechanically operated pump is of the diaphragm form. In each of these views F is the full throttle enrichment valve.

There is a tendency to replace these mechanical devices by those operated by manifold depression. See Section 11.32 and Figs. 11-22, 11.23 etc.

11.18 Dual Characteristic

It thus becomes possible to plot on a basis of mass flow (grams per second or pounds per minute) two characteristic curves of mixture ratio, one for full throttle opening and the other for part throttle, corresponding to (say) normal cruising speed on the level.

For each of these throttle openings a range of flow corresponding to the full range of engine speed may be plotted against the experimentally determined mixture ratio.

A generalized example of the type of characteristic to be aimed at is shown in Fig. 11-15, in which the method of plotting conforms with that used in Fig. 11-7. The part-throttle characteristic extends to the lowest value of the flow, corresponding to the lowest speed, and under these conditions a rich mixture is required to counteract the effect of dilution by exhaust gas, which may be greatly intensified by valve timing overlap.

As the flow increases with increase of speed a weak economy mixture is provided, which continues throughout the part-throttle range, until this range may be supposed to meet the full-throttle

258

characteristic by a final opening of the throttle, indicated by the fine broken line. This curve is closely comparable with that of Fig. 11-13 on page 256.

11.19 Principle of the Intermediate Chamber

A principle which is applied in various forms in different car-burettors, and particularly in idling adjustments, is the device of the intermediate chamber in which the jet or its effective outlet is placed, and through which the necessary air, or some part of it, passes on its way to the choke. In general, both the inlet and outlet of this chamber are adjustable, as for instance, by air and throttle slides in the two lever motor-cycle carburettor, or by throttle stops and air-bleed screws in idling and starting devices.

The principle is illustrated in Fig. 11-16. The absolute pressure p_2 in the intermediate chamber, on which the discharge of the jet depends, is intermediate between p_1 and p_3 depending as it does on the flow and the relative areas of inlet and outlet. At (a) the inlet is larger than the outlet, thus causing the depression d in the inter-mediate chamber to be less than half that in the induction pipe. At (b) the relative sizes of the openings are reversed and adjusted so as not to alter the rate of air flow, with the result that the depression at the jet is more than half the total depression in the induction pipe. This will clearly cause an increase in petrol flow and a richer mixture. Obviously the adjustments may be made with such a degree of fineness as to produce any required change in mixture strength with constant quantity, or the quantity flowing may be altered with or without modification of the quality of the mixture.

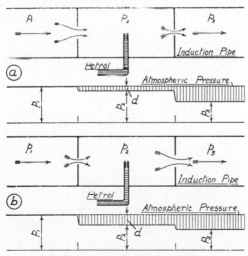

Fig. 11-16: Intermediate chamber

11.20 Idling and Starting Devices

In the fixed choke carburettor the small flow required for idling cannot be obtained from the main choke and jet owing to the very low corresponding depression and velocities of flow. The metering under these conditions becomes uncontrollable and atomization is non-existent.

It is necessary, therefore, to provide idling jets and air orifices constituting in effect a small auxiliary carburettor exposed to the best depression available, which is just on the engine side of the edge of the throttle disc. The small quantity required will thus flow at high velocity, and good atomization will result. In this connection the effect of air leaks into the induction pipe, through faulty joint gaskets or worn valve guides, should be emphasized. A small leak may represent a big proportion of the total flow under idling conditions, and will completely upset the mixture, though at large throttle openings it would be quite immaterial.

When the engine is warmed up, the idling mixture required is a normally rich one, but since the charge is of low density, it must be homogeneous in order to ensure inflammation.

Such a mixture would generally be much too weak to ensure starting from cold, owing to the fact that in cold surroundings only a small proportion of the petrol vaporizes. Hence arose the somewhat discredited expedients, which are now being eliminated, of using the float tickler to cause flooding and the strangler to increase the depression on the jet. These methods, at all events with the ordinary strangler, clearly gave somewhat haphazard and uncertain results.

11.21 Separate Starter Devices—Semi-automatic

Several devices coming under this heading are in successful use. They are brought into action by the operation of a hand control, and there follows a greater or lesser degree of automatic and progressive adjustment of the mixture ratio as the engine warms up. When the engine is ready to run on the idling jet alone the starter is put out of action by release of the control.

The starter jet may be incorporated in a system which uses the ordinary idling ducts for the delivery of the petrol to the induction pipe, or it may be provided with quite independent passages which are closed by the release of the control.

The automatic and progressive weakening of the mixture which is required as the engine warms up may be controlled by depression or temperature or by air velocity, it being borne in mind that increase of depression (lowering of absolute pressure) and increase of temperature both assist evaporation, and a lower petrol-air ratio may be used.

Increased air velocity is the result of higher engine speed and greater depression, and is not strictly a third independent means of control.

11.22   Zenith Starter—VE-type Carburettor

This semi-automatic device is illustrated in Fig. 11-17. Not now in production, it is interesting as representing the separate miniature carburettor to supply the small quantities of rich mixture required for starting and idling. An objection to the arrangement is the difficulty of providing for " inside air." It consists essentially of a small fixed-choke fixed-jet carburettor proportioned to give the correct quantity of suitably rich mixture for starting, and provided

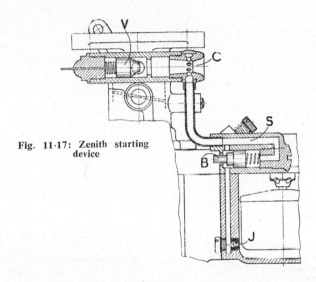

Fig. 11-17: Zenith starting device

with an automatic air bleed valve controlled by the depression at its own choke. This small carburettor is placed in communication with the induction pipe, on the engine side of the throttle, by the lifting of a cone valve by a cable control. Referring to the figure, C is the choke having at its neck a ring of petrol or petrol-air emulsion holes. Here the petrol metered by the jet J joins the air stream in the choke and the rich starting mixture passes through the open cone valve V to the induction pipe.

As the engine speed increases the depression in the space S increases until it is great enough to overcome the control spring and move the air-bleed valve B off its seating. This allows air to enter through the annular area around the reduced stem of the valve. This area remains constant as the valve opens, and adjustment is effected by changing the valve for one having a different diameter of stem as required.

Thus with increase of speed, the bleed air increases the quantity and weakens the proportions of the mixture to compensate for the improved evaporation. In this fashion a fast idling speed is

261

maintained until warming up is complete, and there is no risk of excess petrol reaching the engine, even in the event of the control not being returned to the closed position.

11.23 Solex Starting Device

The Solex " self-starter " is a device similar in principle, but having somewhat different provision for the automatic change in strength of the mixture, which operates on the basis of the time required to exhaust the capacity well from which the initial rich mixture is obtained.

The device, as in the Zenith arrangement described above, is brought into action and finally put out of action by the operation of a hand control on the dash, the connection usually being by cable. The details are described on page 272 in connection with descriptions of recent Solex constructions.

11.24 Inter-connected and Automatic Strangler Control

The Stromberg and Zenith-Stromberg designers have adopted the principle of using the main carburettor to assist the idling devices to give the rich mixture for cold starting.

With the mechanically inter-connected strangler used on the Zenith VIG and VIM models the closing of the strangler by the dash-board control opens the throttle slightly from the idling position.

Thus a large depression is communicated to the main system on the principle of Fig. 11-16 and a rich mixture is obtained. A small automatic flap valve in the strangler provides for the admission of an increasing air flow with a sensibly constant depression in the main choke or, with further reference to Fig. 11-16, the entrance to the intermediate chamber increases with the increased demand while the main jet system is subjected to a depression p_1-p_2 the value of which depends on the area, stiffness, and deflection of the flap valve. The depression is about $\frac{1}{2}$ lb/sq. in., or say 14 in. of water column.

11.25 Thermostatic Control

Automatic control by means of exhaust manifold temperature is employed in the Solex Thermostarter. The starter unit is similar to that of the " self-starter," but communication with the induction pipe is established and cut out automatically by a vacuum-operated diaphragm controlled by a thermally closed leak valve. The control box, which is mounted on the exhaust manifold, contains an adjustable bi-metal strip, which on warming up closes by its flexure the leak valve referred to above, with the result that the diaphragm is then subject to a pressure difference which causes movement of the cut-out valve and puts the starter out of action.

In cases where periods of cooling are frequent, as in door-to-door delivery service, the device tends to give somewhat high consumption, and it is more suitable for applications where one or two starts per day under exceptionally cold conditions have to be accomplished.

11.26 Fully Automatic Devices—"Single Button Control"

There is a demand for, and, in spite of their greater complication, a tendency to supply, fully automatic and progressive devices which shall not require from the driver anything more than the pressing of the starter button.

Under the stimulus of American demand for devices to meet the extremes of climatic conditions the Stromberg Company has been prominent in the development of such arrangements, which are exemplified in the various forms of the Stromberg " automatic choke." Here the term " choke " is used for strangler, which in these designs is of the offset spindle type. These devices have been very fully described and illustrated in articles by Mr. Charles H. Fisher in *Automobile Engineer* and *Modern Motoring*, and the interested reader is referred to these journals for fuller information.

A short description of the Zenith Stromberg thermostatically controlled type is given herewith.

The offset strangler is controlled by three agencies, namely, the spring control of an exhaust-heated thermostat, the action of induction pipe depression on a small vacuum piston, and the torque due to the air stream, which latter is always tending to *open* it. The thermostat is of the bi-metal clock-spring form enclosed in a chamber mounted on the exhaust manifold in a convenient position below the carburettor.

When cold, the tension of the spring, which is provided with an adjustable anchorage, holds the strangler *closed*. As the thermostat box heats up, the difference in coefficient of expansion of the two metals of the spring strip causes the tension to relax, the increasing velocity of the air stream past the strangler overcomes the spring, and the device finally goes out of action with the strangler fully open.

The foregoing describes the change from the fully closed position at the initial start, when only a small quantity of leakage air can pass, to the fully open or out-of-action position. An intermediate " fast idle " position is necessary to give rapid warming up. The strangler and throttle must be automatically set to prevent excessive depression on the main jet system which would result in " loading " with petrol and stalling the engine.

This object is accomplished by the induction pipe vacuum established as the engine accelerates on first firing. The vacuum operates on a small piston, which moves through a short stroke limited by an adjusting screw S in Fig. 11-18. Through the vacuum kick lever K, the fast idle cam lever L is moved slightly downwards,

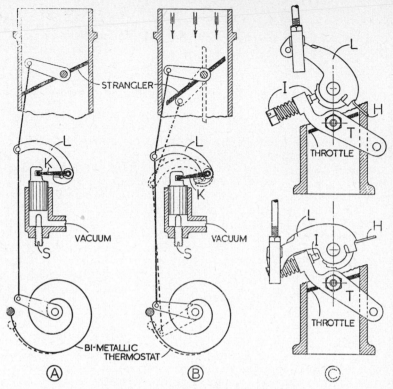

Fig. 11-18: Zenith-Stromberg starting device

overcoming the spring force and slightly opening the strangler. As the thermostat warms up, the relaxing spring tension and the increasing torque due to the air flow relieve the vacuum cylinder of this duty.

The view (A) in Fig. 11-18 shows the closed position at the initial start, while (B) shows the " fast idle " position in full lines and—in broken lines—the out-of-action position which leaves the throttle, and the main and warm idling systems, to function normally.

Views (A) and (B) are purely diagrammatic, while (C) shows in more constructional detail the fast idle cam lever L.

The upper diagram shows the fast idle position and the lower one the free position corresponding to the broken lines in diagram B.

On cooling after shutting down, the clockwise movement of L will result in the cam fouling the fast idle stop screw I, as it would be undesirable to provide a gradual ramp which would impose on the thermostat spring the task of overcoming the throttle closure spring. The fouling is, however, easily released by a flick of the accelerator pedal before operating the starter button, thus allowing

264

the strangler to snap to the closed position. The tang H is provided to enable the throttle lever T to open the strangler mechanically should it be necessary to ventilate the system before the warming up is complete.

For descriptions of other types of thermostatic control the reader is referred to Vol. 28 of *Automobile Engineer*.

11.27 Idling Systems and Progression Jets

A typical idling system incorporating " progression " jets is illustrated in Fig. 11-19, which shows the arrangement used in the Zenith VE up-draught carburettor. The idling jet J draws its petrol supply by way of the emulsion block E from the main and compensating jets. This arrangement ensures that the idling jet is starved of petrol and goes out of action when the main system is in action—it does, in fact, then provide an additional air bleed to the emulsion block. On the same principle the practice of feeding the idling or auxiliary jet direct from the float chamber which was used in the early Solex carburettors has been abandoned, and the feed is now taken from the well, which becomes emptied when the main system is fully in action. In this way some tendency to excess petrol consumption is avoided.

To return to Fig. 11-19, it will be seen that the jet sprays into an intermediate chamber or duct D, into which there are three air bleeds or leaks. The outlet from this chamber is to the induction pipe above the throttle, where a high depression exists—see Fig. 11-1 (page 243).

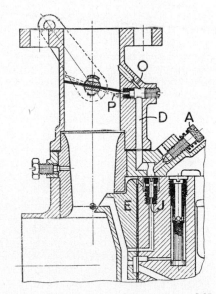

Fig. 11-19: Zenith idling system

The depression in the chamber D (d of Fig. 11-16) is determined by induction pipe depression p_3, the size of the drilling O, and the effects of the three air leaks, which are as follows. The radial holes in the jet plug communicate with the main choke, where the pressure, with the throttle closed or only very slightly open, may be taken to be atmospheric. This fixed bleed supplies the emulsifying air.

The second bleed is provided by the adjustable air screw A, and the third by the fixed calibrated air plug P which constitutes the " progression " device. With the throttle closed this plug acts as a fixed air orifice supplying, with the emulsifying bleed, part of the idling air. The adjustment is thus confined to that part of the idling air entering past the screw A, and thus becomes more accurately controllable.

A further idling adjustment is provided by a slight opening of the throttle as necessary. This slightly reduces the induction pipe depression and gives a larger quantity of weaker mixture, owing to the fact that the petrol flow is reduced concurrently with the increase of air flow.

11.28   Progression or Transfer Action

A difficulty experienced with the fixed choke carburettor is the tendency to a " flat spot " on transfer from the idling system to the main system as the throttle is opened up. The opening of the throttle reduces the depression on the drilling O before sufficient depression becomes available at the main choke, but the gap is bridged by the intense local depression which then develops at the edge of the throttle disc, on the principle expressed in Bernoulli's theorem that in a fluid stream, high velocity and high kinetic energy are accompanied by low potential or pressure energy. With the throttle opened to a moderate extent as shown by the broken lines, the progression jet becomes a delivery jet for the idling system, on which depression is maintained until the main system is in action.

11.29   Accelerating Well or Pump

It has been said that the ideal carburettor should maintain correct mixture strength at all combinations of throttle opening and speed. Certain of these combinations give rise to difficulties. Thus if, after a period of low speed and light load, the throttle is suddenly opened to accelerate the engine the following conditions arise. The high depression previously existing in the induction pipe is momentarily applied to the choke, but the sudden rush of air induced is so momentary that the petrol cannot respond quickly enough owing to its own inertia. Thus the first rush of mixture is very weak. The situation is now as follows. A big throttle opening will have put the idling device out of action, while the poor vacuum producing capacity of the pistons due to the low engine speed, will be producing only a very small depression at the main jet, with the result that a very patchy and poorly atomized mixture will be produced. This will cause hesitation and misfiring.

Suppose, however, that there is a body of petrol available between the throttle and the jet, as in the well of the Zenith and in the jet tube and well of the Solex carburettors. The flow of this petrol is not controlled by the constriction of the main jet and therefore it will flow readily in response to the weak suction, temporarily enriching the mixture until the engine has gained speed. Such a " pick-up " well is practically essential in fixed choke carburettors if satisfactory acceleration at low speeds is desired and in certain models of the majority of leading makes of carburettor this " snap " acceleration is made still more certain by means of a positive pump which delivers a charge of petrol into the choke when the throttle is suddenly opened.

11.30 Zenith Mechanically-operated Pump

The pump fitted to the Zenith VIG down-draught carburettor is operated from the throttle lever by a long bell-crank lever as shown in Fig. 11-20. The pump plunger P is raised by the internal spring S and petrol flows from the bowl through the suction valve V_s. During the delivery stroke caused by rapid movement of the accelerator pedal, the petrol is forced through the double-seated ball valve and pump jet J as a fine spray into the beak of the emulsion block. The upper seat for the ball valve provides a vent to break any suction that might be communicated from the choke and so cause syphoning over. For slow movements of the accelerator, there is sufficient clearance around the pump plunger to allow the petrol to be by-passed and no delivery takes place.

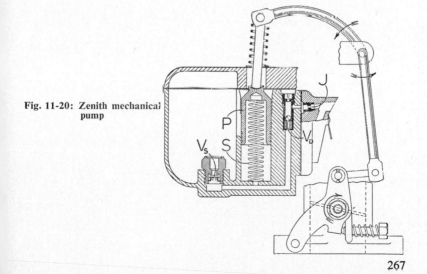

Fig. 11-20: Zenith mechanical pump

11.31   Stromberg Pump: Type DBV Carburettor

This pump is shown in Fig. 11-21.   As the throttle is opened the pump piston rod R is pulled down and, through the compression spring S, drives downwards the pump plunger P, the pump chamber having been filled on the previous return stroke through the plate suction valve V.

The petrol is delivered through the ball valve at a rate controlled by the size of the discharge reducer D and the stiffness of the plunger spring, which by its compression will give a spread-over delivery into the choke through the spraying jet J.   As in the Zenith pump, there is a carefully controlled clearance around the piston to allow of by-passing during slow movement of the accelerator pedal.

11.32   Devices Controlled by Manifold Depression

Variations in manifold depression may be used in various ways for the control of mixture characteristics, as also for ignition advance and retard.   Fig. 11-1 shows that large throttle opening is accompanied by reduced induction pipe vacuum; that is, high absolute pressure in the inlet manifold implies a full cylinder charge, and if the fuel/air ratio is correct, high m.e.p. and power.

Thus power, economy and snap acceleration may all be controlled by sustained or sudden variations of manifold pressure.

In the Stromberg DBV downdraught carburettor shown in Fig. 11-22 a by-pass or power enrichment valve V is opened by the fall of the spring-loaded piston P when the depression sustaining it,

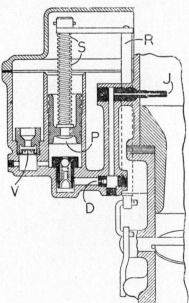

Fig. 11-21: Stromberg mechanical pump

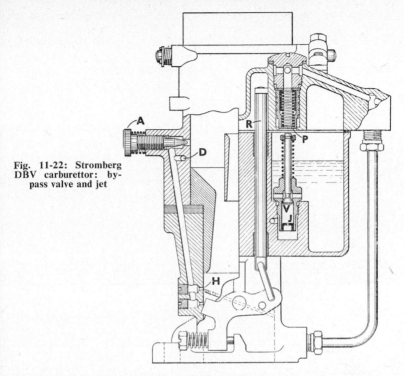

Fig. 11-22: Stromberg DBV carburettor: by-pass valve and jet

and communicated by the external pipe (or in later models by internal drillings) is sufficiently reduced by opening of the throttle.

The flow is metered by the jet J.

The following additional details may be noted in Fig. 11-22; the air adjusting screw A for the idling mixture which is delivered through the discharge holes or progression jets H, and the pump operating rod R, linked to the throttle arm. D is the internal drilling through which is delivered the petrol metered by the idling jet. For diagrammatic clarity certain components are shown out of their actual position and plane in the carburettor body.

11.33 Zenith Vacuum-controlled Economizer

Several Zenith models obtain the part-throttle economy mixture by applying the fullest practicable degree of air bleed to a rich power mixture over the part-throttle range, a diaphragm valve controlled by manifold vacuum being utilized to control the flow of air to the main jet bleed. This arrangement is shown in Fig. 11-29.

The valve V is normally held open by the high manifold vacuum at part throttle, communicated through the passage P. Bleed air then has free access to the emulsion block through the calibration plug A by way of the drilled passages leading from the air horn.

With the low vacuum resulting from full throttle opening, the spring closes the valve and only the small permanent air bleed F, which short-circuits the valve, is available to weaken the mixture.

11.34   Solex Vacuum-controlled Accelerating Pump

This membrane type of pump is fitted to certain Solex down-draught models, and is illustrated in Fig. 11-23 which is partly diagrammatic and applies to the A.I.P. model.

P is the pump chamber supplied through a ball suction valve from the duct D which communicates directly with the float chamber.

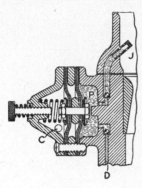

The suction stroke is effected by the induction manifold vacuum on the engine side of the throttle being communicated through an internal drilling to the hole C, the membrane spring being thereby compressed. The collapse of the vacuum consequent on the opening of the throttle allows the spring to deliver the charge of petrol through the ball delivery valve and the side drilling of the jet J, which projects a fine stream into the neck of the choke. The spring may be so adjusted that the pump is filled only at suitably high values of the induction vacuum, during light running, subsequent to which rapid acceleration would be required.

Fig. 11-23

Under " all out " high speed conditions, the depression surrounding the jet J will become large enough to cause continuous spraying, thus providing a rich mixture at the top end of the range.

11.35   Up-draught and Down-draught Systems

The down-draught system has displaced almost universally both the up-draught and horizontal types of carburettor. The functional advantage claimed is that gravity assists instead of hindering the comparatively low spraying velocity of the fuel, thus aiding the atomization and enabling a somewhat larger choke to be used with a corresponding improvement in performance.

Improved accessibility of the carburettor, with convenient accommodation for the air cleaner and silencer, is provided with the down-draught arrangement, and no difficulty is experienced with petrol supply by electrical or mechanical pumps. In some installations provision is made for draining flooded petrol, which naturally falls beyond the throttle to the induction pipe, by means of an " atmospheric " pipe of vertical length sufficient, when filled with petrol, to overcome moderate induction pipe depression and thus allow for drainage through an upwardly closing ball valve at the foot of the pipe.   The ball valve prevents inward air leak under idling conditions.   There has been a return to the external induction manifold from the cast-in distribution systems which had become popular with the horizontal carburettor. These external manifolds incorporate hot spot contact with the exhaust manifold, and in some cases provision of thermostatic shutter control is made to regulate the local flow of the exhaust gases.

11.36 Vauxhall Exhaust-heated Manifold

A successful thermostatically controlled assembly of the above type is illustrated in Fig. 11-24. A four-port exhaust manifold is bolted to the under-side of a three-port inlet manifold of a six-cylinder engine served by a down-draught carburettor. Surrounding the central junction of the carburettor branch with the three inlet branches is a rectangular chamber or jacket through which exhaust gas is circulated under the control of a shutter S. This shutter is moved by the opposing action of a weight W, tending to close it against flow to the jacket, and a bi-metal coil spring giving counter-clockwise rotation to the shutter spindle when cold.

The impact of the exhaust gases also tends to close the shutter, owing to the off-set spindle, particularly at full throttle and high speed when the temperature conditions are high, and little additional heat is needed.

Thus at starting the shutter takes up the position shown by full lines and deflects the bulk of the exhaust gases around the jacket,

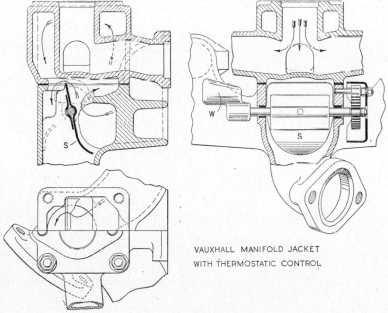

VAUXHALL MANIFOLD JACKET
WITH THERMOSTATIC CONTROL

Fig. 11-24

271

quickly warming this and supplying the necessary heat to the mixture flowing from the carburettor. The thermostatic spring is external to the manifold in a light protective casing, and as it gradually takes up the surrounding temperature of the hot manifold, its tension relaxes and the weight, aided by the impact of the gases, turns the shutter to the stop position shown in broken lines, leaving only a small opening for passage of the exhaust gas to the jacket. Such a device may be linked with the " fast-idle " carburettor control illustrated in Fig. 11-18.

The authors are indebted to the Vauxhall Motor Company for the drawings from which the illustration was prepared.

11.37 Recent Solex Carburettors

The Solex B32 PBI-5 model, referred to earlier as being fitted to the 2·4 litre Jaguar, may be taken as representative of recent Solex designs.

The salient features may be studied with the aid of the general section and the scrap views of Figs. 11-25 and 11-26.

The views on the left show how the fuel reaches the starter, idling system and main diffuser system through the starter jet Gs, main jet G and idling jet g respectively. It will be noticed that the starter jet delivers into the capacity well to which the inlet of air is limited by the calibrated bleed orifice Sb.

From the well, starter petrol is drawn through the two level drillings into the rising branch and over the weir to the starter unit. After the first start with a very rich mixture the well becomes empty and the flow through Gs is determined in a similar manner to the compensating jet in the Baverey system. An automatic reduction of mixture strength occurs as the engine speeds up to a " fast idle " apart from any manipulation of the starter to the " intermediate " position. It will be noticed that a small air bleed is provided at the top of the rising branch from the well, to break any tendency to syphon over the weir.

11.38 Progressive Starter

The starter unit, on the left of the main view of Fig. 11-25, is operated by a manual control from the dashboard. In early models of this unit there were only two positions of this control, giving free communication of manifold depression to the starter chamber and so to the air jet Ga and to the well described above through the duct D, or complete closure with the dashboard control in its " off " position.

No progressive action was provided in the operation of the control.

The bi-starter and the progressive bi-starter are variants of this arrangement, the former a two-step movement with definitely located full, intermediate and off positions. The " progressive " control allows for gradual change from the intermediate to the off position by regulated movement of the dashboard control.

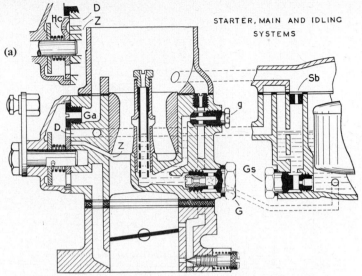

Fig. 11-25: Solex B32-PBI-5 carburettor: starter, main and idling systems

Automatic weakening of mixture strength by the exhaustion of the well takes place as described above.

In the intermediate position shown at Fig. 11-25 (a) the valve disc now presents a small dished hole Hc to the fuel duct D, and at the same time opens a second air vent Z to " inside " atmospheric air. The fuel and the air from this second vent share the restricted entry Hc to the starter chamber, so that a slightly larger quantity of much weaker but better emulsified mixture (for the same engine speed) enters the chamber and reaches the manifold. As the control is gradually pushed home a progressive reduction of all the port areas takes place until they are finally closed at the completion of the last idle warming up period, after which the action is transferred to the idle and main throttle systems.

11.39 Idle System

The idling or pilot jet g takes its fuel from the main jet via the reserve well which feeds the main diffuser system, so that there is little risk of its being starved of fuel when the throttle is suddenly closed after a period of fast running. The delivery of the idling mixture to the manifold follows normal practice.

11.40 Combined Accelerating Pump and Power System

This is mechanically operated by movement of the throttle, and is shown in the sectional view on the right of Fig. 11-26. This is a new feature of Solex carburettors, and is used on models which are fitted to high performance cars used for normal road purposes.

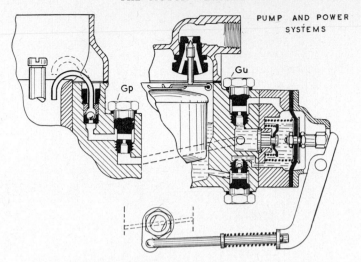

PUMP AND POWER
SYSTEMS

Fig. 11-26: Solex B32-PBI-5 carburettor: pump and power systems

In the figure, counter-clockwise movement of the throttle spindle in the opening direction acts through the lever to move the membrane to the left, compressing the return spring and delivering the additional fuel necessary for snap acceleration through the injector tube via the pump jet Gp and the ball delivery valve. Gu is an economy or by-pass jet which can be added if required.

With further and sustained opening of the throttle the membrane spindle makes contact with the head of the delivery valve spindle

Fig. 11-27: Twin Solex installation on 2·4-litre Jaguar

and holds the valve open, allowing continuous delivery of fuel to the injector tube for sustained full power.

The tube may be bent to alter the level of its outlet and so control the depression at which continuous spraying will take place. A higher level is found advantageous for four-cylinder engines as compared with sixes, owing to the greater pulsation of depression with the former.

The annotation used in the foregoing descriptions and diagrams conforms with that used by the makers, which is standardized and familiar to users.

The photographic view of Fig. 11-27 shows the installation of twin Solex B32-PBI-5 carburettors on the 2·4-litre Jaguar engine.

11.41   Other Recent Constructions by Solex

Carburettor type ZIC-3 is particularly designed for use in very cold climates where starting difficulties and interference by icing may become serious.

As will be seen from Fig. 11-28 the emulsion tube is removed from the centre of the venturi and placed at the side where it is less exposed to the low presure and low temperature conditions at the throat of the carburettor.   An auxiliary venturi or ring diffuser RD is now provided at the throat, the main emulsion being fed to this by the horizontal passage.   This increases the capacity of the

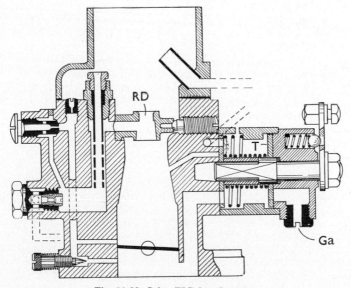

Fig. 11-28: Solex ZIC-3 carburettor

275

carburettor without increasing its size owing to the removal of the obstruction due to the standard emulsion tube assembly.

Owing to the nature and required range of this series, it has been possible to dispense with the separate choke tube and to obtain simplicity by making the venturi integral with the body.

11.42 Progressive Zero Starter

The bi-starter already described is modified as shown in Fig. 11-28. The starting richness is increased by the effect of an additional rotating disc valve T, which blanks off the entry of air through the starter air jet Ga, the small drilling seen at the top of the box providing the sole initial air supply to the starter.

As the engine first fires, the disc T acts as a flat automatic inlet valve, lifting against the inner spring and so opening communication with Ga until the control is moved to the intermediate position, when the necessary opening is provided by a drilling through the disc. The spring ball location device and the dished hole indicated by broken lines are applicable to the intermediate position.

The reader is referred to an important paper by C. H. Fisher " Some Notes on Carburation and other Fuel System Troubles " which deals with the problem of icing. See *Proc. Inst. Mech. Engineers* (Automobile Division), No. 2 (1955–6).

The new Solex B32PAIA compound carburettor is illustrated in Fig. 11-35.

The authors are much indebted to Solex Ltd. for information.

11.43 New Zenith Carburettors

The latest carburettors in the Zenith range are the VN and the W types, both of down-draught construction.

The former is based on the well-established Baverey principle of main and compensating jets with the addition of air-bleed orifices which aid the formation of an atomized emulsion, as well as playing a secondary part in the correction of the mixture ratio.

The latter type is developed from the earlier Zenith-Stromberg designs in which compensation or correction is obtained by the air-bleed method in the multi-hole diffuser illustrated in Fig. 11-11.

Both these new carburettors incorporate cam-controlled inter-connected stranglers for starting and fast idling, a mechanically operated accelerating pump and provision for a full-throttle power mixture combined with part-throttle economy.

The VN carburettor weakens the full throttle mixture at part throttle; the W type enriches the normal mixture at full throttle, by means of a power jet brought into action by mechanical means, or by variation of manifold depression as described on page 268 though the closely fitting piston there shown is replaced by a flexible diaphragm as illustrated in Fig. 11-31.

The VN range of carburettors are all down-draught types, and a particular feature of the series is the manner in which all the jets are centrally mounted in the specially designed emulsion block,

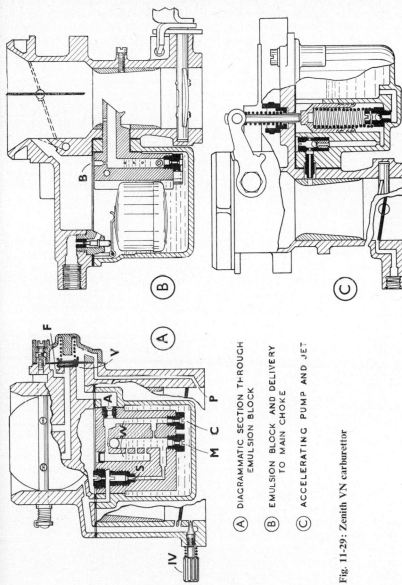

(A) DIAGRAMMATIC SECTION THROUGH
    EMULSION BLOCK

(B) EMULSION BLOCK AND DELIVERY
    TO MAIN CHOKE

(C) ACCELERATING PUMP AND JET

Fig. 11-29: Zenith VN carburettor

instead of partly in the main bowl casting. The emulsion block becomes a larger and wider component inserted from the inside of the float chamber instead of being attached on the outside. The delivery beak of the emulsion block projects into the choke tube at the throat where the main air stream has its highest velocity. The pump jet delivers at the same level, also in a horizontal direction, but in a different radial plane. An exploded pictorial view of the float bowl, float, emulsion block and pump piston with the various jets and air bleed plugs is shown in Fig. 11-30, which the reader will be able to relate to the sectional views of Fig. 11-29.

This latter figure shows a flattened and extended section, perpendicular to the throttle spindle and parallel to the strangler spindle, of the main and compensating jets M and C, the capacity well W, the progressive air holes into the emulsion tube above the main jet and the idling system on the left, fed by the slow-running jet S which is supplied through the main jet.

The idling mixture receives correction and emulsifying air through a fixed drilling from the main air intake, and from the top of the float chamber through a calibrated plug above S. The screw IV controls the *volume* of the idling mixture. On the right is the economy device, the operation of which is explained in principle on page 269.

The mechanical accelerating pump on an earlier model is shown in Fig. 11-20. The general construction remains the same though a ball suction valve is substituted for the disc valve, and the linkage with the throttle movement is modified. This now incorporates a spring controlled lost-motion device, which permits a spread-over in the event of very rapid operation of the accelerator pedal, and also allows for seasonal change of the pump stroke by means of a stop collar provided with lugs of alternative height. This may be seen in the sectional view (c) of Fig. 11-29 as well as in the photographic view of Fig. 11-30.

The small air bleed in the top of the emulsion block, Fig. 11-29, B, has been found advantageous in certain installations.

11.44   Inside Air

It will be observed that in the above illustrations all the air drillings and ducts originate inside the air intake, including the atmospheric vent to the float chamber.

There are two reasons for this, namely, to place all air inlets under the protection of the air cleaner fitted to the intake, and to ensure that any strangling at the air cleaner shall not impose different " atmospheric " pressures on the various air drillings, which would result in disturbance of mixture ratios.

This provision for supplying inside air is now general with the standardized fitting of air cleaners and silencers.

11.45   Zenith W Type Carburettors

These are fitted as standard to some Ford cars, and have basic features developed from Stromberg designs, including bottom feed

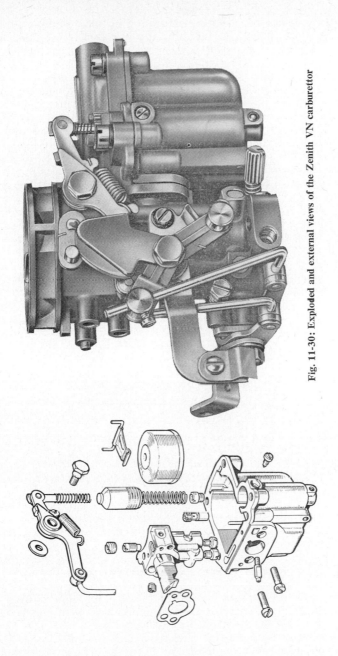

Fig. 11-30: Exploded and external views of the Zenith VN carburettor

to the float chamber, double venturi and air bleed emulsion tube as illustrated in Fig. 11-11, mechanically operated accelerating pump and economizer or power enrichment valve opened for full load conditions as shown in Fig. 11-31 (c), but closed at part throttle.

In the WIA assembly, as in the DBV type shown in Fig. 11-22, the by-pass or enrichment valve is operated by induction vacuum, but instead of a piston, a spring loaded diaphragm is used, the vacuum duct consisting of internal drillings instead of the external pipe shown in Fig. 11-22. At part throttle the induction pipe vacuum lifts the diaphragm and allows the valve to close.

For the WI type a direct mechanical control was developed, an adjustable degree of lost motion ensuring that the valve opened only in the last stages of throttle movement. This has not been widely used but is illustrated in Fig. 11.31 (d).

Both models include direct mechanical operation of the accelerating pump, with spring return of the piston instead of the spread-over spring delivery shown in Fig. 11-21. Seasonal adjustment of the pump stroke is provided by three alternative pin holes in the driven lever of the operating linkage.

The strangler flap is urged by its spindle spring to the shut position, but through its lever and follower pin which bears on the starting cam is prevented from closing until the cam is rotated by the strangler control cable to permit of the spring closure, the throttle being simultaneously cracked open for the start by the connecting rod and lost motion crank.

Fig. 11-31 shows in a diagrammatic manner how provision for these various phases is provided.

A general section is shown at (a) through the float chamber, large and small venturis, and the main jet plug M and emulsion or main discharge tube T.

If Fig. 11-11 is compared, it will be seen that the correction or bleed holes are now placed on the under side of the inclined discharge tube T.

This view also shows the strangler flap in the fully open position, and the " inside air " drilling by way of which bleed air reaches the idle jet discharge by internal drillings.

Fig. 11-31 (b) shows the idling system, the accelerating pump inlet valve and operating crank, and the vacuum duct from the induction manifold to the chamber housing the spring loaded diaphragm which opens the economizer valve. At the bottom of the view, on the right, are the usual features of progression holes at the edge of the throttle disc, and the adjusting screw for *quantity* of idling mixture.

Fig. 11-31 (c) shows a full section of the diaphragm chamber and economizer valve operation, and the pump delivery valve and control jet. This view shows the inclined delivery duct by which the enrichment petrol is led to the outside of the main discharge tube, in which, after passing through the bleed holes, it joins the main emulsion for delivery to the throat of the small venturi.

280

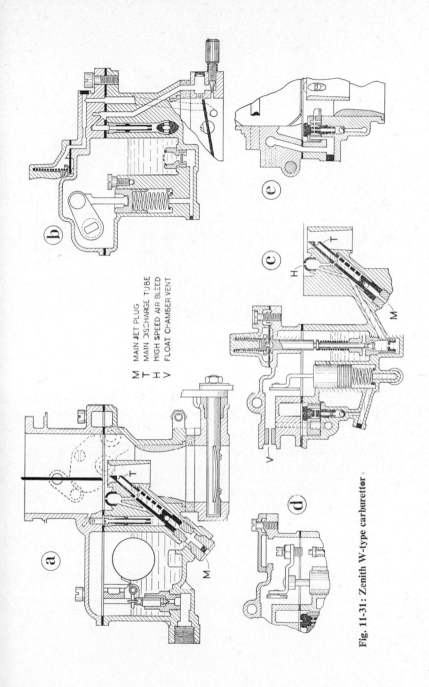

M   MAIN JET PLUG
T   MAIN DISCHARGE TUBE
H   HIGH SPEED AIR BLEED
V   FLOAT CHAMBER VENT

Fig. 11-31 : Zenith W-type carburettor

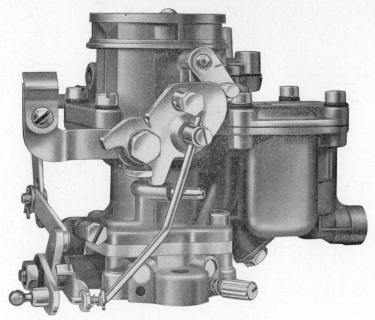

Fig. 11-32: Zenith W-type carburettor

The scrap view (*e*) shows the method of delivery through the pump discharge nozzle into the main choke.

The external view of Fig. 11-32 will give some idea of the actual construction.

11.46   Multi-barrel Carburettors

The intensive development in the U.S.A. of high-powered V-eight engines has naturally been accompanied by corresponding carburettor development by the leading Corporations.

These modern instruments which are all of the " open " choke type have become somewhat complicated units, though in only one major feature do they incorporate any new combination of established principles. This is in the provision of two separately fed venturis with linked throttles which are brought into action successively to full parallel operation on maximum load.

The limitations of the simple or basic " open " or fixed choke class of carburettor are referred to on page 260 in connection with starting and idling devices. A small depression applied to a large orifice is unsatisfactory from the points of view both of metering and spraying or atomization. Conditions are most unsatisfactory in the main choke in the early stages of transfer from the idling system, and progressively improve as the speed and load increase. The desire to provide full flexibility of performance, with, in

282

some cases the highest degree of " press button " automaticity, has
led to the extreme exploitation of the advantages of fixed orifices
provided by the constant choke class of carburettor.

This has resulted in complication, but not necessarily in reduced
reliability, and flexibility of performance is generally greater than is
obtainable with the constant vacuum class, which has its own merits
of simplicity and high full load performance.

Nomenclature is not standardized, but the terms " dual " and
" duplex " are both applied to the two linked venturis mentioned
above, which provide jointly the quantity and quality of mixture
required through the full throttle range, while avoiding the disadvantage of excessive choke area at lower throttle openings.

What are usually referred to in Britain as the " five phases " of
carburation, namely starting, idling, part throttle, acceleration and
power, are usually described in American textbooks and makers'
handbooks in relation to the metering and atomizing jet " systems,"
by which the required conditions are provided. The float chamber
mechanism may be included as a sixth " system." There is no
divergence of objective in the phases or systems, merely in the
degree of completeness and elaboration with which they are provided
in each make and model of carburettor. Details vary but basic
methods have become largely standardized.

The four-barrel instrument, now becoming standard on large
V-eight units, duplicates in one assembly, this " dual " or " duplex "
combination, each of the two combinations serving a selected group
of four cylinders in the two banks which has been found to give the
best distribution in relation to a particular firing order.

11.47   General Motors 4GC Rochester Carburettor

The authors are much indebted to the Rochester Products Division
of General Motors Corporation for the full information and diagrams from which the following notes and the figures have been
prepared.

The Rochester 4GC carburettor is a twin duplex downdraught
instrument incorporating four main venturis and four corresponding
throttles in a detachable throttle block. The venturis may or may
not be of the same diameter.

The carburettor is built as a three-layer " sandwich," the middle
layer incorporating the float bowl, venturis and jet clusters, and
the upper layer forming the air horn for the attachment of the air
cleaner, and carrying the automatic strangler or " choke," with its
thermostatic control, and certain of the control lever pivots.

The two sides of the carburettor are described as the primary or
pump side (since the accelerating pump is situated on this side) and
the secondary side.

The two primary barrels provide for starting (automatic choke),
adjustable idling, and part throttle running, while the power
enrichment valve, operated by manifold vacuum, and the throttle

operated accelerating pump are incorporated in the primary side of the carburettor.

The secondary side of some of the earlier models contributed two " phases," namely a fixed idling contribution (about half the total) delivered to the primary barrels, and the additional quantity of mixture required for full load. The secondary throttles, subject to a brief transition stage, are either shut or fully open.

In most of the later models the idling system is confined to the primary barrels, thus simplifying the secondary jet cluster, and a recent addition is an automatic throttle valve with offset spindle described in connection with Fig. 11-33.

The float chamber completely surrounds the four barrels, and is divided into two horse-shoe sections separated by a wall which in the assembled carburettor extends as a continuous partition from top to bottom, between the primary and secondary sides. The two float bowls are fed by identical inlet needle valves controlled by twin cylindrical floats carried on light horse-shoe arms. A cored passage conveys the petrol from the single inlet and filter connection on the secondary side to the inlet needle valve on the primary side.

A second cored passage in the air-horn casting, slightly above normal fuel level, equalizes any abnormal rise of fuel level between the two bowls.

The valuable effect of this float chamber arrangement is that each cluster of metering orifices and main wells is centrally situated in regard to the surface area of the liquid in the float chamber from which it is supplied. Thus derangement of the mixture due to tilt of the vehicle in either direction is reduced to the minimum.

The detailed construction and action of the carburettor should be clear from the following notes on the four views of Fig. 11-33, taken in conjunction with previously described general principles.

Fig. 11-33 (b) shows a general section through the two barrels of one half of the four-barrel assembly, the primary side on the left and the secondary side on the right. Each of the four barrels is provided with its own throttle T mounted in the throttle block; the two primary barrels share the automatic off-set choke or strangler flap in the primary half of the air-horn, which is controlled in the general manner described on page 264.

In addition, the two secondary barrels are provided with automatic damper valves or auxiliary throttles D, the purpose of which will be described later.

The small venturis on each side of the carburettor are paired in a cluster which carries on the primary side the main air-bleed tubes and idle dip tubes as well as the two pump delivery jets. On the secondary side the cluster carries only the main air bleed tubes, though in earlier models an idle dip tube was provided also on this side. The flow through this was led to the primary side through internal drillings and passage ways.

The four main jets M feed the capacity wells in both halves of the carburettor, those on the primary side being related to the

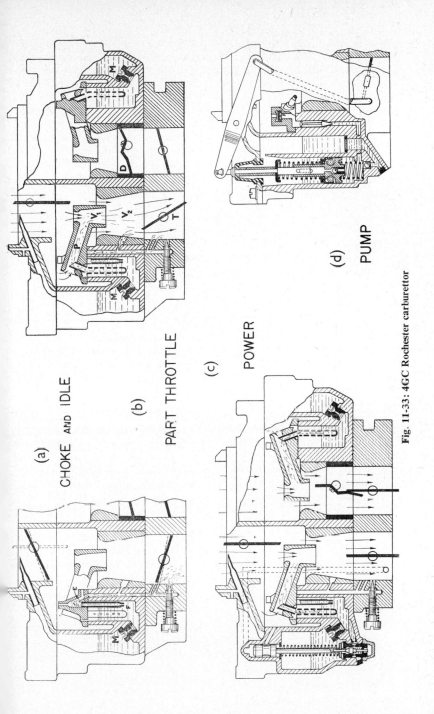

(a)

CHOKE AND IDLE

(b)

PART THROTTLE

(c)

POWER

(d)

PUMP

Fig. 11-33: 4GC Rochester carburettor

primary main venturis so as to provide the part throttle economy mixture, while those on the secondary side provide the additional fuel corresponding to the increased breathing capacity as the secondary throttles move towards their fully open position during the final stage of primary throttle opening, consequent on the mechanical linkage between the primary and secondary throttle spindles. The secondary main jets may be so chosen as to maintain an economy mixture up to the point at which the power system becomes operative with the final stage of throttle opening, or a progressive enrichment of the total mixture may be provided by fitting larger main jets on the secondary side. It will thus be seen that the use of primary and secondary barrels with linked throttles provides limited choke area and good air velocity when the load is small, with additional choke and jet area to meet maximum load.

Referring to the general classification of carburettors given on page 291, it will be seen that the duplex barrel carburettor provides an example of the " mechanical stepped " class, intermediate between the single open choke and the true constant vacuum classes. The limitations of the " fixed orifice " type, with its great variation of depression and air speed are mitigated though not wholly eliminated.

To return to the diagrams of Fig. 11-33. Diagram (a) shows the primary throttles and the strangler flap in the " cracked open " position for starting, in order that the best available depression may be applied to all fuel sources to give the small quantity of very rich mixture required for a cold start. In this position, if Fig. 11-18 is used as a basic reference, the throttle stop screw I is riding on a high step of the cam, and the strangler flap is held slightly open against the closing urge of the cold thermostatic coil.

On the first firing, the increased depression acting on the piston opens the flap slightly, this action being immediately reinforced by the air flow on the off-set flap. The fast idle phase follows, and as the thermostatic coil warms up, the flap opens further and rotates the fast idle cam, allowing the throttle stop screw to drop to a lower step on the cam and causing a slight closing of the throttle.

The lowest step permits the closure of the throttle to the slow idle position, with the strangler flap fully open.

The hot air supply reaches the thermostat housing by a pick-up pipe with its entry close to the exhaust manifold, and is drawn through the same depression duct which operates the piston, this latter being of special form to control both its own effort on the cam lever and the flow of hot air to the coil.

11.48   Idle System

The idle system, fed through the primary main jets, is duplicated in the two halves of the four barrel instrument, and its general functioning, as also that of the progression drillings, should be clear from descriptions elsewhere in this chapter.

The main idle adjusting screw, which is spring locked in the usual

286

manner, controls the *quantity* of emulsion finally delivered to the induction manifold on the engine side of the throttle, where its final quantity and quality is determined by its mixture with the air passing the edge of the throttle from the main venturi.

It will be seen that several air bleeds and vents are provided, as well as metering restrictions F and E for fuel and emulsion, the best position and size of these being a matter of patient experiment in applying basic theory, but having the general purpose of providing the correct quantity and quality of well " atomized " emulsion throughout the idling range, and of avoiding syphoning action and " percolation " of fuel vapour from the float chamber under conditions of a hot engine and cooling system, which might lead to " hot start " difficulties.

11.49 Part Throttle System

Fig. 11-33 (*b*) shows the conditions at part throttle for delivery of the main fuel supply on the primary side through the mixture passage P to the small venturi V_1 (see page 254) and finally into the main air-stream through the large venturi V_2. The situation indicated is the degree of primary throttle opening—from 40° to 50°—at which the opening of the secondary throttle commences. The linkage between them causes them to move together from this point so that they reach the fully open position simultaneously.

Fig. 11-33 (*c*) and (*d*) show the power enrichment valve for sustained full throttle operation and the accelerating pump. Both these features are provided on the primary side of the carburettor only, as single units serving both primary barrels. Diagram (*c*) should make clear how the power piston is lifted by manifold vacuum to close the valve at part throttle, but it is forced down to open the valve by the helical compression spring against the reduced vacuum corresponding to full throttle opening.

A vent to the air-horn is provided to ensure that the induction vacuum is not applied to the float bowl, from which the power valve is fed direct.

Fig. 11 33 (*d*) shows the accelerating pump, intended to supply, as previously explained the additional fuel for snap acceleration, but not responding to slow changes of throttle position owing to piston by-pass effects in combination with carefully chosen volume. The ball suction and vapour release valves will be noted, with the cone pellet delivery valve which, in connection with the double helical piston springs, determines the pressure and spread-over of the delivery through the duplicate pump jets into the two primary main venturis.

The linkage with the throttle is of necessity by a simple direct rod, so that the pump plunger moves continuously with throttle movement. With a fidgety driver and spasmodic accelerator movement there is some risk of fuel waste, as in most accelerating pump installations. The pellet delivery valve may be replaced by a spring loaded ball valve.

11.50 Secondary Throttle Lock-out

Provision is made by the engagement of a short lock-out lever on the secondary throttle spindle with a slot in the fast idle cam plate, to ensure that the secondary throttles cannot open until the choke flap is fully open, otherwise excessive air would be drawn through the open secondary barrels.

Further, since it is not desirable to have the full capacity of the secondary barrels in action at low speed, should all throttles be fully opened, the damper valves or auxiliary throttles D, previously

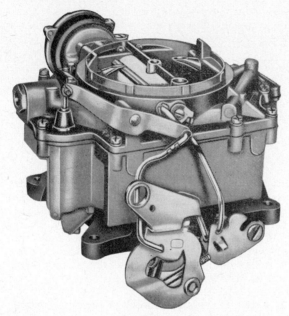

Fig. 11-34: 4GC
Rochester carburettor

mentioned, are provided on the secondary side. These are spring-loaded on off-set spindles, so that the secondary barrels come into action only when the air speed is sufficiently high to ensure good metering in all four barrels.

Space does not permit of a full description of all the ingenious features of these modern instruments, but the photographic view of Fig. 11-34 will assist the reader in understanding the constructional details.

11.51 Solex B32 PAIA " Automatic Twin " Carburettor

This latest Solex production may be compared with the 4GC Rochester carburettor already described, in which the same basic principle is used, but in a duplex assembly designed for application to V8 engines. The PAIA instrument is a " compound " carburettor with two separate choke systems acting in parallel and thus

288

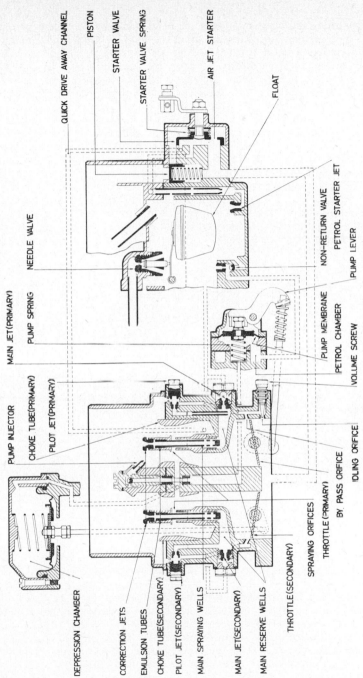

QUICK DRIVE AWAY CHANNEL
PISTON
STARTER VALVE
STARTER VALVE SPRING
AIR JET STARTER
FLOAT

NEEDLE VALVE
PUMP SPRING
MAIN JET(PRIMARY)

NON-RETURN VALVE
PETROL STARTER JET
PUMP LEVER
PUMP MEMBRANE
PETROL CHAMBER
VOLUME SCREW

PUMP INJECTOR
CHOKE TUBE(PRIMARY)
PILOT JET(PRIMARY)

DEPRESSION CHAMBER
CORRECTION JETS
EMULSION TUBES
CHOKE TUBE(SECONDARY)
PILOT JET(SECONDARY)
MAIN SPRAYING WELLS
MAIN JET(SECONDARY)
MAIN RESERVE WELLS
THROTTLE(SECONDARY)
SPRAYING ORIFICES
THROTTLE (PRIMARY)
BY PASS ORIFICE
IDLING ORIFICE

Fig. 11.35: Solex B32 PAIA Carburettor

mitigating the disadvantages of the single fixed choke when required to operate over an extreme range of flow. These disadvantages, of poor atomization at the lower air speeds and strangulation when full power is required, have already been referred to. In this way the stability of the fixed choke type and its freedom from moving parts liable to stick is combined with a useful approach to the merits of the variable choke, constant vacuum class described later.

The primary choke is of limited diameter, to provide for starting, stable idling, low speed running and snap acceleration in the familiar way of fixed or " open " choke instruments, but when top performance is required without restriction of orifice area, the second choke is automatically opened up and thereafter operates in parallel with the primary choke to deliver a combined stream of mixture to the manifold. Careful setting and synchronization is required at the combination point to ensure smooth and economical transition, but the difficulties associated with the synchronization of two independent carburettors throughout the range are avoided.

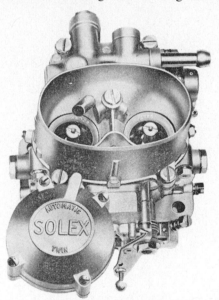

Fig. 11-36: External view PAIA carburettor

The general construction of the instrument can be studied from Fig. 11-35, from which it can be seen that the familiar methods of air-bleed correction, starting and idling devices used by Solex are incorporated. To obtain the progressive choke tube action, the throttle valves have to operate independently of each other. The primary throttle valve is linked directly to the accelerator pedal and is mechanically operated, but the throttle valve of the secondary choke is completely automatic in action. This latter valve is

290

connected by a rod to a diaphragm housed in a depression chamber, which communicates by an internal drilling with a suitably chosen intermediate point in a cross drilling between the waists of the two choke tubes. A mechanically operated accelerator pump is incorporated in the primary assembly.

These two carburettors may be said to represent in some degree the " stepped variation " principle, the one mechanical the other automatic, but they are not constant vacuum instruments.

The Solex design, being automatic, requires a moving part but, as this is of diaphragm form and the operating rod has no close clearances which might cause sticking, no trouble has been experienced from this cause.

In Fig. 11-36 is shown the external top-view of the carburettor, and the following points may be noted. The cover of the depression chamber is very accessible and easily detachable for change of spring if required, though this is not a user's ajustment. On the secondary side may be seen the float chamber vent tube for " inside air ", and on the primary side the pump injector nozzle is just visible.

It is now necessary to deal with the second main class of carburettor, the constant vacuum, or variable choke, type.

CONSTANT VACUUM CARBURETTORS

The second broad class of carburettor is that known as the " constant vacuum " class, of which for long the only surviving example was the S.U. Carburettors in this class are essentially instruments which vary in size, that is as regards the essential air and petrol orifices or the choke and jet, with the variation in demand of the engine for gas, the depression and therefore the air and petrol *velocities* through the choke and jet remaining constant or approximately so.

This variation in size may take place automatically as in the true constant vacuum type—or mechanically, and it may be a continuous process or occur in steps. The S.U. is an example of automatic continuous variation, while stepped and mechanical variation have been represented by various types which are now obsolete, although they have been partially revived in the duplex or compound type.

11.52 S.U. Constant Vacuum Carburettor

The widely used S.U. carburettor in its simplest current form is shown in Fig. 11-37. A plunger or cylinder G integral with the air piston P is rigidly attached to the piston rod R which slides in the close-fitting central bore of the suction chamber S. In some models a steel liner is provided here to minimize wear.

The weight of the piston assembly, and the load of the light auxiliary spring are supported by the necessary degree of vacuum communicated from the throttle chamber through the vent V.

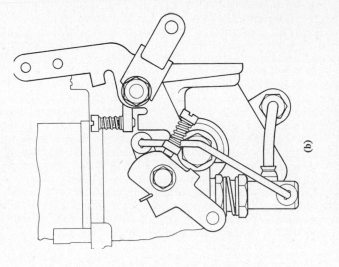

(b)

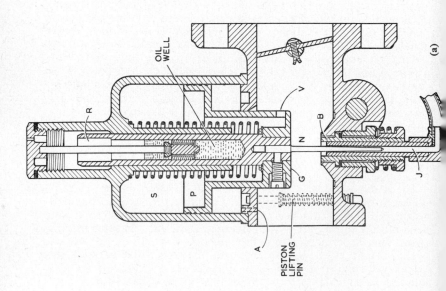

OIL WELL

R

V

B

N

G

J

S

P

A

PISTON LIFTING PIN

(a)

Fig. 11.37: S.U. Carburettor type HS

The load to be supported, subject to the low spring rate, is practically constant, so that for any equilibrium position, the degree of vacuum required on the piston P to support the load is also constant.

Depending on the particular application, this vacuum is about nine or ten inches of water column below the pressure at the entry to the carburettor, and provides the head or pressure difference which forces the air flow demanded by the engine through the variable rectangular choke of constant width but with its height determined by the varying position of the cylinder G. The underside of the piston is vented to atmospheric pressure at A.

The simultaneously varying petrol orifice is the annular area between the bore of the jet sleeve J and the taper needle N which is rigidly attached to the moving cylinder. A great variety of needle profiles is available, to give the correct variation of jet area as determined by the makers for each particular application.

The jet sleeve can be raised or lowered for over-riding adjustment at starting or idling, and there is a radial clearance between the close fitting bush B in which the sleeve slides and the body and gland nut, to allow for the operation of centring the jet. The petrol supply from the float chamber is taken through flexible nylon tubing directly to the inside of the jet tube, instead of through drillings from the outside as in earlier models, which required packing glands to prevent leakage.

A damping piston is provided in the bore of the piston rod to prevent too rapid rise of the cylinder on sudden throttle opening, which would lead to weakening of the mixture when a rich one is required.

The movement of the jet sleeve is effected by the dash-board control with cam plate interconnection with the throttle lever to provide for the small opening required at starting.

The cam and connecting link can be seen in the outside view (b), of Fig. 11-37.

A single bolt and spigotted boss is used for the attachment of the float chamber to the body of the carburettor, thus providing a simple adjustment should a semi-downdraught assembly be required. The head of this bolt is seen behind the connecting link.

11.53   The Stromberg C.D. Carburettor

Before the advent of the Stromberg C.D. carburettor, now produced in the country by the Zenith Carburetter company, the S.U. instrument held a monopoly of the constant vacuum class, with its well known high performance at the " top end " due to unrestricted air flow.

The design of the Stromberg C.D. is based on the same principle, of a vacuum operated cylinder carrying a tapered jet needle and moving in a slide to form a rectangular choke area which varies automatically with the demand for mixture by the engine as determined by the speed and throttle opening. The needle moving in the

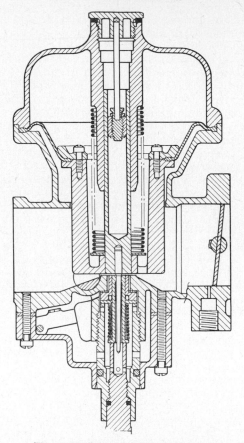

Fig. 11.38: Stromberg C.D. carburettor

stationary jet tube simultaneously varies the annular area constituting the jet orifice. This needle has a very carefully ground profile to
determine the size of the jet orifice, which varies approximately
with that of the choke orifice, but provides for changes in mixture
ratio required at various points throughout the range. The
construction can be seen in Fig. 11-38.

There are certain structural differences between the two carburettors. In the Stromberg design a diaphragm is employed in
place of the closely fitting piston; in both downward movement of the
cylinder is spring-assisted as in the semi-downdraft S.U. Suitable
choice of spring stiffness enables adjustment of the operating depression to be made readily. This depression is normally about nine
inches of water column.

Another feature of the Stromberg design is the concentric float
chamber which is claimed, as in other instances of its use, to have

294

the merit that there is less disturbance of the petrol level at the jet during cornering, acceleration and braking.

An oil damping cylinder or dashpot is provided to prevent too sudden increase of choke area on sudden opening of the throttle. This results in the carburettor behaving momentarily as the fixed choke type, a richer mixture resulting from the temporarily increased depression. This feature is common to both makes.

Provision is made for cold starting in the following manner. A cylindrical bar lies across the bottom of the air port and is given a slight rotation by the choke control. This causes the edge of a flat, formed in the bar and blending with the bottom of the port, to raise the cylinder while masking the choke opening and restricting the air flow. At the same time the needle rises in the jet, which is fixed in position, and so provides a larger jet area to enrich the mixture. The throttle movement is linked with the rotation of the starter bar through a cam plate which is directly operated by the control on the dash.

11.54 Mixture Ratio Curves

Mixture ratio curves may be drawn for these carburettors of the same form as those in Fig. 11-15, the weight of air flow being plotted horizontally, but with no dual characteristic.

This weight of air flow may be taken as directly proportional to the lift of the cylinder, since the rectangular choke area is proportional to this lift, and is subjected to a constant depression or head.

For each position, that is for each value of the flow, there will be a definite ratio of jet area to choke area and therefore a definite mixture ratio dependent on the diameter of the

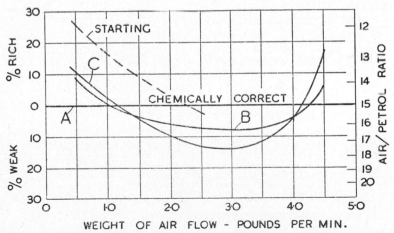

Fig. 11-39: Mixture ratio curves for constant vacuum carburettors

needle. The annular form of the jet area, it should be noted, renders it subject to viscosity effects, and the flow is not exactly proportional to this area since it is not of geometrically constant form. Fig. 11-39 illustrates the manner in which any desired curve can be obtained by modifying the profile of the needle. At A the profile is so chosen as to make the petrol flow just proportional to the air flow and in the chemically correct ratio. If now the needle were changed for one having a slightly larger diameter than the first at all points near the middle of its length, but reduced at its two ends, curve B would be obtained, while C, giving a 12 per cent weak mixture over the middle range and considerable enrichment at the two ends, would result from still further reduction at the ends of the needle and enlargement of its centre portion. It should be realized that, just as in the ordinary fixed choke carburettor, the mixture ratio is a function of flow only, and not of throttle opening, so that the double characteristic of Fig. 11-15 is obtainable only by use of the overriding jet control shown in Fig. 11-37(b). In certain special models thermostatic and throttle controls are provided.

11.55 Automatic Governor

The dangers of excessive speed will have been appreciated by the reader in studying the chapter on balancing, in which the nature and magnitude of the inertia forces were discussed. These dangers are intensified in vehicles with specially low emergency gear ratios, and it is possible for modern high-performance engines to suffer serious damage from over-speeding without the driver appreciating the danger, owing to the relatively low speed of the vehicle.

The provision of a mechanical centrifugal governor operating on a separate throttle has been resorted to from time to time by commercial vehicle makers, but the objections of increased cost, liability to derangement or deliberate tampering on the part of the driver, and interference with mixture distribution by the second throttle have militated against their general adoption.

A fleet operator desiring to protect from over-speeding the vehicles in his charge, which may include a variety of designs with and without governors, will naturally welcome any simple and reliable device which may be readily fitted to any engine.

Such a device should be inexpensive, so designed and installed that it cannot easily be tampered with, and it should not restrict engine performance beyond the essential function of limiting the maximum speed to a safe value. The precise performance of an accurate centrifugal governor is not required.

11.56 Velocity Governor

A device successfully meeting these requirements is the " velocity " governor illustrated in Fig. 11-40. Originally associated with and developed by the Solex Company, it is now more widely available,

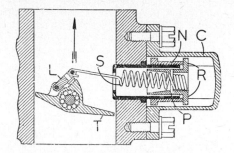

Fig. 11-40: Solex automatic
governor

and has been successfully adapted to certain assemblies of the Zenith carburettor.

The air velocity past a specially formed and mounted butterfly, which takes the place of the normal throttle, is used to obtain automatic closure when the piston speed reaches a desirable maximum value.

Fig. 11-40 illustrates an up-draught form of the assembly.

The butterfly is mounted on an offset spindle which is hardened and ground and furnished with a race of needle rollers to give the greatest possible freedom of movement.

The spindle takes its bearing in the usual way in the throttle barrel and is rotated by the operation of the accelerator pedal. The butterfly is free to rotate relatively to the spindle in the closing direction, but is held against a limiting dog on the spindle in the other direction by the control spring.

The equilibrium position of the butterfly is thus controlled by three factors as follows—

(1) The action of the spring S always tending to open the throttle.

(2) The pressure due to the air flow always tending to close it in virtue of the greater torque in the counter-clockwise direction caused by the greater area of the tail portion T of the butterfly.

(3) The limit to the opening imposed by the accelerator pedal, movement of which against its own return spring permits the governor spring to open the throttle to the required degree. Failure of the governor spring would immediately result in the closure of the throttle by the air flow, even if the accelerator pedal remained depressed.

The mode of operation is as follows—

Suppose the operation of the accelerator pedal has permitted full opening of the throttle at a moderate engine or piston speed. The pressure on the butterfly—which is partly due to static pressure difference between the two sides of the throttle and partly due to impact pressures—will be light, and will not overcome the spring. Induction pipe depression will be small.

297

If the external conditions result in an increase of road speed there will be an increase of air speed, accompanied by an increase of pressure difference and closing torque on the butterfly, and the spring tension may be so adjusted as just to be overcome at the highest desired piston speed. The butterfly will then begin to close, and for the same piston speed the air speed, pressure difference and closing torque will increase sharply. If the spring force or moment did not increase correspondingly the throttle would snap shut and unstable hunting would be initiated.

For each throttle position there is, for a given piston speed, a certain pressure difference, air velocity and closing torque on the throttle (see Fig. 11-1 and Fig. 11-2).

The stiffness of the governor spring and its effective moment may be arranged to balance this closing torque with a suitable degree of accuracy, so that the throttle will close independently of accelerator movement when the air velocity reaches the value which, for the particular throttle position concerned, corresponds to the desired limiting piston speed.

The spring may be adjusted for stiffness by cutting out a suitable number of coils by rotating the regulating sleeve R, when the diametral steel peg P, which forms the spring anchorage, will alter the number of active coils. The initial tension of the spring is adjusted by means of the tension nut N. After adjustment the locking and sealing cover C is secured.

The spring anchorage link L enables the spring leverage to be maintained practically constant, so that the moment increases with the spring force from, say, 1 pound-inch with $\frac{1}{4}$ in. of throttle opening to $2\frac{1}{2}$ pound-inches when the throttle is shut, the exact figures depending on requirements.

CHAPTER 12

Fuel Supply : Air Cleaning

Tank position. Relative height of tank and carburettor. Gravity feed Autovac and pump systems. Electric and mechanical pumps. Air cleaners.

DEVELOPMENTS in body design, considerations of safety, and the general adoption of down-draught carburettors, involving a high position of the float chamber, have rendered obsolete the simple arrangements of gravity feed from the fuel tank that were popular in small cars and many commercial vehicles.

Only in isolated cases of small car design is the tank still located under the scuttle, though a few vehicles with this arrangement are still on the roads. If the position of the carburettor is sufficiently low a direct gravity feed may be employed, and the highest degree of simplicity and reliability is secured.

A two-level change-over cock may be fitted to the tank to ensure an emergency reserve of petrol, and a readily accessible filter should be provided in addition to that in the carburettor inlet. Such an arrangement is usually free from inaccessible pipe stoppages and vapour locks, though in the event of collision the large bulk of petrol near the engine adds considerably to the fire risk.

In modern designs the rear position of the tank for private cars and the side position for commercial vehicles have become standardized, the level being at or below that of the side members of the frame. With a down-draught carburettor situated at the top of the engine, this may involve a vertical lift of 2 ft or more in addition to the overcoming of the resistance of a considerable run of pipe from the tank to the carburettor.

Thus some means of pumping or forcing the petrol from tank to carburettor must be provided. The principle, at one time popular, of sealing the tank and maintaining in it by a hand-operated air pump sufficient pressure to force the petrol to the carburettor, has been abandoned except for racing and special applications, and after a period of general adoption of the " Autovac " system, the modern practice of installing one or more pumps of the diaphragm type has become standardized. These pumps may be electrically or mechanically operated, both types being in wide general use. The former enables the carburettor float chamber to be filled independently of engine rotation, and since they may be fitted close to the tank and below the fuel level, the whole pipeline can be under positive pressure, thus minimizing the risk of vapour lock as compared with the mechanical pump located on the side of the crank case, where it must exert a suction lift and is exposed to higher temperatures; but these advantages are partly negatived by

299

what is generally regarded as the superior reliability of the mechanically operated types.

Rotary pumps of the gear or multi-plunger type which are in general use on aircraft engines are less suited to the large-scale economic manufacture necessary in automobile work.

12.1 Positive Displacement Pumps

The Autovac, which utilized the induction pipe depression to raise the fuel to a high-level auxiliary tank, was extensively and successfully used in the fuel supply of large petrol engines, but is now generally superseded by the positive displacement type of pump, for both petrol and diesel engines.

These pumps are of either the metallic bellows or the fabric diaphragm type, there being a tendency towards the general adoption of the latter.

The metallic bellows has proved an extremely reliable device in thermostatic applications, in which it is frequently referred to as " the sylphon " from the proprietary name used by the firm to which its commercial development is largely due, but with the rapid and continuous flexure arising in pumping applications there is some risk of failure of the metal due to fatigue, which results in the development of cracks and consequent failure.

Fabric diaphragms are not immune from the development of punctures, but very reliable types are now being obtained by the successful use of woven gut, which is being employed in both electrically and mechanically operated pumps.

12.2 S.U. Pump

A successful pump of the electrically operated diaphragm type which is in wide use in this country is the S.U. horizontal pump which has superseded the S.U. Petrolift. This is shown in longitudinal section in Fig. 12-1. The diaphragm D consists of a number of layers of impregnated fine gut fabric. The middle of the diaphragm is clamped to the armature A, which is centred in the stepped mouth of the magnet pot M by a ring of spherical discs or rollers, which swing with a rolling action as the armature moves to right or left. These roller discs also serve to support the free portion of the diaphragm.

The steps at the mouth of the magnet pot are so proportioned that as the lines of force passing across vary in density and direction to find the shortest path, so the component axial pull on the armature remains approximately constant throughout the travel.

The magnetic circuit is completed through the core C over which is threaded the winding spool W. A fibre disc is inserted in the central recess of the armature to prevent metal-to-metal contact of armature and core, which, as a result of residual magnetism, might prevent the return of the armature under the action of the delivery

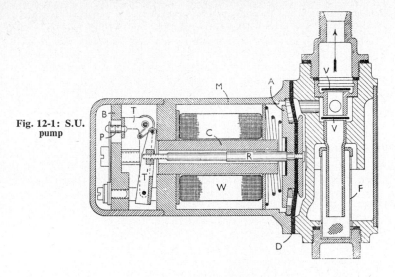

Fig. 12-1: S.U.
pump

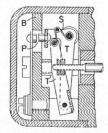

Fig. 12-2

spring. The suction stroke occurs when the armature and diaphragm
are moved to the left by the magnetic pull, and petrol then enters
the pump chamber through the filter F and the lower of the two
plate valves V. On the breaking of the circuit by the flick-over
mechanism the diaphragm is returned by the compression spring,
and petrol is delivered to the float chamber of the carburettor
through the upper plate valve. Should the float chamber be so
full as to close the needle valve, the diaphragm will remain at rest
(with the electric circuit broken) until further delivery is required.

The float mechanism of the carburettor must be matched with
the spring of the pump so that flooding cannot occur.

The stroke of the pump is about $\frac{1}{8}$ in. and the maximum delivery
pressure about 1 lb/sq. in. A wide margin of delivery capacity is
provided.

The flick-over mechanism for the make-and-break of the current
is operated by the rod R, the outer end of which is pivoted to the
primary rocker T′. This controls the outer twin rocker T, which
carries on a cross yoke one of the contact-breaker points P. The

301

bottom ends of both rockers are pivoted on a pin passing through two of the legs of the bakelite moulding B. The second contact point is carried on a spring blade which rests against this moulding when the contacts are open. The auxiliary diagram Fig. 12-2 should make clear how the movement of T′ causes T to flick to the right and open the contacts under the action of the coil spring S mounted on a floating pin. This spring acts as a compression spring between the two rockers.

12.3 Mechanical Diaphragm Pump

A successful and reliable mechanical pump which is very widely used is the A.C., one form of which is illustrated in Fig. 12-3. The particular model shown is adapted for high level application to a V8 engine, and its location at carburettor level may be observed in Fig. 7-15. It is there operated from the camshaft by a vertical push rod engaging with the inverted cup at the end of the level L_1. This lever is maintained in close contact with the push rod by the compression spring shown.

In the majority of applications the pump is mounted on the side of the crank case at camshaft level, and the operating lever L_1 takes the form shown by the broken lines, acting as a flat cam follower. This lower position of the pump is preferable as it reduces the suction lift. In faulty installations trouble may arise through vapour lock caused by too close proximity of the petrol pipe to the hot exhaust pipe. The high temperature combined with reduced pressure due to excessive suction lift leads to vaporization of the petrol and interference with the flow.

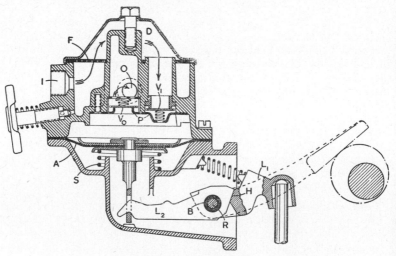

Fig. 12-3: A.C. fuel pump

To return to Fig. 12-3, the inner portion L_2 of the operating lever fits between the jaws of L_1 and is free to rotate on the bush B. The cross spindle R forms the pivot on which the combined lever turns. L_2 will be driven in a counter-clockwise direction by the rise of the push rod if there is contact at the heel H of L_2.

This will draw down the diaphragm A, compressing the spring S and providing the suction stroke of the pump. Petrol enters at I and, passing to the dome D through the circular filter gauze F which surrounds the central turret, enters the pump chamber through the inlet valve V_1. This valve with the outlet valve V_0 is mounted in a brass plate P screwed to the under-side of the turret. The valves are small discs of bakelized fabric of octagonal shape, which allows for passage of the petrol while keeping the valve central. The outlet to the carburettor is indicated at O which leads to a union on the outside of the pump body.

The illustration shows the diaphragm in the lowest position. If the float chamber control of the carburettor permits delivery, the spring S will raise the diaphragm as the push rod falls. If not, the diaphragm and L_2 will remain at rest and lost motion will arise at H.

12.4 Air Cleaners and Silencers

America has taken the lead in adopting as a standard fitting in all installations some form of air filter or cleaner for the carburettor intake air. Undoubtedly general road conditions in America result in a greater intake of dust than in this country, but it is probable

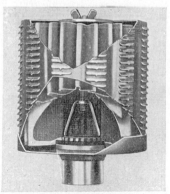

Fig. 12-4: Vokes filter

that a great reduction in cylinder wear is resulting from the general adoption of these accessories in England. When it is realized that in only one hour's normal running a 2-litre engine consumes the air content of a large room, some idea of the quantity of grit and dust that might pass through the engine can be formed.

Air cleaners may be classified as dry filters, centrifugal separators, and the washer type in which the air is actually drawn over oil-coated surfaces. A popular and successful form of the filter type is the Vokes Protectomotor shown in Fig. 12-4. The air is cleaned by being drawn through a thickness of a special felt which, as can be

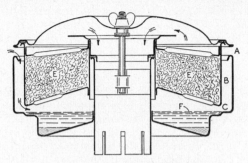

Fig. 12-5 : A.C. oil-bath air cleaner

seen, is supported on a star-shaped frame. In this way a very large area is obtained in a small space. A large area is required for two reasons, first to reduce the restriction to the passage of the air to the minimum, and second to make the " life," before cleaning is necessary, as long as possible. The filter is arranged with the felt vertical, so that the air passes through it horizontally and the dust that is intercepted tends to fall off to the bottom of the device.

12.5   Oil-bath Cleaner: Air Silencing

Fig. 12-5 shows a section through the widely used A.C. oil-bath cleaner. Entering at the circumferential gap A, the air passes down the annular space B to the restricted gap C at the oil level F. Impinging on the surface of the oil at high velocity after the right-angle turn, the bulk of the heavier particles are deposited at once in the oil bath and sink to the bottom as sludge. An oil mist is whipped up from the surface and entrains the finer particles which are arrested by the oil-wetted mesh of metal wool E, after which the cleaned air passes down the vertical intake to the carburettor or induction manifold of the c.i. engine. An outer casing can be provided to protect the unit from rain, if used in the open, and to facilitate the fitting of a single entry.

Under bad conditions of dirty and dusty atmosphere regular servicing of these cleaners is essential, by washing in paraffin or petrol and refilling with oil to the correct level, in accordance with the makers' instructions.

A variety of assemblies is available incorporating centrifugal extraction of the larger particles by means of abrupt changes in direction of the air stream by deflector vanes and catchment louvres and, in cases where the silencing function is to be combined with

304

cleaning, units can be supplied with suitable resonance chambers and absorbent pads adapted to individual designs of power unit.

12.6 Paper-element Air Cleaners

The successful development of paper-element fuel and oil cleaners has been followed by an extension of the method to carburettor air intake systems.

It is now possible to provide air cleaners with the high efficiency of the oil-bath type at a lower cost and with simpler maintenance.

Messrs. Delco-Remy and other makers now market paper-element cleaners having a filtering efficiency of 99·1 to 99·7 per cent when tested in accordance with B.S.I. Specification No. 1701.

The following advantages are claimed: they are lighter and more compact than most oil-bath cleaners, and do not normally require supplementary support brackets.

The resin-impregnated paper-elements, which must be discarded and replaced usually at every 10,000 to 12,000 miles, are easy to change and cost only a few shillings.

The large filtering surface area provides minimum air flow restriction and maximum dirt retention capacity.

The surface area of the paper element is related primarily to the air flow requirements of the engine, and may range from 450 sq. in.

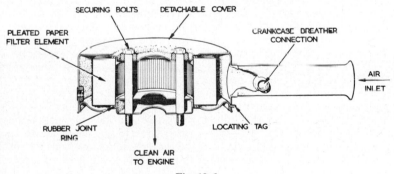

Fig. 12-6

for a flow of 60-80 cu. ft/min to 1,350 sq. in. for a flow rating of 200–250 cu. ft/min, or about 6 sq. in. per cu. ft. of flow per minute.

The authors are indebted to Messrs. A.C.-Delco Ltd. for particulars and for the illustration from which Fig. 12-6 was prepared.

CHAPTER 13

Supercharging and Superchargers

General principles. " Prestige " and commercial objectives. Characteristics of petrol and diesel engines. Relative merits of different systems. Types and characteristics of superchargers. New developments.

INCREASED output for a given size of engine is becoming more and more desirable in view of the trend towards weight reduction. It is also important because of the increasing emphasis on the need for providing, within the limits imposed by legal and practical restrictions on overall dimensions, the greatest possible space for pay-load.

There is more scope for supercharging in commercial vehicles than private cars, mainly because the diesel engine offers greater opportunities of gain and fewer consequential difficulties than does the petrol engine, in which the possibilities are limited by risk of detonation and all the troubles of greater waste heat disposal.

Considerably more heat can be handled in a well designed diesel engine than is represented by unblown conditions, provided sufficient air is supplied and utilized by adequate combustion arrangements.

Low speed torque may be improved and a flat torque-speed curve maintained without increased risk of bearing troubles if maximum speed is not increased. Recent years have witnessed a great increase in interest in the various systems of supercharging, and the development of new forms of supercharger.

The characteristic curves of speed, mean effective pressure, and horse power shown in Fig. 4-6 illustrate the loss of power arising at high speeds from the failure to charge the cylinder completely by the agency of the atmospheric pressure alone. With aeroplane engines at high altitudes this loss becomes serious, and there is full practical justification for the adoption of positive methods of forcing the charge into the cylinders in order to maintain at such altitudes the full mean effective pressure and torque obtainable at ground level. Here the extra complication and weight of the supercharging apparatus is necessary to avoid loss of performance.

In competitive track and road racing under rating rules based on cylinder swept volume, the use of specially tuned " blown " engines became universal, and such engines have made a natural appeal to the private owner of a " sports " model, apart from organized professional and amateur racing, with its " prestige " value.

These engines are, however, in no sense normal production engines, being usually fitted with specially stiffened crankshafts, high compression heads and valves of special and expensive steels. They use specially blended fuels of high octane rating.

306

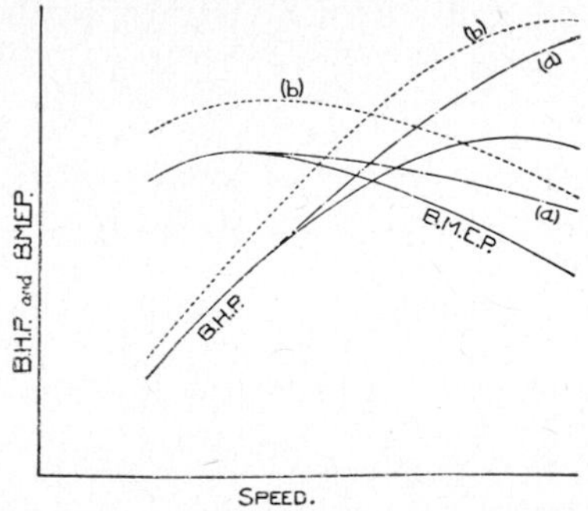

Fig. 13-1: Supercharging

Attempts to increase the performance throughout the whole range of speed, or to increase the normal peaking speed of a standard engine by fitting a supercharger, are liable to develop serious bearing and waste-heat troubles.

Fig. 13-1 illustrates two aspects of supercharging and its effect on b.m.e.p. (or torque) and power.

The full lines represent the performance curves of an unblown engine with a somewhat steeply falling b.m.e.p. characteristic. The broken lines *a* and *b* represent two different degrees of supercharge applied to the same engine.

The curves *a* indicate a degree of progressive supercharge barely sufficient to maintain the volumetric efficiency, b.m.e.p. and torque, at their maximum value, through the speed range.

There would be no increase of maximum piston load or maximum torque, though there would be an appreciable increase in maximum road speed if an overspeed top gear ratio were provided—the engine speed range remaining the same.

Curves *b* show an increase of power torque throughout the whole range, due to a greater degree of supercharging. The *maximum* values of piston loads and crankshaft torque would also be increased unless modifications to compression ratio and possibly to ignition timing were made with a view to reducing peak pressures. This would have an adverse effect on specific fuel consumption, and would tend to increase waste heat troubles, but the former might be offset by fuel saving arising from the use of a smaller engine operating on a higher load factor under road conditions, and careful attention to exhaust valve design and directed cooling of local hot spots would minimize the latter risk.

13.1 Supercharging of Commercial Petrol Engines

Spark ignition petrol engines consume virtually all the air supplied to them, and the power developed depends almost entirely on the breathing capacity of the unit. Supercharging can be applied to increase the maximum power but this tends to lead to detonation

307

and high thermal loading, particularly on the piston, rings and exhaust valves. The tendency to detonation can be reduced by lowering the compression ratio, but this leads to a reduction in thermal efficiency over the cruising range. Increased maximum temperature of the cycle leads directly and indirectly to loss of thermal efficiency and higher fuel consumption, with increased waste heat troubles.

This aspect of supercharging is appropriate to specially tuned engines for racing purposes, where maximum performance from given cylinder dimensions is the all important objective. In commercial vehicle applications maintenance of torque at low speeds with a light engine, and utmost possible fuel economy for a given cost, weight and bulk of the power unit are the paramount considerations.

In the U.S.A. the petrol engine is in more extensive use for commercial purposes than the diesel engine, since fuel running cost is of less importance than engine first cost. Petrol engines of low cost and high power have been very extensively developed, and supercharging developments have been related to petrol engines to a greater extent than in this country, where fuel costs have encouraged the development of the more economical diesel engine.

Figs. 13-2 to 13-4 record results obtained some years ago on General Motors six-cylinder petrol coach engines. Fig. 13-2 refers to an engine of 477 cu. in. and Fig. 13-3 to one of 450 cu. in. They both show improvement in performance of the same nature and similar amount to that indicated in the curves a of Fig. 13-1, but obtained by quite different means. The improvement in performance of the 477 cu. in. engine of Fig. 13-2 is due to the substitution of two carburettors for one and increase of compression ratio from 6·0 to 6·5. The breathing characteristics of the engine and the thermal efficiency were susceptible of improvement by normal means.

The 450 cu. in. engine of Fig. 13-3 was by contrast supercharged by means of a centrifugal blower, driven by belt and gearing at

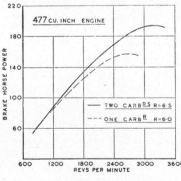

Fig. 13-2

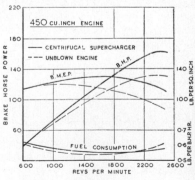

Fig. 13-3

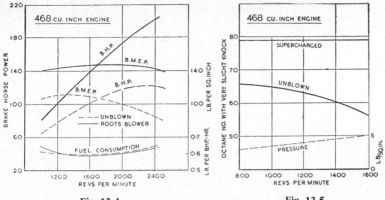

Fig. 13-4   Fig. 13-5

ten times crankshaft speed. No clutch provision was made in the blower drive, and the compression ratio was lowered slightly to avoid any alteration in the octane requirement of the fuel.

Fig. 13-4 shows the results obtained with and without supercharge on a 468 cu. in. engine, the blower in this case being of the Roots type, arranged so that its drive is engaged by a magnetic clutch only after full throttle conditions are reached.

It is recorded that the supercharged power output of the 468 cu. in. engine was equal to the normal output of a larger engine of 616 cu. in. capacity, with a relative petrol saving thereto of about 20 per cent under road conditions.

No alteration of compression ratio was made in this case, but a higher octane fuel was used, and it was found that 79 octane fuel was satisfactory throughout the whole speed range with the Roots type supercharger in contrast to increasing octane requirement at lower speeds when not blown, as shown in Fig. 13-5, in which the broken line indicates the boost pressure in lb/sq. in. above normal atmospheric pressure.

The effect of supercharging on the specific fuel consumption is seen to be small in these instances.

13.2 Diesel Engines

Because the mixing of fuel with air in diesel engines has to take place within a period of 35–40° of crank rotation, it is possible to utilize a maximum of only about 80 per cent of the air supplied. For a given maximum power output, the cylinder dimensions are therefore larger than those of the spark ignition engine. At maximum speed and power output, the thermal loading is generally about as great as the engine can safely withstand, unless it has been specially designed for supercharged conditions. At lower speeds, however, the margin is greater, and thermal loading is not a critical factor, and full benefit may be obtained from a blower with good

309

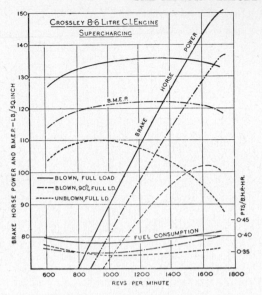

Fig. 13-6: Performance curves of supercharged Crossley c.i. engines.

low-speed characteristics giving an engine torque which rises with decrease of speed and obviates the need for frequent gear changes.

This capacity to "tug" at low speeds is one of the most valuable features of the diesel in modern applications.

The denser air of the supercharge tends to reduce the delay period, and gives better control over the rate of pressure rise. As a result, to double the normal torque calls for an increase in maximum pressure of only about 30 per cent.

Running is smoother and quieter. A smaller engine, with higher maximum speed may be used for a given power.

Fig. 13-6 shows the performance curves obtained with Roots blowers in a series of supercharged Crossley engines supplied to the Netherlands State Railways, a full description of this important contract being given in *Automobile Engineer*, Vol. 38, No. 2.

13.3 Two-Stroke Engines

In two-stroke engines, excess air must be supplied for scavenging of the cylinders. There is normally a wastage through the exhaust ports of abour 40 per cent of the total air delivery. This loss is not entirely without benefit, for the additional cooling obtained reduces the thermal loading on the engine components. Because of the exhaust porting normally used in two-stroke engines, it is possible to apply a reasonable degree of supercharge only if there is back-pressure in the exhaust system.

This seems to indicate that the two-stroke engine provides a suitable field for the application of turbo-blowers. From the point of view of cylinder charge, the resistance to flow through poppet exhaust valves, where used, would have the same effect, but without the subsequent utilization of exhaust heat obtained from a turbine. Back-pressure effects are referred to in Chapter 10.

13.4 Blower Characteristics

The curves of Figs. 13-3 and 13-4 bring out clearly the comparative speed-delivery characteristics of two usual types of blower, the delivery of the centrifugal type being negligible at low speeds and giving the characteristic supercharging results indicated in the *a* curves of Fig. 13-1.

The Roots displacement type shows a positive delivery throughout the range, rising slowly with speed. The volumetric efficiency of this type increases with speed owing to the smaller proportional effect of the rotor tip clearances, but the power absorbed goes up in a greater proportion owing to the turbulence due to the right-angle turns in the flow path. The consequent warming of the charge is valuable from a carburation point of view.

The most positive delivery at low speeds and higher pressures is given by the eccentric rotor, sliding vane type of blower, such as the Zoller, Centric and Cozette designs, but very thorough provision for lubrication is required owing to the high-speed sliding contacts, and the side loading of the blades is liable to produce distortion. This type can be made very silent.

The Centric vane type blower is of interesting construction. Fig. 13-8 shows the original construction as used for moderate powers. A central stub shaft S, on the axis of the main cylindrical casing, supports on ball bearings the balanced vane carriers C, which are interlaced in symmetrical pairs, each vane being riveted to a pair. The vanes pass through slotted trunnions of bakelized fibre carried in the cylindrical recesses formed at the junctions of the segmental sections of the built-up, eccentric drum D.

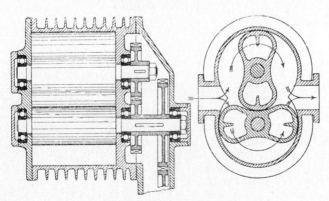

Fig. 13-7: Roots type blower

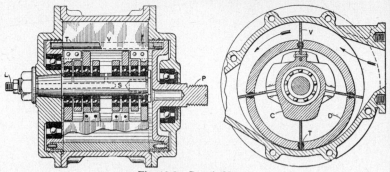

Fig. 13-8: Centric blower

The drum D is rotated by the power shaft P, and carries round the vanes on their free running carriers. It will be noted that the vanes remain always radial to the outer drum, though not at a constant angular pitch. A surface seal is thus obtained at the outer edge of the vanes, as well as where they pass through the revolving drum. Actual contact is avoided by providing a very slight clearance, as the vanes are accurately constrained radially by their carriers.

The construction thus provides positive and accurate driving of the vanes without high speed sliding contacts, and the internal friction is a minimum, provision for lubrication being made at L.

With units designed for higher powers and speeds it was found that there was some tendency of the stub shaft to deflect under the unidirectional forces arising from the angular acceleration and retardation of the vanes, and a new construction was developed.

In this construction, the central shaft is carried through and becomes the primary driving shaft, the drum being driven through a pinion and internally toothed ring at a speed reduction depending on the designed eccentricity. The primary drive shaft may, of course, be driven at any suitable speed through a train of gearing from the engine. The carrier bearings now undergo a relatively small oscillating movement.

Although in wide and successful use for scavenging and blowing two-stroke engines, and for supercharging of four-stroke engines to moderate pressures, the Roots blower has evinced certain limitations in efficiency and in suitability for supercharge pressure ratios higher than 1·5.

The design operates as a displacer rather than a compressor, as indeed do the other types so far mentioned, there being no general compression of the charge until the delivery port is uncovered, with the result that at high ratios, pulsations and high frequency shock waves tend to be formed with loss of volumetric efficiency, and with high fluctuations of torque on the rotor shafts.

More recent developments are the Lysholm and Saurer types of meshing rotors which constitute true compressors. The general

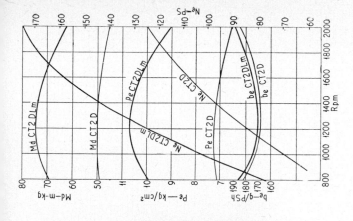

Fig. 13-11: Saurer supercharger
performance curves

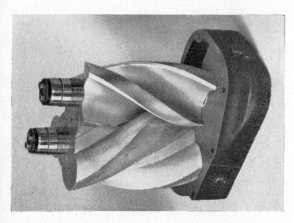

Fig. 13-10: Saurer rotors

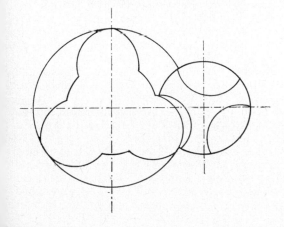

Fig. 13-9: General section of
Saurer rotors

form of the cross-section of these is shown in Fig. 13-9, three helical lobes being used. As in the Roots type, actual contact between the meshing profiles is avoided by the mating of the precision synchronizing gears at the ends of the shafts, and there is no contact with the casing, so that complete freedom from rubbing friction is obtained.

A pair of rotors of the Saurer compressor are shown in Fig. 13-10 from which it will be realized that very great problems of precision production have been overcome. Pressure ratios up to 2·0 and speeds up to 10,000 r.p.m. have been obtained, and at 5,000 r.p.m. and 1·5 pressure ratio the Saurer unit has shown an adiabatic efficiency of 80 per cent compared with 60 per cent of a comparable Roots unit.

Performance curves of the Saurer six-cylinder diesel of bore and stroke 115 mm and 140 mm are given in Fig. 13-11 showing the normally aspirated and supercharged results. The blower in this case has a displacement of 2·07 litres.

13.5 Symposium of Papers on Supercharging

An important symposium of papers on supercharging and new forms of supercharger was presented before the Automobile Division of the Institution of Mechanical Engineers in April, 1957, by a number of acknowledged authorities.

Space does not permit here of more than a very brief summary of the information given and the views expressed by the authors, and in the following discussion, published in *Proc. Aut. Div., Inst. Mech. Engineers.*

Important new forms of positive displacement supercharger described and discussed were the B.I.C.E.R.A.* positive rotary compressor and the Wellworthy-Ricardo axial multi-cylinder, " wobble-plate " or Z-crank compressor.

A cross-section of the former is given in Fig. 13-12.

Two interrupted drums each carry a symmetrical pair of wing-like vanes or lobes acting as pistons in the annular working spaces between their outside surface and the casing. The rotation of the drums by any suitable mechanical means, is synchronized by precision spur gearing.

Intermeshing and counter movement of the vanes causes the variation of volume of the two working spaces which effects the aspiration, compression and delivery of the charge. The charge enters and leaves these working spaces by axial ducts formed by the annular spaces between the rotor bosses and shafts and the inside of two fixed sleeves fitting closely to the rotor bores.

Large ports running the full length of the rotors and extending over appropriate arcs provide communication with the working spaces. The arc of the delivery port is about 90° and of the inlet port about 170°. The latter may be varied by means of a lip L attached

* British Internal Combustion Engine Research Association.

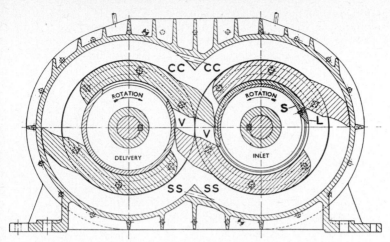

Fig. 13-12: B.I.C.E.R.A. compressor

to an inner sleeve S which may be rotated relatively to the fixed sleeve by an external control wheel operating a toothed sector. It has been found advantageous to apply this variation of port edge to the inlet closing only.

In the position shown in Fig. 13-12 all the vane tips lie on the transverse centre line of the shafts.

It will thus be seen that the two rotating drums provide the pistons in the form of the lobes or wings and also act as the outer members of sleeve valves controlling inlet and outlet of the air. In this way rapid opening of valves of large area is provided, an essential for efficient operation of a rotary compression, in which there is no convenient harmonic slowing of the piston movement during the opening of the valves.

There are essentially two working spaces undergoing the changes in volume which effect suction, compression and delivery.

The double annular spaces SS at the bottom of the housing form the suction volume, which is initiated as the vane tips commence to withdraw from over-lap, and reaches a steady rate of increase as the two wing tips simultaneously reach the lower point of bifurcation of the annular spaces SS, about 40° of rotation from the position shown in Fig. 13-12. This is also the point at which the previously aspired charge is split into two portions for the carry-round to the upper portion CC of the annular spaces, in which compression of the re-combined portions of the carry-round is effected, followed by delivery.

A fresh charge is aspired every half revolution, and delivery is completed one and a half revolutions later. Carry-round and direct compression of the previous charge occur simultaneously with the aspiration of the new one, and together occupy the same

315

period of half a revolution. Delivery occupies the remaining half revolution. The cycle time of one and a half revolutions includes a dead period of about 20° between delivery and suction during which the residue of the charge occupies the constant volume clearance space VV.

The reader may care to trace the events of the cycle by means of tracings or cut-outs of the rotor sections.

The loss due to the unresisted expansion of this residual air cannot be recovered. During carry-round leakage compression takes place between thc high pressure delivery space past the rotor tips into the carry-round charge. This represents a rise of pressure at constant volume to the compression curve, and saves both volume and work at the toe of the indicator diagram. Since the rotor surfaces between the lobes have pure rolling contact, the corresponding clearances and leakages can be kept small.

This compressor is in the early stages of development but appears to possess favourable characteristics.

13.6 Wellworthy-Ricardo Compressor

A longitudinal section of this most interesting example of the " wobble-plate " or Z-crank multi-cylinder construction is shown in Fig. 13-13.

To obtain the most even delivery flow practically possible, fourteen double acting cylinders are disposed in two symmetrically arranged banks of seven tandem pairs. Two rotary distributing valves are mounted on the central driving shaft and carry ports which connect each cylinder in turn to the suction trunks S and the delivery

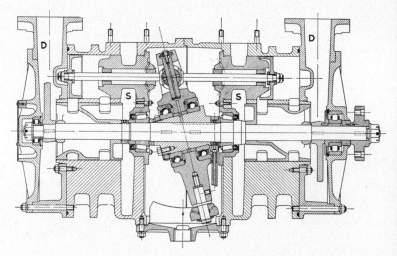

Fig. 13-13: Wellworthy-Ricardo compressor

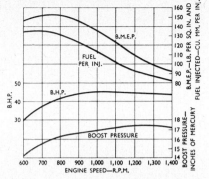

Fig. 13-14: High torque at low speed

trunks D. To eliminate piston and valve rubbing friction, both valves and pistons run with an actual clearance, and piston rings are dispensed with, labyrinth grooves being turned in the pistons to reduce leakage.

Experimental work is being carried out to determine whether diametral clearance between piston and bore—both are of light alloy—can be reduced to 0·00225 in. The pistons are accurately guided by the long piston rods moving in widely spaced bushes mounted in the closing plugs. Clearly a high degree of precision machining is required if the desired small piston clearances are to be maintained. The diametral valve clearances are even more important, as it is stated that the overall performance of the compressor is more dependent on maintaining this clearance at a minimum than on any other single factor.

The constraint from rotation of the wobble-plate or spider introduces kinematic problems of some difficulty, as points in the central plane when moving freely but without rotation, describe a series of "lemniscate" or figure-of-eight curves on a spherical surface. The point of actuation of the piston rod clearly moves in a straight line parallel to the axis of the compressor.

After various solutions had been tried, satisfactory results were obtained with the simple form of separate restrainer seen at the bottom of Fig. 13-13. A stub spindle on the spider carries an aluminium alloy (Lo-ex) slipper block working with minimum clearance in a cast iron guide.

Cylindrical bobbins working in the knuckles of the nitralloy piston rods, provide the small lateral movement that is required in addition to the sliding and rotation on the spider pins.

This has proved an entirely satisfactory means of taking the driving torque reaction while providing the necessary freedom for lemniscate motion, which will have the maximum lateral amplitude opposite the restraint arm which moves in a plane arc.

Fig. 13-14 shows the interesting performance of a 4·4 litre diesel engine for excavator application supercharged by a Ricardo compressor. Since it was only sought to increase the engine torque at

317

low speeds, a torque control governor as described on page 192 was fitted. This is a striking instance of how special performance characteristics may be obtained by appropriate means.

The following advantages of supercharging by an engine-driven compressor are claimed by the makers, in general, and with particular reference to the design under consideration.

(1) An increase of torque of 50 per cent to 60 per cent at low and medium engine speeds with an increase of only about 20 per cent in cylinder peak pressure.

(2) A reduction in specific fuel consumption when the load factor is high enough to justify supercharging.

(3) Complete elimination of diesel knock even when idling, and a marked reduction of noise at all loads.

(4) Elimination of exhaust smoke, more especially when accelerating from low speeds.

(5) Much improved cold starting due to the increased air density even at cranking speeds.

In particular, the Ricardo-Wellworthy design has a high adiabatic and overall efficiency, runs at a relatively low speed, usually between 1·2 to 1·7 times engine speed so that it can be driven by belt without the need for any step-up gearing, and the delivery of air is oil-free and uniform.

In this latter connection it is of interest to note that in addition to the intended development as an engine supercharger, a somewhat unexpected but widespread application is being found in the pneumatic handling of powder materials by air-lift. The complementary problems of feeding dust-free air to the compressor and delivering clean, oil free air to the air-lift are being solved.

Lubrication of the wobble-plate components and piston rod guides is necessarily provided.

13.7 Exhaust-turbo Supercharging

The development of condensing and compounded steam engines, and of low-pressure steam turbines, all represented attempts to utilize more of the energy available at the low pressure end of the expansion curve instead of discharging it to waste as previously, at pressures up to 50 lb/sq. in. or more according to the type of engine and conditions of working; the most heinous offender, largely in the interests of a strong chimney draught, being the ordinary steam locomotive.

A logical development of the combination of high pressure reciprocating engines with steam turbines referred to on page 395 is the combination of exhaust-gas turbines with reciprocating diesel engines, but unfortunately in automobile applications the power delivered from low-speed and high-speed shafts cannot be readily combined for propulsion purposes, nor applied independently as in marine propulsion.

Supercharging, however, offers an attractive application and has

318

Fig. 13-15: Typical supercharger

been extensively used in conjunction with marine diesels, on what
is generally referred to as the Buchi system.*

The exhaust-turbo supercharger runs as a self-contained unit
without any mechanical connection with the main engine, and
utilizes what would normally be waste heat energy, thus increasing
both the power and efficiency of the power unit.

It is in this respect that the turbo-charged engine shows its greatest
advantages. By utilizing the exhaust energy to drive the supercharger, mechanical losses associated with engine-driven blowers are
greatly minimized and the performance may be from 5 to 7 per cent
better than when atmospherically charged owing to the additional
work obtained from the completion of the expansion down to
atmospheric pressure in an apparatus which, moreover, has a
higher mechanical efficiency than that of the reciprocating engine.

Thanks to the pioneer work of Dr. Buchi, these benefits have
long been realized in the fields of marine propulsion and stationary
generating plant, where the conditions of constant speed and steady
load are favourable factors in determining reliable and economical
performance.

Two of the papers in the symposium deal very fully with the
problems involved in the extension of these benefits to automobile
work, in which new and special problems arise.

These may be summarized briefly as due to great fluctuation of
speed and load of the reciprocating engine, and the very much

* Buchi, A. J., "Exhaust Turbo Charging of Internal Combustion Engines—
Its Origin, Evolution, Present State of Development and Future Potentialities,"
Monograph No. 1 *J. Franklin Inst.* (1953).

smaller power requirements, perhaps only one-fiftieth or less of that employed in big marine or generating installations. Moreover, the maintenance of high torque at medium and low powers, which is essential in automobile applications, is difficult of attainment with the characteristics of the rotary compressor. The high rotational inertia of these small, very high-speed units introduces difficulties during periods of rapid acceleration, when delay in response of the turbine unit will cause a temporary shortage of air delivery relative to the increased fuel delivery from the injection pump, with corresponding development of exhaust smoke.

13.8   Valve Overlap and Combustion Conditions

To take advantage of the low-pressure periods of the exhaust pressure wave to aid scavenging it is necessary in some engines to employ valve overlap much in excess of normal amounts.

An overlap of 140° is quite common, and this results in both valves being nearly in the full open position at top dead centre.

This calls for large valve clearance slots in the piston crown, which has two disadvantages. The compression ratio is reduced, and the form of the combustion chamber may become unfavourable.

Cold starting may be adversely affected, and for this reason small high-speed engines seek a compromise between scavenge period and compression ratio.

These disadvantages do not appear to arise in all cases, for Messrs. Thornycroft, who have carried out extensive development work with their 6-cylinder, 11·3 litre engine, both normally aspirated and supercharged by an Eberspacher supercharger, state that no

Fig. 13-16: Thornycroft supercharging

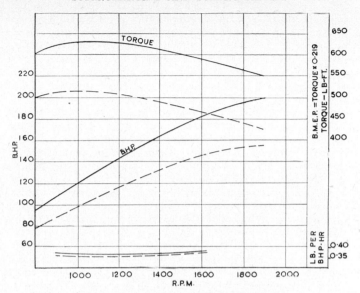

Fig. 13-17: Thornycroft supercharging curves

modification of the valve timing was called for owing to the successful matching of the turbine and engine characteristics.

The rotor is mounted on ball races and its moment of inertia has been reduced to a minimum. With these high-speed rotors (in the above case the maximum is about 35,000 r.p.m.) dynamic balance must be meticulously carried out to very fine limits.

Fig. 13-15 shows a cut-away view of such a supercharger; while Fig. 13-16, which reveals the turbine guide and rotor blading, shows how compactly the unit may be mounted and ducted; and Fig. 13-17 gives the power curves both normally aspirated and supercharged. It will be noticed that there is no appreciable difference in the fuel consumption based on a one-hour rating.

The curves, which are plotted for the net automotive rating as installed in a vehicle, may be compared with those of Fig. 13-14.

For full information on this important development the reader should refer to *Automobile Engineer*, Vol. 47, No. 2.

Intensive development of the automobile turbo-charger is being undertaken by many firms of great repute and experience, and improvement in construction and performance should be rapid. Large scale manufacturing techniques should ensure competitive costs with other methods of improvement of engine output.

13.9 Differential Supercharging

The unfavourable characteristics of the i.c. engine for traction purposes as compared with steam engines and electric motors are referred to on pages 53 and 447 where the ideal torque–speed curve

321

corresponding to constant engine power at all vehicle speeds is dealt with. As is explained in Chapter 20 the i.c. engine requires a gearbox or other variable ratio drive to transform its approximately flat torque–speed curve into something approaching the ideal hyperbolic curve. The tendency in heavy vehicles is therefore towards the use of gear boxes giving a large number of ratios, sometimes as many as 24.

In the D.D.E. (Differential Diesel Engine) system developed by F. Perkins Ltd., of Peterborough an attempt has been made to improve the characteristics of the diesel engine, particularly at low speeds, by using a constant fraction of the engine torque to drive a supercharger, the remainder being passed on to the driving wheels. At low speeds the increase in engine torque due to the use of the supercharger is such that the torque passed on to the transmission and driving wheels is increased enough to enable a transmission employing only a single-stage torque converter and a two-speed and reverse epicyclic gear box to be used. Indeed, for certain applications, only a single forward speed and reverse gear box may be needed. The division of the engine torque between the supercharger and the transmission is effected by an epicyclic gear as is explained on page 509 where the transmission is illustrated and described.

The use of supercharging in this way introduces problems in respect of the mechanical stresses set up in engine components such as pistons, connecting rods and crankshafts but it is claimed that the thermal stresses in the engine are not increased.

In the D.D.E. system both the b.m.e.p. and the maximum cylinder pressure have been rather more than doubled in comparison with an unblown engine and development is taking place in respect of cylinder head gaskets and pistons.

It will be interesting to follow the future development of the connecting rod and main engine bearings, where bearing pressure up to 8,000 lb/sq. in. may arise.

Surprisingly it has been found that many difficulties proved greater with the turbo-charged engine developed in parallel with the D.D.E., and it is claimed that this is largely due to the lower thermal loading with the latter at lower engine speeds. The standard reticular aluminium–tin shell type bearings have stood up well.

Considerable modifications to the distributor type injection pump have been necessary to obtain the injection characteristics required, but it is claimed that these have been highly successful.

A paper fully describing this interesting development, by three authors, was presented to the Automobile Division of the Institution of Mechanical Engineers in April, 1964, and reported in the Minutes of Proceedings of the Institution and in *Automobile Engineer* for May and November of 1964.

Commercial developments depending on relative costs will be awaited with great interest.

CHAPTER 14

Fuels for Automobile Engines

Commercial considerations. Power output, consumption and safety. Chemical and physical properties. Pinking and octane number. Dopes. Fuels for compression-ignition engines. Cetane number. Diesel index. Turbine fuels.

THE fuel problem may be conveniently considered under the following three heads—

   (1) Commercial and political considerations of supply and cost.

   (2) Power output, consumption and safety.

   (3) Fuel quality, in terms of chemical and physical properties.

14.1 Commercial and Political Considerations

The vitally important question of engine fuels, from the point of view of national defence and supply during emergency, cannot be dealt with here, and the following summary covers, therefore, the technical aspects of commercial applications only. In these applications we are almost entirely restricted to—

   (1) Fuels derived from petroleum. These are hydrocarbons principally in the liquid form, although to a limited extent and in special circumstances they may be compressed gases or liquefied petroleum gases (L.P.G.).

   (2) Fuels derived from other sources. These include hydrocarbon fuels from oil shale or from coal, gaseous fuels and alcohols.

In normal times, economic considerations and availability practically confine commercial engine fuels to group (1). A limited amount of benzole is used in some countries, particularly in Germany, and alcohol fuels have been used in the past in racing engines and are still incorporated in petrols in some wine-producing countries.

Britain, apart from the Scottish shale deposits, possesses only limited resources of crude petroleum. These were intensively exploited during the 1939–45 war, and cannot now be regarded as of great importance. During peace-time, petroleum products are so readily imported and may be made to provide such a large Customs revenue that there is no great stimulus to the use of fuels home-produced from coal, in view of the fact that, on the grounds of both capital and production cost, these fuels cannot compete on economic terms with imported fuels unless favoured by preferential taxation.

The use of gaseous fuels, such as producer gas and liquefied petroleum gases, in the spark-ignition engine may be mentioned in passing.

Producer gas, the chief combustibles in which are hydrogen and carbon monoxide with a large proportion of diluent nitrogen, may be made from " capital " fuels such as anthracite and coke, or from " income " sources represented by wood charcoal, wood shavings, seed pods and other vegetable carbonaceous matter. In France and Germany and similar agricultural countries where it may be desirable to restrict imports of petroleum fuels, compact producer gas plants burning charcoal or wood refuse have been used to some extent on motor vehicles. Fuel costs may then be very low, but there is a loss of net load-carrying capacity of the vehicle, range of action is limited and the plants have their own running and maintenance troubles.

During the war period 1939–45 there was a considerable development of gas generators for road vehicles on the Continent, and to some extent in Great Britain, the solid fuel being burnt in a " producer " fitted near the engine or, alternatively, mounted on a special trailer. The popularity of this system can, perhaps, be gauged from the rapid reversion to liquid fuel when war ended.

During the 1914–18 war some pioneer work was done in the use of coal gas carried in light rubberized fabric bags on the roof of the vehicle, the supply being obtained from the ordinary town mains at the usual pressure of a few inches of water head above atmosphere. This represented a somewhat crude improvisation with a very limited range of action, corresponding in most cases to that of less than half a gallon of petrol.

The application of town gas has been experimentally developed in recent years by the use of gas compressed in special steel cylinders to about 3,000 lb/sq. in., by which means a range of action of 80 to 100 miles has been obtained with medium commercial vehicles.

The central compressing stations represent, however, a fixed " anchorage " and high overhead costs, disadvantages which in times of peace prevent the system from competing successfully with the convenience and mobility of the petrol-driven vehicle, while the weight of the cylinders represents a considerable loss of net pay load.

In the event of war, however, necessity or expediency dictates the utmost possible use of home-produced fuels, including the above-mentioned gases, and the liquid fuels represented by power alcohol, benzole and other liquid hydrocarbons produced by various processes from coal.

14.2 Power Output, Consumption and Safety

In the ordinary explosion engine which draws in a combustible mixture there is remarkably little difference, for a given compression ratio, in the power output of a given size of cylinder as between petrol, benzole and alcohol. Ricardo has pointed out that the mixture strength or heat content per cubic foot of chemically correct explosive mixture is almost exactly the same for all the volatile hydrocarbon fuels, though the bulk and weight of fuel in which this heat is carried vary with the calorific value and density of the particular fuel under consideration. In the case of benzole the heat content per pound of fuel is less, and that per gallon greater, than with petrol, while with alcohol both heat contents are considerably less.

Commercial paraffin or kerosene and the heavier diesel and fuel oils are intermediate between petrol and benzole per pound and about the same as benzole per gallon. Alcohol has the advantage of giving under comparable conditions rather better filling of the cylinder or volumetric efficiency owing to the cooling effect of its higher latent heat, that is, the heat required for vaporization, this heat being largely picked up inside the cylinder.

Benzole and alcohol have a fairly high resistance to pinking and in this respect were formerly superior to the straight-run petrols obtained by straight distillation from crude oil. However, with the development of new refining processes, "high-octane" petroleum fuels are now available to the ordinary motorist, and this has been accompanied by the general adoption of high compression engines in recent years.

Thus the thermodynamic conditions for power and economy can now be met as the result of improvement in fuels and carburation.

With regard to safety, there is little to choose between the volatile fuels as marketed, owing to the necessity for including in all cases constituents which will make starting of the engine easy in cold weather. Practical immunity from fire risk can, however, be obtained by the use of "heavy" oils in the compression-ignition engine, in addition to the great advantages of a saving in fuel consumption of 25 to 30 per cent which is inherent in the higher compression ratio of the diesel cycle. The relative *price* of the two classes of fuel is determined under present commercial and fiscal conditions very largely by taxation, and it must be borne in mind that the oil companies' prices for the different classes of fuel are determined by relative demand and the variation in production cost resulting from that relative demand.

The replacement for aircraft purposes of the piston engine by the gas turbine, whatever particular combination of propeller and jet may be used, will call for an increased production of specially prepared kerosene, and a reduced consumption of high-octane fuel. This may well imply that better anti-knock petrols will become available for road work.

There is nothing fixed in the relative price of petrol and diesel oil, though normally the latter is, with the same tax, a few pence per gallon cheaper.

14.3 Sources and Characteristics of Motor Fuels

Motor fuels suitable for the petrol engine are obtained from several sources, the proportion derived from each source depending

325

on accessibility, cost, availability, and a variety of fiscal and defence problems, such as have already been suggested.

14.4 Petroleum

Almost the whole of the spirit with a world-wide distribution is of petroleum origin, and is composed of one or more of the following—

(a) Straight-run petrol (distilled from crude petroleum).

(b) Natural and " casing-head " gasoline (very light spirits, used in blending, to produce easy starting).

(c) Cracked or re-formed spirits, made by thermal and catalytic treatment of certain petroleum fractions.

(d) Spirits made by special methods, such as polymerization, alkylation, isomerization and aromatization. In all these cases various treating methods such as " sweetening " and desulphurization are employed to remove sulphur and to make components more stable for extended storage periods.

All petroleum products are derived from capital resources, which are being used up at a disconcerting rate in U.S.A., for so long a major source of supply.

Fortunately, prolific fields have been discovered in the Middle East and Venezuela, and are now rapidly being exploited.

14.5 Shale Petrol

Although at present a very subsidiary fuel, petrol obtained by distillation of oil shale may assume increasing importance as the world's petroleum reserves diminish. The cost of mining, handling and processing of oil shale is a handicap at existing world prices of fuel.

The world possesses enormous deposits of oil shale, but these deposits are capital resources which will not last for ever, and the presence of minerals, such as uranium, in many of these shales may become an incentive towards their speedier utilization, in view of the latest developments in the use of atomic energy.

Indeed, it is not impossible that the oil might become merely a by-product.

14.6 Benzole

Benzole (commercial benzene) is mainly a by-product of those industries which use large quantities of coal, such as the gas and steel industries.

It is never used as a motor fuel alone, but is normally blended with petrol at a concentration of 10 to 30 per cent. Increasing quantities of benzene are now being manufactured from petroleum, but mainly for use as a chemical solvent or feedstock. Since for this type of use benzole commands a fairly high price, its use in motor spirit is restricted.

326

14.7 Alcohols

Although methanol was formerly widely used as racing fuel, where economy was not so important, the use of either methanol or ethanol as conventional motor spirit is entirely impractical. Alcohol from agricultural products such as, for example, sugar or grain, costs up to four times as much as the motor spirit it would displace, yet it has only two-thirds of the heat energy content of motor spirit.

Alcohol has, however, excellent anti-knock quality, but the cost to the consumer for octane improvement would be nearly twenty times as much as with T.E.L. (tetra-ethyl lead). In the case of methanol, its tendency to absorb water creates problems in motor spirit distribution and storage.   Water causes the alcohol to separate from the motor spirit in an alcohol-water layer.   Cleveland Discol (the name given before the second world war to a fuel blended with some benzole and about 15 per cent of ethanol) still contains a very small percentage of alcohol.

14.8 Manufactured Fuels

A miscellaneous collection of fuels is made by chemical processes; they represent a relatively small proportion of world output, but tend to increase each year.   They include—

(a) Petrol made by hydrogenation of bituminous coal or brown coal.

(b) Petrol made by hydrogenation of certain types of coal tar products such as low-temperature tar and creosote.

(c) Petrol made from " synthesis " gas, specially made for the purpose, such as mixtures of carbon monoxide and hydrogen.
This includes the important Fischer-Tropsch process.

(d) Actual hydrocarbon compounds of " technical " purity possessing very high octane rating such as *iso*octane, *iso*decane and triptane, made by special processes.

(e) Tetra-ethyl lead (T.E.L.), though not strictly a fuel, should be included, as it is used in most petrols nowadays in order to improve anti-knock characteristics.

14.9 Chemical and Physical Properties

Practically all petroleum hydrocarbons found in motor fuels are members of four groups—paraffins, olefines, naphthenes (cyclo-paraffins) and aromatics.   Crude oil does not contain olefines and these result from certain refinery processes.

Paraffins. These occur as chain structure hydrocarbons. The hydrogen and carbon atoms are related to each other by the general formula C_nH_{2n+2}, in which n indicates the number of carbon atoms. The table (Fig. 14-1) lists a number of paraffinic hydrocarbons and illustrates some of the characteristics of all hydrocarbons.

327

Isomers. Hydrocarbons listed in Fig. 14-1 are called " normal hydrocarbons " when they have a straight-chain structure, as in normal octane. However, starting with butane, it is possible to have two or more distinctly different compounds with the same number of hydrogen and carbon atoms (see numbers in parentheses, Fig. 14-1). Many of these compounds have been isolated in the laboratory and, for example, one of the *iso*octanes, C_8H_{18}, is well known as a component of the reference fuel used in the octane number determination. This is a branched-chain compound. The

Name of paraffin[a]	Formula	Usual form at room temperature	Approx. boiling point ($°F$)	Major uses
Methane	CH_4	Gas	−259	As gas for industrial and domestic fuel; source for petroleum chemicals
Ethane	C_2H_6	Gas	−128	
Propane	C_3H_8	Gas	− 44	
(2) Butane	C_4H_{10}	Gas	31	In gas and motor fuels
(3) Pentane	C_5H_{12}	Gas and liquid	97	Motor fuels
(5) Hexane	C_6H_{14}	Liquid	156	Motor fuels[d]
(9) Heptane	C_7H_{16}	Liquid	209	Motor fuels[d]
(18) Octane	C_8H_{18}	Liquid	258	Motor fuels[d]
(35) Nonane	C_9H_{20}	Liquid	303	Motor fuels[d]
(75) Decane	$C_{10}H_{22}$	Liquid	345	Kerosene and motor fuel
Hexadecane	$C_{16}H_{34}$	Solid	550[b]	Dissolved in heavy oils
Pentatriacontane	$C_{35}H_{72}$	Solid	166[c]	Waxes

[a] Numbers in parentheses at left indicate number of isomers which can exist.
[b] Melting point 64 ° F.
[c] Melting point.
[d] Usually converted to other forms for motor fuel (see isomers).

Fig. 14-1: Paraffinic hydrocarbons and their characteristics

more compact arrangement of *iso*octane, compared to that of normal octane, has a marked effect in engines. *Iso*octane is rated 100 octane number; normal octane, in contrast, is less than zero.

Petroleum companies have spent millions of pounds on research to develop processes for converting normal hydrocarbons to isomers of higher anti-knock value or to other types of hydrocarbons.

Olefines. Similar to paraffins, these compounds have two hydrogen atoms fewer and contain one chemical " double bond " between two of the carbon atoms. As in the case of paraffins, isomers of olefines can exist, such as *iso*butylene. Olefines are generally much less stable than paraffins and have a greater tendency to react with oxygen, with other compounds and with each other.

328

	FUEL	Percentage by weight of		Specific gravity	Density lb/cu. ft	Boiling point °C	Air/fuel ratio by weight	Lower calorific value in pound calories	
		Carbon	Hydrogen					per lb	per gallon
Chemical Series	*Paraffins* C_nH_{2n+2}								
	Hexane C_6H_{14}	83·7	16·3	0·67	41·8	69	15·3	10,760	72,150
	Heptane C_7H_{16}	84·0	16·0	0·69	43·1	98	15·2	10,680	73,800
	etc. etc.								
	Pentadecane $C_{15}H_{32}$	84·9	15·1	0·81	50·5	266	15·0	10,460	84,800
	Hexadecane $C_{16}H_{34}$	84·95	15·05	0·82	51·1	282	15·0	10,440	85,800
	Naphthenes C_nH_{2n}								
	Cyclohexane C_6H_{12}	85·7	14·3	0·79	49·3	80	14·7	10,530	83,300
	Cycloheptane C_7H_{14}	85·7	14·3	0·78	48·7	100	14·7	10,500	82,000
	Cyclooctane C_8H_{16}	85·7	14·3	0·74	46·1	120	14·7	10,500	77,800
	Aromatics C_nH_{2n-6}								
	Benzene C_6H_6	92·3	7·7	0·88	54·9	80	13·2	9,710	85,400
	Toluene C_7H_8	91·3	8·7	0·87	54·3	110	13·4	9,810	85,400
	Xylene C_8H_{10}	90·5	9·5	0·86	53·7	140	13·6	9,980	85,900
	Alcohol ether								
	Ethanol (98%)C_2H_5OH	52·2	13·0	0·80	49·9	78	8·9	6,560	52,500
	Ether$(C_2H_5)_2O$	64·9	13·5	0·74	46·2	35	11·1	9,340	69,100
Commercial Fuels	PETROL	A refined distillate of petroleum having a final boiling point not greater than 200° C (approx.).							
	KEROSENE	A refined distillate of petroleum boiling between 150° C and about 300° C.							
	BENZOLE	A refined distillate of coal tar. Chiefly benzene and toluene.							
	GAS OIL	A refined distillate boiling between about 180–360° C.							
	DIESEL FUEL	A gas oil of specially selected characteristics for automotive use.							
	FUEL OILS	Blends of petroleum residue from distillation with gas oil or similar distillates.							
	ALCOHOL BLENDS	Petrol containing approximately 15% alcohol, possibly with a similar proportion of benzole.							

Fig. 14-2: Properties of liquid fuels

Apart from open-chain olefines, there are a number of ring-type olefines and diolefines.

Naphthenes (cycloparaffins). Compounds of the general formula C_nH_{2n}, C_nH_{2n-2} etc., can also occur in a ring structure such as cyclohexane.

This family of hydrocarbons is known as cycloparaffins and behaves quite differently from the paraffins and olefines, in both anti-knock quality and stability. Pennsylvania crude oil is very high in its percentage of paraffins whereas the asphaltic or naphthenic crude oils of the U.S.S.R., California and parts of Texas are lower in their percentage of paraffins but much higher in their percentage of naphthenic materials (cycloparaffins).

Aromatics. This term was originally applied to benzene and its derivatives because of their distinctive odour. Aromatics form part of the ring-type hydrocarbons of the general formula C_nH_{2n-6} and contain three double bonds in the ring. The basic structure of aromatics is typified by benzene itself but aromatics include many hundreds of related compounds such as toluene (methyl benzene), xylene (dimethyl benzene) and cumene (*iso*propyl benzene).

14.10   Pinking

Perhaps the most important property of a fuel from a performance point of view is its freedom or otherwise from liability to " pinking," the popular term used to describe the results of an extremely rapid rate of inflammation and combustion which yet falls short of the practically instantaneous phenomenon of " detonation " which occurs in high-explosive shells. The phenomenon is accompanied by the generation of pressure waves of very great intensity but of too short duration to be recorded by ordinary indicators. The impact of wave fronts on each other and on the walls of the combustion chamber give rise to the characteristic sound known as " pinking." Its occurrence results in rough running, overheating and loss of efficiency. The phenomenon *follows* ignition, and represents a very greatly accelerated rate of inflammation due to compression at the flame front. The effects are sometimes confused with those of early ignition due to excessive spark advance or pre-ignition due to glowing carbon and other incandescent points in the cylinder.

This pre-ignition results in a normal process of combustion and rate of pressure rise, but occurring too early in the cycle with the result that excessive negative torque arises at the crank, with bumpy running.

The chemical and physical processes associated with pinking are still matters of controversy, but the nature of the fuel is so definitely the fundamental factor that the relative merits of fuels can be consistently indicated by an " octane number," such that a fuel of high octane number will be less liable to pinking than one of low octane number, in the same engine. This does not mean, however, that a given fuel will show the same actual tendency towards, or immunity from, pinking in all engines, even of the same compression ratio. The pinking tendency is aggravated or reduced by the form of the combustion chamber and the position of the sparking plug, as well as by the compression ratio. The two former factors determine the extreme distance which the flame front has to travel and whether the last portion of the charge to be ignited—the " end-gas "—will be in a hot or a well-cooled portion of the combustion space.

If the final stages of inflammation occur on a flame front of wide area near the hot exhaust valve, and remote from the sparking plug, detonation is extremely likely to occur, while with the off-set type of head illustrated in Fig. 6-29, the last part of the charge to be ignited is situated in the narrow clearance space between the piston crown and the head; it is attacked on a narrow flame front and is so adequately cooled by the high surface volume ratio that excessive rate of pressure and temperature rise is prevented. The old T-head cylinder, in which the most remote part of the charge was situated near the hot exhaust valve, was a notorious offender from the detonation point of view.

An important paper by G. D. Boerlage and Dr. W. J. van Dyck on the causes of detonation is published in Vol. XXVIII of the *Proc. Inst. Aut. Engineers*. In the paper and in the discussion as to the chemical causes of detonation, the possible influence of peroxides, formed in the early stages of combustion, as " activating " agents, was referred to.

14.11 Octane Number

The earlier " toluene number," introduced by Ricardo and his associates in connection with his original variable compression engine, has been superseded by the general adoption of the " octane

	Super grade	Premium grade	Regular grade
Specific gravity at 60° F	0·755	0·740	0·715
Initial boiling point °C	30	30	30
Final boiling point °C	190	200	200
Aromatics (% by wt)	40	30	15
Tetra-ethyl lead MLS/IG	2·4	2·0	2·0
Research octane No. (F1)	101	97	83

Fig. 14-3: Particulars of commercial fuels

number " as determined by the variable compression engine of the Co-operative Fuel Research (C.F.R.) Committee using the earlier Midgley " bouncing pin " indication of pinking or one of the modern electronic indicators.

The anti-detonation quality of toluene is somewhat higher than that of *iso*octane, but the latter has proved more convenient and more consistent in behaviour, when mixed with normal heptane, as a standard of comparison. Normal heptane and normal octane are two members of the paraffin series that are present in ordinary petrols.

The tendency towards pinking of the paraffin series increases with the size of the molecule, octane being worse than heptane. The compound *iso*octane, which contains the same number of carbon and hydrogen atoms in the molecule as normal octane, but in a different grouping, has on the other hand high *anti*-pinking properties.

The " octane number " of a fuel is determined by comparison in the C.F.R. engine of the fuel with a mixture of normal heptane and *iso*octane, the percentage of the latter in the mixture, which gives the same tendency to pink on the gradual increase of the compression ratio as does the fuel under consideration, being known as the octane number.

Thus, if a fuel shows the same tendency to pinking as a mixture of 15 per cent heptane and 85 per cent *iso*octane, its octane number is 85. With this system the octane number of heptane is 0, and of *iso*octane 100.

Two somewhat different techniques are in use, the " Research Method " and the " Motor Method." The first is less severe than the Motor Method and, as a result, most fuels will have a higher octane number by the Research Method.

The Research octane numbers of fuels ordinarily obtainable from kerb-side pumps range from about 83 for ordinary motor spirit to about 101 for highest grade spirit.

Special fuels can be produced, if circumstances justify the cost, which are much more highly resistant to pinking than *iso*octane, with octane numbers higher than 100, and suitable for use in special engines with very high compression ratios. Such fuels are already available for aircraft use.

14.12 Fuels for High-performance Engines

Development and supply of high octane fuels for the general public came practically to a standstill in this country during the second world war, owing to the demands of the fighting services, and it was not until 1953 that premium fuels became again available.

Progress in the U.S.A. was steadier because less restricted, but with the removal of military and economic barriers, the British petroleum industry has made immense strides and more than equalled American progress.

Fig. 14-4, which is based on an authoritative article by J. G. Withers and H. J. Eatwell in *Automobile Engineer*, Vol. 46, No. 12, shows in a striking manner both the actual and relative progress of the two countries.

The upper half of Fig. 14-4 shows the progress made in average compression ratio in the first ten years after the war, and as has

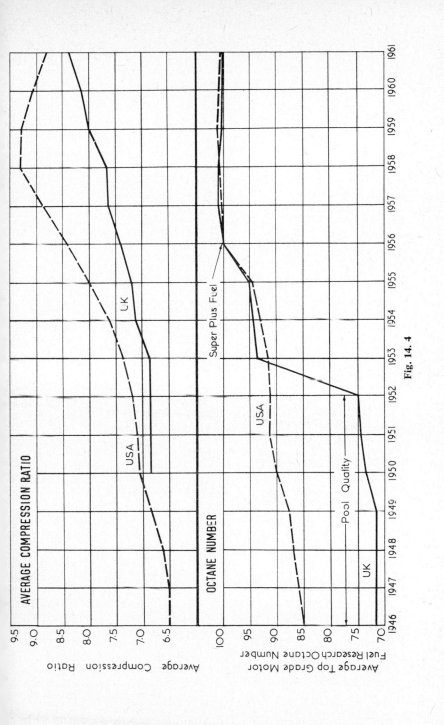

Fig. 14. 4

been mentioned elsewhere in this book, these figures are now greatly exceeded in high-performance engines.

The lower half of Fig. 14-4 illustrates the corresponding progress in the provision of the special high octane fuels that enable these high compression ratios to be used, with the direct thermodynamic gain which results.

14.13 Other Properties

Besides high resistance to pinking, there are many other properties which a good motor spirit must have. Thus its volatility, normally measured by distillation characteristics and vapour pressure must be carefully balanced. The volatility must be high enough to ensure ready starting and rapid " warm up " but is limited by the necessity to give freedom from vapour lock, carburettor percolation and carburettor icing.

In practice this means that the volatility of a petrol is adjusted to the particular climatic conditions in which it will be used, and in this country, for instance, it varies according to the season of the year.

The storage stability of a petrol is another important property. It must be refined and specially treated so that it will be capable of being stored without appreciable oxidation with the resulting formation of gum.

14.14 Fuels for Compression-ignition Engines

Among fuel technologists the name " diesel " is still in wider use than the phrase " compression-ignition " when describing fuels, which are referred to as light, medium and heavy diesel fuels and by such industrial or trade names as Gas Oil, Solar Oil, Diesolene, Derv, etc.

For the high speed automotive diesel engine, a fully distillate fuel is required. This is a gas oil, with certain specially selected characteristics, and has a boiling range of 180–360° C approximately, and S.G. of between about 0·83 and 0·86. It should conform to the requirements for a Class A fuel in B.S. 2869 : 1957.

Larger stationary and marine diesels may be less fuel sensitive and can use blends of gas oil and fuel oil. These are covered by Class B of B.S. 2869 : 1957, but even heavier residual fuels have been used.

14.15 Ignition Quality and Cetane Number

The most important quality of a fuel for a high-speed c.i. engine is its ignition quality, or its readiness for self-ignition with the minimum desirable delay period after the commencement of injection.

Just as *iso*octane is an effective anti-knock fuel, so a hydrocarbon of good self-ignition quality for comparative testing purposes is found in hexadecane or cetane as it is more usually called, which has

334

replaced cetene for this purpose. The complementary fuel of very low ignition quality with which cetane is blended is alpha-methyl-naphthalene ($C_{10}H_7CH_3$). The percentage of cetane in a reference mixture of these two compounds, which gives the same ignition characteristics as the fuel under consideration, is called the " cetane value " of that fuel. This figure ranges from 30 to 70. In general a high octane number implies a low cetane number.

14.16 Diesel Index

Alternative methods, which do not require the involved procedure of an engine test, may also be used to express ignition quality, and the most common of these is known as the diesel index. The ignition quality of a fuel depends on the relative proportions of the different types of hydrocarbons which are present in the fuel; thus it can be measured by means of a simple laboratory test known as Aniline Point.

The Aniline Point is defined as the lowest temperature at which the fuel is completely miscible with an equal volume of aniline and when this has been determined, as well as the specific gravity (which is then converted to °API), the following equation is used:—

$$\text{Diesel index} = \frac{GA}{100}$$

where G is API gravity

A is Aniline Point in °F

The diesel index will be found to give a reasonable assessment of the ignition quality of a fuel, but in value it will be numerically different from the cetane number and the exact relationship between these two methods will depend on the hydrocarbon make-up of the fuel. Because of its simplicity, the diesel index is widely used to express ignition quality; however, it cannot always be relied on to give a true estimate. Moreover, it will not be raised, as will be the cetane number, if ignition improvers are added to the fuel.

A more accurate method of assessing ignition quality is the cal-culated cetane index, using an empirical formula which has as its variables the mid-boiling point and the specific gravity of the fuel.

14.17 Fuel Dopes

Corresponding to the anti-knock petrol dopes, there are certain ignition accelerators which may be added to diesel fuels in propor-tions ranging from 1 per cent to 5 per cent, which is higher than the corresponding percentage of ethyl fluid in petrols.

These reduce the delay period, and so tend to suppress " diesel knock " in the second phase of combustion, in virtue of the smaller accumulation of fuel in the combustion chamber at the commencement of burning, the rate of pressure rise being consequently reduced.

Typical substances are ethyl nitrate and amyl nitrite. The effects of such an addition on the delay period and rate of pressure rise in the second phase of combustion are shown in Fig. 14-5, which was taken from an A.E.C. engine.

The speed in each case was 1,000 r.p.m. and the b.m.e.p. 83·5 lb/sq. in. It will be seen that the delay period was reduced by the

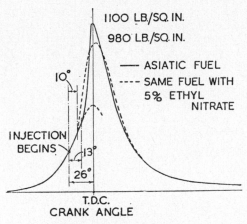

Fig. 14-5: Ignition accelerator

addition of 5 per cent of ethyl nitrate from 13° to 10°, while the rate of pressure rise during the second phase of combustion was reduced from over 60 lb/sq. in. per degree to less than 40. There was a corresponding reduction in maximum pressure of over 100 lb/sq. in. with much improved running.

It must not be assumed that these results would be obtained in all circumstances. Modern high speed diesel fuels are usually of sufficiently high quality to satisfy the needs of even the most critical engine, and hence these additives do not enjoy a wide commercial use.

14.18 Diesel Fuels from Coal

Early pioneer work on fuels made by the distillation of coal or its by-products were disappointing, as the ignition quality of the fuels obtained was much inferior to that of the paraffin hydrocarbons, and supplies were dependent on by-products of major industries, with corresponding uncertainty as regards availability.

Considerable progress has since been made, especially in Germany, where Fischer and Tropsch as well as later workers have developed a complicated but successful process, whereby on final distillation a high-speed diesel fuel of excellent characteristics is obtained.

14.19 Gas Turbine Fuels

Even the most optimistic forecasts of progress in thermal efficiency of the gas turbine accept the fact that it is likely to remain considerably below that of the piston engine and, unless cheap fuels can be successfully used, fuel running costs will greatly exceed those of existing prime movers. Capital and overhead operating costs then become the determining commercial consideration.

Apart from improvement due to higher turbine operating temperature as new materials for blades are developed, higher thermal efficiency involves bulky and troublesome heat interchangers.

Further, the use of low-priced liquid and pulverized solid fuel will almost certainly require more complicated and far more bulky types of injection equipment and combustion chamber than those at present in use with aircraft plants.

Fuel	Specific gravity	Net calorific value (C.H.U.)
Premium grade petrol	0·740	10,470
Avtag	0·756	10,400
Avtur	0·790	10,350
Gas/Diesel oil	0·835	10,200
Light fuel oil	0·935	9,850
Heavy fuel oil	0·970	9,750

For automobile work, bulk and weight are ruled out, and the automobile turbine will, for the sake of simplicity and lightness, be compelled to shoulder the handicap of high consumption of a fuel of similar nature to present diesel or light furnace oils, showing little or no price advantage apart from differential taxation.

The fuels used for aircraft jet engines are of two types:—

(1) Avtur. A grade of kerosene with special characteristics.
(2) Avtag. A " wide cut " gasoline, i.e. a fraction boiling over the gasoline and kerosene ranges. It contains no T.E.L.

Fuels having a high calorific value per unit volume are most desirable for automotive gas turbine use and the table above gives net calorific values (in C.H.U.) for various fuels. See also Fig. 14-2.

14.20 Filtration of Diesel Fuel

The question of fuel cleanliness regarding compression ignition engines is quite different from that problem when dealing with petrol engines. With carburettors, jets must be kept clear and any sliding parts free from small particles of grit, sand or dirt that may get into the petrol, but this can be satisfactorily achieved by the use of very fine gauze filters. With fuel injection equipment, however, the pump elements, delivery valves, and nozzles are finished to exceptionally fine precision fits, of almost optical standards of perfection, on account of the very high pressures which have to be handled.

The working tolerances are very small (the plunger has only 1 micron—one thousandth of a millimetre—clearance in its barrel, the two being hand-lapped together). Fuel cleanliness is therefore of the utmost importance; gauze filters are quite inadequate for the purpose, and only filters specially designed for the purpose are permissible.

Even the finest of dust carried in suspension in the air is liable to cause trouble by wear and scuffing of the fine surfaces. Even with care in fuel delivery, storage and filling up, some dust enters the system through breathers and filter caps, etc., and efficient filters are the only safeguard. These must be serviced regularly according to the makers' instructions.

CHAPTER 15

Lubrication

Friction, heat and wear.   Viscosity.   Lubrication systems.   Circulation and level indicators.   Oil pumps and filters.

THE purposes of a lubricant are primarily two in number—

(1) To reduce the resistance to relative motion between two surfaces in contact under pressure.
(2) To reduce wear of the surfaces and eliminate as far as possible any danger of seizure.

The resistance to relative motion between two bodies in contact depends on a variety of factors and their various possible combinations. Three broad types of contact are recognized, but the conditions in an actual bearing rarely fall exactly into one of these divisions, being usually intermediate between two.

15.1 Dry Friction

Here complete absence of lubricant is assumed. The frictional resistance is proportional to the load on the bearing and independent of the area of contact, and usually decreases somewhat with increase of speed. The coefficient of friction is high and fairly constant, and depends on the materials and fineness of finish, since there is actual contact between the surfaces. Continuous running under load would not be possible under such conditions owing to the excessive amount of heat developed.

15.2 Boundary Friction

Here some lubricant is present but not sufficient to completely separate the surfaces. The coefficient of friction is reduced, but the resistance to motion is still dependent on the load and the nature of the surfaces. Oils differ considerably in their lubricating quality under these " boundary " conditions, the animal and vegetable oils, such as sperm, rape and castor, being somewhat superior to mineral oils in the maintenance of a film at high pressures and low speeds. They suffer, however, from the tendency to gum at high temperatures, and experience has shown that the greater freedom from carbonization and the freer running with high-class mineral oils, particularly in combination with suitable additives, are not offset by any greater risk of failure of the film if the lubrication system is correctly designed.

It is only in recent years that physicists and chemists have made appreciable progress in understanding the phenomena of lubrication, and the boundary conditions are now known to involve far more

339

complicated phenomena than was formerly supposed. The existence of an extremely thin " adsorbed " layer is now recognized, where the lubricant enters into some form of chemical or physical bond with the bearing metal of such a nature that, after being once formed, it can be removed only by mechanical polishing, by abrasive means, or, under certain conditions, by " desorption ".

Substances which have valuable properties under these boundary conditions are zinc oxide and colloidal graphite—that is specially purified graphite in an extremely fine state of subdivision, the suspension of which in a suitable carrier oil is maintained not only by the fineness of the subdivision but also by the application of a suitable electric charge to the particles. The exact mechanism involved in the action of these substances has been the object of much recent research. Certain compounds involving sulphur and chlorine have also found application in this field.

15.3 Viscous Friction or Fluid Friction

Under certain conditions of oil-bath, flooded or force-feed lubrication it is possible for the surfaces of the bearing to be completely separated by the lubricant. In these circumstances, the resistance to relative movement is a fluid one arising from the viscosity, or resistance to shearing of the oil film itself. This viscosity increases considerably with pressure, especially at very high pressures, and decreases, in some cases rapidly, with increase of temperature.

The resistance to motion is proportional to the area in contact, the speed and the viscosity coefficient and inversely proportional to the thickness of the oil film. It is far less than in the preceding cases.

It should be realized that the viscosity of the oil is itself a source of resistance, which in certain circumstances may make the total

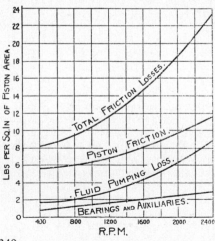

Fig. 15-1: Sources of engine friction

resistance with lubrication greater than without any lubrication. This may readily be tested with a valve stem and guide. If no side thrust is exerted, it will be found that the addition of lubricating oil will produce a resistance which was not previously present, the resistance arising from the process of shearing the oil film. As the clearance is increased and the viscosity of the oil reduced, the resistance to motion decreases.

This is one reason why the pistons of racing engines are made an easy fit, and the design of the slipper piston is due to the realization by racing men of the necessity for reducing to a minimum the area of the film to be sheared between the piston and cylinder wall, the areas in contact being reduced to the least amount that will safely take the side thrust and at the same time allow for conduction of heat from the piston body to the cylinder walls. The importance of this reduction will be realized from a study of Fig. 15-1, which shows curves, due to Ricardo, of mean effective pressure required to overcome the various sources of friction in a certain engine at different speeds. It will be seen that piston friction forms about 60 per cent of the whole.

From the foregoing it will be seen that, in order that the resistance to motion should be a minimum, the oil film should have considerable thickness and small extent, while the viscosity should be low. Unfortunately, these conditions are mutually incompatible, as it is impossible to confine a thin oil in such a manner as to maintain a thick film. It is necessary to use in internal combustion engines an oil of such a nature that under the high temperature of operation the viscosity will still be sufficiently high to prevent the film from being completely squeezed out and so avoid conditions approaching those of dry friction which would lead to immediate disaster.

In most engine bearings the conditions are somewhere between the boundary and flooded conditions, so that both the pressure on the bearing and the viscosity of the oil are factors in determining the resistance.

15.4 Choice of Viscosity

The provision and maintenance of a suitable viscosity in the oil to meet all requirements and conditions of use is a difficult matter. To give easy starting under cold conditions, to ensure rapid and early distribution of lubricant to all working parts as the engine speeds up, and to minimize " oil drag " under all conditions, an oil of low viscosity is required; while to ensure the continued maintenance of a lubricating film under difficult conditions of high temperature and extreme bearing loads, and to reduce oil consumption arising from excessive pumping past the piston rings at high speed and small throttle opening, the viscosity should not fall below some suitable minimum value depending on the conditions of service.

The physical property of viscosity does not in itself imply lubricating value, and recent research in extreme pressure lubrication

341

has shown that the best local protection against the " scuffing " effects of excessive bearing pressures, such as arise in some forms of tooth gearing, is given by the addition of certain organic compounds of quite low viscosity, or other additives.

15.5 Change of Viscosity with Temperature: Viscosity Index

To meet the requirements of low resistance or breakaway torque at starting, combined with adequate viscosity at normal operating temperature, the oil should have a high " viscosity index," that is, while having a suitably low viscosity when cold, it should be of such a nature that the rise of temperature as the engine reaches normal running conditions will not lower the viscosity unduly. The viscosity-temperature curve should be as flat as possible.

The index is a number based upon an empirical scale having 100 for the best Pennsylvanian blends, and 0 for certain asphaltic oils which show a very steep viscosity-temperature curve.

Modern refining methods, and particularly the new solvent extraction processes whereby the less desirable asphaltic constituents of the oil are abstracted by suitable solvents, have resulted in the marketing of oils of high viscosity index. In recent years further improvements have been effected by the use of additives.

These oils have suitably low viscosity to provide the required conditions for starting, while the viscosity is well maintained at higher temperatures.

15.6 Heat Generated and Wear

The work done against friction appears as heat, which will cause the temperature of the bearing to rise to a point where the loss by conduction, convection and radiation is just equal to the rate of generation. If the temperature so reached is high, the viscosity of the oil may be reduced so much that the oil film will be broken when actual metallic contact will occur, and seizing or running out of the white metal may take place. The great virtue of the modern system of forced lubrication, presently to be described, is its action as a cooling system to the crankshaft and big-end bearings. The excess of oil flowing over the surfaces effectively cools them and prevents undue reduction of the viscosity.

It is now generally recognized that the best combination of materials for resisting wear is one in which the materials differ widely in hardness. Mild steel on mild steel is notoriously bad, mild steel on phosphor bronze is not good, whereas case-hardened steel on phosphor bronze and mild steel on white metal are excellent. The accepted explanation is that the small particles of foreign matter which cause wear must so readily embed themselves in the softer of the two metals as to minimize their capacity for cutting the harder.

With metals of equal hardness the particles are not pressed into one metal sufficiently deeply to prevent their abrading the other. It has been observed that, when wear does take place in a

342

bearing formed of two metals of different hardness, it is usually the harder metal which shows the greater amount of wear.

In any case, the more completely the oil film is maintained, the less will be the wear, though it is open to question whether a supply of oil largely in excess of what is used in maintaining this film is advantageous from the point of view of wear. Though its cooling effect is good, it is possible that a larger amount of abrasive material is thereby carried into the bearing.

15.7 Corrosive Wear

Extensive researches into the phenomena of cylinder bore wear, which is notoriously greater under conditions of frequent starting under cold or partially warmed conditions, have shown that corrosion, as distinct from abrasion, plays a very large part. This corrosion is caused by the condensation on the walls of acid products of combustion at coolant temperatures below about 70° C, and hence arises the necessity for rapid warming up and free distribution of the lubricating oil. The use of lower viscosity oils and the fast idling starting devices of modern carburettors have led to considerable improvement in this direction, while the use of special alloy cylinder irons, or hardened liners, has further reduced both abrasive and corrosive wear.

15.8 Systems of Lubrication

Modern " full forced " systems of lubrication have developed by stages from the crude " all loss " system as represented by the early motor-cycle engine in which a pumpful of oil was delivered to the crank case at uncertain intervals by the action of the rider, the oil being splashed around by the internal flywheels and connecting rod, and reaching the cylinder walls and various bearings in a somewhat fortuitous manner.

Unless the rider was careful and attentive, the engine suffered from alternate periods of over-oiling and starvation, occasionally with disastrous results.

In multi-cylinder engines a phase of pump circulation to distribution and dipper troughs followed, dippers on the big-end bearing caps, sometimes but not always of hollow scoop form, picking up oil from the troughs and leading it to the crank-pin bearings. There was no drilling of internal oilways through the crankshaft.

Lubrication became a little more regular, and the objectional splashing of a large body of oil in the crank case was avoided, but the direction of oil to the vital bearings was insufficiently positive and certain.

15.9 Full Forced System

In the full forced system, which has now replaced the earlier systems referred to above, the oil is drawn from a sump as in the trough system, and is delivered at a pressure of from 5 to 30 lb/sq. in.

343

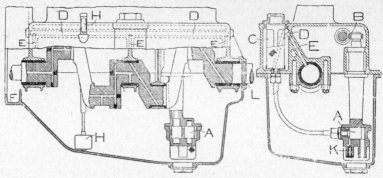

Fig. 15-2: Full forced lubrication system

to a system of distributing pipes which carry it to the main crank-shaft bearings and other points. After entering the main bearings a certain amount escapes along the bearings and either drains directly back to the lower half of the crank case and so to the sump or is splashed from the crank webs to the cylinder walls, etc. The remainder of the oil delivered to the main bearings finds its way through holes drilled diagonally from the bearing journals through the crank webs to the adjacent crank pins, thus carrying a full flow of oil to the big-end bearing. Each big-end bearing is thus lubricated under pressure from an adjacent main bearing.

In the full forced system, strictly speaking, oil is led from the big-end bearings through pipes secured to the connecting rods, or through holes drilled in those rods, to the gudgeon pins, but in the majority of systems, which are called full forced, the gudgeon pins are lubricated by the oil which escapes along the big-end bearing and which is flung off by centrifugal force. Very occasionally in special cases pipes lead oil direct to the cylinder walls and pistons, but usually those parts are lubricated by the " fling-off " from the big ends. Other leads also go to the camshaft bearings, timing gears, etc., but again the " fling off " is frequently relied upon.

Overhead camshafts are almost always lubricated by a separate pipe conveying a portion of the pump discharge to the camshaft bearings, and the camshaft itself is sometimes drilled along its centre so that oil can be led to the cam faces through suitable radial holes. In most cases oil is also led directly to the hollow valve rocker shafts and thence through holes drilled in those shafts to the rocker bearings.

Another method of camshaft lubrication, where the camshaft is in the crank case, is to place it in an oil bath fed by a separate pipe.

Fig. 15-2 illustrates a full forced system. The gear type pump A has its suction branch protected by a gauze filter and is fitted with an integral relief valve K which returns a portion of the oil from the delivery side direct to the suction in the event of excessive pressure arising in the system when starting in cold weather with an oil of high viscosity. The pump is driven by a vertical shaft through the skew gears B from the camshaft, and can be withdrawn as a unit after removing the sump. C is a large " high pressure " filter of which the gauze is readily accessible for cleaning without sacrificing the bulk of the oil, as is sometimes unavoidable in cases where a filter is provided only on the suction side. D is a gallery or delivery pipe with branches E to the three main bearings, whence it reaches the crank pins by the drilled passages shown, two alternative methods of drilling being indicated. The connection to the pressure indicator on the dashboard is usually taken from the gallery.

H is a float type level indicator with a pointer outside the top half of the crank case, while F is an oil bath for the timing gears (often fed by the overflow from a relief valve), and L a screw type oil thrower or baffle.

15.10 Wet and Dry Sump Systems

With the forced system of lubrication either the " wet " sump or the " dry " sump system may be employed. The former is that already described, where there is only one pump which draws its oil from the bulk supply contained in the sump formed in the lower half of the crank case.

The dry sump system, which is universal in aircraft engines and in other engines which frequently operate at a considerable inclination to the horizontal, employs two pumps. Very little oil is retained in the crank-case sump, from which the oil is scavenged by a pump and delivered to a main oil tank situated in any convenient position. This tank is often arranged as a cooling radiator. From the main tank oil is drawn by the second or " pressure " pump,

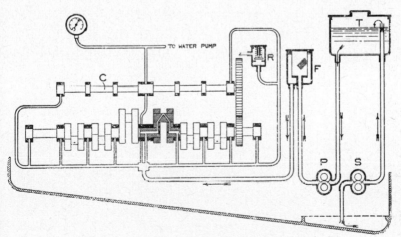

Fig. 15-3: Dry sump system

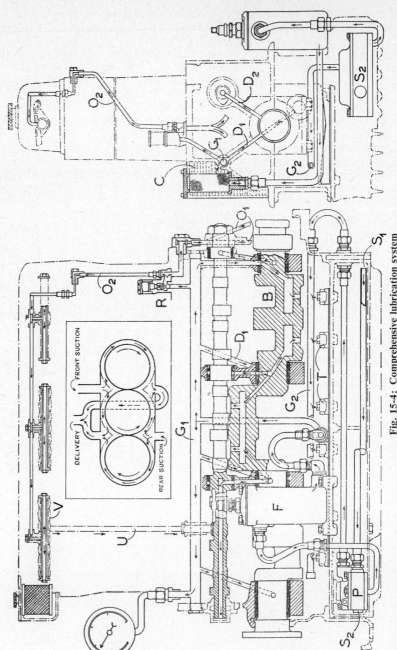

Fig. 15·4: Comprehensive lubrication system

and is circulated under pressure through the piping system, to the various bearings and gears.

Fig. 15-3 illustrates diagrammatically such a system, applied to an engine fitted with a built-up crankshaft. The two pumps S and P would be combined in a single unit. Pressure feed is led to the three main bearings of the camshaft C, the others being lubricated by splash. F is the high pressure filter, R the relief valve and T the oil tank and cooler.

Occasionally two scavenge pumps are fitted, one being placed at either end of the crank case, each in a small sump. When only a single scavenge pump is fitted it is usually placed at the centre, in a deep sump, if the engine is likely to operate at large inclinations. The scavenge pump is of larger capacity than the pressure pump as its work is liable to be intermittent owing to the variation of oil level in the sump.

15.11 Comprehensive Lubrication System

A well-thought-out lubricating system which incorporates most of the features already referred to is illustrated in Fig. 15-4 in semi-diagrammatic form. The provision of dipper troughs in addition to pressure oil ways and a drilled crankshaft is unusual, but the additional oil-mist formed by the pick-up of the connecting-rod peckers should materially assist the general distribution of the oil and by splashing it to the crank-case walls, ensure its better cooling.

The pump P is of unusual construction, comprising twin pumps each containing three meshing gears. The centre gears are driven by the vertical splined shaft, and the four outer gears thus all revolve in the same direction. Two suction ports are provided, one of these taking oil from the front of the sump through the pipe S_1 while the other S_2 draws its supply from the rear end. The front intake supplies oil to the suction space between the centre and offside gears of both the upper and lower pump, while the rear intake S_2 feeds the suction spaces of the centre and near side gears. The dual deliveries of the upper pump feed in parallel the gallery G_2 which supplies the troughs T. The corresponding dual deliveries from the lower and larger pump lead to the external filter F.

When the engine is level both suction ports are in action, but when considerably tilted, as in cross-country vehicle applications, either inlet may be uncovered and draw air, but under these conditions both pumps can still obtain their supply of oil from the other inlet and no interference with the flow will occur. An insert diagram of the pump is given.

The main delivery from the pump passes to the externally mounted Autoklean filter F, whence it passes by an internal transverse pipe to the capacity chamber C, which contains a readily accessible cylindrical filter screen. From this chamber, where a steady pressure is maintained, the oil enters the gallery G_1 and is led by the ducts D_1 to the four main bearings, and thence by the crankshaft drillings to the six crank pins B. A further set of ducts D_2 leads to

347

three of the camshaft bearings, while oil reaches the fourth by the centre drilling of the rear portion of the camshaft.

The pressure gauge and relief valve R are in direct communication with the main gallery G_1 and the oil which is by-passed at the relief valve is taken to the timing chain wheels, and the valve rockers V, through delivery pipes O_1 and O_2 respectively. The return oil from the valve rockers, together with the oil required for replenishment which is inserted through the filler and breather in the valve gear cover, passes to the crank case through the tappet rod tunnels as indicated at U. The sump is protected by a flat filter screen of large area and, if required, an oil cooler may be inserted in place of the short external pipe delivering oil to the gallery G_2.

15.12 Pumps

The pumps used for oil circulation have taken a variety of forms, but that now almost universally used, on account of its simplicity and reliability, is the double gearwheel type illustrated in Fig. 15-5. It consists of two meshing gearwheels, one of which A is driven by the engine by means of the vertical shaft C which carries a skew gear meshing with another gear integral with the camshaft, while the second wheel B is driven by the first. The two are mounted in a casing with as small clearances as possible. The casing is provided with suction and delivery ports S and D. The wheels do not " mangle " the oil through, as might be thought at first sight, but it is carried round the outer peripheries as indicated by the arrows, in the spaces formed by the tooth spaces and the walls of the casing. The meshing of the teeth displaces the oil from the

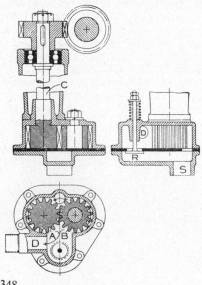

Fig. 15-5: Gear type pump

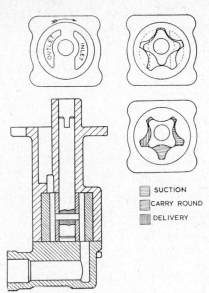

Fig. 15-6: Hobourn-Eaton pump

SUCTION
CARRY ROUND
DELIVERY

tooth spaces and it is thus forced through the delivery port.   R is a relief valve.

This type of pump cannot be regarded as a strictly positive one owing to the inevitable leakage at high pressures, but if it is used " drowned," that is, immersed in the oil at the bottom of the sump, and if it is the proper size for its work, no trouble is likely to occur in operation.   Should it be necessary for any reason to mount it in such a position that it has to lift the oil on the suction side, some arrangement should be provided for " priming " it, that is, for filling it with oil in the event of its becoming empty through standing. In that event the pump might fail to draw the oil up, as owing to the clearances in the pump the air would escape back from the delivery side to the suction side and thus prevent the pressure on that side being reduced sufficiently to draw up the oil.

15.13   Hobourn-Eaton Oil Pump

This pump, shown in a simplified form in Fig. 15-6, is of the internally meshing double rotor type.

It has been recently developed, and the patent specifications cover a variety of devices and arrangements aimed at automatic control of the by-passing of surplus delivery at high speeds.

The pump is intended more particularly for servo applications such as power-operated steering, where the demands may at times be only a small fraction of the available displacement volume during periods of high-speed operation of the prime-mover.   It is highly desirable under these conditions that surplus delivery should

349

be by-passed to the suction side of the pump without noise, excessive pressure or emulsification.

As a lubrication pump, units of simplified form such as that illustrated can be supplied.

Referring to Fig. 15-6, which is partly diagrammatic, R is the driven, internal rotor having four teeth, meshing with and driving the external annular rotor A which has five tooth spaces. Displacement of oil from suction to delivery side takes place in a similar manner to that in the more usual externally meshing gear pump.

Larger pumps employ a greater number of teeth and spaces, but these always differ by one in number.

15.14 Filters

It is not possible even with the finest gauze to intercept all the minute particles of grit and abraded metal which cause wear of bearings, and it is essential to have in the oil circuit adequate filters of large total area for the interception of all dangerous abrasive material.

It is usual to provide two filters in the circuit, one, the low pressure, being placed on the suction side of the pump, and the other on the delivery side. The low-pressure filter is of comparatively coarse mesh so as to minimize the risk of strangling the suction. It takes the form, in some cases, of a large shallow cylindrical float connected by a hinged connection to the pump suction. The intake periphery is protected by a medium mesh wire gauze, and as this entry is always completely submerged below the surface of the oil but clear of the bottom, both floating matter and sediment are unlikely to be picked up.

A floating intake of this type is shown in Fig. 7-13.

15.15 High-pressure Filter

The thorough filtering of the oil, which should ideally remove all abrasive particles large enough to span the oil films in the various bearings, is accomplished on the pressure side of the system between the pressure relief valve and the delivery galleries.

The filtration may be of the full flow or the by-pass type; in the latter, the filter is arranged as a shunt to the main flow, and passes only a portion of the total oil stream. This proportion will depend on the relative hydraulic " conductivities " of the two circuits through the filter to the sump and through the various bearings to the sump, just as does the amount delivered to any particular bearing depend on its conductivity relatively to its fellows. If one of a pair of adjacent big ends, for instance, fed from the same main journal, is worn or adjusted with too great clearance, it will rob its neighbour of the proper share of oil. In the event of bearing seizure, attention is not always given to the bearing which is the real source of the trouble.

It is not possible to estimate accurately the time that will elapse before every oil-borne abrasive particle will be carried to the filter, as it depends on the element of chance and the rate of introduction of new particles. It is, however, clearly related to the rate of pump circulation as compared with the total oil capacity of the system, and the relative quantities flowing through the filter and by-passing it.

Should a large quantity of dirt be carelessly introduced to the sump during topping up, there is serious risk with the by-pass system that much of this dirt will reach the bearings before it reaches the filter.

The reason for the introduction of the by-pass system was the difficulty (experienced when the paper or fabric type of fine filter was first introduced) of providing a sufficiently large filter area to deal with the rapid rates of circulation used in present-day lubricating systems.

This difficulty has been largely met by the use of long fabric strips folded into multi-point star formations on a suitable perforated frame, or incorporating a sandwich arrangement of wire gauze and fabric. There should be no serious difficulty in designing *ab initio* for a full flow filter of adequate size to pass at moderate pressure the full delivery of the oil pump, thus eliminating the risks associated with the partial flow, by-pass system.

There may be many applications in industrial work where it is necessary to make provision for cleaning the filter without stopping the engine, but in these cases a duplicate installation with change-over cocks and suitable access doors is the correct solution.

15.16 Relief Valve Incorporated in Filter

A fabric-type filter for use on the pressure side of the pump, incorporating good features of design, is the Vokes outward flow arrangement shown in Fig. 15-7. Both entry and exit are at the top of the container, and the relief valve which short-circuits the element is formed by a synthetic rubber ring bearing on an annular seating formed in the head casting.

The whole filter element slides on a central rod and bears on a coil spring which determines the limiting pressure difference permitted on the element, this difference being small owing to the provision of a very large filter area.

With this arrangement it will be seen that there is no risk of the accumulated silt being discharged into the delivery either by opening of the relief valve or on removal of the element for cleaning or replacement.

It is claimed that the danger of the relief valve being prevented from seating by a particle of dirt, as is possible with the metallic cone or ball valve, is eliminated by the capacity of the rubber seating to accommodate small particles without causing leakage.

15.17 Purolator " Micronic " Filter

An interesting new filtering material has been introduced in the Purolator filter to which the name " micronic " has been given in

351

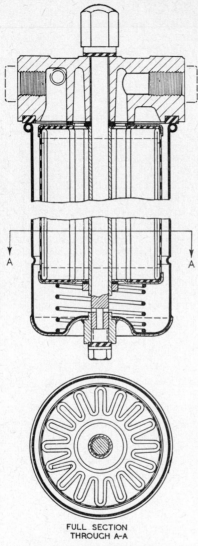

FULL SECTION
THROUGH A-A

Fig. 15-7: Vokes full-flow filter

reference to the physicist's unit of very small measurement, the "micron." This is one thousandth of a millimetre, and the material, which is a plastics impregnated paper, is claimed to be able to stop particles approaching this size. Even very much larger particles would be unlikely to cause damage to bearings.

Relatively high rates of oil flow are possible, and it is claimed that the extraction of additives in detergent-type oils is negligible.

The element is easily and cheaply renewed as necessary in place of cleaning.

15.18 Autoklean Filter

An application of the principle of edge filtration, providing satisfactory freedom of flow combined with ready means of clearing the filter elements without dismantling, is employed in the Autoklean filter, in wide use in its various forms.

The filter element is formed by threading alternately on to a flatted spindle a thin perforated metal plate of circular form and a spoked spacing washer $\frac{3}{1000}$ in thick. These elements are assembled as a cartridge of convenient length and capable of rotation by the centre spindle. During assembly of the pack a series of intermeshing cleaning blades is threaded on a stationary square rod. These cleaning blades are $\frac{2}{1000}$ in thick and penetrate between the circular plates nearly to the spokes of the spacing washers.

Periodical rotation of the centre spindle, which may be linked with clutch operation, enables the cleaning blades to clean the narrow filtering spaces between the edges of the circular plates.

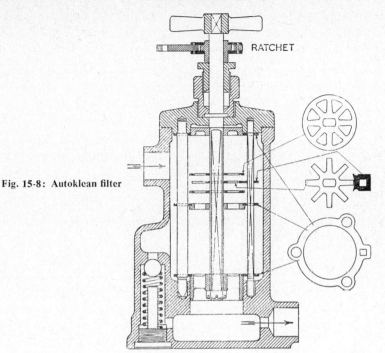

RATCHET

Fig. 15-8: Autoklean filter

The oil flows radially inwards between the discs and axially through the perforations to the outlet of the filter. The details of the assembly should be clear from Fig. 15-8, while Fig. 15-4 shows the arrangement and location of the filter in a typical application.

15.19 Circulation Indicators

Some indication that the lubrication system is functioning correctly is desirable, but it is to be regretted that in the majority of instances the only indicator provided is of the pressure gauge type, which is no certain guide to the oil circulation either qualitatively or quantitatively, and which may lull the driver into a false sense of security.

Any abnormal pressure, whether high or low, should be regarded as an indication that something is wrong, though changes in the viscosity of the oil due to changes in temperature produce changes of pressure. Where a pressure relief valve or other by-pass arrangement is fitted, an obstruction in the circulating system may cause the whole of the pump delivery to be by-passed through the relief valve so that although a high pressure might be indicated the circulation system would not be receiving any oil at all.

15.20 Oil Level Indicators

The oil level in the sump must be maintained between certain limits to ensure that the pump is never starved, while at the same time excess is avoided. One of the simplest devices, and one which gives reliable indications if carefully used, is the dip stick marked for high and low level. In using this it should be removed and wiped and then reinserted to take an observation, otherwise a false reading may be obtained, owing to creep and splash of the oil.

In all cases it is desirable to check the oil level only after the engine has been running and has reached its normal temperature so that the variation in sump level due to the quantity of oil in circulation and increase in volume with rise of temperature may be allowed for.

The float type of indicator illustrated in Fig. 15-2, while giving an immediate indication, is somewhat liable to derangement from puncture of the float or bending of the rod.

CHAPTER 16

Engine Cooling

Cooling problems. Pump and thermo-syphon systems. Temperature control. Pressurized cooling system. Directed cooling. Radiator construction.

THE high working temperatures of the internal combustion engine which are the cause of its high efficiency are at the same time a source of great practical difficulty in construction and operation. No known materials are capable of enduring continuously the high temperatures to which the cylinder, piston and valves are subjected while at the same time retaining sufficient strength to withstand the high working loads.

The maximum temperature of the explosion is approximately the melting point of platinum and the temperature even of the exhaust gases is above that of aluminium. It is thus essential that heat be abstracted from the parts enumerated above at a sufficient rate to prevent a dangerous temperature being reached, for, unfortunately, it is quite impossible to prevent heat entering the metal from the hot gases.

Nevertheless, it must always be borne in mind that such abstraction of heat is a direct thermodynamic loss, and if high thermal efficiency is desired the abstraction of heat should not be more than is necessary to prevent dangerous overheating and consequent distortion of the cylinder, etc. Excessive cooling will also prevent proper vaporization of the fuel, leading to further waste and also to objectionable dilution of the crank case oil by unvaporized fuel, which gets down past the piston. On the other hand, too high an operating temperature is bad from the point of view of the power developed, since it results in reduced volumetric efficiency on account of the excessive heating of the incoming charge with the consequent reduction of charge weight and thus of power.

In any given set of conditions there is some particular operating temperature which produces the most satisfactory results, and only experience with a particular engine will determine this temperature. If it were not for the loss of water and the interference with cooling as a result of boiling in an ordinary water-cooled system, the temperature of boiling at atmospheric pressure, namely 100° C or even higher, would not be too high a general operating temperature in the majority of engines. To prevent boiling a lower operating temperature is necessary, as local overheating must be guarded against. It is usually in the neighbourhood of 75° to 90° C.

It follows that to obtain the best running in all conditions of climate and fuel, etc., the amount of cooling should be controllable. American design, stimulated by the extreme variations of climate

355

to be provided for, is somewhat ahead of British in this respect, but the problem is now receiving a good deal of attention in this country.

To come to the actual cooling means employed, whatever these may be, the ultimate result is the dissipation of the dangerous heat to the surrounding air. Direct dissipation of heat from the cylinder barrel and head to the surrounding air, or air-cooling as it is called, is feasible with small engines and is practically universal with motor cycles. The heat is dissipated by radiation and convection from thin cooling fins cast on the cylinder head and barrel.

Natural flow air-cooling is at best very difficult to regulate, and as the size of the cylinder increases the difficulties become very serious, for the heat developed increases as the cube of the linear dimensions, while the radiating surface increases only as the square.

In multi-cylinder engines the flow of the air is controlled by suitable cowlings so as to be distributed equally to all the cylinders. However, in large engines, if air-cooling is used, it is generally in conjunction with a large fan which delivers a considerable volume of air to the cylinders, and this fan besides being bulky requires a considerable expenditure of power to drive it, so that unless other considerations enter into the question the chief gain, which is the elimination of the necessity for a radiator and water jackets to the cylinders, with the consequent saving in weight, is not always realized. Air-cooled engines have the reputation of being noisier than the water-cooled form, and very few instances of large fan-cooled engines are on the market, though in the special application of large power units to armoured fighting vehicles, important developments have recently taken place in the United States Army. Extremes of climate, difficulty in replacing water lost by evaporation, and all the complications involved in frost precautions in operational theatres, added to the probable greater vulnerability of liquid cooling, are powerful inducements towards the adoption of direct air-cooling in this field.

For the normal medium and large passenger and commercial vehicle water-cooling is practically universal.

Heat is far more readily transferred from metal to water than from metal to air, while the final transfer of heat from the water to the air, in order that the water may be returned to circulate through the engine jackets, can be readily accomplished in a radiator provided with a large cooling surface in contact on one side with the hot water from the engine and exposed on the other side to a strong current of air arising from the motion of the car, aided by a fan driven from the engine.

A steady operating temperature will be reached when the difference between the temperatures of the air and radiator is sufficient, in conjunction with the area of radiating surface and air flow to dissipate heat at the same rate as it is being received from the jackets. During a long climb with a following wind equilibrium may not be reached and the water will boil.

356

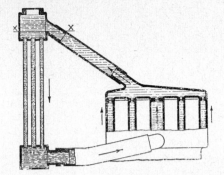

Fig. 16-1: Thermosyphon system

The radiator is normally placed in front of the engine, but whatever the position may be there are two methods in general use for circulating the water through the engine jackets and radiator, namely—

(1) Thermosyphon system.
(2) Pump system.

In the former the water circulates in virtue of the pressure difference arising from the difference in density between the hot water in the jackets and the cooler water in the radiator. For success in operation the passages through the jackets and radiator should be free and the connecting pipes large, while the jackets should be placed as low as possible relatively to the radiator, in order that the " hot leg " shall have as great a height as possible.

In operation the water level must on no account be allowed to fall below the level of the delivery pipe to the radiator top, otherwise circulation will cease.

Fig. 16-1 shows as simply as possible the essentials of the system, X X showing the critical water level.

In general the thermosyphon system requires a larger radiator and carries a greater body of water than the pump circulation system and a somewhat excessive temperature difference is necessary to produce the requisite circulation. On the other hand to some extent it automatically prevents the engine being run too cold.

These defects have, however, resulted in the pump circulation system becoming universal in high-powered vehicles. The pump is either a radial flow centrifugal pump, driven in the larger engines by positive gearing, and forcing the circulation from the bottom of the radiator to the bottom of the jackets, or a simpler axial flow impeller, placed usually at the outlet from the cylinder head, and driven by an all round belt drive including the dynamo. This arrangement is popular with the smaller engines, and the fan is usually mounted on the impeller spindle. These impellers have less forcing power than the centrifugal type, but give appreciable assistance to the circulation.

Neither type is a positive pump in the sense of being able to force a fixed rate of flow independently of the hydraulic resistance of the circuit.

Fig. 16-2 shows the construction of a centrifugal pump. It consists simply of a casing inside which an " impeller " P, provided with vanes V, is rotated. The water enters the casing at the centre of the impeller and, being caught up by the vanes, is whirled round. Centrifugal force causes the water to pass to the periphery of the impeller where it is thrown out into the stationary casing. The kinetic energy imparted to the water by the impeller is converted in the stationary casing into pressure or potential energy so that a pressure difference is established between the inlet and the outlet D of the pump. A seal is provided where the impeller spindle passes through the casing, in order to maintain a water-tight joint. This seal is made in modern designs by means of the face contact of a graphitic carbon ring which may revolve with the impeller or be stationary in the housing, on either the suction or pressure sides, according to convenience in design. The face contact avoids wear of the shaft, and the carbon, bearing on a suitable alloy iron, hardened steel or phosphor bronze surface, develops a hard, wear-free surface which requires no lubrication and provides an effective seal against leakage.

Alternative arrangements of the " Morganite Unit Seal," supplied by the Morgan Crucible Company as a proprietary fitting, are shown on the left of the figure. The carbon ring is bonded to a flexible rubber casing which takes the friction torque. Inside the casing is a light stainless steel spring proportioned to give appropriate pressure between the rubbing surfaces. The whole provides a readily inserted unit assembly requiring renewal only at long intervals.

The authors are indebted to the makers for details of the unit.

Pressure relief holes may be provided through the impeller boss to prevent the delivery pressure developing undue end thrust on the back.

A pump circulation system is illustrated diagrammatically in

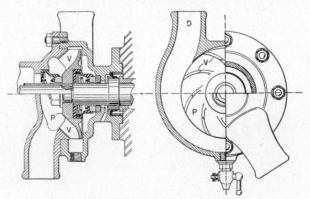

Fig. 16-2: Centrifugal pump

Fig. 16-3. A is the centrifugal pump delivering to the bottom of the jackets and B shows a thermostatically controlled by-pass valve by which the radiator can be short-circuited and the water returned to the pump suction until its temperature reaches a desirable value. In the diagram the valve is in a mid position.

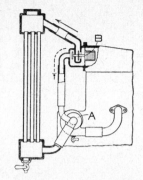

Fig. 16-3: Pump circulation

16.1 Temperature Control

There are broadly two methods of regulation in use the first being practically universal in automobile practice:—

(1) Automatic control by means of a thermostat.

(2) Hand control by means of radiator shutters.

The thermostat consists of a concertina or bellows-like vessel of thin metal, similar to those employed in the aneroid barometer but filled with a suitable liquid. In some cases expansion is magnified by a system of levers to operate the valve. In most modern designs, the large movement necessary for the valve is obtained directly from the bellows by *evaporation* of the liquid, which should be one boiling at about 60° to 80° C. Such liquids are acetone, alcohol, etc.

The valve may control a by-pass as in Fig. 16-3, or it may simply be placed in the main circuit as depicted in Fig. 16-4, where *a* shows the valve as part of the engine construction and *b* illustrates the convenient and simple " Motorstat " hose-line type, which can be readily installed in any engine in place of the hose connection to the top of the radiator.

Where the thermostatic valve closes the main circuit without a by-pass, which has been the usual practice, it must be capable of

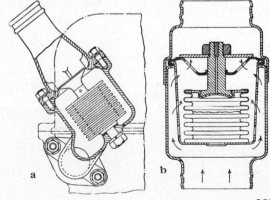

Fig. 16-4: Bellows type thermostat

a

b

359

closing the circuit against the pressure developed by the centrifugal pump, but no great difficulty is experienced in meeting this condition, since the bellows can be arranged to act as a tension spring, the initial tension being regulated to give any opening temperature desired within the vapour pressure and temperature characteristics of the liquid employed.

When carefully designed and installed these devices are reliable, and their use in various forms has become general.

16.2 Wax Element Thermostats

The recently developed thermostats of the wax-element type are incorporated almost exclusively in the pressurized cooling systems of current American cars and commercial vehicles, and are widely favoured by the German and Italian automobile industries. They are now becoming the rule, too, in Great Britain after a delay, probably attributable to the local temperate climate, because of which there is not such an urgent stimulus to change over to the reputedly superior wax type. However, the number of makers who now fit the latter type as standard equipment is increasing rapidly.

Western-Thomson Controls Ltd., of Reading, are now developing the original designs of their American associates for the British market, and are supplying units for the leading makers of automobile petrol and diesel engines, either as replacement units or as original equipment.

The waxes used are broadly in the microcrystalline group which covers the higher melting point range of paraffin waxes. In many cases the wax is mixed with a very finely divided copper to increase the thermal conductivity of the charge as a whole. This results in a more thermally sensitive element. Over the working range the wax remains in the plastic state, having a coefficient of volumetric expansion of about 0·5 per cent/deg F. A maximum lift of $\frac{3}{8}$ in. and a thrust of no less than 35 lb are given by the standard automotive element.

A tapered piston rod is enclosed in a synthetic rubber boot sealed in the upper end of the capsule (a brass pressing) which contains the wax. The upper end of this rod is screwed into a central hole in a bridge carried by the main seating ring, and after adjustment for calibration, the screw is locked by solder.

As the wax expands on heating, it forces the body of the capsule downwards against the return spring carrying with it the valve which opens against the pump pressure.

To avoid the harmful effects that might arise from a stalled water pump when the valve is shut in a closed circuit, the makers recommend a by-pass system, and when this cannot be arranged without extensive modification, a suitable bleed orifice may suffice.

Failure of the wax capsule would cause the valve to remain closed, with possible disastrous consequences, but the same results would arise with a punctured or cracked bellows. The wax capsule

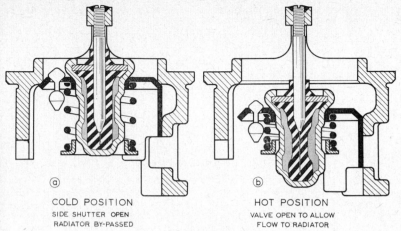

COLD POSITION
SIDE SHUTTER OPEN
RADIATOR BY-PASSED

HOT POSITION
VALVE OPEN TO ALLOW
FLOW TO RADIATOR

Fig. 16-5

is claimed to be less liable to failure owing to its robust construction and freedom from fatigue effects which may arise in the bellows type due to cyclical distortion.

Fig. 16-5 illustrates a wax element thermostat in one of its simpler forms. The valve, side-shutter type, is pressed on to the outside of the capsule against the swell in diameter, and seats on the main annular pressing which carries the bridge and return spring abutment. The form of the rubber boot and seal will be clear.

The authors are indebted to the makers for information, and a full description will be found in *Automobile Engineer* for March 1962.

The second means of regulation, namely by hand-operated shutters, has both the advantages and disadvantages of being under the direct control of the driver. By the use of these shutters, placed usually in front of the radiator, the air flow may be wholly or partly blanked off in order to obtain the desired working temperature. The shutters and their controls require to be well designed and made if they are to be free from rattle. Radiator shutters controlled by a thermostat have been used.

The radiator and bonnet muff so much used in this country, while useful in cold weather to prevent cooling off while the car is standing, is at best a makeshift and unsatisfactory means of control.

16.3 Pressurized Cooling System

Experience with evaporative cooling systems in closed water jackets of complicated form appears to have emphasized the danger of local steam pockets forming at critical positions around exhaust valve pockets and spark-plug bosses.

In such locations rapid extraction of heat from the metal is essential, but stagnant or superheated steam which is not rapidly scoured away by fresh supplies of water at boiling point is relatively

361

a very poor agent for the purpose, and local overheating and water hammer action is very likely to take place.

A system which combines the reliability of the more familiar arrangements with some of the advantages of steam cooling is the pressurized system incorporating a light relief valve with an automatic vacuum break valve, the relief valve being spring loaded to open at a pressure of 3 to 4 lb/sq. in. above prevailing atmospheric pressure. This is illustrated in Fig. 16-6, which shows the combined pressure and vacuum relief valve fitted to the Vauxhall Velox cooling system and supplied as an accessory by A. C. Sphinx, Ltd.

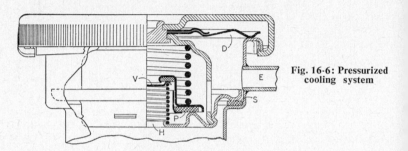

Fig. 16-6: Pressurized cooling system

The pressure inside the radiator block is communicated through the central port H to the pressure disc valve P and the vacuum valve V. These are loaded to pressures of about $3\frac{1}{2}$ and 1 lb/sq. in. respectively. An escape pipe is provided at E. To guard against spurting on removal of the cap, the spring disc D does not leave its seating until the main body is well clear of the sealing washer S, and the pressure is reduced to that of the atmosphere.

In a closed water system of this type the pressure reached depends on the temperature attained according to the table below—

Temperature (° C)	94	100	107	121
Pressure (lb/sq. in. absolute)	12	15	19	30

The pressure of 12 lb/sq. in. corresponds to an altitude of 6,000 to 7,000 ft, so that boiling would occur at 94° C at this altitude in an open system, whereas in a closed system loaded to 3 lb/sq. in. the temperature would be raised to the normal sea level figure before loss occurred. At sea level a margin of 6° or 7° is provided by the pressurized system. These increases may well prove sufficient to avoid the necessity of stopping to cool off in order to prevent loss of water under arduous conditions of hill climbing at high altitudes. The heat dissipating capacity of the radiator surface would be appreciably increased by such a temperature increase.

A higher loading of the relief valve up to (say) 15 lb/sq. in. would give such a gain in temperature that economy in size of radiator

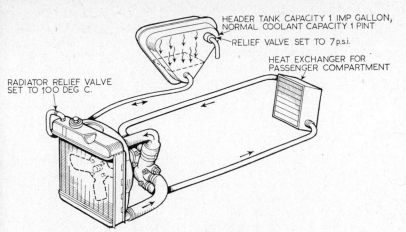

HEADER TANK CAPACITY 1 IMP GALLON, NORMAL COOLANT CAPACITY 1 PINT

RELIEF VALVE SET TO 7 p.s.i.

HEAT EXCHANGER FOR PASSENGER COMPARTMENT

RADIATOR RELIEF VALVE SET TO 100 DEG C.

Fig. 16-7: Renault sealed system

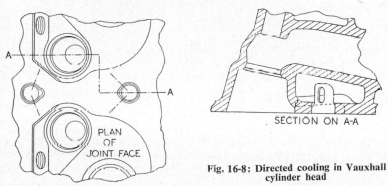

A

A

PLAN OF JOINT FACE

SECTION ON A-A

Fig. 16-8: Directed cooling in Vauxhall cylinder head

Fig. 16-9 (*left*): Honeycomb radiator

Fig. 16-10 (*below*): Honeycomb tubes

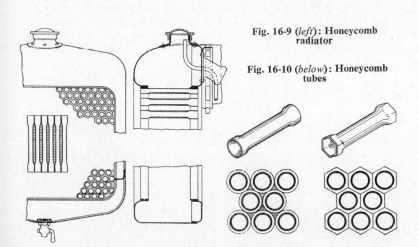

might be possible, though the probable necessity of strengthening the block would rule out any saving in weight. With the lower figure of 3 to 4 lb/sq. in. above atmosphere special provision for strengthening will not normally be necessary.

16.4 Renault R4-L Sealed Coolant System

A recent and interesting development of the pressurized cooling system is the sealed arrangement adopted on the R4-L Renault front-engined vehicle.

Described as a " sealed for life " system, both temperature and pressure controls are provided. Communication with a relatively large expansion tank situated under the offside front wing is opened by a thermostatic valve when the coolant reaches a temperature of 100° C. The expansion tank is provided with a pressure relief valve set to about 7 lb/sq. in.

The coolant is a 50-50 mixture of water and glycol charged and sealed permanently subject to abnormal leaks. The air capacity of the expansion tank is sufficient to prevent the pressure (at 100° C) from reaching the above relief pressure, and in any case only air would be discharged.

Fig. 16-7 indicates the arrangement diagrammatically. All connections are made with rubber hose including those to the space heater for the passenger compartment.

16.5 Directed Cooling

Considerable care is taken in modern designs of cylinder head to provide carefully directed jets of coolant to local hot spots such as valve seats and spark-plug bosses. This may be accomplished by means of a suitably drilled gallery pipe fed directly from the water pump, or by nozzles pressed into the head casting at each of the communicating holes between the cylinder block and head jackets. In the Vauxhall head, shown in section through the exhaust valve in Fig. 16-8, the nozzles take the form of thimbles provided with one or two ports suitably positioned in each case to direct vigorous local streams to the spots desired. A pressed locating snug ensures correct positioning in each case. The six-cylinder head has a total of ten of these jets directed in general towards the exhaust valve pockets. The authors are indebted to Vauxhall Motors, Ltd., for drawings and particulars.

16.6 Radiator Construction

Radiators have now developed into two main types of water-tube construction, the early honeycomb or cellular construction shown in Figs. 16-9 and 16-10 being obsolete. Though having certain advantages in appearance, ease of repair and smaller proportionate immobilization by a single obstruction, the earlier types suffer from the important heat transfer defect that the ratio of metal-air to water-metal dissipating surface is practically unity instead of being many times that figure.

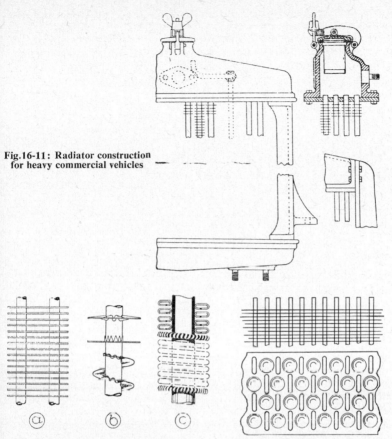

Fig.16-11: Radiator construction
for heavy commercial vehicles

Fig. 16-12: Radiator tubes   Fig. 16-13

In modern tubular constructions, appearance and protection are provided by the ornamental grille which is now universal in passenger vehicles, and the radiator block can be designed simply as an efficient heat exchanger of the lightest possible weight.

Fig. 16-11 shows the vertical water tube type which is to be found on heavier types of commercial vehicles. The construction consists essentially of cast light alloy top and bottom tanks bolted to cast side pillars. The cooling element consists of a nest of copper tubes soldered into brass upper and lower tube plates which are bolted to the top and bottom tanks. This construction is inexpensive and makes for accessibility and ease of repair.

The tubes take various forms, and if of normal circular section, are usually provided with external gills to give additional surface to aid transfer of heat from metal to air. Various forms are illustrated in Fig. 16-12. At (a) is indicated a construction in which a

365

nest of six or eight tubes, running from back to front of the block, is sweated into common gill plates.

Different forms of plate gills applied to individual tubes are shown at (*b*), while (*c*) shows the efficient and widely used Still tube which employs a continuous coil of copper wire wound spirally around, and sweated to, the plain tube.

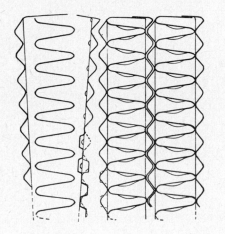

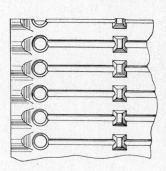

Fig. 16-14: Film tube construction

Fig. 16-13 shows a popular current form of flattened tube and plate gill type, which can be assembled and sweated up to the size of block required. The flattened tubes give a more favourable ratio of transfer area to water weight than the circular tube, and they are fabricated from very thin strip metal with a folded and sweated longitudinal joint. The ratio of air surface to water surface can be varied very conveniently by the appropriate choice of the number of gill plates through which the tubes are threaded. The dimples help to ensure the desirable turbulent motion of the air.

Fig. 16-14 illustrates the extreme development of the film-tube type in which the core is built up of units formed from thin embossed copper strip of a width equal to the required thickness of block. This is normally from two to three inches thick.

The block is built by first forming air-way units of the full height of the block. This is done by folding the embossed strip round serpentine dimpled strip to provide the additional air surface, locating dimples being provided on the embossed strip to position the serpentine strip until the final soldering operation.

These air-way units are then assembled in a jig in the required number and sweated together at the corrugated edges, leaving straight vertical water-ways of a lateral width equal to the full depth of the edge corrugations. The embossing of the strip provides, in addition, strengthening flutes and spacing supports on the vertical centre line. The full-size drawing of Fig. 16-14 should make the construction clear. The ratio of air area to water area in the example illustrated is about five to one.

The Authors are indebted to Serck Radiators, Ltd., and Coventry Radiator & Presswork Co., Ltd., for information.

16.7 Horizontal Disposition of Tubes

The marked tendency towards wider and lower bonnet lines has encouraged designers to test the merits of the horizontally disposed radiator block. As pump or forced circulation is now practically universal, thermo-syphon action has little significance, and the high and narrow constructions of block previously called for can no longer be accommodated easily. Increase of width and reduction of height of the block result in a less favourable surface/weight ratio, owing to the greater proportional weight of the top and bottom headers. The larger number of shorter tubes calls for a greater number of soldered joints and increased risk of leakage. Favourable proportions are restored by laying a " long tube " block on its side, and if desired, introducing baffles so that inlet and outlet may be on the same side of the bonnet, the water traversing the bonnet width twice.

The increased length and smaller total cross section of the flow area naturally increase the hydraulic resistance, but by careful pump design and choice of speed, the power consumption need not be excessive. The flattened tube type of block shown in Fig. 16-13 is well suited to this horizontal lay-out.

CHAPTER 17

Future Trends

Petrol injection.　**The gas turbine.**　**The free piston gas generator.**

THIS chapter is devoted to brief notes on two possible developments of the power unit which have aroused considerable
interest in recent years, the one involving an alternative to the
normal carburettor in existing types of engine, and the other
representing a complete change in the mechanical nature of the
prime mover.

Successful development has taken place in both directions in
connection with aircraft engines, and speculation has naturally
arisen as to the possibilities of application to road automobiles.

The advantages of metering the fuel supply by means of the
positive displacement pump of either the high or low pressure type
have been demonstrated, and the issue is the commercial one of
deciding whether improved performance is sufficient to justify the
cost of applying more or less familiar techniques.

The application of the gas turbine to the smaller types of road
vehicle is a much more revolutionary and conjectural possibility,
though the successful enterprise of the Rover Company in producing
the first turbine-driven car has attracted world-wide interest.

Since these post-war developments were first noticed here, research
and technical advance have continued, but though the great U.S.
corporations and many European firms of high standing are patenting and developing a great variety of appliances, there is no evidence
yet of pending large-scale applications in the automobile field.

Regarding heavy road vehicles, interest and commercial development here are increasingly concentrated on the supercharged diesel.
In the medium car field, the four-cylinder, carburettor and spark
ignition engine seems to be more firmly established than ever for
this country's home and export market, while on the Continent the
small utility car with the simplest form of power unit is increasingly
popular.

Only in the U.S.A., where pioneering resources are immense and
very high-powered vehicles are the rule, does petrol injection seem
likely to make headway. The cost of injection equipment is a much
smaller proportion of the total cost of the vehicle, and may be
justified by improved performance and fuel economy.

In this country the great experience in aircraft applications of the
Lucas organization has been utilized in a " prestige " installation in
the racing Jaguar cars, but this cannot be regarded as of immediate
commercial significance. A valuable descriptive article will be
found in *Automobile Engineer*, Vol. 47, No. 1.

368

It is significant that at the 1957 Motor Show at Earls Court London, the only example shown of petrol injection was on the high-powered Mercedes-Benz engine, using conventional multi-plunger Bosch equipment which, with its auxiliary mixture control gear, represents a costly item.

The small four- or six-cylinder carburettor engine is on the whole performing so well and reliably, and such great vested interests of capital, skills and experience are brought to its production and maintenance, that revolutionary change seems highly unlikely in the near future.

The gas turbine is developing rapidly in applications for bulk power production and marine propulsion, but is up against diesel competition for heavy road and rail transport, and is at present quite out of court for light road transport.

A promising development which may be successful in combining diesel economy with the low cost and convenience of rotary equipment is the free-piston gas-generator, of which some description is given later. The general matter on petrol injection and the gas turbine, with some additional notes on rotary heat exchangers, has been retained as covering, if briefly, the first essentials.

PETROL INJECTION

The limitations of the float chamber and jet carburettor for aircraft purposes, and the serious disturbances arising in fighter machines during aerobatics, led in the second world war to the general adoption of petrol injection by means of positive displacement pumps, in Germany of the " jerk " type delivering to separate injectors for each cylinder, as in the diesel engine; or as applied in the low-pressure Stromberg system used by the Western Allies.

In both systems, float chambers with their gravitational disturbances, and the dangers of refrigeration ice were eliminated, in the Stromberg system by directing the metered spray to the supercharger side of the throttle, and so into the eye of the impeller.

The Stromberg system employed metering jets of the normal type, but subject to a pressure head accurately controlled by the entry and throat pressures of the air-intake venturi. The pressure head averaged about 5 lb/sq. in., and the requisite jets were cut in and out by both automatic and manual means.

There was no special provision for ensuring uniform distribution of the air and fuel to the various cylinders, though this was helped by the effects of the supercharger. In both cases the fundamental cycle, whether four- or two-stroke, and the use of electric spark ignition, remained unchanged.

Since the compression-ignition engine has now a virtual monopoly of the heavy vehicle and passenger transport field and is steadily extending its range to lighter commercial vehicles, there remains little but the private car field and in the special high performance engines demanded by the racing fraternity in which petrol injection could replace existing carburettor systems.

The volatile fuel, spark-ignition reciprocating engine is likely to persist for many years as the most suitable and cheapest small power unit for the private car. Experienced opinion does not visualize an early substitution of either the compression-ignition engine or, still less, the gas turbine. The problems involved in both these developments—particularly the latter—increase rapidly with diminution in size, apart from questions of fuel availability.

Before considering the details of the petrol injection principle, a brief consideration of the advantages offered relatively to the normal carburettor may be of interest.

The limitations in performance and economy of current designs of carburettor and induction systems arise from two main causes. Firstly, loss of volumetric efficiency arising from restriction of air flow by the carburettor choke and by necessary pre-heating; and secondly from the effects of unequal distribution of the fuel between the various cylinders in a multi-cylinder engine.

As has been seen earlier, the necessity of ensuring that the weakest charge arising in any one cylinder shall not fall below the limits of ignitability, requires that the general setting of the carburettor must give a richer average mixture than is consistent with economy. Even the most successful designs of induction manifold fail to ensure uniform distribution of the air charge and still less of the fuel. It will be realized that the Stromberg system offers no advantages in these two directions, and only the "individual injector" systems will be dealt with here.

It is rightly claimed that injection of petrol by individual injectors to the respective engine cylinders will largely solve the distribution problem, while simplified induction manifolds free from a strangled entry will aid volumetric efficiency and air distribution. Moreover, since there is no necessity to maintain a stable ignitable mixture in the manifold, induction heating, with the consequent reduction of weight of charge, is eliminated.

The immediately following information is based on an important paper by K. Brook and W. E. W. Nicolls read before the Automobile Division of the Institution of Mechanical Engineers. The present authors are indebted to the Council of the Institution for permission to reproduce diagrams and abstract subject matter.

For full information Part I of the *Proceedings of the Automobile Division* for 1947–48 should be consulted.

17.1 Location of Injector

There are three alternative locations for the injector, which have been subject to development work.

These are the "cylinder (direct)," "port," and "manifold" systems. Figs. 17-1, 17-2 and 17-3 show these.

The diagrams are self-explanatory, and it will be noticed that the first in order follows closely the practice in direct injection c.i. engines, though the duration and timing are different.

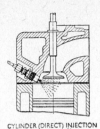 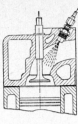 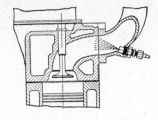

CYLINDER (DIRECT) INJECTION   PORT INJECTION   MANIFOLD INJECTION

Fig. 17-1   **Fig. 17-2**   **Fig. 17-3**

The other two arrangements move the injector progressively farther from the combustion chamber, with the idea of providing a longer period for mixing and warming the charge. With manifold injection, in order to realize the essential advantages of the system, it is necessary to employ individual injectors delivering locally to each port, the twinning of ports being ruled out.

The second, or port system, appears at present to hold the balance of favour in development work. Compared with the direct system, there is less interference with cooling water spaces in the crowded valve region, and the high-speed turbulent passage of the inlet valve assists in forming a homogeneous mixture, while the heat of compression, together with the contact of the charge with the hot exhaust valve, provides the bulk of the warming and vaporizing heat prior to ignition.

It is not easy to ensure " downstream " injection and freedom from mutual interference between cylinders if the injectors are placed far from the valve ports, though location of these in the manifold casting has the great merit of freeing the cylinder head from complication.

Only continued development and test will establish the most desirable compromise in any given design.

17.2 Timing of the Injection

Figs. 17-4 and 17-5 show typical valve and injection timing diagrams for four- and two-stroke engines respectively. The four-stroke diagram illustrates a timing system, with constant start and variable end of the injection period, comparable with that used in c.i. engines, and employing a normal helix on the pump plunger (see Fig. 9-17). The injection period is considerably longer than in the case of the c.i. engine, and is timed as early as possible consistent with the avoidance of fuel loss through the exhaust valve—it will be noticed that there is 10° margin in the diagram.

The two-stroke diagram shows a different system calling for an " inverted " helix on the pump plunger, giving constant " spill " or end of injection combined with variable commencement. It was found in this particular engine that the end of injection could not

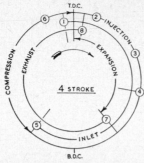
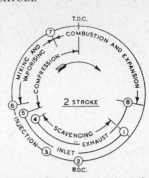

① INLET OPENS .0° B.T.D.C.   ⑤ INLET CLOSES 40° A.B.D.C.
② INJECTION STARTS 20°A.T.D.C.   ⑥ IGNITION (ADVANCED)
③ INJECTION PART LOAD ENDS ⑦ EXHAUST OPENS 40°B.B.D.C.
④ INJ. FULL LD. ENDS 80°B.B.D.C. ⑧ EXHAUST CLOSES 10°A.T.D.C.

Fig. 17-4

① INLET OPENS 50° B.B.D.C.   ⑤ INLET CLOSES 70°A.B.D.C.
② INJECTION FULL LD. STARTS⑥ INJECTION ENDS 80°A.B.D.C.
③ INJECTION PART LD. STARTS⑦ IGNITION (ADVANCED)
④ EXHAUST CLOSES 60°A.B.D.C.⑧ EXHAUST OPENS 80°B.B.D.C.

Fig. 17-5

be delayed later than 80° after b.d.c. without adversely affecting the combustion efficiency. The later point of commencement on part load minimizes the risk of fuel loss at cruising speeds by reducing the period of overlap between injection and scavenge. The remote location of the injector from the exhaust ports minimizes such loss, but it is liable to occur at full load.

17.3 Control of Fuel Delivery and Mixture Strength

It has been seen that normally the compression-ignition engine is controlled by variation of fuel charge only, the amount of injection being always less than that corresponding to chemically correct combination. This constitutes quality control with " mixtures " that are always weak, and which meet without further complications the requirements for economy. The impossibility of obtaining complete combustion of either fuel or air by injection, after compression, of chemically correct or excess fuel, rules out the possibility of using high fuel-air ratios to obtain high b.m.e.p. in the c.i. engine.

The spark-ignition engine on the other hand permits the use of rich mixtures, and the air and fuel metering device, whether carburettor

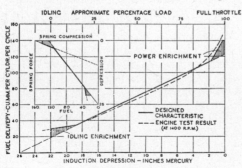

Fig. 17-6: Mixture control by manifold depression

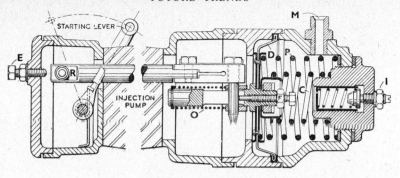

STARTING LEVER

E

R

INJECTION
PUMP

M

D P

F

C

O

I

R	PUMP CONTROL RACK	F	MAXIMUM FUEL ADJUSTMENT	P	MAXIMUM POWER SPRING
E	EXCESS FUEL ADJUSTMENT	M	CONNECTION TO INDUCTION	C	CENTRE CRUISING SPRING
O	OVER-RIDE SPRING	D	FLEXIBLE LEATHER DIAPHRAGM	I	IDLING SPRING ADJUSTMENT

Fig. 17-7

or injection pump, must provide accurately the corresponding control of the air-fuel ratio.

It was seen on page 256 that the simple carburettor delivers a mixture determined by rate of air flow, and not directly by load or speed, hence the necessity for correction in accordance with throttle opening to provide a weak economy mixture for cruising and a rich mixture for maximum load, that is for maximum b.m.e.p. and torque.

The situation with the injection pump is different—its delivery per cycle, for any given position of the control rack, is sensibly constant, and has no direct relation to the air flow. The two must be matched by a suitable mixture control device.

With aircraft engines these devices become extremely complicated, since large and rapid variations of atmospheric pressure and temperature, in addition to variations of load, must be provided for.

For normal conditions at ground level, variations of barometric pressure and temperature may, to a first approximation, be neglected, and the weight of air aspired per cycle may be assumed to be proportional to the absolute pressure in the manifold. If, then, the weight of fuel injected per cycle be made proportional to the same absolute pressure, constant mixture strength in any desired ratio at all speeds, subject to the speed-delivery characteristic of the pump, may be provided throughout the cruising range with suitable provision for enrichment at the extremes of throttle position for idling and for maximum b.m.e.p.

Fig. 17-6 illustrates such control as designed and as realized in an actual engine. Fuel delivery is plotted for convenience against a reversed scale of manifold depression, horizontal co-ordinates measured from the left representing absolute pressure.

Fig. 17-7 shows the direct acting mechanical device by which the above control was obtained.

Manifold depression reduces fuel delivery, spring loads increase it. The control-rod position and pump delivery corresponding to

373

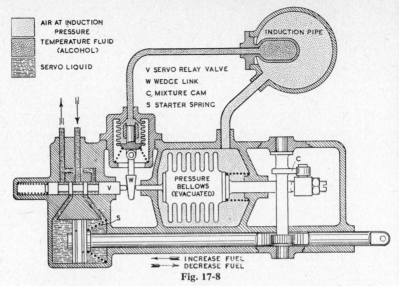

AIR AT INDUCTION PRESSURE
TEMPERATURE FLUID (ALCOHOL)
SERVO LIQUID

INDUCTION PIPE

V SERVO RELAY VALVE
W WEDGE LINK
C MIXTURE CAM
S STARTER SPRING

PRESSURE BELLOWS (EVACUATED)

V

W

S

C

← INCREASE FUEL
→ DECREASE FUEL

Fig. 17-8

any given depression is determined by the combined load of the three nested springs. Their cumulative effect is indicated in the small insert diagram in which control movement (fuel delivery) is plotted horizontally and depression vertically. The relationship between the three diagrams should be clear.

A servo-type mixture control is shown diagrammatically in Fig. 17-8. The servo-type mechanism would be employed where adequate power could be obtained only by excessive diameter of the bellows in the direct acting type. Oil under pressure from the lubricating circuit is used as the servo fluid. The action is as follows—

Assume the servo relay valve to be in the neutral position, causing the servo piston to be hydraulically locked in position. Should a reduction of depression, that is an increase of absolute pressure, occur in the induction manifold as a result of increased throttle opening, this will compress the bellows and allow the relay valve to move to the right under its own spring, the right-hand end of the bellows being located by the spring loaded follower of the mixture cam.

The valve movement allows fluid pressure to move the servo piston to the left and increase the fuel injection. At the same time this piston movement is fed back to the right-hand end of the bellows (which has taken up its new length) through the rack and pinion and the mixture cam to restore the valve to its central position and to lock the control in its new location. The exact relationship between the control-rod position and bellows configuration, that is between fuel delivery and manifold pressure, will be determined by the profile of the mixture cam.

374

A temperature correction is included in this apparatus, the principle of which will be clear from the diagram. A rise of temperature, calling for a reduction of fuel to compensate the reduced density of the air, will result in the lowering of the wedge link. This will partly neutralize the compression of the bellows referred to above, and so reduce the amount of control-rod movement required to restore equilibrium. Thus the increase in fuel delivery will be less than it would be without the temperature correction.

This device tends to over-correction at part load if correctly designed for maximum output, but an acceptable compromise can be arranged for moderate temperature changes.

17.4 Relative Performance

Performance figures obtained by Messrs. Brook and Nicolls on a four-cylinder engine of 1·4 litres capacity using the manifold location for the injector are shown in Fig. 17-9.

In the figure, the b.m.e.p. and volumetric efficiency curves are for full throttle conditions, while specific fuel consumption is plotted for half and three-quarter loads. At low speeds and quarter load, the injection system shows even greater relative economy, while at high speed and full throttle there is little to choose between the two systems.

The authors deal very fully in the paper with the development of the injection equipment in the new direction, and their work appears to indicate that there is little difficulty in designing and producing smaller and lighter types, while the less exacting conditions compared

Fig. 17-9: Relative performance with carburettor and
injection plugs

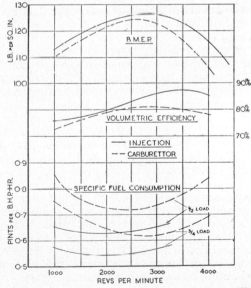

with the c.i. engine as regards pressure and timing, may lead to the development of simpler pumps and injectors.

Reduction in size alone does not appear to result in reduction of cost, which remains the overriding consideration in assessing prospects of future use and development.

When to the cost of the injection pump and injectors is added that of the mixture control devices, the injection system labours under a very serious handicap relatively to the cheap and readily maintained carburettor. Since there is no countervailing saving by elimination of the ignition equipment, it is inevitable that prices would be higher for the injection system though this would be offset to a greater or less degree by saving in fuel consumption.

An interesting paper was presented to the Automobile Division of the Institution of Mechanical Engineers on 4th April, 1950, by R. Barrington and E. W. Downing, describing work carried out by them for Messrs. Joseph Lucas, Ltd., and the Rover Company.

In this work, individual injectors were used, but an entirely different pumping and metering system. This comprised a low pressure pump delivering fuel at a constant pressure of 100 lb/sq. in. to a metering and distributor unit—for a four-cylinder engine—in which the same actual metering displacement was used for all cylinders, thus ensuring close uniformity of fuel distribution.

It is of great interest that this work has satisfactorily confirmed the general conclusions of Messrs. Brook and Nicolls.

17.5 Recent Developments

Since this early work was reported, very large sums have been spent on development in Europe and the U.S.A. However, there have been no important commercial applications in the ordinary car field, owing to the lack of interest of both manufacturers and users. Development was most active in the middle 50's, but interest has since decreased except in the case of a few expensive and high performance cars where the advantages can be utilized and paid for.

The main advantages are well established, namely improved performance and economy, both arising from better distribution and less restricted breathing. Valuable secondary advantages are: freedom from icing troubles, avoidance of acceleration disturbances during cornering and braking, quick starting and warm-up, and greater freedom in choice of fuels. However, the disadvantages of high cost, complication and lack of ordinary servicing facilities and experience still remain unsolved. In the U.S.A. the movement to " soft-pedal " claims for ever increasing power, speed and acceleration has tended to confine the main advantages to fuel economy. This movement may well have to be followed in Great Britain, until radically altered road and driving conditions have reduced the present carnage of road accidents. Moreover, the current simple and reliable four-cylinder petrol engine with a modern carburettor undoubtedly meets the requirements of the average responsible road user more than adequately.

Modern large scale production involving the investment of very large sums in automatic machinery and techniques militates against innovations unless they promise commercially adequate rewards.

In an important symposium referred to later, the American contributor, Errol J. Gay, gave the following estimated cost figures, which may of course already be somewhat out of date. They are American figures reduced to sterling, and relate to the more elaborate multibarrel carburettor systems. To compete in cost with even these relatively expensive modern systems, of around £12–18 per vehicle, the cost of injection equipment to the vehicle manufacturer would have to be reduced to this figure from the present estimate of £140 per unit. This reduction could be achieved by an increase in production from 100 units per week to 1,000 units per day, but would call for an expenditure of about £2 million in automatic machinery and tooling. So far there is no sign of a demand large and stable enough to justify this outlay.

Referring to Figs. 17-1, 2 and 3, most current systems are based on either port or manifold injection. The system may be of either the " timed " or " continuous " flow type. In the former, of which the Lucas system is an example, the movement of a shuttle, plunger or piston usually both meters and times the charge. In the latter, of which the Holley R-83 and the recently developed Tecalemit–Jackson system are examples, there is continuous flow through the ring main from which the fuel is distributed and metered to the injectors on the " rate of flow multiplied by time " principle.

The symposium referred to previously consists of a summary of developments in petrol injection in Britain by E. W. Downing, in U.S.A. by Errol J. Gay and in Germany by H. Heinrich and H. Stoll. The papers were read and discussed before the Automobile Division of the Institution of Mechanical Engineers on 15th April 1958 and reported in the *Auto. Division Proceedings* 1957–58 (No. 6). Very well illustrated descriptions of all the important developments up to that date, some of great complexity, are included in the Symposium, to which the interested reader is referred for detailed information.

17.6 Tecalemit–Jackson System

The recently produced Tecalemit–Jackson low pressure system holds out prospects of mitigating the handicaps of high cost and multiplication of precision parts, and should help to relieve the call for skilled staff and extensive resources in the maintenance field.

Though a considerable number of auxiliary control units is provided for in the design, as in all systems, these are of simple form and may not all be required in any particular installation.

The system is of the continuous flow, ring main type, the injectors discharging into the valve ports as shown in Fig. 17–10, but being of a tubular form, so that their length and position can be adjusted experimentally to determine the most favourable location and direction. The form of the injector is shown in Fig. 17–11.

377

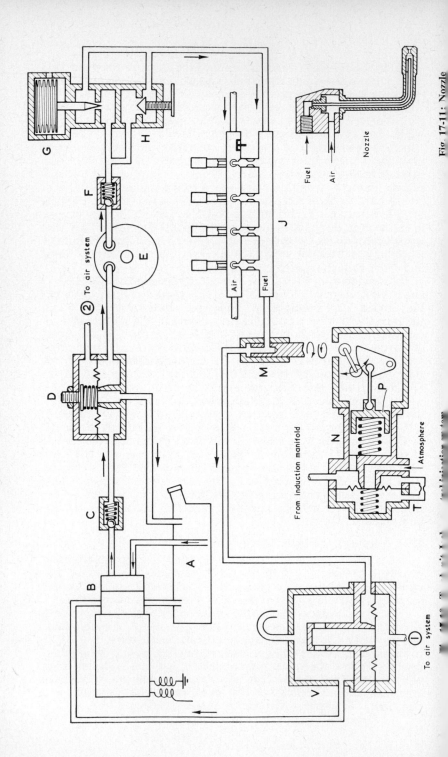

Fig 17-11: Nozzle

Equal distribution to all ports is ensured by restrictors in the tubes delivering the fuel to the injectors. It has been found that tubular restrictors of experimentally determined length give more accurate and stable control than short jets of the carburettor type. According to the manufacturers, adjustment can be made to ± 1 per cent.

The process of continuous delivery, during the closed as well as during the shorter open period of the inlet valves, would at first sight appear liable to derange the distribution by straying of the fuel charge from the appropriate valve port to its neighbours, but experience indicates that this does not occur. The rate of evaporation during this "waiting" period can be controlled by varying the size of the droplets caused by the atomizing air in the injector, and though the closed period is a large proportion of the total time of the valve cycle, it is yet a very small interval at cruising speeds, say one fiftieth of a second.

The basic units in the metering process are three pumps, scavenge, lift and pressure all of the same very simple construction, and a rotary variable restrictor valve operated by manifold vacuum. This rotary control valve provides the variable by-pass orifice which under the operating pressure determines the "time rate" of flow in parallel through the nozzles. The pressure pump is engine driven and develops a pressure proportional to the square of engine speed, with a maximum of about 90 lb/sq. in. at 6,000 r.p.m. The *velocity* of flow, applying the orifice formula, thus becomes proportional to engine speed, and multiplying by the orifice area, the rate of flow in say c.c./sec is obtained.

These basic units are shown at B, E, M and N of Fig. 17-10 while J is the fuel rail with four sets of distribution restrictors and injection nozzles.

The very simple construction of the three fuel pumps will be seen

Fig 17-12

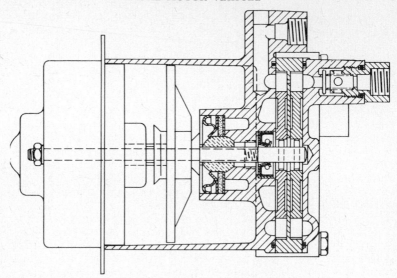

Fig. 17-13: Scavenge and lift pumps

in the photographic view, Fig. 17-12, and in the line illustration, Fig. 17-13, which shows the back-to-back assembly of the electrically driven scavenge and lift pumps. The disc-type rotors run closely between the bottom of a shallow recess in the body and the cover plate, which carries a semicircular annular groove extending around the greater part of the circumference.

Inlet and delivery ports are formed at the ends of the groove. The disc rotors are " gashed " to form rectangular cells the volume of which is partly in the rotor and partly in the groove.

The pumping action is somewhat as follows: centrifugal force sets up a spiral vortex between the rotor and the groove with a steadily increasing angular velocity. At the end of the groove this vortex is abruptly destroyed, and the velocity energy is converted to pressure energy proportional to the square of the rotor speed, up to the maximum value quoted above. The action is broadly similar to that in a fluid flywheel or Froude brake. This form of pump is simple and inexpensive to make and may be a sealed assembly.

The method of operation of the control mechanism N is as follows: Variations of vacuum in the engine manifold are transmitted to the chamber immediately above the piston P, so that the position of this piston is determined by the balance between the vacuum and the coil spring in the chamber. The movement of the piston is communicated to the rotary valve (which is practically the only component calling for precision production) by the cam and lever shown. When the vacuum is reduced by the opening of the throttle, the by-pass orifice becomes smaller, which results in a

380

greater proportion of the total flow passing to the injectors, this flow being continuous and uniformly distributed by the tubular restrictors previously mentioned.

The chamber on the left of the diagram deals with the rapid change of manifold pressure which results from sudden opening of the throttle, performing a similar function to the accelerating pump of the fixed choke carburettor and the dashpot piston of the constant vacuum class. Induction pipe pressure is applied to both sides of the spring-loaded diaphragm valve through the balance connection shown at T which is provided with a restrictor. This restrictor has no effect on slow changes, but a sudden reduction of vacuum (increase in absolute pressure) which may be subject to delay in communication from the induction pipe, is further delayed by the restrictor in reaching the back of the diaphragm. The unbalance of pressure results in opening the valve to atmospheric pressure which is immediately communicated to the back of the piston, causing rapid movement of the control valve to give increased flow of fuel. When pressure balance on the diaphragm is quickly restored, normal control by induction manifold depression and engine speed only, is resumed.

Secondary units in the ring main comprise the following. Non-return check valve C; relief valve D for surplus fuel; check valve F set to the same opening pressure as D, in order to ensure that the engine pump delivery head shall depend on the square of pump speed only; aneroid device G subject to ambient air pressure; enrichment device H for cold starting, and fuel return collector V with air balance valve.

Connections 1 and 2 are made to communicate the pressure of the atomizing air to the diaphragms of D and V, in order to ensure that the fuel pressure shall always exceed the air pressure, and so prevent the latter interfering with the fuel flow.

The relative absolute pressures at the fuel, air and delivery orifices of the nozzles are indicated diagrammatically in Fig. 17-14

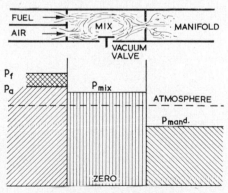

Fig. 17-14: Pressures in nozzle

which is of the same form as Figs. 11-1 and 11-16. The actual construction of the injection nozzles is shown in Fig. 17-11 from which the method of introducing the atomising air should be clear. The delivery orifice plays no part in the metering of the fuel. The air circuit is very simply arranged, and consists of an ordinary A.C.-Delco mechanical pump delivering air at about 3 lb/sq.in, a diaphragm operated electrical switch assembly to control the electric pump, and an air distribution manifold. The latter is provided with a vacuum break valve to ensure that the pressure behind the delivery orifice cannot fall below atmospheric, thus ensuring that the main induction pipe vacuum cannot interfere with the flow.

A comprehensive description, with details of construction of the various units will be found in *Automobile Engineer* of July 1964. It will be seen that, while numerous, these components are of simple and inexpensive construction, and lend themselves to " package " assembly as required.

THE GAS TURBINE

The gas turbine, which for many years has been the dream of inventors, has inspired a wealth of technical literature and experimental enterprise, but has shown very limited practical and commercial progress until the last three decades, culminating in the spectacular development of the turbo-jet propulsion of aircraft.

It is natural to consider whether the turbine is likely to become a serious competitor of the piston engine for road vehicles.

The following articles, published by the *Automobile Engineer*, should be consulted for further reference: F. R. Bell, " The Gas Turbine Car," Vol. 43, No. 3, and " Gas Turbine Arrangements," Vol. 43, No. 8. The most recent paper on the Chrysler gas turbine car is that which was presented before the Automobile Division of the Institution of Mechanical Engineers on 13th April 1965. Readers interested in the theory of the design of gas turbines are advised to consult *Jet Propulsion Engines*, edited by O. E. Lancaster and published by the Oxford University Press, London (1959).

17.7 Two Fields of Successful Application

The ultimate objective of automobile and power plant engineers is the replacement of the complicated, noisy, and vibration-prone reciprocating piston engine by a self-contained power unit which shall deliver energy by direct rotative motion.

The valuable features of mechanical simplicity, lightness and ultimately, cheapness, can certainly be achieved, and if fuel economy and reasonable reliability and life can be realized, the piston engine will gradually be superseded.

Unfortunately very great difficulties arise in satisfying these latter conditions, and the two fields in which successful development

382

has taken place represent special applications in favourable circumstances.

The first of these is in the use of the turbine as an adjunct to the piston engine for supercharging purposes, on which some notes are included in Chapter 13, and the second as a means of supplying kinetic energy to the jet used for the propulsion by reaction of high speed aircraft.

It should be realized that jet propulsion is quite unsuitable for the efficient propulsion of low speed vehicles, apart from traffic conditions.

The " turbo-prop " system represents an approach to the self-contained unit delivering shaft power, but in an application where economy and endurance are not factors of overriding importance as in ordinary commercial fields. The system has a higher efficiency than the pure jet system at lower altitudes and speeds.

Fig. 17-15 represents in simple diagram form the turbo-jet and turbo-prop jet systems. The success achieved represents a remarkable advance in overcoming two of the main problems of the rotative unit, the provision of an efficient rotary compressor and the

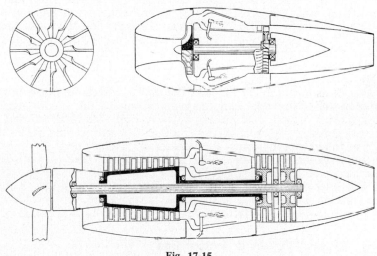

Fig. 17-15

production of turbine blade materials which will give an acceptable endurance in this application.

The thermal efficiency, however, remains far below that of the supercharged diesel engine, and even below that of the best steam plant.

In Fig. 17-15, a centrifugal compressor is indicated in the pure jet system, feeding multiple combustion chambers which usually

383

fill the available annular space. An enlarged front view of the impeller is shown on the left, and indicates how the blades are curved to provide for axial entry to the eye with the minimum of shock. It should be noted that as the vanes have no curvature in diametral planes, centrifugal force has no tendency to distort their shape.

The lower diagram indicates an axial flow compressor, this type showing higher efficiency than the centrifugal type. It will be noticed that the two turbines are mechanically quite independent, but utilize the combustion gases in series. The compressors are required to supply a great excess of air over that required for complete combustion, not only to prevent excessive heating of the parts, but also to provide the necessary mass-velocity characteristics of the propulsive jet.

17.8   Essential Processes in I.C. Power Units

The three essential processes in any internal combustion power unit are compression of the air charge, combustion of the fuel, and expansion of the products as completely as possible to produce mechanical work. The greater the degree of compression and expansion, and the greater the range of temperature effectively utilized, the higher will be the thermal efficiency and the lower the specific fuel consumption. These conditions apply to both piston and turbine engines.

The piston engine can accomplish the first two processes with high efficiency and reliability, but is less successful with the third owing to its unsuitability for handling the large volumes at the low pressure end of the expansion, this being incomplete unless continued in a turbine, which is admirably suited to deal with large volumes at low pressure. Hence, as explained in Chapter 13, the exhaust turbo supercharger forms a mechanically independent but not thermodynamically self-contained high-speed unit which increases the power of the main engine but does not require to be geared to the low-speed power shaft. Moreover, since the gases reach the turbine blades at a manageable temperature, no insoluble temperature-stress-time factor arises with the material of the blading.

17.9   Essential Organs in Turbine Unit

In a self-contained turbine unit separate organs must be provided for all three processes, the compressor as well as the turbine being of the rotary form, and driven by the main or an auxiliary turbine. The combustion chamber or chambers must receive the compressed air, the liquid fuel must be injected, and the combustion be completed before the products are passed to the turbine. This combustion must be done in a light and compact arrangement, capable of withstanding the high temperature of continuous combustion over an acceptable working life.

384

In the present stage of the art, and with available materials, it is not possible to produce organs which in combination can approach the efficiency of the piston unit, in spite of the ability of the turbine to provide complete expansion.

The most successful rotary compressors yet built achieve at best only about 80 per cent of the efficiency of their piston counterparts, owing to the inherent aerodynamic difficulty of controlling by high-speed rotary means the flow of light fluids. The pressure ratios that can be used are restricted both by the limitations of the compressor and also indirectly by the inability of the turbine blading and rotor to withstand for sufficiently long periods the combination of high temperature and high centrifugal stresses that are involved in the subsequent expansion process.

The net useful output of the plant is the difference between the power developed by the turbine and the power absorbed by the compressor, and it is interesting to note that the net 2,000 h.p. of the Brown-Boveri gas turbine locomotive,* corrected for losses in electric transmission, is the difference between the turbine output of about 10,000 h.p. and the compressor consumption of nearly 8,000 h.p. It will be readily realized that a reduction of 10 per cent in efficiency of both units would eliminate this net difference, and the early days of gas turbine development involved a succession of failures in which the output of the turbine proved insufficient to drive its own compressor. Thus fundamental aerodynamic difficulties in compressor design and material limitations in the turbine have resulted in efficiencies so low as to make the specific fuel consumption of the most successful gas turbine units greater than the average steam plant and far above the best diesel engine practice.

On the other hand, there are many actual and prospective advantages which fully justify expenditure on research and development. The most hopeful field appears to lie in the range of 2,000 to 10,000 b.h.p.

In the case of jet propulsion there are certain favourable factors which are not realized in industrial applications. The low air temperature at high altitudes results in the turbine blading being exposed to less destructive temperatures than would normally arise. The time period during which the blades are so exposed is less, both on account of load factor and the limited endurance that is required or expected, fuel economy is not a first consideration, and finally in the pure jet unit the useful power output is not subject to turbine blading losses as in the case of power delivery by shaft.

17.10   Gas Turbines for Road Transport

Here the situation is much less favourable, in spite of the ultimate advantages of lightness, simplicity and compactness, absence of

*See *Proc. I. Mech. E.*, Vol. 141, No. 3, and *Automobile Engineer*, Vol. 32, No. 6.

necessity for a cooling system and negligible oil consumption, all added to the much acclaimed advantage of direct production of rotative effort. This latter may even prove to some extent an embarrassment owing to the extremely high rotational speeds involved relatively to road wheel speeds, necessitating a large gear reduction.

17.11 Essential Characteristics of Turbine Prime Movers

When the energy of expansion of high-temperature gases is expended in giving kinetic jet energy to the gases themselves, gas velocities of several thousand feet per second are generated, depending on the temperature range of the expansion, which in turn is limited by the maximum temperature to which the turbine blades may be continuously exposed.

The efficient extraction and utilization of this energy involves correspondingly high speeds of movement of the parts operated upon, whether these parts are the blades of a turbine or the vehicle on which a propulsive jet reacts.

As with the Pelton water-wheel, which is the simplest form of impulse turbine, for maximum efficiency the blade speed should be about half the jet speed, and with single-stage impulse wheels peripheral blade speeds of 1,000 to 1,200 ft/sec are now normal practice in gas turbine work.

These speeds may be reduced by using multiple stages, and a gas turbine impulse wheel may be provided with two rows of blades with stationary deflector vanes between them. With this arrangement the gas velocity is extracted in two steps, and the peripheral blade speed may be about one-third of the initial gas velocity. Even so, since the power normally required for automobile work can be obtained from wheels of 6 in to 8 in diameter, rotational speeds of 40,000 to 50,000 r.p.m. will have to be provided for in design. The high rotational inertia consequent on such speeds leads to troublesome time-lag in response to throttle control.

A turbine is a high-speed, unidirectional prime mover capable of handling very large volumes of fluid flow with high mechanical efficiency—actually of the order of 85 to 90 per cent if correctly designed—and its torque will increase with a decrease of speed for a given input; but this will be accompanied by loss of efficiency, since the fixed angles of the blading are correct only for certain relative speeds of jet and blades.

17.12 Automobile Power Unit

For automobile work it becomes necessary to use either electrical transmission, which is expensive and heavy, or a separate work turbine independent of the turbo-compressor shaft. This power turbine is geared to the road wheels, while the compressor unit can be run up to speed with the car stationary. The exhaust from

386

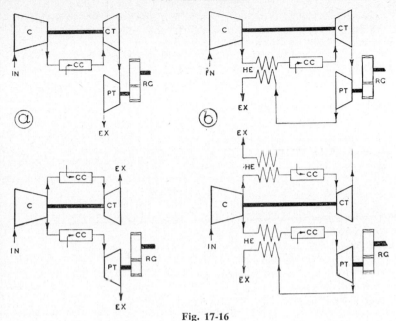

Fig. 17-16

the compressor turbine would thus develop a fluid drive effect on the power turbine and exert on it a starting torque. This arrangement of the power unit is shown in simple diagram form in the upper diagrams of (a) and (b) in Fig. 17-16. A single combustion chamber CC feeds the compressor turbine CT and the power turbine PT in series. The lower diagrams show two combustion chambers in parallel, so providing independent control for the power turbine. Diagrams (a) show the simplest possible layout for each system, while diagrams (b) indicate the use of heat exchangers HE which improve thermal efficiency by transferring some of the waste heat in the exhaust to the combustion air between the compressor and the combustion chamber. RG is the reduction gearing between the turbine and the propellor shaft, a very large ratio being required.

17.13 Fuel Consumption

Low thermal efficiency remains the great stumbling-block. Unless a heat exchanger is used, the specific fuel consumption will probably be twice that of the average petrol engine and three times that of the diesel, though possibly of a cheaper fuel. While the commercial user will assess lower capital and maintenance costs as a set-off against higher fuel consumption and cost, this aspect will appeal less to the private motorist, whose accounts rarely include depreciation and interest.

It will, moreover, be many years before a low selling price can be realized, even with reduced production costs, owing to the necessarily very high cost of development work.

All things considered, the gas turbine for the private car can be regarded only as a somewhat remote prospect.

17.14 Heat Exchangers

Heat exchangers are essential in large plants to reduce fuel consumption, but their bulk and weight are objections in automobile applications. Much theoretical and practical research is being devoted to improve their construction and performance, and the ultimate position of the turbine power plant in the automobile field will depend vitally on these developments.

Heat exchangers for the application under discussion may be classified into two types. Firstly, the static recuperative type, in which the heat passes by conduction from one fluid stream to the other through plate and tubular surfaces. This type is familiar in a great variety of domestic and industrial applications. In relation to performance the type is bulky and heavy. Secondly, the regenerative, or change-over type, in which the two streams alternately deposit in, and extract the heat from, the refractory material, which in large industrial applications usually consists of a nest of fire bricks, through which the streams are directed in turn.

For light power applications attention is now concentrated on the development of compact revolving units, in which matrices of a suitable material in mesh form are carried in a drum revolving at 20 to 30 r.p.m., the two streams passing continuously, each through an appropriate portion of the rotor profile. Each portion of the matrix picks up and deposits heat as it passes from one stream to the other. The Ford research organization has published information* in regard to a rotor construction in which a dual band of stainless steel strip is wound between a 4 in diameter hub and an outer drum about 20 in diameter. The drive is through a small pinion engaging a toothed ring on the periphery of the drum.

The material of the strip is 2 thousandths of an inch thick, the two layers being plain and corrugated alternately. This provides an extremely high surface volume ratio, and a number of flow passages estimated at a quarter of a million. This ensures that the matrix is an extremely efficient means of transfer of heat for its bulk and weight. This is known as the " flame trap system."

Clearly, means of pressure sealing are required where the rotor profile passes through the boundary wall separating the two streams, and formidable constructional difficulties call for solution.

* " Engineering Details of Ford Rotary Heat Exchanger for Gas Turbine Engines," by W. Wai Chao, Section Supervisor, Combustor and Heat Exchanger Section, Scientific Laboratory, Ford Motor Co. Abstract of a Paper presented by the Author at the 17th Annual Meeting of the American Power Conference in Chicago. *Automotive Industries*, 15th May, 1955, p. 54.

17.15   Current Turbine Developments

The Rover Company achieved striking success in the 1963 and 1965 Le Mans twenty-four hours race with their Rover–B.R.M sports car, the first turbine powered car to compete in this race.

In 1963 no regenerator was fitted, and the fuel consumption was naturally high at 6·9 m.p.g., but power output and mechanical reliability enabled the car to finish 8th at an average speed of 108 m.p.h.

In 1964 a heat-exchanger of the regenerator type, incorporating ceramic drums, had been developed, but time for reliability tests was limited, and it was decided not to enter for the race.

The race of 1965 saw a remarkable step forward in fuel economy, achieved by the use of the heat exchanger referred to above, though unfortunately it was necessary to limit performance owing to a mishap to the blading of the compressor turbine early in the race. None the less the car was the leading British entrant, and was placed tenth in a field of fifty-one of which only fourteen finished. At an average speed of 99 m.p.h. the consumption was at 13·5 m.p.g. —little more than half the 1963 figure.

An informative illustrated article will be found in *Automobile Engineer*, Vol. 55 No. 9.

The Firebird II Chassis, which is being developed by General Motors, is powered by the G.T.-304 " Whirlfire " turbine unit which incorporates a rotary regenerative type heat exchanger.

All the basic components will be under test in combination, and some reliable forecast of eventual efficiencies should be possible. Improvement in aero-dynamic efficiency of the compressor and turbine units will be a slower and less spectacular long-term advance, though since final power output is the net difference between positive and negative powers of the same order, relatively small improvements result in considerable gains.

Metallurgical advance and manufacturing techniques determine cost and endurance rather than thermodynamic efficiency.

The general lay-out of the G.T.304 " Whirlfire " unit is shown diagrammatically in Fig. 17-17. This specially drawn schematic illustration is based on information given in one of two papers, describing the Firebird II chassis and its power unit, by four members of the research staff of the General Motors Corporation and published in *J. Soc. Automotive Eng.*, Vol. 64, 1956. The present Authors are much indebted to the above society for permission to make this brief extract indicating the present stage of development.

The general lay-out consists of an accessories section incorporating a gear-driven hydraulic pump for powering the hydraulic motors which drive the rotary regenerators, fuel injection control and lubricating apparatus, and other auxiliary units.

The gasifier section comprises a single-stage centrifugal air-compressor delivering to a plenum from which the compressed and warmed air passes radially through a symmetrical pair of revolving

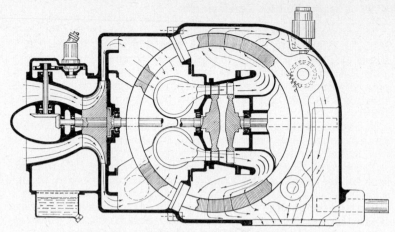

Fig. 17-17: General Motors G.T. 304 " Whirlfire " unit

drum-type regenerators. The heat picked up by the matrix of each regenerator as it passes through the hot exhaust stream is imparted to the air as it passes to the four symmetrically placed " can-type " combustors. From the combustors the high-temperature gases pass through the nozzle ring mounted in a dividing bulkhead to the turbine chamber. The velocity acquired in the nozzle ring is extracted in the two separate single-stage impulse turbines in series, the power turbine discharging the hot exhaust to a deflector ring which directs the stream to pass radially outwards through the regenerators. The matrices are thereby heated and the cooled exhaust passes out at the bottom of the casing.

The driving pinions, supporting rollers and floating seals where the regenerator drums pass through the dividing bulkhead, are indicated. The construction of the seals is the subject of intensive research and development, and little information is available.

Reduction gearing is provided to the power output shaft, whence a long transmission shaft leads to the final gearing at the rear of the chassis. The normal speeds of the compressor and power turbines are 35,000 and 28,000 r.p.m. respectively, and the regenerators revolve at 20 to 30 r.p.m.

17.16 New Ford Power Unit

Automobile Engineer, Vol. 49, No. 8, contains a description of a new turbine power unit currently under development by the Ford Motor Company of America. This unit, known as the 704 model, is making a successful attack on the problem of high fuel consumption by novel arrangement of the various units, giving a somewhat complicated assembly.

Two stage compression, with intercooling, is employed, the compression ratio of each stage being 4 to 1. The secondary, or

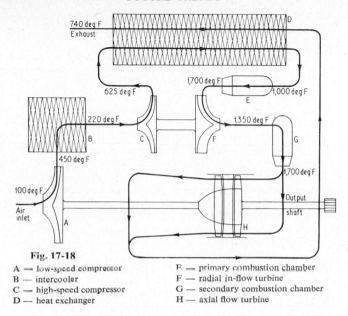

Fig. 17-18

A — low-speed compressor
B — intercooler
C — high-speed compressor
D — heat exchanger

E — primary combustion chamber
F — radial in-flow turbine
G — secondary combustion chamber
H — axial flow turbine

high speed compressor runs at the very high speed of 91,000 r.p.m. as compared with 46,500 r.p.m. of the low speed unit. There are also two combustion chambers, the first interposed between the heat exchanger and the high speed inward flow radial turbine, from which the gases pass to the secondary combustion chamber where a further supply of fuel is introduced. The exhaust products then pass to the main axial turbine which drives the low speed compressor and the output shaft. The arrangement of the components is shown diagrammatically in Fig. 17-18 with approximate gas temperature at the various stages.

The weight is stated to be 650 lb for a power output of about 300 b.h.p., or about one-quarter of the weight of a corresponding diesel engine. The overall dimensions are about 38 in long, 29 in high and 28 in wide. A wide variety of fuels can be used, with a consumption of only 0·48 to 0·58 lb/b.h.r.-hr. according to load.

17.17   Chrysler Turbine Car

In 1963 the Chrysler Corporation achieved limited production of a completely new turbine driven car which they are supplying to selected customers in order to obtain user experience.

This will be an expensive form of development, but one likely to prove most fruitful.

The basic arrangement of the power plant follows the generally accepted system of two mechanically independent turbine wheels of the single-stage impulse type, through which the gas stream

391

passes in series. They are axial flow wheels, the front one driving the single stage radial compressor with an extension shaft serving the auxiliaries.

Of the two, the rearmost is the power turbine. This is larger than the compressor wheel, and is provided with a novel arrangement of variable angle guide vanes which is one of the many interesting features of the power unit. The direction of the gas stream on to the turbine blading may be varied from maximum power, through economy and idling to a braking position. The operating gear is one of the hydraulic auxiliaries all fed from a single pump.

A heat exchanger system consisting of a symmetrical pair of rotary regenerators of the multicellular type is employed. These regenerators are about 15 in. diameter and driven by spur reduction gearing from the compressor shaft at 9 to 22 r.p.m. Designed for axial flow, the compactly arranged and well insulated ducting leads the air-flow from the compressor volute through the front halves of the regenerator wheels, where it is pre-heated, to the single combustion chamber mounted underneath the main casing. The

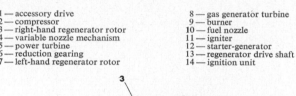

1 — accessory drive	8 — gas generator turbine
2 — compressor	9 — burner
3 — right-hand regenerator rotor	10 — fuel nozzle
4 — variable nozzle mechanism	11 — igniter
5 — power turbine	12 — starter-generator
6 — reduction gearing	13 — regenerator drive shaft
7 — left-hand regenerator rotor	14 — ignition unit

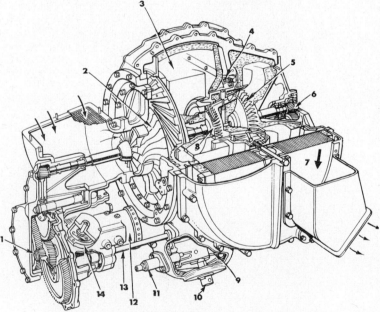

Fig. 17-19: Chrysler turbine unit

housing of the outer diametral seal of the left hand regenerator may be noted in Fig. 17-19. No details of the sealing strips are available.

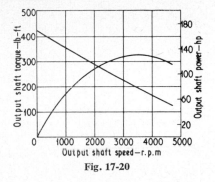

Fig. 17-20

As it is injected the fuel burns with excess air, and the combustion products pass first, through fixed guide vanes, to the compressor turbine, and thence through the variable angle guide vanes for the second stage of expansion in the power turbine.

The hot exhaust is ducted to the rear halves of the interchangers where the wheels absorb heat and transfer it to the contrary air stream from the compressor. A pair of aluminium alloy ducts leads the exhaust to the rear of the car.

In the part sectioned pictorial view, Fig. 17-19, is shown the general arrangement, and many of the details can be seen.

The heat exchangers and ducting are skilfully and compactly arranged, and indeed a great part of the total bulk is due to the auxiliaries and their drives, and the front air intake and cleaner.

Fig. 17-20 gives torque and power plotted against output shaft speed, and the valuable feature of high torque at low speed will be noted.

The power turbine may be stalled to zero speed, but will continue to develop full torque, as the compressor unit will run independently.

An informative article giving particulars of transmission and automatic controls, and further structural details, will be found in *Automobile Engineer* Vol. 53, No. 12.

FREE-PISTON GAS GENERATOR

The relatively high efficiency of the piston compressor as compared with the centrifugal type has revived interest in the " free-piston " engine in combination with an expansion turbine in the hope that it may be possible to " make the best of both worlds."

The conventional connecting-rod and crankshaft arrangement, and any attempt at mechanical linkage between the high-speed rotary turbine and a low-speed reciprocating mechanism has been discarded, the free-piston engine-compressor unit being a self-contained provider of high-pressure, moderate-temperature gases ready for delivery to the expansion turbine with which it is associated. The exhaust gases from the diesel cycle are diluted with a large excess of scavenge air and the temperature of the mixture is determined almost completely by the delivery pressure. Compression of air and combustion of fuel are complete in the gas-generator unit, and the turbine unit then has the duty of developing the mechanical

393

power output, there being no net delivery of power from the piston " compressor-combustion " unit.

The free-piston engine has been known in various forms for many years, and the present revival of interest is based on the Pescara free-piston engine system as developed by S.E.M.E./ S.I.G.M.A. in France and Alan Muntz & Co., Ltd., in the U.K.

The term gas generator or " gasifier " is used to describe these units in a general sense, and to cover a variety of applications using a wide range of fuels.

To date two sizes have been developed, the 1,250 gas h.p. " GS-34 " in France and the 420 gas h.p. " CS-75 " in England. These run at moderate speeds, 600 and 1,080 oscillations per minute respectively, but research and development are being actively prosecuted with a view to developing much smaller, higher speed versions for heavy road vehicle application with the objective of combining rotary power with diesel economy.

Though the gasifier is somewhat bulky, the space and the weight of a heat exchanger is saved, and the overall thermal efficiency is considerably greater than that at present obtainable with the rotary compressor, combustion-chamber turbine combination even if a heat exchanger is used.

Some details are now available of an experimental unit developed by the Research Department of General Motors Corporation, and described in a paper presented to the Society of Automotive Engineers by A. F. Underwood of the Research Department. A brief description is given later.

The diagram shown in Fig. 17-21 is based on illustrations given in an interesting and comprehensive paper by E. S. L. Beale, M.A., F.Inst. Pet., A.M.I.Mech.E., and P. Watson, B.A., read before the Diesel Engineers and Users Association. The present authors are indebted to the Council of the Association for permission to extract information, and also to Mr. F. A. I. Muntz, B.A., for many helpful suggestions. The paper describes development work in France in connection with power-plant for generating stations, cargo ships and locomotives and deals authoritatively with the basic principles and constructional problems.

Alan Muntz and Co., Ltd., of Feltham, Middlesex, hold the exclusive licence for manufacture under Pescara S.E.P. and Alan Muntz Patents for the British Commonwealth and Egypt, and they have supplied to General Motors Corporation and Renault 420 gas h.p. CS-75 units for experimental purposes. The diagram shown in Fig. 17-21 is applicable to this unit.

It will be seen that the unit consists of two opposed two-stroke diesel pistons fed with scavenge air by integral compressor pistons.

The backs of the compressor pistons compress air in closed cushion or " bounce " cylinders, starting being effected by the application of a compressed air supply to these.

Synchronous movement of the two opposed piston units is ensured either by a light twin rack and pinion or by a link rod

394

mechanism which serves to absorb any slight inequalities of frictional resistance and pressure discrepancies, and is quite lightly loaded.

Dynamic balance is ensured by the opposed motions of the two piston assemblies of equal weight, but unlike the ordinary opposed piston engine described elsewhere, in which large forces are mutually balanced by linkages involving heavily loaded and vulnerable bearings, in the free-piston engine or " gasifier " mutual reaction is provided by air pressures and longitudinal tension in the casing, unlikely to give any operational trouble.

An overstroke fuel trip to eliminate any risk of mechanical impact, and a cushion air stabilizing device are provided.

The motion and cycle time of the moving parts are determined automatically by their inertias and the " spring reaction " of the compressed air in the bounce cylinders. Normally the rate of oscillation at minimum output is about 60 per cent of that at maximum output.

As far as individual gasifiers are concerned, surplus air must be blown to waste below about 30 per cent of maximum output, but where a single turbine is fed from several gasifiers, an arrangement incidentally which achieves a wider range of load control and at the same time reduces the risk of shut-down through a single mechanical failure, output can be reduced by shutting down one or more units.

Within the limited range of output variation which is possible, stability is obtained automatically by transfer of air between the bounce cylinders and the engine-case in the appropriate direction through a stabilizer valve.

A gasifier power unit may thus be defined as one in which the power is first generated in the form of moderately hot gas under pressure and then converted into mechanical power at the shaft of a turbine or reciprocating engine. The gas horse-power (g.h.p.) is the potential horse-power in the gases leaving the gasifier measured as the product of the " adiabatic heat drop " of the hot gases if expanded to atmospheric pressure and the mass flow per minute.

It is of interest to compare and contrast three power systems in which the superiority of the piston engine for dealing with high pressures and temperatures and small volumes is, or has been, exploited.

In a transition stage of marine steam propulsion, reciprocating engines dealt with the high-pressure stages of expansion, and turbines with the lower, or large-volume stages. Similarly in the case of both the exhaust-turbo supercharged diesel engine and the free-piston gasifier, the high-pressure compression and the high-temperature combustion, as well as the initial stages of the expansion and cooling, take place in the piston units.

In the first system a high proportion of the net power output is delivered by the reciprocating unit, in the second, the whole of it, and in the third the whole is delivered by the turbine.

In none of the three is there any mechanical link between the reciprocating and the turbine mechanisms.

395

It has been suggested that just as the marine combined system represented a transition stage during the gradual improvement in materials and manufacturing technique, so the free-piston gasifier may represent only an ephemeral development.

The two cases are not quite parallel however, and moreover the difficulties presented by the design of an efficient, compact and inexpensive heat exchanger are immediately solved in the free-piston engine by the direct application of expansive energy to accomplish the necessary compression.

There is also the very important advantage that neither the free-piston gasifier, nor the complementary turbine which is relieved of extreme temperature conditions, require any better or more expensive materials than those in widespread and familiar use in steam turbines for many years.

Accessibility and ease of maintenance compare very favourably with the large diesel engine.

Turning to Fig. 17-21 the general arrangement of the complete power-unit will be clear.

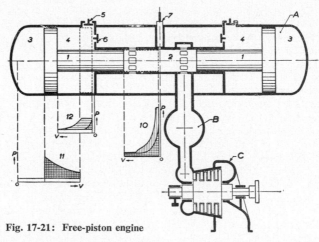

Fig. 17-21: Free-piston engine

The two-stroke diesel cylinder, 2, in which move the opposed pistons, 1, is charged with scavenge air from the annular engine case surrounding the cylinder, this case being supplied with air from the inward compressing spaces, 4, through automatic delivery valves, 6. At the " dead centre " a light linkage operates the fuel injectors, 7, and the pistons are driven apart, compressing the air in the cushion or " bounce " chambers, 3. When the exhaust ports are uncovered the gases are delivered to the gas collector chamber, B, from which the turbine, C, is fed, at a temperature normally less than 500° C (900° F).

In the small indicator diagrams, which are not plotted to the same pressure scale, the areas, when applied to the appropriate

396

volumes and corrected for friction and cooling losses will show no net positive work, because the whole of the positive work of the diesel pistons is absorbed by the compressor pistons. The useful work delivered by the turbine is the available energy from the net heat in the exhaust from the diesel cylinder when the gases are expanded in the turbine down to atmospheric pressure.

The overall compression ratio and pressure in the diesel cylinder will depend on load and will usually be considerably higher than in an ordinary diesel engine because this engine is very highly supercharged, but piston and piston ring problems are now well understood, and there are no cylinder-head distortion and gasket difficulties to be solved.

The diagram shows the " inward compression " system.

17.18 General Motors Free-piston Developments

In the paper mentioned above, and presented by A. F. Underwood of the Research Department of General Motors Corporation before the Society of Automotive Engineers, some account is given of a free-piston turbine unit installed in a chassis similar to that used for the experimental " Firebird " turbine installation. This free-piston project is referred to as XP500.

An interesting and valuable comparison should eventually be possible between these two turbine systems.

A twin compressing unit is employed which enables the advantages of simplicity and accessibility, with freedom from ducting, to be realized without the accompanying disadvantage of unfavourable phasing of the periods of scavenge delivery and cylinder port opening, which is avoided by " outward compression," but at the cost of ducting and sacrifice of accessibility.

The twinned units may be started in phase to give full combined delivery and will then automatically, under the action of a pneumatic de-phaser, take up a 180° phase motion, each pair of pistons providing the scavenge air for the other. It is stated that this system of twinned units emanated from the Societé des Études Mécaniques et Energetiques (S.E.M.E.).

The name " Hyprex " has been given to the twin General Motors unit which is nominally rated at 250 g.h.p. but is probably equivalent to a 300 h.p. conventional engine when the high starting torque of the turbine at low vehicle speeds is taken into account.

The overall dimensions of the free piston unit are 3 ft 4 in. long, 2 ft 10 in. wide and 1 ft 6 in. deep.

Two power pistons of 4 in. diameter are integral with compressor pistons of 11 in. diameter, the operating stroke being about 5 in. at maximum cycle speed of 2,400 cycles per minute.

The compression ratio ranges from 30 : 1 to 50 : 1.

The temperature of the gases entering the turbine ranges from 450° to 900° F.

397

A synchronizing linkage of parallelogram form is used, the work of this being confined to compensating friction differences, injection pump drive and controls.

As an alternative to blowing off air at reduced loads, " recirculation " by by-passing air between the receiver, or engine casing, and the compressor air intake, is used. This warms the air and assists ignition at the lower compression ratio on light loads.

The gas turbine is a five-stage axial-flow unit driving through a gear box with 7 : 1 reduction ratio.

A specific fuel consumption of less than 0·45 lb/gas h.p.-hr. was recorded during preliminary testing.

Satisfactory weight distribution is obtained by mounting the gasifier at the front of the chassis and piping the gases to the turbine and transmission unit at the rear.

PART 3 : TRANSMISSION

CHAPTER 18
Transmission Requirements

Arrangement of clutch, gear box and rear axle transmission.   Four-wheel drive. De Dion drive.

IT has been seen in the previous chapters that the internal combustion engine, as used in motor cars and lorries, has, broadly, the following characteristics—

(1) It has to be started by being turned by the application of external energy.

(2) Its maximum torque is small compared with that of a steam engine or traction electric motor of the same maximum horse power.

(3) It is a comparatively high-speed engine, its maximum power being developed at speeds ranging from about 2,000 r.p.m. in lorries up to as much as 12,000 r.p.m. in racing cars.

These characteristics have their effect on the nature of the transmission, causing it to be very different in many respects from that of a steam-engined vehicle.

Thus in order that when starting the engine the necessary effort, which has to be supplied either manually or by electrical storage batteries, shall be as small as possible, the engine is arranged to be disconnected from the driving wheels when being started.   Once started the engine has then to be connected to the driving wheels so as to propel the car along.   This connection must be accomplished smoothly and without shock so that the passengers are not incommoded or the mechanism of the car damaged.

The torque developed by the engine is then transmitted to the road wheels where it gives rise to a propulsive force, or " tractive effort," between those wheels and the road.   When the vehicle is starting from rest a large tractive effort is required in order that the acceleration shall be rapid.   This necessitates the introduction of considerable " leverage " between the engine and the driving wheels so that the small torque available shall produce a large tractive effort.   This large leverage is also required when climbing hills or traversing very rough or sandy roads.

It is necessary, however, to be able to vary this leverage, because if the same leverage were used when travelling on the level as when climbing steep hills, the maximum speed possible would be unduly low.   A large leverage implies a large reduction in speed between the engine and the driving wheels and at quite moderate road speeds the engine speed would be very high.   But at high speeds the engine torque falls off so that the tractive effort available would be reduced and the road speed limited.

A comfortable cruising speed for a passenger car is about sixty miles per hour, and since their road wheels are usually about 26

401

inches in diameter the corresponding road wheel speed will be about 800 r.p.m. Now the engine speed at a road speed of 60 m.p.h. would be about 3,500 r.p.m. and so the engine would have to be geared down to the road wheels in the ratio of 3,500 to 800, that is at about 4·5 to 1. This ratio will vary somewhat with the weight of the car and the size of the engine. In cars with large engines the ratio might be only 3·0 to 1, in light lorries it might be about 5·5 to 1 and in heavy lorries possibly 10 to 1 or even higher.

While the nature of the transmission is not affected greatly by changes in the form of the " carriage unit," so that the transmission of a four-wheel driven vehicle is similar in nature to that of a two-wheel rear-driven vehicle, the arrangement of the transmission will vary in these cases.

The majority of cars and lorries, however, have their engines fitted at the front, parallel to the fore and aft centre line of the car, and since the axes of the driving wheels must necessarily be perpendicular to the centre line of the car, the drive between the engine and the driving wheels must be turned round through 90° at some point of the transmission. With transversely disposed engines this 90-degree turn is not necessary.

The driving wheels will also traverse circles of different radii when the vehicle moves in a circle, but the engine must continue to drive them, although they will be moving at different speeds.

Again, the engine is universally carried on the frame of the carriage unit while the driving wheels are carried on axles attached to the frame by springs. When the springs flex the relative positions of the engine and the driving wheels will alter, and this relative movement must be allowed for in the transmission.

The transmission must therefore—

(1) Enable the engine to be disconnected from the driving wheels.
(2) Enable the engine, when running, to be connected smoothly and without shock to the driving wheels.
(3) Enable the leverage between the engine and the driving wheels to be varied.
(4) Reduce the speed of the engine in the ratio of about 4 to 1 in passenger cars and in a greater ratio in lorries.
(5) Turn the drive round through 90°.
(6) Enable the driving wheels to be driven at different speeds.
(7) Provide for the relative movement between the engine and the driving wheels due to flexing of the road springs.

These requirements can be met by a number of constructions working on different principles. Thus transmission systems may be classified under three heads—

(1) Mechanical.
(2) Hydraulic, (a) Hydrostatic,
(b) Hydrodynamic.
(3) Electrical and electromagnetic.

Of these the first is by far the commonest. Vehicles with full hydraulic transmissions have been built but have not gone into production, although some agricultural tractors currently employ them. Vehicles in which hydraulic components are used in the transmissions are now fairly common. Electric transmissions have been used for road vehicles but they are no longer made; they are, however, extensively used in diesel-electric locomotives and have been used in tanks. Both hydraulic and electric transmissions nearly always incorporate mechanical components; with the former, in fact, the hydraulic portion merely replaces the clutch and gear box of a mechanical transmission.

Mechanical transmissions are very numerous, but the majority fall within the following categories—

(1) Clutch, gear box and " live " axle transmissions.
(2) Clutch, gear box and " dead " axle transmissions.
(3) Clutch, gear box, axleless transmissions.

A very large percentage of the passenger cars and lorries in use to-day are provided with transmissions of the first type, but since all the types have in common the clutch and gear box, the constructions of those components may be considered without reference to the transmission systems in which they are to be used.

Before considering these components it will be useful to consider the general arrangements of some typical mechanical transmissions.

18.1 General Arrangement of the Clutch, Gear Box and Live Axle Transmission

The general arrangement of this system is shown in Fig. 18-1. The engine is situated at the front with its crankshaft parallel

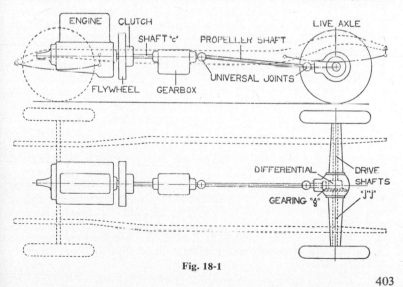

Fig. 18-1

403

to the centre line of the car. From the engine the drive is transmitted through a clutch and a short shaft c to the gear box. It is then taken by a " propeller " or " cardan " shaft, which has a universal joint at each end, to the live back axle. Bevel or worm gearing g within the axle casing turns the drive round through 90° and a " differential " divides it equally between the two shafts jj which convey it to the driving wheels.

The functions of the several components are as follows:

The clutch enables the engine to be disconnected from the driving wheels, but its principal function is to enable the engine, when running, to be connected smoothly and without shock to the driving wheels. A spring keeps the clutch in the " engaged " position, disengagement being effected by the pressure of the foot on a pedal. To disengage the clutch, therefore, the driver must be sitting in the car. For starting purposes, and when it is desired to leave the car with the engine running, the disconnection between the engine and the driving wheels is obtained in the gear box.

The principal function of the gear box is to enable the leverage between the engine and the driving wheels to be varied to suit the prevailing conditions, this being necessary as indicated above.

The universal joints permit the back axle to move up and down relatively to the frame as the road springs flex. The gearing g, usually called the " final drive," turns the drive round through 90° and reduces the speed in the ratio of about 4 to 1, so as to bring the high speed of the engine down to the comparatively low speed of the driving wheels. The differential enables the two road wheels to be driven equally by the engine and yet to be able to turn at unequal speeds.

In the above arrangement the gear box is a separate unit, but there are two other dispositions in use. In one the gear box casing is made integral with, or is bolted rigidly to, the engine crank case so as to form a single unit—giving what is called " unit construction." In the other the gear box is incorporated with the back axle.

The unit construction is almost universal on cars and is very common on lorries. Its chief advantages are cleanliness, neatness of appearance and a slight reduction in manufacturing cost while its chief disadvantage is inaccessibility of the clutch. Incorporation of the gear box with the axle is now extremely rare.

With certain forms of gear box, notably in epicyclic types, the clutch action is obtained in the gear box itself. When these types of gear box are used there will be no separate clutch in the transmission, the drive going straight from the engine to the gear box.

The live axle itself is built in several forms. That indicated in the figure is called a " single reduction " axle, because the reduction in speed between the propeller shaft and the road wheels is obtained in one step in the final drive at g. In lorries the reduction, which has then to be about 8 to 1 or more, is sometimes obtained in two or three steps, the axles being called " double " or " triple " reduction axles.

404

18.2   General Arrangement of Rear-engined Vehicles with Live Axles

In Fig. 18-2 the gear box is built as a unit with the engine, which is placed behind the rear axle with its crankshaft axis situated transversely.   The clutch is between the engine and the gear box and the output shaft of the latter carries a bevel gear which meshes with a second gear on a short shaft carried in bearings in the gear box casing.   This short shaft is coupled by a propeller shaft having a universal joint at each end to the pinion shaft of the axle.   The angles between the axes of both pairs of bevel gears are no longer right angles but this makes the design of those gears somewhat simpler. The chief difficulty in this arrangement is to find room for

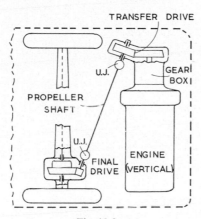

Fig. 18-2

the rather lengthy engine, clutch and gear box unit in the limited transverse space available and this also makes it essential to use a rather short propeller shaft. The universal joints therefore have sometimes to work at rather large angular deflections when the axle moves up or down.

In Fig. 18-3 the engine is again placed behind the axle but now with its crankshaft axis placed longitudinally; the gear box is a separate unit and is placed in front of the axle more or less where it would be if the engine were at the front.   Thus a reasonably long propeller shaft can be used to couple the gear box to the axle. The universal joints between the engine and the gear box only have to allow for the relative movements between those units consequent on deflections of the frame or body structure and they can be of a simple type. It may be necessary to place a bearing in the middle of the engine gear box shaft

A separate gear box is also used in the transmission shown in Fig. 18.4 but, as the axle is now well forward, it is feasible to use a propeller shaft that is parallel to the centre line of the vehicle.

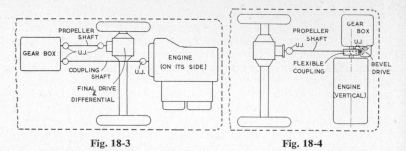

Fig. 18-3   Fig. 18-4

All three of the above arrangements are suitable chiefly for coaches and large vehicles.

18.3   General Arrangement of Dead-axle and Axleless Transmissions

The chain drive, which is now used only occasionally for special vehicles, is an example of a dead axle transmission. It is shown in Fig. 18-5. The drive passes from the engine through the clutch to the gear box and at the rear of the latter, and usually housed in the same casing, is the gearing G that turns the drive through 90°. The differential is also located there. The drive then goes along the two shafts JJ to the chain sprockets KK which are connected by the driving chains LL to the chain wheels MM. The latter are rigidly bolted to the road wheels which revolve on the ends of the dead axle D.

The sprockets being usually smaller than the chain wheels there is a reduction in speed between them and the road wheels. This reduction is in addition to that given by the gearing G and this is an advantage when a very large reduction is required, as it is in large tractors.

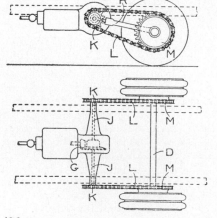

Fig. 18-5: Chain drive

The relative movement between the axle and frame when the road springs flex is taken up by the chains which wrap and unwrap round the sprockets and chain wheels when the axle moves up and down.

The De Dion Company in their early cars used a shaft drive in conjunction with a dead axle and although this arrangement is now seldom used the transmissions of modern cars having independently

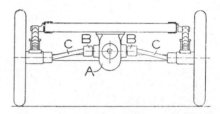

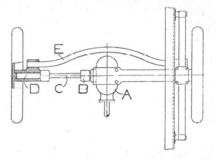

Fig. 18-6: De Dion drive

sprung wheels are similar to it. It is shown in Fig. 18-6. The clutch and gearbox are normal and so is the arrangement of the final drive except that its casing A is fixed to the frame. The differential shafts are quite short and are coupled by universal joints BB to intermediate shafts CC the outer ends of which are coupled by further universal joints to the shafts D and thus to the road wheels. The latter revolve on bearings carried by brackets fixed to the ends of the dead axle E. The springs connecting the dead axle E to the frame are also fixed to those brackets. Some sliding freedom must be provided in the shafts CC by making them in two portions splined together or in some other way.

This system has the advantage, shared by all dead axle and axleless systems, of low unsprung weight and it also obviates the troubles involved in the use of chains. The shafts C, however, must necessarily be rather short and hence the universal joints are called upon to work at rather large angles when the axle movements are large. With modern universal joints this does not matter seriously.

When there is no axle the road wheels are connected to the frame in various ways which are considered in the chapter on independent suspension. With some of these arrangements the

407

Fig. 18-7

Fig. 18-8

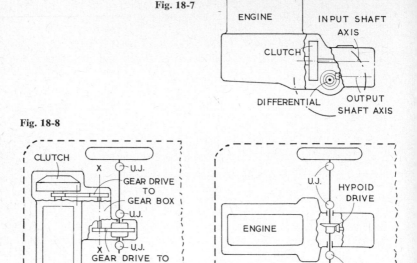

transmission may be exactly as described above for the De Dion drive but in some arrangements it is possible to dispense with the outer universal joints and with the sliding freedom in the shafts CC. Fig. 18-7 shows an axleless transmission for a front-wheel drive vehicle in which the engine axis is longitudinal and is placed in front of the wheels while the gearbox is behind them. This helps in getting a suitable weight distribution between front and rear wheels. The gearbox is an " all indirect " type as is described in Section 21.26 and the output shaft is placed below the input shaft. The pinion of the hypoid final drive is carried by the output shaft and meshes with the crown wheel on the differential case. The latter is carried in bearings in the common casing of the engine and gearbox unit. The half-shafts project outside of this casing and are coupled to the road wheels by shafts as in the De Dion transmission.

The transmission used in the B.M.C. front-wheel driven cars is shown in the diagram Fig. 18-8. The engine and gearbox shaft axes are transverse to the centre line of the car and spur gears are used to transmit the drive from the driven member of the clutch to the input shaft of the gearbox and from the output shaft to the differential case.

Both the above arrangements are particularly suitable for small and medium-sized cars.

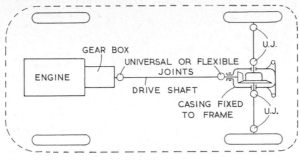

Fig. 18.9

Fig. 18-9 shows the transmission of a vehicle having a front engine and independently sprung rear-wheel drive. Although the final drive casing is carried by the frame, which also carries the engine and gearbox, universal or flexible joints are provided at the ends of the shaft coupling the gearbox to the final drive. These joints are required to accommodate the slight movements that may occur between the units owing to flexure of the body or frame unit and also because the units are carried on relatively flexible rubber supports.

18.4 Four-wheel Drive Transmission

The general arrangement of the transmission of a four-wheel driven lorry is shown in Fig. 18-10. The engine and clutch and the gear box are normal but at the back of the latter is situated a gear drive consisting of the pinion A fixed to the gear box shaft, the intermediate wheel B and driven wheel C. The latter houses a differential and the two shafts coming out from this differential are coupled by propeller shafts one to the back axle and the other to the front axle. The back axle is a normal live axle and has a normal final drive and differential. The front axle is similar to

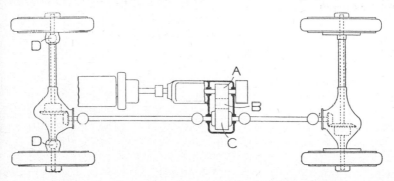

Fig. 18-10: General arrangement of four-wheel driven chassis

the back axle except for the universal joints DD which are situated on the axes of the swivel pins about which the wheels are swung for steering purposes. The joints DD are required to accommodate this swinging of the wheels when steering.

The differential inside the wheel C is required in order to distribute the drive equally between the two axles and to allow for the fact that when the vehicle moves in a circle the mean of the speeds of the front wheels will be different from the mean of the speeds of the back wheels so that the speeds of the two propeller shafts will not be the same. This differential can usually be put out of action in order to improve the performance of the vehicle on slippery ground and in vehicles that are intended chiefly for work on bad ground it is generally omitted altogether. When independently sprung wheels are used the transmission is essentially the same as described above but the final drives will be carried on the frame of the vehicle, and universal joints will be provided at both ends of the shafts connecting the differentials to the road wheels (as in a De Dion drive).

Beyond the fact that in a four-wheel driven vehicle the whole of the available adhesion between the wheels and the road can be utilized, the chief advantage of having the front wheels driven is that when they drop into a steep-sided ditch they can climb out, whereas when the front wheels are not driven and they drop into a ditch they can only be got out by going backwards, and not always then.

CHAPTER 19

Clutches

Principle of the friction clutch.   Types of cone clutch.   Single and multiple plate types.   Clutch stops.

CLUTCHES are mechanisms which enable the rotary motion of one shaft to be transmitted at will to a second shaft, whose axis is coincident with that of the first.   They are of two types—

(1) Positive clutches.

(2) Gradual engagement clutches.

In positive types the clutch is either " in," so that the two shafts are rigidly connected and must revolve at the same speed; or it is " out," when the shafts are entirely disconnected.   It is obvious, therefore, that this type of clutch is not suitable for use between the engine and gear box.   The positive clutch is used inside the gear box, and in other places, and will be described later.

In gradual engagement clutches it is possible for one shaft to be revolving rapidly while the other is either stationary or revolving at a lower speed.   As the engagement of the clutch proceeds the speeds of the two shafts gradually become the same, and when the clutch is fully engaged the shafts revolve as one.   This is the type used between the engine and gear box.   In the motor car the gradual engagement clutch depends for its action upon the frictional force which acts between two bodies when they are pressed together.   Such clutches are called friction clutches.   There are, of course, hydraulic and other gradual engagement clutches employed in engineering, but since they are not used on motor cars they will not be described.

19.1   Principle of the Friction Clutch

Consider the two shafts A and B shown in Fig. 19-1.   They are supported in bearings C and D and are free to rotate about the common axis XY.   Keyed on to the ends of the shafts are circular discs E and F which face each other. Suppose the shaft A and its disc to be revolving while the shaft B and its disc are at rest, and let the two shafts be pressed together endways.   Then as soon as the faces of the discs come into contact a frictional force will act between them tending to slow down the disc E and to speed up the disc F.

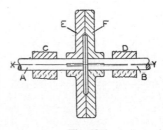

Fig. 19-1

411

At first, when the force pressing the discs together is small, the frictional force may not be large enough to overcome the resistances to the motion of the shaft B, but if the force pressing the discs together is gradually increased the frictional force will increase also, until it is sufficient to overcome the resistances and cause the shaft B to move. That shaft will then gradually speed up until ultimately it will be going at the same speed as the shaft A, the clutch being then fully engaged.

Until the clutch is fully engaged the disc E is going faster than the disc F, so that slip is taking place between the faces of the discs. When the clutch is fully engaged the discs are rotating at the same speed and there is no slip between them.

This is the basic principle of all friction clutches. In motor car clutches a spring is used to press the discs together. The spring tends to keep the clutch always in engagement, and when it is desired to disengage the clutch the discs are separated by pulling one of them back against the pressure of the spring.

19.2 Torque Transmitted

Suppose the spring used to press the discs together exerts a total force of P lb. This then is the normal force between the discs, upon which depends the magnitude of the frictional force tending to prevent slip between them. The value of the frictional force will be $\mu \times P$ where μ is the coefficient of friction. This frictional force is the sum, or resultant, of a large number of small component frictional forces acting all over the surfaces in contact, which, in this case, it will be noticed are comparatively narrow rings near to the outsides of the discs. The resultant frictional force may be taken to act at the mean radius of the ring of contact and it will act, of course, tangentially. If the mean radius of the ring of contact R inches, then, since the frictional force is $\mu = P$ lb its moment about the axis of the shafts is $\mu \times P \times R$ lb-in. This moment is the torque tending to stop the shaft A and to drive the shaft B, that is, it is the torque transmitted by the clutch.

If the ring of contact were not comparatively narrow there would be some inaccuracy in taking the resultant frictional force to act at the mean radius. By making the ring of contact very narrow, and thereby increasing its mean radius, the torque that the clutch can transmit will be increased. The ring must not be made too narrow, however, or the wear that occurs when the clutch is slipping during engagement will be excessive. While the area of the ring of contact affects directly the amount of wear that will occur, it only affects the torque that the clutch can transmit in that it affects the mean radius at which the frictional force acts.

The torque that a clutch can transmit depends therefore upon three factors, the coefficient of friction, the spring force, and the mean radius of the contact surfaces.

The coefficient of friction depends upon the materials composing the friction surfaces, and has a definite maximum value which cannot be exceeded. Constructional difficulties prevent the mean radius from being increased beyond a certain amount, and the spring force is limited to that which a driver can overcome without undue effort when provided with the maximum leverage conveniently possible. When all these three factors have been made as large as possible, a clutch of the elementary form considered would not transmit the large torques met with in large cars and lorries, and the constructional form of the clutch has to be modified so that it will transmit a greater torque. The basic principle involved remains the same, however.

The practical adaptations of this principle have resulted in three principal types of construction in motor car clutches. They are—

(1) Cone clutch.
(2) Single-plate or few-plate clutch.
(3) Multiple-plate clutch.

The cone clutch, however, is no longer used and the multiple-plate clutch is used only in certain epicyclic gear boxes but it has been thought advisable to retain descriptions of them for historical purposes and because cone clutches are used in the synchromesh mechanisms in gear boxes.

19.3 Cone Clutch

In the cone clutch the contact surfaces of the members corresponding to the discs E and F are made portions of cones for a reason that will be explained later.

A typical cone clutch is shown in Fig. 19-2. The flywheel A is

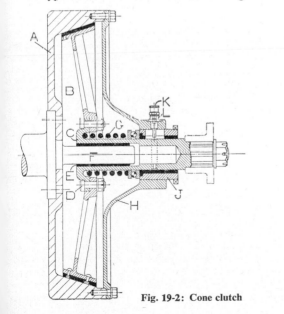

Fig. 19-2: Cone clutch

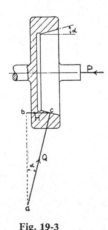

Fig. 19-3

413

attached to the crankshaft by bolts passing through the web of the flywheel and a flange integral with the crankshaft. The male member is made in two parts, the cone B being bolted to the centre C by bolts D. This enables the cone to be made of aluminium so as to secure lightness while the centre is made of steel to ensure the necessary strength. The composite male member is carried on the crankshaft spigot F, a bush E being provided. The spring G presses the male cone into the female cone of the flywheel. The spring reaction is taken through a ball thrust bearing on to the cover plate H which is bolted to the rim of the flywheel by a number of hexagon headed screws, two of which are seen in the drawing.

To disengage the clutch so that the engine no longer drives the gear box shaft, the male cone is drawn back along the spigot F against the pressure of the spring. The faces of the cones are thereby separated and the flywheel no longer drives the male cone. If the latter comes to rest while the flywheel continues to revolve relative motion must occur either between the spring G and the male cone C or between the spring and the plug J. Actually it will occur between the last-named members because there is a ball thrust bearing between them. This bearing is essential as otherwise the friction would be considerable and it would be impossible entirely to disconnect the drive between the engine and gear box and, moreover, excessive wear would occur.

19.4 Reason for Using Cones

The reason for using cones for the engaging surfaces is to enable greater torques to be transmitted without having to employ extremely heavy clutch springs.

It has been seen that the frictional force between two surfaces depends upon the *normal* force between them. By using conical surfaces the normal force between them can be increased considerably without increase of spring pressure, because a wedging action is introduced. Referring to Fig. 19-3, the axial force P of the clutch spring gives rise to a normal force Q between the surfaces of the cones. This force Q is actually distributed all over the cone surfaces as a pressure. We may, however, so far as the frictional force is concerned, consider it to act at a point at the middle of the cone surface as shown. Now the only forces acting on the male cone in the axial direction are the spring force P and the axial componect H of the normal force Q. This axial component must therefore be equal to the force P. The axial component H is obtained by drawing the triangle abc, in which ac represents the force Q, and bc the component H. Obviously Q is much greater than H and therefore than P.

Usually the angle of the cone is such that H is about one-fifth of Q so that Q is about five times as large as P. The frictional force between the cones is equal to $\mu \times Q$, that is, equal to about $5 \times P \times \mu$ and the moment of the frictional force about the axis of the clutch is $5 \times P \times \mu \times R$ where R is the mean radius of the cones. If this mean radius is equal to the mean radius of the ring of contact in the elementary clutch shown in Fig. 19-1, and if the spring force and the coefficient of friction are the same in each clutch, then the cone clutch will transmit about five times the torque that is possible with the elementary clutch.

The angle of the cones cannot be made much smaller than about 20° because the male cone would tend to bind or stick in the female cone and the clutch would be difficult to disengage, and also because a small amount of wear on the cone surfaces would result in a considerable axial movement of the male cone, for which it would be difficult to allow.

19.5 Clutch Linings

Cone clutches have been used in which the metal male cone engaged with the metal female cone thus giving a metal to metal contact. Such clutches were usually enclosed so that oil could be kept in them to lubricate the engaging surfaces. The oil, of course, reduced the coefficient of friction between the engaging surfaces, but made the engagement more progressive.

Most cone clutches ran " dry," oil being kept away from the engaging surfaces and the male cone was covered with a friction fabric or a composition lining, so that the coefficient of friction was higher than with a metal to metal contact. The lining was secured to the male cone usually by means of copper or aluminium rivets which passed through both the lining and the rim of the cone as seen in Fig. 19-2. The rivet heads were sunk well below the surface of the lining so that they did not come into contact with the surface of the female cone.

19.6 Friction Materials

There are two main types of friction lining, namely—
(1) Woven type.
(2) Moulded or composition type.

The first type is made by spinning threads from asbestos fibres, sometimes on brass wire, weaving this thread into a cloth and then impregnating it with a bonding material. This type of material can be sub-divided into two classes; (a) the laminated variety and (b) the " solid " woven variety. The former consists of layers of cloth placed on top of each other and held together by the bonding material sometimes aided by stitching. The second variety is woven to the required thickness in one operation and the result, being an interlocked structure and not a layered one, has a much greater mechanical strength. Both types may incorporate metallic (usually brass) wire. This was originally used because it was impossible to spin asbestos fibres into a thread without using a metallic wire to provide strength but this is now possible and the wire is not always used. The woven materials are usually used with one of the first three types of bond mentioned in Section 19.7.

415

The moulded or composition type of lining is composed of asbestos fibres in their natural state mixed with a bonding material and then moulded in dies under pressure and at elevated temperatures. Metallic wires are sometimes included but only to increase the wearing qualities and to eliminate scoring of the metal faces against which the lining rubs.

19.7 Bonding Materials

A very large number of different bonding materials have been used but they can be roughly classified as follows—

(1) Asphaltic bases with additions of natural gums and oils.
(2) Vegetable gums.
(3) Rubber.
(4) Synthetic resins, (a) alcohol soluble.
(b) oil soluble.

The frictional properties of the materials depend chiefly on the bonding material and the above bonds have broadly the following characteristics—

(1) Coefficient of friction from 0·3 to 0·4 at any temperature up to about 250° C. The coefficient tends to rise at higher temperatures due largely to exudation of the bonding material. Higher coefficients can be obtained by using excessive bonding material but such coefficients are not maintained after the excess of bond has been driven off by a rise of temperature. The wearing properties of materials (usually fabrics) impregnated with this bond are good, particularly when the product is die pressed.

(2) Coefficient of friction from 0·35 to 0·45 up to about 250° C. The wearing properties are rather better than type 1 but otherwise it has similar properties.

(3) The coefficient of friction can be made to have almost any value up to about 0·6 by the incorporation of filling materials and the vulcanization of the rubber may be arranged to produce either a flexible or a rigid product. Both types tend to disintegrate under severe conditions, the flexible type being very bad in this respect. The rigid type has a very destructive effect on the surfaces on which it runs. Both types are more affected by water than the other types of bond.

(4) (a) Coefficient of friction from 0·4 to 0·5 at any temperature up to about 230° C but at higher temperatures the coefficient falls off and may become as low as 0·1. This " fading " has been eliminated in some recent materials using this type of bond. This type of bond is not affected by lubricating oil and can withstand heavy pressures; they consequently find a field of usefulness in epicyclic gear boxes, etc.

(4) (b) Coefficient of friction from 0·35 to 0·38 which is maintained at quite high temperatures. Vegetable gum and

asphaltic bases are often used in conjunction with this type of bond. Both 4a and 4b have excellent wearing qualities.

The rubber bonded materials are very little used outside the United States of America.

While most asbestos friction materials will stand surface pressures up to 200 lb/sq. in. or more, such pressures are not often used in clutches although they may be approached in brakes. In clutches the surface pressure is usually about 15 to 30 lb/sq. in. The fabric materials being more porous than the moulded materials will absorb oil more readily and though this makes the effect of very small quantities of oil less the effect persists longer than with the moulded materials.

Cotton is occasionally used instead of, or mixed with, asbestos and such fabrics can be made to give high coefficients of friction, up to 0·6, but materials containing cotton cannot withstand a temperature exceeding about 150° C without being charred and ruined. They are used only for clutches. Cork is also used occasionally for clutches, almost always being arranged to run in oil. It has a coefficient of about 0·3 and surface pressures up to about 20 lb/sq. in. may be used.

19.8   Single-plate Clutch

A simple single-plate clutch is shown in Fig. 19-4, from which the principle of operation may be gathered. The flywheel is a simple disc with a thick rim having a flat face, into which are screwed six studs A. These studs carry a thick plate B, which is thus fixed to the flywheel as regards rotation; it is, however, free to slide axially along the studs. In between the plate B and the flywheel is situated the driven plate F; this is riveted to the flange of a hub G, which is connected with the clutch shaft C by splines E. When the parts are disposed as shown there is no tendency for the flywheel

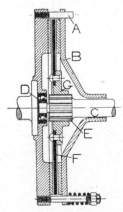

Fig. 19-4: Single-plate clutch

to turn the plate F, but if the plate B is moved along the studs so as to squeeze the plate F between itself and the flywheel the frictional forces set up between the surfaces in contact will prevent slip between them.

The necessary axial force is applied to the plate B by a number of springs which are usually arranged to surround the studs A. The latter are then provided with nuts as shown at the bottom of the figure. The face of the flywheel and the inner face of the plate B are sometimes lined with some form of friction fabric or composition, but usually the linings are riveted to the faces of the plate F. The latter arrangement has the advantage that the heat generated when the clutch is slipping during engagement is more easily dissipated, as it can be conducted directly away into the body of the flywheel and outer plate B.

In the former arrangement the heat has to pass through the linings before it can be absorbed and, as the linings are not good conductors of heat, the absorption and dissipation are not so rapid and the clutch will heat up more rapidly. On the other hand, the second arrangement increases the rotational inertia of the driven element which is undesirable; this does not outweigh the advantage obtained.

19.9 Torque Transmitted

It will be observed that if slip occurs at one face of the plate F it must also do so at the other face, so that there are two frictional forces tending to prevent slip, each of which will be equal to μP where P lb is the total spring force and μ the coefficient of friction. Each of the frictional forces acts at the mean radius of the ring of contact, so that if that radius is R inches the torque transmitted will be $2\mu PR$ lb-in.

To transmit the same torque as a cone clutch of equal overall diameter a single-plate clutch would generally have to be provided with a greater spring force because the wedging action of the cones is lost and also the mean radius of the ring of contact is, owing to constructional exigencies, smaller. The reduction due to these causes is offset by the fact that there are two frictional surfaces in the single-plate clutch as against the single surface in the cone type, but the net result is a reduction necessitating an increased spring pressure.

The spring pressure necessary may, however, be reduced by using more than one driven plate, as is done in the clutch shown in Fig. 19.5.

There are three driven plates which are riveted to hubs that are free to slide on the splined clutch and these are gripped between the flywheel, the pressure plate B and the intermediate plates A A. Thus there are six slipping surfaces and the clutch can transmit three times the torque that a similar single-plate clutch having only two slipping surfaces could do. The intermediate plates are positioned on and are driven by square-headed pegs A A which engage

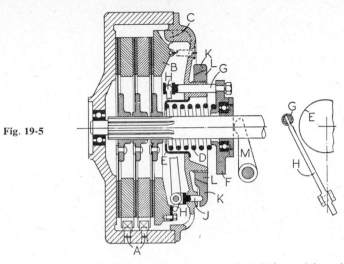

Fig. 19-5

slots formed in their peripheries. The pressure plate B is positioned and driven by three lugs C formed on the cover plate of the clutch and which engage three slots machined in the pressure plate. The force pressing all the plates together so as to transmit the drive is supplied by a single coil spring D; this bears at one end against the pressed steel cup E which seats in a hole in the cover plate and at the other end against the housing F. Secured to the latter are three plungers G that are free to slide in holes in the cover plate and which engage the ends of the three levers H. These levers are pivoted on pins carried by small brackets J and, at their outer ends, they bear against renewable hardened pads fixed to the pressure plate. The force of the spring is thus increased by the leverage of the levers H. To ensure that all three of the levers press equally on the pressure plate the brackets J are not fixed in the cover plate but their stems are left free to slide in the holes in which they are placed and, at their outside ends, they bear against a disc K which seats on a spherical surface on the nut L. Because the disc K is free to rock in any direction on its spherical seating the forces acting on the brackets J, and hence the forces applied by the levers to the pressure plate, must be equal. The nut L, being screwed on the boss of the cover plate, enables the pressure plate to be adjusted bodily to the left to take up any wear that occurs. The clutch is disengaged by the withdraw fingers M which press against the inner member of the thrust race housed inside the member F, thereby pressing the latter to the left and relieving the pressure plate of the spring force. The pressure plate is pulled back by a number of small coil springs one of which can be seen at the top, and spring loaded levers, not shown, then separate the intermediate plates. The levers H are not arranged radially but as shown in the scrap end view where it will be seen that they pass to the side of the cup E;

419

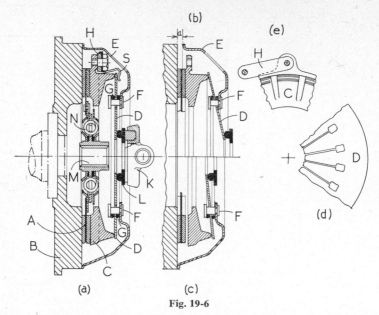

Fig. 19-6

this enables a longer lever to be used than could otherwise be got in. In the figure the plunger G is shown out of its true position.

The use of a single spring in this manner is, however, no longer current practice.

19.10   The Diaphragm-spring Clutch

In this type of clutch, two examples of which are shown in Figs. 19-6 and 19-8, the basic form is the same as that of Fig. 19-4, the driven plate A being clamped between the flywheel B and the pressure plate C but the clamping is done by the single diaphragm spring D which is a steel disc which, when unloaded, has a conical form as indicated in the part end view at (b). During assembly of the clutch the cover pressing E has to be forced axially through the final movement a during which the diaphragm is flattened into the simple disc as seen in the view (a). This change in shape is made easier by forming a number of radial slots at the centre of the diaphragm as indicated at (d).

The spring is held in place between two circular wire rings G, G which are carried on the shouldered pins F (nine in number) and which form a "fulcrum" for the diaphragm when the clutch is being disengaged. This is done by forcing the centre of the diaphragm to the left so that it again becomes a cone but now with the apex on the left as shown at (c). Spring clips S ensure retraction of the pressure plate when the spring pressure is thus removed.

The method of centring and driving the pressure plate in this clutch is different from those used in the clutches described above.

420

Three strap links are used, one of which is seen at H in the views (*a*) and (*e*). These are pivoted at one end to the pressure plate and at the other end to the cover pressing. The principle involved is shown in Fig. 19-7 and a little consideration will show that if the link Hz were removed then the disc D could move by reason of the pivoting of the links Hx and Hy about their pivots U and V. But consideration will also show that in this motion the point Z of the disc would have to move in the direction *z* and as this is prohibited by the link Hz the disc cannot move when all three links are in position. The straps will, however, permit the pressure plate to move axially (in Fig. 19-6 (*a*)) by the small amount required for disengagement of the clutch.

Disengagement is effected through the medium of the clutch release bearing K which, in this example, houses a graphite block which bears against the ring L when the housing K is moved to the left by depression of the clutch pedal. This ring L is also carried by three straps in the same manner as for the pressure plate.

The driven plate of this clutch is fitted with a *spring centre;* this is very common in clutches in cars and light lorries but is not much used in heavy vehicles. The plate A is free to rotate on the hub M but this freedom is restricted by several small coil springs N which are housed in rectangular holes formed in the flange of the hub and which also engage corresponding recesses in the pressings which form the centre part of the plate assembly. This arrangement provides a little torsional flexibility and makes the engagement of the clutch smoother. Discs made of frictional material are placed between the flange of the hub and the centre pressings of the plate and the friction thereby introduced helps to damp out torsional vibrations between the engine and the gear box.

The chief advantages of the diaphragm spring are, first, that it is more compact than other designs; secondly, that it is easier to

Fig. 19-8

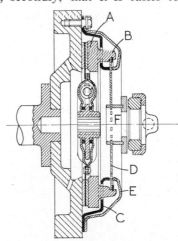

Fig. 19-7

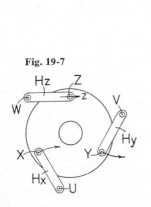

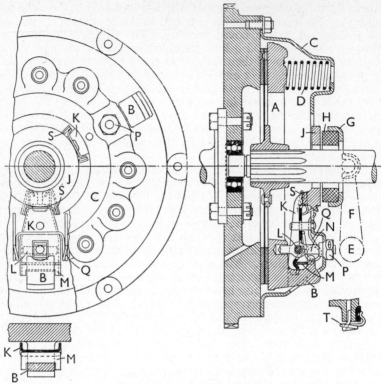

Fig. 19-9: Borg and Beck clutch

balance rotationally and is less subject to unwanted effects due to centrifugal force at high rotational speeds; and, thirdly, that it gives a uniformly distributed pressure on the pressure plate.

The Laycock design of the diaphragm clutch is shown in Fig. 19-8. In this the pressure plate A is centred in relation to the flywheel and is driven by six lugs B which fit into slots formed in the pressing C. The diaphragm spring D is carried in a recess formed inside the lugs and is kept in place by a circlip. The " fulcrum " for the spring is formed by the lips of the pressings C and E which are bolted to the face of the flywheel. The diaphragm has eighteen radial slots at its centre and the inner ends of the fingers thus formed engage the sleeve F which is pressed to the left by the clutch release bearing when the clutch pedal is depressed.

19.11   Another Single-plate Clutch

A clutch designed and manufactured by the Borg and Beck Company is shown in Fig. 19-9. It is intended for use with unit construction of engine and gear box and so the driven shaft is supported at its right-hand end in the gear box and at its left-hand end in the spigot ball bearing shown housed in a hole in the flywheel web. The presser plate A is held in position by reason of three projecting pieces B which fit in slots cut in the pressed steel cover plate C. The latter is bolted to the face of the flywheel. The projections B also serve to make the presser plate revolve with the flywheel. A number (nine in the clutch shown) of springs O, housed in pockets formed in the cover plate, cause the driven plate to be squeezed between the presser plate and flywheel face unless the spring force is overcome by the disengaging mechanism. The latter acts as follows. When the clutch pedal is depressed the shaft E (which is supported in bearings in the bell-housing connecting the crank case and gear box) is rotated and the fingers F move the housing G to the left and the graphite impregnated block H comes into contact with the plate J and pushes it to the left. The inner ends of the levers K (of which there are three) are moved to the left and as the levers fulcrum on the pins L their outer ends move to the right. Small struts M inserted between the outer ends of the levers and the projecting portions of the presser plate transmit the motion to the latter and the clutch is disengaged. The pins L pass through D-shaped holes in the members N and bear on the flat sides of the holes. Thus when the levers are moved a rolling action occurs between the pins and the members N instead of the sliding that would occur if the pins fitted the holes in the members N. This eliminates considerable friction. The struts M are used to allow for the small radial motion that is produced by this rolling action. The members M are screwed at their outer ends and carry nuts P which have spherical seatings on the cover plate C. The spherical seats permit the members N to adjust themselves to a position of repose. Springs Q keep the levers pressing against the struts M and this pressure helps to keep the latter in position. Sideways movement of the struts is prevented by shaping them as shown in the part plan view where it will be seen that the projections B fit in recesses formed in the struts. The plate J is supported entirely by the levers K whose inner ends have slots formed in them. This is shown more clearly in Fig. 19-10. These slots fit projections R formed integral with the plate J and the springs S keep the parts in contact.

The clutch is non-adjustable after final assembly. After assembly the nuts P are adjusted until the face of the plate J is truly

Fig. 19-10

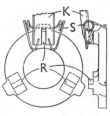

perpendicular to the axis of the clutch, this adjustment being made while a cast-iron dummy driven plate takes the place of the actual driven plate. While still in position the nuts P are then drilled and split pins are inserted. The clutch is then taken off the flywheel and is reassembled with the real driven plate but this is done without disturbing the levers and associated parts. If the adjustment is disturbed at any time then new members N and nuts P must be used on reassembly and the procedure described above must be adopted. Any attempt to use the old parts will almost certainly result in faulty adjustment. The housing G has trunnions which rest in slots formed in the ends of the fingers F and it is kept in place by springs T as shown in the part plan view.

The driven plates of single-plate clutches are made of a high quality steel similar to saw steel, and vary in thickness from $\frac{1}{16}$ to $\frac{1}{8}$ in. To prevent them from buckling when they get hot through the continued use of the clutch, radial slots are usually cut in them. These slots end in small circular holes in order to avoid the sharp corners that would otherwise exist and which would lead to the formation of cracks.

Instead of fabric or composition linings cork inserts are sometimes used in single- and few-plate clutches. They are usually of about $\frac{5}{8}$ in. diameter and about $\frac{1}{4}$ in. thick, being pressed into holes formed in the driven plates which are made comparatively thick to support them. They are comparatively easily compressed, thus ensuring smooth engagement.

19.12 Multiple-plate Clutch

The multiple-plate clutch is now practically obsolete as a main clutch but is still used in epicyclic gear boxes and one example will be briefly described; it is shown in Fig. 19-11. Bolted to the flywheel is a drum which on its inner circumference is splined to

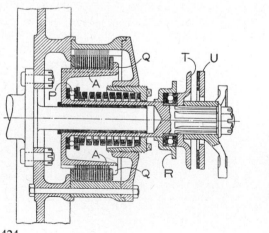

Fig. 19-11

carry a number of thin metal plates; these must consequently revolve with the drum but are able to slide axially. Interleaved with these outer plates is a number of inner plates that are splined to an inner drum (A) which is coupled rotationally to the gear box shaft. This drum is supported on a spigot extension of the crankshaft, a suitable bearing bush being provided. Between the web of the inner drum and a sleeve screwed into the cover plate of the outer drum is a strong coil spring. The inner drum is thus pressed to the left and, being provided with a flange Q, it squeezes the outer and inner plates together so that friction between them transmits the driving torque from the outer drum to the inner one. The clutch is disengaged by pulling the inner drum to the right against the pressure of the spring. The fingers of the withdraw shaft bear against the flange R of the housing of the clutch withdrawal thrust race. A ball bearing P eliminates friction between the spring and the inner drum when the clutch is disengaged. The screwed cup at the right-hand end of the spring enables the spring force to be adjusted. The plates of multiple-plate clutches were at one time made alternately of steel and phosphor bronze but now are all of steel or one set may be lined with a friction material. With metal to metal contact lubrication is essential and so the clutch is made oil-tight and is partly filled with oil. The oil tends to make the plates drag when the clutch is disengaged and so a clutch stop or brake is fitted. It consists of a disc T fixed to the inner drum hub and which comes into contact with a spring loaded disc U carried by any convenient part of the gear box casing or clutch housing; the disc U has a friction material lining.

19.13 Dry Multiple-plate Clutches

Multiple-plate clutches are also made to work dry, that is, without any oil. The driving plates are then lined on each side with a friction fabric. In such clutches the driving plates are sometimes carried on a number of studs screwed into the web of the flywheel in the same way as the outer plate of a single-plate clutch is sometimes carried. This construction is inconvenient when oil is used. Several small springs can be used instead of a single spring.

19.14 Clutch Release Gear

The disengagement of almost all clutches involves the axial movement of a shaft or sleeve that is rotating and this involves the use of a bearing that will permit the motion and transmit the force. A ball bearing is frequently used and is nowadays a dual purpose bearing capable of supporting both axial and radial loads. In the past bearings which could support only axial loads were used, an example being shown in Fig. 19-11, and the housing R of the bearing had itself to be supported by letting it bear on the clutch shaft. Instead of a ball bearing a graphite block bearing may be used, as has been mentioned, and in this case the housing of the block can itself be supported by the fingers which transmit the axial thrust as is shown

425

in Fig. 19-9. Referring to that figure the shaft E has to be connected to the clutch pedal and this used to be done by means of links and rods, a method that is still sometimes used in commercial vehicles. But the drawbacks to such a linkage are that it would be difficult to arrange it in modern vehicles where the clutch and the clutch pedal are not conveniently near to each other and that because the engine is carried on the frame or body structure on rubber mountings and the clutch pedal is mounted on a separate part of the body or frame the relative movements that occur between these two units give rise to poor engagement of the clutch and also to rattles. Hydraulic actuation of the clutch is therefore now used. The units employed are similar to those used for brake actuation and which are described in Chapter 29. The pedal actuates a piston which forces fluid through piping into an actuating cylinder carried on the bell housing surrounding the clutch and whose piston is connected to a lever carried by the shaft on which the withdraw fingers are fixed. Part or all of the piping can be made flexible and thus both of the difficulties associated with mechanical linkages are obviated.

19.15 Clutch Brakes or Stops

When a clutch is disengaged while the engine is running the inertia of the driven member will tend to keep it revolving. This inertia is proportional to the weight of the member and to the square of the " radius of gyration " which is the equivalent radius at which the weight may be considered to act. Since this tendency to continue revolving may render gear changing difficult small brakes are often arranged to act on the driven member when the clutch is *fully* withdrawn. The stop member or brake is sometimes backed up by springs so that a gradually increasing pressure acts on the brake.

Careful adjustment of the clutch stop will sometimes convert a difficult gear change to an easy one. The brake should not come into action at all when the clutch is only just disengaged because in " changing down " the driven member has to be speeded up instead of slowed down, and consequently the brake is not required to act.

In order to reduce the work done by these brakes the weight of the driven member of the clutch, and more particularly its radius of gyration, are kept as small as possible. One of the advantages of the single-plate clutch is the small weight and radius of gyration of its driven member.

19.16 " Automatic " Clutch Action

Many attempts have been made to produce motor vehicles that can be controlled by the accelerator pedal and brakes only; this can be done in several ways. A centrifugal clutch which automatically disengages itself when the speed falls below and which reengages when the speed rises above some predetermined value may be used. Alternatively, a fluid coupling, a fluid torque converter or some special form of clutch may be employed. Examples of each of these solutions of the problem will be described in the following sections.

19.17 Centrifugal Clutches

The principle of these is shown in the simple arrangement in Fig. 19-12 (*a*) where a single-plate clutch of ordinary construction has its presser plate A actuated by the " centrifugal " forces acting on masses B formed on the ends of bell-crank levers pivoted on pins in the cover plate C. This arrangement has two principal drawbacks. Firstly, there would be some force acting on the presser plate whenever the clutch was rotating and thus the clutch would never be completely disengaged. Secondly, if the force P due to the centrifugal force C.F. were sufficient to engage the clutch fully at say 1,000 r.p.m. then it would become nine times as great at 3,000 r.p.m. and it would require nine times the force necessary with an ordinary clutch to produce disengagement at that higher speed by pulling the presser plate back in the ordinary way, and it is desirable to be able to disengage the clutch in that way.

The first drawback can be overcome by putting in springs D (shown dotted) which apply a force Q opposing the force P. The centrifugal forces will then not give rise to any pressure on the driven plate until they have increased sufficiently to overcome the force Q and until then the clutch will be completely disengaged. By choosing the magnitude of Q suitably, the commencement of the engagement can be made to occur at any desired speed. Usually in motor car clutches a speed of about 500 r.p.m. is chosen. The second drawback can be overcome by modifying the construction as shown at (*b*) where the bell-crank levers press on a floating plate E between which and the presser plate are placed springs F. These springs transmit the force P from the floating plate to the presser plate. A stop G limits the outward motion of the masses B and thus limits the amount the springs F can be compressed. The force that must be applied to the presser plate in order to pull it

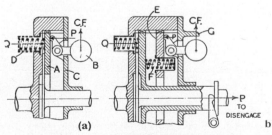

Fig. 19-12: Principle of centrifugal clutch

back so as to disengage the clutch is now limited to the difference between the force Q and the force exerted by the springs F when the masses (having come against the stops G) have compressed them fully. This difference can be made to have any desired value. The

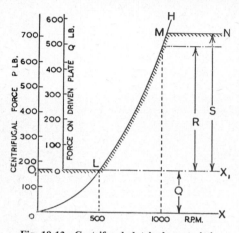

Fig. 19-13: Centrifugal clutch characteristic

pressure exerted on the driven plate will now be represented by a graph whose shape is the shaded line in Fig. 19-13. The curve OLMH whose ordinates are measured from the line OX as axis shows how the centrifugal force CMF varies with speed. If a new axis O_1X_1 is drawn so that OO_1 equals the force Q exerted by the springs D then the graph O_1LH measured from O_1X_1 gives the pressure on the driven plate when the springs D are fitted. Finally, if the line MN is drawn so that its height above OX is equal to the force exerted by the springs F when fully compressed the graph O_1LMN will represent the pressure on the driven plate in the modified arrangement of Fig. 19-12 (b). This is what is desirable for the variation of pressure with speed, that is, no pressure at speeds below about 500 r.p.m., a rapid increase of pressure between 500 r.p.m. and about 1,000 r.p.m. so that at the latter speed the clutch is fully engaged, and no great increase in pressure at speeds above 1,000 r.p.m. In Fig. 19-13, S is the force that must be used to disengage the clutch at speeds over 1,000 r.p.m. and R the force required to enable the clutch to transmit full engine torque. If the torque developed by the engine is less than full torque (that is, if the throttle is not wide open) then a force less than R will enable that reduced torque to be transmitted and the clutch will be fully engaged at some speed less than 1,000 r.p.m.

19.18   Magnetic Particle Clutches

The construction of these and the principles on which they operate are best explained by considering a typical example. Fig. 19-14 shows the dual coupling developed by Messrs. Smith's Motor Accessories, Ltd., for their automatic transmissions. These are used by several motor car manufacturers, in particular by Rootes, Ltd., in their Hillman Minx cars.

There are four main components: (1) the stator A which is fixed in the bell-housing connecting the engine crankcase to the gear box casing; (2) the driving member B which is bolted up at its left-hand end to the engine flywheel; (3) and (4) the driven members C and D. The member C is connected through a spring cushioning centre E (see Section 19.10) to the shaft F, and the member D through the spring centre G to the sleeve H.   Baffles J, K, L and M enable the spaces N, O, P and Q to be partly filled with very small particles of a magnetic material.

The stator A has two windings, R and S, which can be energized by current from the car generator or, when necessary, from the battery.   Supposing the winding R to be energized, then there will be a magnetic field set up whose direction will be as indicated by the elliptical arrow and it will be seen that this field intersects the gap between the members B and C approximately perpendicularly. The direction of the field is controlled by the gap in the stator and by the grooves formed in both the driving member B and the driven member C.   Because of the magnetic field, each magnetic particle in the gap between B and C becomes magnetized and the particles thus tend to cohere to each other and to the surfaces of the members B and C.   The result is that when the winding is fully energized, sufficient friction is generated at those surfaces and between the particles to enable full engine torque to be transmitted without appreciable slip occurring.

When the energizing current is cut off the friction falls to a negligible value and the clutch is disengaged.   By controlling the energizing current the " take-up " is made smooth and gradual. This can be done directly by means of rheostats in the winding circuit or indirectly by controlling the build-up of the generator current as its speed rises during acceleration.

The excitation current is about one and a half amps with a 12 volt supply, i.e., the excitation power is about 30 watts.

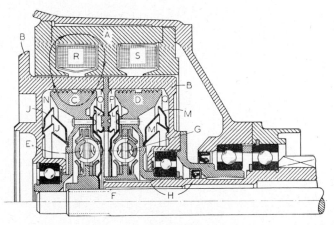

Fig. 19-14

19.19 Eddy Current Couplings

The constructional form of one of these is shown in Fig. 19-15. There are two main members, A and B, which are coupled respectively to the engine crankshaft and the input shaft of the gear box. The member A resembles and, if required can form, the flywheel but its rim is cut away by a number of semicircular recesses as shown in the view (a). The metal left between the recesses forms a series of axial " bars "—connected together at their ends by the continuous portions of the rim. The member A thus resembles the rotor of a " squirrel-cage " electric motor.

The shape of the outside of the member B is shown in the view (b). There is an electrical winding running round the annular space C and the ends of this winding are connected to slip rings D and E on which stationary brushes bear, so that current can be passed through the winding from a battery or generator. When this is done, a magnetic field is built up whose direction will be as shown by the dotted line. The field will take this path rather than pass from the " fingers " F to the fingers G because the air-gap between these fingers is large compared with the gap between the members A and B and the magnetic " resistance " or reluctance is consequently less through the latter.

If the member A now rotates relative to B, the magnetic flux will " cut " the bars of the member A and eddy currents will be generated in that member. There will consequently be a magnetic drag between the members which will tend to make B rotate in unison with A. Some difference of speed will, however, always exist because if there were no such difference, there would be no eddy currents and no drag.

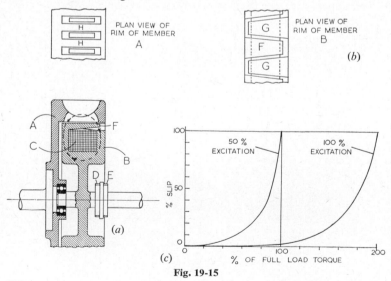

Fig. 19-15

The torque that can be transmitted from A to B depends on the difference in speed that exists between them, on the magnitude of the exciting current (up to that value which will produce saturation of the magnetic " circuit ") and on the size of the coupling.   When transmitting the full designed torque, the difference in speed will usually be about 3 per cent of the speed of the driving member. The variation of the percentage slip

[i.e., 100 × (speed of A — speed of B)/(speed of A)]

with the torque transmitted and for two values of the magnitude of the excitation current is shown in Fig. 19-15 (c).   The take-up characteristics of this type of coupling are very similar to those of a fluid coupling (see Section 19.21).   Take-up is brought about by increasing the speed of the driving member and by controlling the value of the excitation current.

It should be noted that the output torque from the coupling is for all practical purposes equal to the input torque so that the device is the equivalent of a clutch and not of a gear box or torque converter. Couplings of this kind are largely used in industrial applications and have been employed in a few automobile vehicles.   By fixing the member B relative to the chassis and by driving the member A off the propeller shaft, the device can be used as a brake and this has been done to some extent in heavy lorries.

19.20   The Ferlec Electro-magnetic Clutch

This is basically a single-plate friction clutch in which the clamping force is provided by an electro-magnet instead of by springs.   Its construction is shown in Fig. 19-16, the driven plate A has a spring damper hub which is splined on the output shaft B.   The latter is

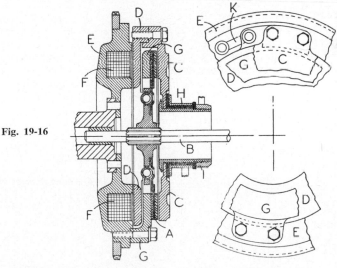

Fig. 19-16

carried in a spigot bearing at the left and in a bearing in the gearbox at the right. The pressure plate C is bolted to an armature disc D which itself is secured to the flywheel by three tangentially disposed links K, as shown in the scrap end view. These links isolate the flywheel from the armature disc magnetically while positioning it and causing it to rotate with the flywheel. The links K also permit the small axial movement required for the engagement of the clutch. There is an air-gap of 0·45 mm between the armature and the face of the flywheel when the clutch is disengaged. When the winding F is energized the armature D with the pressure plate C is attracted to the flywheel so that the driven plate is squeezed between the pressure plate and the member G, which is rigidly bolted to the flywheel at three points, as indicated in the scrap end view at the bottom of the figure. The current for energizing the winding is led in and out through brushes which bear on slip rings H and I, connected to the ends of the winding.

To provide a smooth engagement the energizing current is made to build up gradually, either automatically as the dynamo speed increases or, when the battery supplies the current, by two variable resistances (one for low and one for high gears) which are decreased as the accelerator is depressed. The change from one resistance to the other is made by the selecting movement of the gear lever, the striking motion of which also provides an interruption of the current to the clutch coil and gives the momentary clutch disengagement to enable a gear change to be made. A cam actuated by the accelerator pedal also opens a switch when the pedal is in the idling and starting position, thus ensuring disengagement of the clutch at starting and during idling.

19.21 Fluid Flywheel

This consists of two castings (called rotors), almost identical in form, one of which is fixed to the crankshaft of the engine and the other to the gear box shaft. These castings are roughly circular discs in which passages XX (Fig. 19-17) are formed. Since the areas of these passages perpendicular to their centre line (XXX in the sectional view) must be kept approximately constant and since the circumferential width of the opening a is less than that of b the

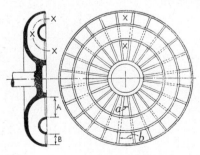

Fig. 19-17: Fluid flywheel rotor

radial size of the opening A is made greater than that of B. In a simplified form the passages may be represented by tubes A and B with right-angled corners as shown in Fig. 19-18.

Imagine these tubes to be full of fluid and suppose them to be rotating about the axis XX with speeds N and n. Then if the outer end of the tube A were closed by a diaphragm C the fluid would be exerting a pressure P_a on that diaphragm, and this pressure can be shown to be proportional to N^2. Similarly, if the tube B were closed by a diaphragm D the fluid would be exerting a pressure P_b on that diaphragm. Now if n is less than N the pressure P_b will be less than the pressure P_a and if the diaphragms were removed the fluid in the tube A would commence to flow in the direction of the arrow E and would force the fluid in the tube B to flow in the direction of the arrow F against its inclination to flow the other way. Thus if the speeds N and n are unequal, the fluid in the tubes will be caused to circulate round and round. If N is greater than n then the circulation will be as indicated by the arrows E and F, that is, clockwise, but if n were greater than N then the circulation would be in the opposite direction and if the speeds of the rotors were equal there would be no circulation at all. Since there will always be some resistance to the flow of the fluid the speed at which the fluid will circulate will reach a steady value which can be shown to be proportional to the difference between N^2 and n^2. Of course, if the speeds of the rotors are not equal then any particular tube A will not always be opposite any particular tube B but there will always be a tube B for the fluid from any tube A to flow into although there may be a certain amount of impinging of the fluid on the walls of the tubes, that is, on the webs of metal between the passages XXX in Fig. 19-17.

Having seen that a difference in the speeds of the two rotors will cause a circulation of the fluid from one rotor to the other it can now be explained how the energy developed by the engine is transmitted to the gear box. Consider Fig. 19-18. At K is indicated a

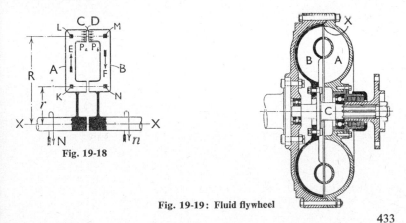

Fig. 19-18

Fig. 19-19: Fluid flywheel

particle of fluid which is at a distance r from the axis XX. This particle has to rotate in a circle radius r with the angular speed of the tube, that is, N. Its linear speed in the circle is thus $2\pi rN$ and its kinetic energy is $\frac{1}{2}\frac{w}{g}(2\pi r)N^2$ where w is the weight of the particle.

Now if the fluid is circulating as described above (N being assumed greater than n) the particle K will, in a short space of time, arrive at L. It will then be rotating in a circle whose radius is R at the speed N and its kinetic energy will be $\frac{1}{2}\frac{w}{g}(2\pi RN)^2$. Since R is greater than r the kinetic energy of the particle when it arrives at L is greater than it was at K. The increase in the kinetic energy of the particle as it moves from K to L is derived from the energy developed by the engine, the whole of which is utilized in increasing the kinetic energy of the fluid as it flows from the centre to the outside of the tubes A.

Continuing our consideration of the particle we find that a short time after it was at L it will have arrived at M. It will then be rotating in a circle radius R as at L but now at the slower speed n. Its kinetic energy is now $\frac{1}{2}\frac{w}{g}(2\pi Rn)^2$ and since n is less than N the kinetic energy at M is less than it was at L. Some of this difference in the kinetic energy will have been passed to the rotor B but some will have been converted into heat by impact with the webs of metal between the tubes and will for all practical purposes be lost. Finally, a short time after the particle was at M it will have arrived at N where it will be once more rotating in a circle of radius r but now at the speed n. Its kinetic energy will be $\frac{1}{2}\frac{w}{g}(2\pi rn)^2$ and is less than it was at M. Thus, as the particle moves from M to N it loses kinetic energy and the energy it loses is passed to the rotor B and thus to the gear box.

19.22 Prevention of Leakage

It has been tacitly assumed that the fluid cannot escape between the faces of the rotors and it might be thought that those faces would have to be in rubbing contact in order to prevent such leakage. In actual fact, however, there is a gap of about $\frac{1}{16}$ in between the faces and escape of the fluid is prevented by making one rotor with a cover which embraces the other rotor as will be seen in Fig. 19-19.

The relative position of the rotors has been changed in that figure to correspond with the disposition generally adopted in fluid flywheels for motor vehicles. The rotor that is fixed to the flywheel is now the right-hand one A which is bolted to the rim of the flywheel while the left-hand rotor B is fixed to the gear box shaft C. Fluid does escape between the faces of the rotors and fills the space between the outside of the rotors and the inside of the flywheel. Centrifugal force keeps this fluid in position and maintains a pressure at X which prevents escape of fluid from the insides of the rotors once sufficient fluid has accumulated outside to enable a state of equilibrium to be reached.

19.23 Characteristic of the Fluid Flywheel

The characteristic which is of chief importance is the way in which the " percentage slip " varies with the speed of rotation. The percentage slip is defined as the quantity $(N - n) \times 100/N$ and is a measure of the difference in the speed of the two rotors. If n were equal to N then the percentage slip would be zero and if n were zero then the percentage slip would be 100. When the percentage slip is plotted against engine speed (N) the resulting graph is of the form shown in Fig. 19-20. At any speed less than about 600 r.p.m.

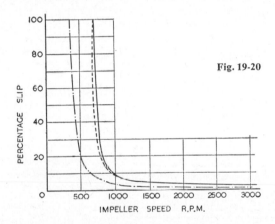

Fig. 19-20

(this speed can be made to have any desired value by suitably modifying the design) the percentage slip is 100, that is, the gear box shaft is stationary and we have the equivalent of a completely disengaged clutch. As the engine speed increases from 600 to 1,000 r.p.m. the percentage slip falls rapidly to about 12. This corresponds to the period of actual engagement of an ordinary clutch, the speed of the gear box shaft being rapidly brought up to roughly the same value as the engine speed. From 1,000 r.p.m. up to the maximum speed the percentage slip decreases comparatively slowly from 12 down to possibly as little as 2. The percentage slip at any engine speed depends, however, on the torque being transmitted, the curve above being based on the assumption that the engine exerts full torque at every speed. If the engine torque is reduced below the full torque (open throttle) value then the percentage slip will be reduced. Thus

435

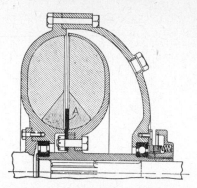

Fig. 19-21

under easy running conditions when the throttle is only slightly opened the percentage slip may be less than 1 per cent. The chain dotted curve indicates the variation of the percentage slip with the speed for such conditions, that is, level road and no head wind. Whatever the value of the percentage slip, however, it represents a direct loss of energy and thus an increase in the petrol consumption. Thus it is an abuse of the fluid flywheel to allow the engine speed to fall to the region between 1,000 and 600 r.p.m., on full throttle, when the percentage slip becomes considerable and such use is comparable to the slipping of an ordinary clutch, which also increases the petrol consumption, the difference being that whereas an ordinary friction clutch would be damaged by prolonged slipping the fluid flywheel will not suffer any damage although it may become so hot as to burn one's hand if one touches it.

19.24   " Open Circuit " Fluid Coupling

In an alternative design of fluid flywheel the " torus-ring " that forms the inner wall of the passage round which the fluid circulates is omitted, as is shown in Fig. 19-21. A " baffle plate," as shown at A, is also sometimes fitted. The open circuit and baffle ring modify the characteristics of the coupling slightly as may be seen from the dotted curve in Fig. 19-20. The most important difference is a reduction in the drag torque when the coupling is stalled.

Figs. 19-22 and 19-23 illustrate the modern forms of seal used with fluid couplings and torque converters. The sealing surfaces are the flat faces of a steel ring C and a bronze or graphite ring D which are pressed together by a spring or springs E. The sealing faces are finished to optical limits of flatness and to ensure proper seating one ring is carried on a flexible diaphragm or bellows F. The design shown in Fig. 19-22 takes up less axial but more radial space than that of Fig. 19-23. In the latter the graphite ring D is left free to float between the metal faces on either side of it.

It can be shown quite easily that the torque exerted by the flywheel

436

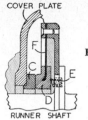

Fig. 19-22

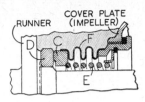

Fig. 19-23

on the gear box shaft is equal to the torque exerted by the engine on the fluid flywheel.

Thus the fluid flywheel does not give any increase of torque and is not the equivalent of a gear box, the chief function of which is to give an increase of torque when required.

In addition to giving " accelerator pedal control " the fluid flywheel also reduces the shocks transmitted by the engine to the transmission and vice versa.

The qualities required of the fluid are high density, low viscosity, chemical stability and absence of corrosive action and the fluid that is generally used is a very thin engine oil. A thick, viscous oil would increase the percentage slip, other factors being the same, and would thus reduce the efficiency.

The only important drawback of the fluid flywheel is that even when the percentage slip is 100 per cent, there is a drag on the gear box shaft which renders gear changing with ordinary types of gear box very difficult. Consequently, the fluid flywheel is generally used in combination with epicyclic gear boxes which eliminate the difficulty. In the fluid coupling made by the MAAG company of Zurich and used in the automatic gear box of their design, the driven member is carried on the output shaft on a quick-pitch screw thread so that, when the speed of the driving member falls below that of the driven member, and the latter therefore tends to drive the former, the driven member is itself " unscrewed " along the thread and moves away from the driving member. This reduces the drag in the coupling and assists in the gear changing.

When it is desired to use an ordinary type of gear box a friction clutch is sometimes used in conjunction with a fluid flywheel. This clutch is intended to be used only for gear changing and not for taking up the drive during starting and acceleration of the car; it can therefore be made with smaller friction surface areas than a clutch that had to take up the drive but it must, of course, be capable of transmitting the full engine torque. However, if the engine is accelerated with the friction clutch disengaged and then the clutch is engaged it will have to take up the drive. To obviate this misuse of the clutch it may be interconnected with the accelerator pedal so that the latter cannot be depressed while the clutch is disengaged.

19.25 Fluid-friction Clutch

The losses that occur in fluid couplings due to the continuous slip at normal running speeds are eliminated in a combination of fluid coupling and centrifugal clutch made by Self Changing Gears, Ltd., of Coventry, and called by them the Fluid-friction clutch. Its construction is shown in Fig. 19-24. The impeller A is bolted to the flywheel and the driven member C is fixed to the output shaft D in the usual way. A spider E is also fixed to the shaft D and carries four shoes F lined with friction fabric. These shoes are pivoted on pins carried in blocks H which are free to slide radially in slots formed in the flange of the spider E. At low speeds the shoes are

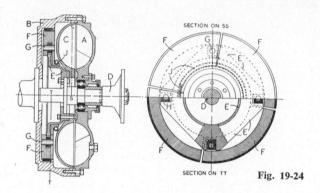

Fig. 19-24

held out of contact with the inside of the flywheel B by a spring J, which encircles flanges formed on the shoes, but when the speed rises beyond a certain value, the shoes move outwards under the action of centrifugal force and engage the flywheel. The slip between the latter and the driven shaft D is thereby reduced to zero. Thus the smooth take-up of the fluid coupling is retained but the continuous slip associated with it is eliminated. The shoes can be mounted on their pivots so that they either " trail " or " lead " (see Chapter 29).

19.26 Connection Between the Clutch and Gear Box

The driven members of the clutches shown in Figs. 19-2 and 19-11 are fully supported by the spigot bearings provided within the clutch. The driven members therefore revolve about the same axis as the crankshaft, and they have to be coupled up to the gear box shaft.

If a *rigid* coupling is used to join two shafts, which have to revolve, it is essential that the axes of the shafts shall always coincide. Otherwise very heavy loads will be imposed on the bearings supporting the shafts and on the shafts themselves.

When the engine and the gear box are independently mounted on the frame it is impossible to ensure that the axes of their shafts,

438

which have to be coupled together, shall always coincide. Although initially the shafts may be " in alignment," as it is termed, unavoidable flexures of the frame will upset that alignment. A rigid coupling cannot then be used; the coupling must be able to allow for the misalignment. The latter may be of two kinds, an angular displacement as in Fig. 19-25, or a bodily displacement as in Fig. 19-26.

The first kind of misalignment can be allowed for by using either a *flexible* coupling or what is known as a " universal " joint. These

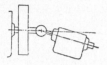

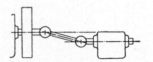

Fig. 19-25   Fig. 19-26

will be dealt with later. The second kind of misalignment necessitates the use of two such joints and a short intermediate shaft as shown in Fig. 19-26. When the engine and the gear box are separate units, therefore, the driven member of the clutch, or the clutch shaft, will be coupled to the gear box by an intermediate shaft with a flexible or universal joint at each end.

When the gear box is made integral with, or is rigidly bolted to the crank case of the engine, so as to form a single unit with the latter, it is possible to ensure the permanent coincidence of the clutch and gear box shaft axes. Those shafts may then be coupled by a rigid coupling, but usually the clutch shaft will be one with the gear box shaft. In that case the single clutch gear box shaft will be supported at one end in the spigot bearing of the clutch and at the other end in the gear box bearings. The clutches shown in Figs. 19-5, 6, 7 and 8 are intended to be used in this manner.

CHAPTER 20

Object of the Gear Box

**Air, gradient and rolling resistances.   Tractive effort.   Performance curves.
Selection of gear ratios.**

IN order to explain the object of the gear box it will be necessary
to consider briefly the resistances to the motion of a vehicle.
When a car is moving along a road at a uniform speed there are
various forces opposing its motion, and in order to keep it moving
at that speed a driving force or " tractive effort " equal to the sum
of all the opposing forces has to be applied to it.   If the tractive
effort should exceed the sum of all the resistances then the excess
tractive effort will accelerate the vehicle.   On the other hand if the
tractive effort is less than the sum of the resistances then the excess
of the resistances will decelerate the vehicle.

The forces opposing the motion can be divided into the following
three groups—

(1) Air or " wind " resistance.
(2) Gradient resistance.
(3) Rolling resistance.

20.1 Air Resistance

The air offers a resistance to the passage of bodies through it.
This resistance depends on the size and shape of the body, and
upon its speed through the air.   Thus, the resistance to the motion
of an airship that is " stream-lined " is very much less than it would
be for a simple cylinder with flat ends.   However, the effect of the
shape and size of a vehicle on its air resistance need not be considered
here, because for any given vehicle the shape and size are fixed
quantities.   The effect of speed on the air resistance must, however,
be considered, and this is illustrated in Fig. 20-1, which is a graph of
air resistance plotted against speed.   It will be seen that when the
speed is zero the resistance is zero and that as the speed increases
so does the air resistance, the rise being at an increasing rate as the
speed gets higher.   In practice the air resistance is taken to vary as
the square of the speed, so that if the speed is doubled the resistance
is increased four times.

It should be clear from the graph that for slow-speed vehicles,
such as heavy lorries, the air resistance will be very small and may
be neglected, but with high-speed vehicles it becomes important.
In racing cars it is of paramount importance.

Since it is the speed of a vehicle through the air that determines
the air resistance, the latter may be considerable even for lorries
if a strong head wind prevails.

440

Fig. 20-1

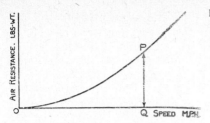

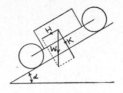

Fig. 20-2

20.2   Gradient Resistance

Fig. 20-2 shows a car standing on a gradient, and it will be seen that the weight of the car, which of course acts vertically downwards, can be resolved into two components H and K. The component K is perpendicular to the road surface and the component H is parallel to that surface. To prevent the car from running down the gradient a force equal and opposite to H must be applied to it, while if the car is being propelled up the hill part of the driving force goes to neutralize the force H. That force is an additional resistance to the motion of the car and may be called the " gradient resistance." It depends simply on the steepness of the gradient and the weight of the car. It is not affected by the speed of the car up the gradient.

20.3   Rolling Resistance

Under this heading are included all the remaining external resistances and also, sometimes, the internal frictional resistances of the transmission system. However, in what follows the latter is not so included and, if not neglected altogether, is dealt with by deducting it from the driving effort due to the engine.

The rolling resistance in this restricted sense is due chiefly to the deformation of road and tyre, and to the dissipation of energy through impact. It depends chiefly on the nature of the road surface, the nature of the tyres with which the vehicle is fitted and the total weight of vehicle and load. On soft, muddy and sandy roads it is greater than on hard dry macadam or wood paving; it is less with pneumatic than with solid rubber or steel tyres and it is generally taken to be directly proportional to the total weight of vehicle and load. That part of it which is due to impact undoubtedly depends also on the speed and springing of the vehicle and the remainder probably does so to a small extent. However, on roads having a hard dry surface free from large bumps and holes, the impact losses are probably only a small part of the total rolling resistance, and the effect of speed on the latter will not be great. Reliable information on this matter is lacking, however, and in what follows the rolling resistance has been assumed to be independent of the speed, but even if this assumption is not justified the value of the present chapter will be but slightly reduced.

441

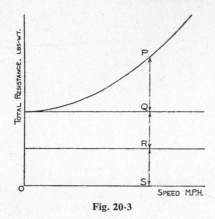

Fig. 20-3

20.4 Total Resistance

The total resistance to the motion of a vehicle is the sum of the above three resistances and is thus composed of two parts that are independent of the speed of the vehicle—the rolling resistance and the gradient resistance—and of one part that is dependent on the speed—the air resistance.

A curve of total resistance against speed is therefore obtained by shifting the curve of Fig. 20-1 up vertically by the amount of the rolling and gradient resistances as is shown in Fig. 20-3.

Thus when the speed is OS m.p.h. the total resistance SP is composed of the rolling resistance SR, the gradient resistance RQ and the air resistance QP. If either the gradient resistance or the rolling resistance increases or decreases then the curve would simply shift up or down by the amount of the increase or decrease.

In Fig. 20-4 the curves A, B and C are the curve of Fig. 20-1 shifted up by various amounts, they therefore represent total resistance curves for a given vehicle on roads of either different surfaces or different gradients. Considering the road surface to remain unchanged then curve A might represent the total resistance on the level, curve B the total resistance on a gradient of say 1 in 30, and so on.

20.5 Tractive Effort

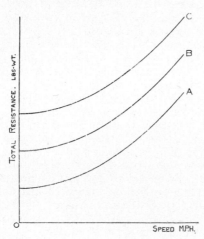

Fig. 20-4

Having dealt with the resistance to the motion of the vehicle, let us turn to the driving effort. The source of this is of course the engine, which turns the clutch shaft with a torque T. This torque is transmitted to the gear box. Now by applying the principle of the conservation of energy as stated on page 32, we shall find that if frictional losses are neglected, and if there is no storing of energy, the whole of the energy put into the gear box at the engine end must be given out at the propeller shaft end. Since the work done in unit time is measured (when rotations are considered) by the product of the torque and the speed, it follows that the product of the engine torque and the speed of the clutch shaft must equal the product of the torque acting on the propeller shaft and the propeller shaft speed. If, therefore, the propeller shaft speed is $1/n$th the engine speed, then the torque acting on the propeller shaft must be n times the engine torque. We have then, propeller shaft torque $= n \times T$, n being the gear box gear ratio between the speeds of the engine and the propeller shaft and T being the engine torque.

The propeller shaft drives the road wheels through the final drive where another reduction of speed occurs. If the road wheel speed is $1/m$th of the propeller shaft speed then the torque acting on the road wheel (the two wheels being considered as a single wheel) will be m times the propeller shaft torque, again neglecting frictional losses and energy storage. The torque acting on the road wheel is therefore $t = n \times m \times T$ where n is the gear box ratio, m the final drive ratio and T the engine torque.

The way in which this torque produces a driving force to propel the car along the road is shown in Fig. 20-5. If the wheel there shown is regarded as being in equilibrium (as defined in the section on mechanics), then the forces that act upon it must be in equilibrium and the couples also. Now at every instant the wheel can be considered as a lever (as shown by the dotted lines) fulcrumed at the point of contact of the wheel and the ground.

Under the action of the torque t the lever will tend to rotate about the point of contact with the ground and the centre of the wheel will tend to go forwards and to take the axle and the vehicle with it. At its centre therefore the wheel is pressing forwards on the axle casing with a force which we will call P_1. The reaction P_2 of this force (P_1) acts backwards on the wheel. Since the wheel is in equilibrium there must be an equal and opposite force P_3 acting on it. This is the adhesive force between the wheel and the road.

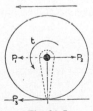

Fig. 20-5

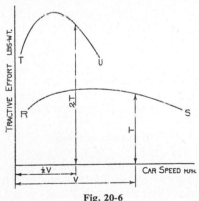

Fig. 20-6

443

The forces $P_2\ P_3$ constitute a couple tending to turn the wheel in the clockwise direction and since the wheel is in equilibrium, and the couples acting on it are therefore also in equilibrium, the couple $P_2\ P_3$ must equal the couple t applied to the wheel by the driving shaft. Now the magnitude of the couple $P_2\ P_3$ is $P_3 \times R$ where R is the distance between the forces $P_2\ P_3$, in this case the radius of the wheel. Hence $t = P_3 \times R$ and since $t = n \times m \times T$ we have $n \times m \times T = P_3 \times R$ or $P_3 = \dfrac{n \times m \times T}{R}$.

Now the values of the final drive ratio m and the wheel radius R are, for any given vehicle, constants and for any particular gear box gear the value of the ratio n is constant. Hence for any particular gear box gear the value of the fraction $\dfrac{n \times m}{R}$ is a constant which may be called K.

The tractive effort is then given by the equation $P = K \times T$ where T is the engine torque and K is a constant whose value depends upon the road wheel radius, the final drive ratio and upon the gear box gear ratio.

20.6 Variation of the Tractive Effort with Speed

Now, since the engine is geared to the driving wheels, a particular engine speed corresponds to a particular vehicle speed, and since the tractive effort is proportional to the engine torque, the variation of the tractive effort with the variation of the vehicle speed will depend upon the variation of the engine torque with the variation of engine speed. This last relation has already been considered and a curve showing it is given in Fig. 4-7, page 51. The curve showing the relation between tractive effort and vehicle speed will be of the same shape; in fact, the same curve might be used provided the scales were suitably altered.

A tractive-effort vehicle-speed curve for a given gear box ratio, a given final drive ratio and a given road wheel radius is shown at RS in Fig. 20-6. If the gear box ratio is altered we shall get another curve of tractive effort. Thus if the gear box ratio is altered so that the total gear ratio between the engine and the back wheels is double what it originally was then the curve RS will become the curve TU, the relation between the curves being that all the horizontal distances of RS are halved and the corresponding vertical distances are doubled to give curve TU, since for a given engine speed doubling the total gear ratio will halve the vehicle speed but will double the tractive effort.

20.7 Performance Curves

Having thus obtained curves showing the variation, with varying vehicle speed, of both the tractive effort and the total resistance to be overcome let these curves be plotted, to the same scales, on the same sheet of paper, as has been done in Fig. 20-7. In that figure

444

the curves A-F are curves of total resistance for a road with a uniform surface but of varying gradient, curve A being the level and curve F the steepest gradient. Curves RS, TU and VW are curves of tractive effort for three different gear ratios, RS being, say, the top gear, TU the next lower gear, etc.

Suppose the vehicle is travelling on the level at a speed represented by OX. Then the resistance to be overcome is XY, while the tractive effort available is XZ. The tractive effort available is therefore greater than the resistance to be overcome and the excess tractive effort YZ will go to increase the speed of the vehicle. Now as the speed increases the resistance also increases but the tractive effort, it will be noticed, falls off. The excess tractive effort, given by the intercepts corresponding to YZ, which is available for acceleration, becomes smaller and smaller as the speed increases until, when the speed is OM, the tractive effort available is only just equal to the resistance to be overcome. There is therefore no excess tractive effort available for acceleration, and the speed cannot be increased further, OM represents the highest speed the vehicle can reach on the level road to which the curve A applies.

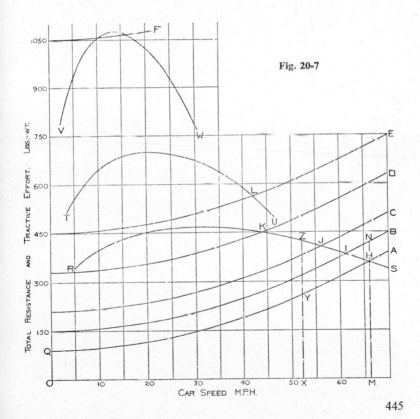

Fig. 20-7

The curve RS represents the tractive effort with the engine running with the throttle wide open. If it is not desired to increase the speed beyond the value OX then the throttle would be closed until the tractive effort was equal to XY, and the speed would be maintained but not increased.

Now suppose the vehicle is travelling on the level at the maximum speed OM, and that it comes to a gradient to which the curve B applies. At the speed OM on the gradient B the resistance is MN, but the tractive effort available is only MH. Hence the excess resistance HN will slow the vehicle down and the speed will fall to the value given by the point I, at which the tractive effort is equal to the resistance to be overcome.

Now suppose that the gradient becomes steeper and steeper so that we pass in succession from curve B to curve C and so on. The speed that can be maintained gets progressively lower as indicated by the points J, K, etc., and it will be seen that we cannot traverse the gradient E at any speed since the tractive effort curve lies everywhere below the resistance curve.

Now, with ordinary sized engines, if the gear ratio is such as to give a reasonable maximum speed on the level, then quite a medium gradient would bring about the conditions represented by the curve E, and the vehicle would be brought to rest. But if the gear ratio between the engine and the driving wheels can be altered we can pass from the tractive effort curve RS to the curve TU and then the gradient E can be traversed at the speed given by the point L.

Thus in order to permit a reasonably high maximum speed on the level and at the same time to be able to climb medium gradients we require to have available two different gear ratios. Similarly in order to permit reasonably high speeds up medium gradients and yet be able to climb steep gradients, we need a third gear ratio, and a fourth or fifth ratio may be desirable.

It should also be clear that at the lower speeds, when quick acceleration is especially desirable, there is a greater excess of tractive effort available on a lower gear than on a higher one.

The above is the complete explanation of the *raison d'être* of the gear box, and it should be clear that the ideal gear box would provide an infinite range of gear ratios so that the engine speed could be kept at or near that at which maximum power was developed, whatever the speed of the vehicle. This assumes that maximum speed is the objective. If maximum economy is desired, the engine requires to be run at the highest torque possible for a given power output. Many of the developments in transmissions, such as the various hydraulic and electrical mechanisms, have as their principal object the multiplication of the number of ratios available. The ideal is not yet attainable, however, and, as in the case of most engineering problems, a compromise is adopted and three, four or more gear ratios are provided depending on the size of engine fitted and other considerations.

446

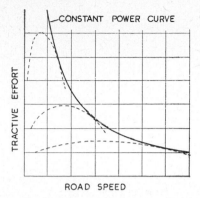

CONSTANT POWER CURVE

TRACTIVE EFFORT

ROAD SPEED

Fig. 20-8

20.8   Clutch Action

Fig. 20-7 also serves to show how the clutch enables a car to be started up from rest. When the car is at rest the resistance to be overcome before the car will move is, for the level road A, given by OQ.   If the engine were in permanent connection with the driving wheels it would, of course, be at rest and the tractive effort would be zero.   The clutch, however, allows the engine to be run at a speed at which a torque giving a greater tractive effort than OQ is developed and enables this torque to be transmitted to the driving wheels, though at the start the latter are at rest.

20.9   Constant Power T.E.-Speed Curve

If the engine of a vehicle could be made to give its maximum power at all speeds then, since *Power = T.E. × Speed*, it follows that the T.E. will be inversely proportional to the road speed.   The graph of the T.E. plotted against the road speed would then be like the full-line curve in Fig. 20-8.   The T.E. curves for an actual engine and gear box combination will touch this constant power curve at one point (corresponding to the engine speed at which the engine gives its maximum power), but will lie everywhere else inside it, as shown by the dotted line curves.   The constant power curve is the ideal form of T.E. curve and its shape is approached by those of a steam engine and of traction electric motors; it could be obtained with any engine if an infinitely variable gear box of 100 per cent efficiency were available.

20.10   Performance Curves on a H.P. Basis

Instead of considering the performance as a balance between the tractive effort available and the resistance to be overcome, that is, as a balance of forces, we may consider it as a balance between the rate of producing energy by the engine and the rate of using energy at the road wheels, that is, as a balance of powers.

447

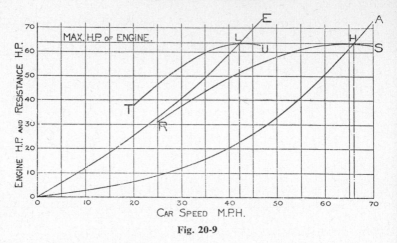

Fig. 20-9

This is shown in Fig. 20-9. The curves A and E represent the horse power required to overcome the resistances represented by the curves A and E of Fig. 20-7 at corresponding speeds, and the curves RS and TU represent the horse power available at the road wheels on the two gears corresponding to the curves RS and TU of Fig. 20-7. The power available at any moment is, of course, equal to the power developed by the engine at that moment if frictional losses are neglected, the only effect of a change of gear ratio being to alter the road speed corresponding to a given engine speed.

The greatest speeds possible on the roads to which A and E refer are given by the intersections of the horizontal line representing the maximum horse power of the engine and the curves A and E, and the best gear ratios for those roads will be such that at those greatest road speeds the engine speed is that at which the maximum power is developed. Any variation of gear ratio from these optimum values will result in a lowering of the maximum speed attainable. The maximum speeds possible with the gear ratios for which the curves RS and TU are drawn are given by the intersections H and L respectively.

The process of settling the gear ratios for a vehicle is ultimately an experimental one, but approximate values which will serve as a starting point may be derived as follows—

A curve corresponding to the curve A of Fig. 20-9 is drawn, and from its intersection with the line of maximum engine horse power the greatest possible road speed found. The top gear ratio is then made such that this road speed corresponds to the engine speed at which maximum horse power is obtained. Next the maximum gradient that is to be negotiable must be assumed and the corresponding gradient resistance found. This gives the maximum tractive effort required, and the maximum engine torque being known the gear ratio necessary to enable this tractive effort to be

448

obtained may be determined. The top and bottom gear ratios are thus settled and the remaining ratios may be put in so that they form a geometric progression, this step being justified as follows—

The engine has a certain range of speed within which the power developed is not very much less than the maximum, and the gear ratios should be such that the engine speed can be kept within that range. Let the lower limit of the range be L r.p.m. and the higher limit be M r.p.m. Suppose the car to be moving in lowest gear and the engine to be speeded to the higher limit.

If the engine speed is to be kept within the specified range the gear must now be changed. Immediately after the change has been made the engine speed should be down to the lower limit L while the road speed of the car will be unaltered. If the low gear ratio is A to 1 then the road speed corresponding to an engine speed of M r.p.m. will be equal to $K \times M/A$, where K is a constant depending on the size of the road wheels, and if the next gear ratio is B to 1 the road speed corresponding to an engine speed of L r.p.m. will be equal to $K \times L/B$. But these two road speeds are the same; hence $K \times M/A = K \times L/B$ or $B = A \times L/M$, that is, $B = c \times A$ where c is a constant equal to L/M. By similar reasoning it will be found that the next gear ratio C to 1 is given by $C = c \times B = c^2 \times A$. Hence the gear ratios form a geometric progression.

Now for an engine having a sharply peaked horse power curve c will be greater than for an engine having a flatter curve, and the number of intermediate gears required to bridge the gap between the top and bottom gears will be greater. Hence a peaked horse power curve calls for a multiplicity of gear ratios, while a flatter power curve needs but two or three. As an example, suppose the top gear is to be 4 to 1 and the bottom gear 16 to 1. Then if $c = 0.5$ the ratios will be 16 : 1, 8 : 1, 4 : 1; while if $c = 0.63$ the ratios will be 16 : 1, 10.1 : 1, 6.35 : 1, 4 : 1, so that in the first case three gears are required and in the second, four.

If performance curves on a tractive-effort basis are now plotted, using the ratios found as above, the performance can be examined and modifications tried.

CHAPTER 21

Constructional Arrangements of Gear Boxes

Sliding-mesh and constant-mesh types. Control mechanism. Lubrication of the gear box. Free-wheel devices.

THE gear boxes which are, or have been, used in motor vehicles may be divided into those in which the drive in every ratio is transmitted through gear teeth which mesh together and those in which a direct drive is provided for one of the ratios and only for the others has the drive to be transmitted through gear teeth. Gear boxes may also be classified as follows—
(1) Sliding-mesh type.
(2) Constant-mesh type.
(3) Epicyclic type.
Gear boxes which are a mixture of two of these types are not uncommon. Spur gearing is used in all three types, the differences between which lie in the manner in which the gears are brought into action.

The sliding-mesh type is the simplest and is the oldest historically; it may conveniently be dealt with first although the constant-mesh type is now the most widely used type.

21.1 Sliding-mesh Gear Box

A sliding-mesh gear box is shown in Fig. 21-1. The engine is coupled, through the clutch and clutch-shaft, to the short shaft A which is integral with the spur pinion B. The shaft A is supported in two journal ball bearings and is fixed axially in a manner that will be described later. The pinion B meshes continuously with the spur wheel D secured to the "layshaft" E, which is arranged

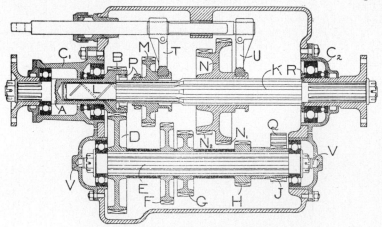

Fig. 21-1: Sliding-mesh gear box

450

parallel to the shaft A and carried at its ends in the ball bearings shown. Secured to the layshaft (which is splined throughout its length) are four other spur gears, F, G, H and J. The latter is continuously in mesh with a pinion Q which is free to revolve on a pin fixed in the casing. A third shaft (usually called the " mainshaft ") is arranged in line with the shaft A, being supported at one end in a ball bearing housed in the casing C_2 and at the other end by the " spigot " L which

Fig. 21-2

is part of the shaft K and which fits in a bushed hole in the shaft A.

The shaft K is splined for nearly its whole length and carries the independent members M and N. M is a single spur gear while N is a double gear, being in effect two gears N_1 and N_2 made in one piece. The gears M and N can be slid along the mainshaft when required by " selector forks " T and U respectively. These forks are secured to rods that can slide in bushed holes in the casing as shown, and their prongs fit into grooves cut in the bosses of the gears so that the latter can revolve freely, but must slide axially when the forks are moved. Teeth P, similar to spur gear teeth, are cut on the boss of the gear M and corresponding internal teeth are cut inside the constant-mesh pinion B and when the gear M is slid along its shaft to the left its teeth P fit into the spaces of the teeth P of the pinion B thus locking those members together. This arrangement is one form of positive clutch; an alternative form is composed of two members, each like that shown in Fig. 21-2. This latter form gives rise to the name " dog-tooth clutch."

The mainshaft K is connected, through the propeller shaft, to the road wheels. The layshaft is fixed axially by thrust buttons V. The spigot L has a spiral groove cut on it to lead oil to the bearing and at its left-hand end bears, through a thrust button, against the engine shaft A. The mainshaft is thus fixed axially by the thrust button at the left and at the right by the single-thrust ball bearing in the casing C_2. The engine shaft A is fixed axially at the right by the thrust button bearing against the end of the mainshaft and at the left by the single-thrust ball bearing in the casing C_1. The proper clearance for the thrust bearings is obtained by grinding the washer R to the proper thickness. Separate ball thrust bearings are not always provided, the journal bearings being arranged to position the shafts axially.

The gear box shown provides four forward speeds and one reverse, as follows—

21.2 First or Low Gear

The gear M occupies the position shown in Fig. 21-1. The gear N is slid along the mainshaft K until it occupies the position shown in Fig. 21-3 (a). It then meshes with the gear H of the layshaft. The drive comes from the engine shaft through the constant-mesh gears B and D to the layshaft, is then transmitted through that

451

shaft to the gear H and thence through the gear N_1 to the main shaft. The "gear ratio" or the ratio between the speeds of the engine and mainshafts is—

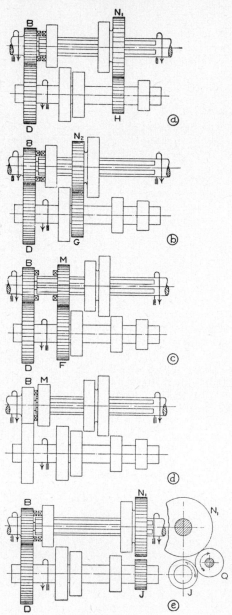

Fig. 21-3: Four-speed gear showing the various ratio combinations

$$\frac{\text{Speed of engine shaft}}{\text{Speed of mainshaft}} = \frac{\text{No. teeth in D}}{\text{No. teeth in B}} \times \frac{\text{No. teeth in N}}{\text{No. teeth in H}} = n_1.$$

The torque driving the mainshaft is now n_1 times the torque acting on the engine shaft.

21.3 Second Gear

The gear M continues to occupy the same position, but the gear N is slid over to the left as shown in Fig. 21-3 (b). It then meshes with the gear G of the layshaft. The drive is from the engine shaft through the constant-mesh gears to the layshaft, through that shaft to the gear G thence to the wheel N_2 and the mainshaft. The gear ratio is—

$$\frac{\text{Speed of engine shaft}}{\text{Speed of mainshaft}} = \frac{\text{No. teeth in D}}{\text{No. teeth in B}} \times \frac{\text{No. teeth in } N_2}{\text{No. teeth in G}}.$$

21.4 Third Gear

The gear N occupies the position shown in Fig. 21-1. The gear M is slid to the right into the position shown in Fig. 20-3 (c), where it meshes with the gear F of the layshaft. The drive is from the engine shaft through the constant-mesh gears to the layshaft, thence to the gear F, through that gear to the gear M and the mainshaft. The gear ratio is—

$$\frac{\text{Speed of engine shaft}}{\text{Speed of mainshaft}} = \frac{\text{No. teeth in D}}{\text{No. teeth in B}} \times \frac{\text{No. teeth in M}}{\text{No. teeth in F}}.$$

21.5 Fourth or Top Gear

The gear N occupies the position shown in Fig. 21-1, while the gear M is slid over to the left as shown in Fig. 21-3 (d). The dog teeth on M then engage in the spaces between the dog teeth on B, thus connecting B and M and giving a direct drive between the engine and the mainshaft. The gear ratio is then 1 to 1. The layshaft now revolves idly.

On all the above gears the direction of rotation of the layshaft is the opposite to that of the engine shaft, while the direction of rotation of the mainshaft is opposite to that of the layshaft. The mainshaft, therefore, rotates in the same direction as the engine shaft.

21.6 Reverse Gear

The member M occupies the position shown in Fig. 21-1. The gear N is slid over to the right, but farther than when first gear was being obtained. It reaches the position shown in Fig. 21-3 (e), but in this position it does *not* mesh with the pinion J of the layshaft, since that pinion is made small enough to clear the gear N_1. The gear N_1 does, however, mesh with the reverse " idler " Q which is carried on a shaft on which it is free to revolve. The shaft is fixed in the gear box casing and the idler Q is constantly in mesh with the pinion J of the layshaft.

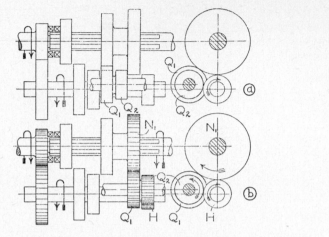

Fig. 21-4

The drive is from the engine shaft through the constant-mesh gears and the layshaft to the pinion J, thence to the idler Q, and thence to the wheel N_1 and the mainshaft. The direction of rotation of the idler Q is the opposite to that of the layshaft, and hence is the same as that of the engine shaft. The direction of rotation of the gear N_1 is the opposite to that of the idler Q, and hence is opposite to that of the engine shaft. The gear ratio is—

$$\frac{\text{Speed of engine shaft}}{\text{Speed of mainshaft}} = \frac{\text{No. teeth in D}}{\text{No. teeth in B}} \times \frac{\text{No. teeth in } N_1}{\text{No. teeth in J}}$$

It will be noticed that the number of teeth in the idler does not affect the gear *ratio*, but only the direction of rotation.

A different method of engaging the reverse gear is shown in Fig. 21-4, which shows a gear box otherwise identical with that just described. The layshaft now carries only four gears, the constant-mesh gear, the third-speed gear, the second-speed gear and the first-speed pinion H. Instead of a simple reverse idler there is now a compound one Q_{1-2}, the two portions of which are of different diameters. This idler is carried on a shaft arranged parallel to the mainshaft, but besides being free to revolve on that shaft it can also be slid axially along it in order to engage the reverse gear.

In the position shown at (*a*) the idler is in the neutral position and there is no drive between the engine shaft and the mainshaft. If, however, the idler is slid to the right, to the position shown at (*b*), the part Q_2 will engage with the pinion H of the layshaft, while the part Q_1 will engage with the gear N_1 on the mainshaft. The drive will then be from the engine shaft through the constant-mesh gears and the layshaft to the pinion H, which then drives the idler Q_2; Q_1 being integral with Q_2 is also driven, and in turn drives the gear N_1 and thus the mainshaft. As before, the mainshaft

454

goes in the opposite direction to the engine shaft, thus giving a reverse drive. The gear ratio is—

$$\frac{\text{Speed of engine shaft}}{\text{Speed of mainshaft}} =$$

$$\frac{\text{No. teeth in D}}{\text{No. teeth in B}} \times \frac{\text{No. teeth in Q}_2}{\text{No. teeth in H}} \times \frac{\text{No. teeth in N}_1}{\text{No. teeth in Q}_1}.$$

The chief advantage of this method of obtaining the reverse is that the mainshaft and the layshaft can be made shorter than when the first method is used. The deflection of the shorter shafts under a given load will be less than that of the longer shafts, if the diameters are the same, and one cause of noisy operation is reduced. If the longer shafts are sufficiently stiff then the shorter shafts may be made smaller in diameter. A gear box of the second type will generally be less bulky than a similar one of the first type. The second construction, however, involves the use of three sliding members instead of two, and makes the control mechanism slightly more complicated.

21.7 Control Mechanism

The sliding of the members M, N and (when required) Q, is effected by means of selector forks, an example of which is shown in Fig. 21-7. The fork fits into a groove formed in the boss of the gear to be moved, so that although the gear is left free to revolve, it must partake of any sideways movement that is given to the fork. There will be a selector fork for each sliding member in the gear box. The selector forks either slide on rods fixed in the gear box casing or are fixed to rods which can slide in that casing, the rods being parallel to the shafts upon which the gears slide. The necessary sliding motions are given to the selector forks by the motion of a gear change lever actuated by the driver, but since there is only one gear change lever and there are two or three selector forks, the driver must be able to select the one belonging to the gear he desires to move. The principal forms of the mechanism that enables this to be done will now be dealt with.

21.8 Sliding Type Selector Mechanism

This type is now hardly ever used but it has been thought advisable to retain a description of it; an example is shown in Fig. 21-5. View 1 is a sectional elevation, the plane of the section being indicated by the line SS in the end view 2. The latter is a section on AB. The third view is a part plan. There are three moving members in the gear box to which this particular mechanism is fitted so that there are three selector forks, C, D and E. The forks C and D slide on rods F and G fixed in the casing, while E is carried by a pivoted lever Q which is actuated by a member that slides on the third rod H. The forks are moved by a fore and aft rocking motion of the gear lever J which is carried by a shaft L pivoted in the casing and to the inner end of which is secured the

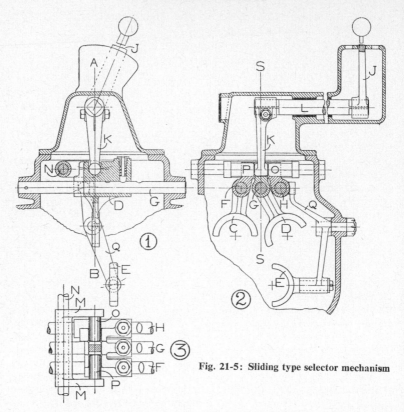

Fig. 21-5: Sliding type selector mechanism

striking lever K. The particular fork that is to be moved is selected by a sideways sliding motion of the member JLK. To hold the forks in their various positions spring plungers, one of which is seen in view 1, and which spring into grooves cut in the rods FGH, are fitted.

To prevent two forks from being moved at once a locking piece M is provided. This slides on a cross rod N fixed in the casing, and is provided with horns O and P which project into the slots in the sliding members. Between the horns O and P is situated the end of the striking lever K so that the sideways movement of the latter causes the member M to slide on its rod. The gap between the horns O and P is only slightly wider than each of the sliding members, so that the latter can be moved only one at a time.

21.9 Ball Type Selector Mechanism

This form of selector mechanism is shown in Fig. 21-6; it is becoming obsolete in cars because modern practice is to put the gear lever on the steering column; however, even in the latter case

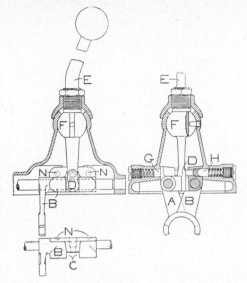

Fig. 21-6: Ball type selector

Fig. 21-7

the principle of the ball type mechanism is often used. The selector forks A and B slide on rods fixed in the gear box lid, which in this design carries the whole of the selector mechanism. The shape of the forks is shown by the perspective sketch Fig. 21-7; they are provided with slots C to receive the end D of the striking arm. The latter is the lower end of the gear lever E which is ball jointed in the casing at F. By rocking the lever sideways its end D may be brought into engagement with either of the selector forks, when a fore and aft rocking motion will slide that fork along its rod.

No gate is provided, but small plungers G and H prevent both forks from being moved at once. When both the forks are in the neutral position, and the slots C are opposite each other, the plungers are forced by small springs into holes in the forks, and before either fork can be moved the plunger that locks it must be pressed back into the casing. This is done by the sideways motion of the gear lever. Obviously when one plunger is pressed in to release one of the forks the other plunger is out, and is locking the other fork. These plungers also serve to lock the forks in position when the gears are properly engaged, being arranged to spring into shallow recesses NN in the forks.

Another selector mechanism, suitable for the remote control of the gear box, is shown in Fig. 21-8. The gear lever A is carried in a ball and socket bearing O and its spherical lower end engages a cylindrical hole formed in an arm fixed to a shaft C that is free both to turn and to slide in bearings. This shaft is coupled rigidly to a shaft carried in the gear box casing (see also Fig. 21-14). The striking arm D is fixed to the latter shaft and its lower end engages the selector forks. A sideways rocking motion of the gear lever

457

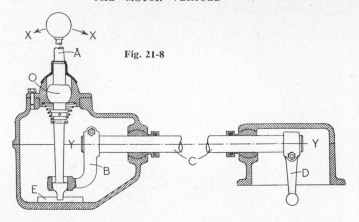

Fig. 21-8

produces a rotation of the shaft and enables the striking arm to select any desired selector rod and a fore and aft rocking motion of the gear lever then slides the shaft and thus the selector fork that has been engaged, thereby engaging the gears as required. The use of spherical bearings for the intermediate shaft accommodates any relative movement between the gear box and the bracket carrying the gear lever, alternatively plain cylindrical bearings may be used and universal joints be provided at each end of the intermediate shaft. The lower end of the gear lever engages a grooved plate E which prevents reverse gear being engaged inadvertently. The lever must be lifted up to clear the plate E in order to engage reverse.

21.10 Hillman Minx Mechanism

This is shown in Fig. 21-9 and forms a good example of the selector and striking mechanism of a gear box arranged for steering column control. The gear box is a four speed and reverse one and there are three striking forks A, B and C of which A is for the reverse and B and C for the forward gears. The striking forks are slid along their rods by the striking lever D when the lever E is rotated about the axis OO. The appropriate fork is selected by operating the lever F; the lever G then rotates the interlocking member H about the axis XX and pivots the lever D about the pin J, thereby moving it into engagement with the appropriate fork. The other two forks are locked in neutral position by the fingers K and L of the interlocking member which is shown separately in perspective in the lower left-hand corner of the figure.

21.11 Steering Column Gear Change

As has previously been mentioned modern practice is to place the gear lever on the steering column, chiefly in order to make it practicable to seat three persons in the front seat. The gear change mechanisms then used vary considerably in detail construction but the principles involved are shown by two examples described.

458

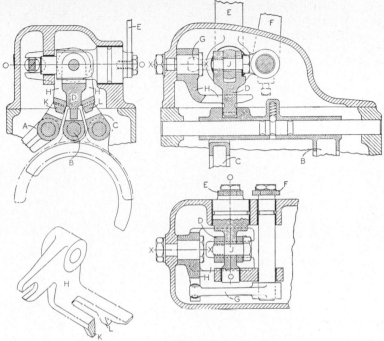

Fig. 21-9

In the mechanism shown in Fig. 21-10 the selection is done at the bottom of the steering column and two separate linkages (one for each striking fork in the gear box) run from there to the gear box. The selecting motion of the gear lever A is a rocking motion in a plane perpendicular to that of the steering wheel and is indicated by the arrows XX; it is permitted by the ball and socket connection between the lever A and the bracket B which is fixed to the steering column. This motion moves the rod D axially, because the ball end of the rod engages the socket C which is free to slide inside the lever A, and thus slides the dog-clutch member E into engagement with either the lever F or G. The striking motion is perpendicular to the plane of the drawing and rotates the rod D and thus also the lever engaged with it. This motion is transmitted by rods and levers to the gear box and strikes or slides the selected dog-clutch member.

In the arrangement shown in Fig. 21-11 the selection is done in the gear box and the two motions of the gear lever corresponding to selection and striking are transmitted separately from the bottom of the steering column to the gear box. The selecting motion of the gear box is a rocking motion about the pin H and produces an axial motion of the rod C which is transmitted by the bell-crank lever M'and a Bowden cable N to the selector lever P of the gear box

459

where it moves the striking arm into engagement with the appropriate striking fork. The striking motion of the gear lever A is a rotation about the axis of the rod C; this turns the bracket D in its housing E on the steering column and the motion is transmitted to the rod C by a key which is a sliding fit in the keyway inside the bracket D. The rotation of the rod C is carried by the arm J, bell-crank K and lever L to the striking lever inside the gear box.

The actual construction of a mechanism which in principle is similar to the mechanism just described is shown in Fig. 21-12. The lever A is now pivoted to the enlarged end of the rod C by the pin B and so the pivot pin H now engages a slot formed in the arm of the bracket D. The selecting motion

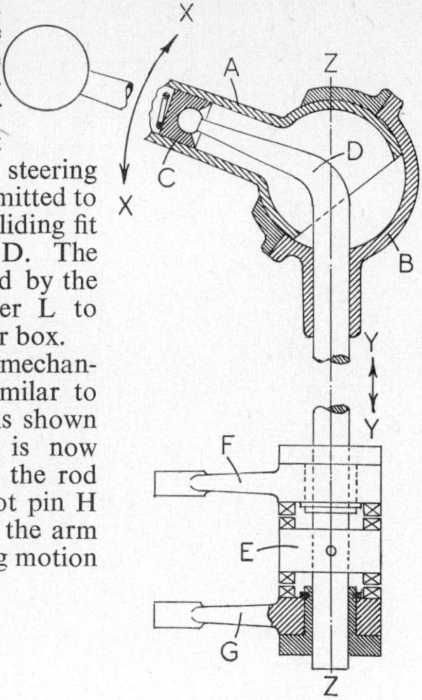

Fig. 21-10

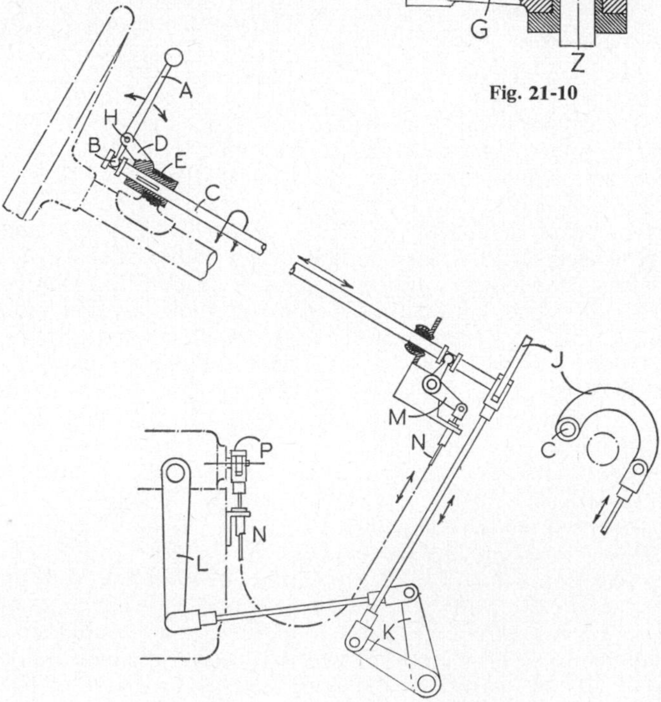

Fig. 21-11

460

Fig. 21·12

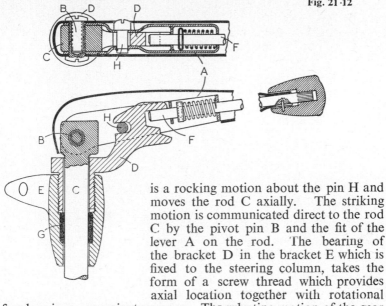

is a rocking motion about the pin H and moves the rod C axially. The striking motion is communicated direct to the rod C by the pivot pin B and the fit of the lever A on the rod. The bearing of the bracket D in the bracket E which is fixed to the steering column, takes the form of a screw thread which provides axial location together with rotational freedom in a convenient manner. The selecting motion of the gear lever is normally limited by the engagement of the rod F with a recess in the bracket D so that only the forward gears are obtained. To get reverse the knob is pulled out against the spring and the lever can then be moved down far enough to select the reverse striking fork in the gear box. A rubber bush G prevents rattles developing.

21.12 Constant-mesh Gear Box

There are many different forms of constant-mesh gear box, in some of which the various gears slide axially along their shafts, while in others they have no axial freedom. The characteristic feature of this type of gear box is, however, that all the pairs of wheels are always in mesh.

The principle of the commonest form of constant-mesh gear box is shown in Fig. 21-13; the engine shaft A is integral with a pinion B, which meshes with the wheel C on the layshaft. The latter is, therefore, driven by the engine shaft. Wheels E, F and G are fixed to the layshaft just as in a sliding-mesh gear box, and the mainshaft D is also similarly arranged. The gears E, F and G (the latter through a reverse idler) are, however, in constant mesh with the wheels H, I and J, which are perfectly free to turn on the main-shaft, bronze bushes, or ball or roller bearings, being provided between them and the shaft. The gears H, I and J, therefore, are constantly driven by the engine shaft, but at different speeds, since the wheels E, F and G are of different sizes. The wheel J, being

461

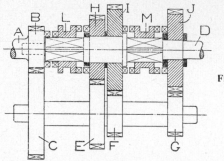

Fig. 21-13: Constant-mesh gear box

driven through an idler, revolves, of course, in the opposite direction to the engine shaft.

If any one of the gears H, I or J is coupled up to the mainshaft then there will be a driving connection between that shaft and the engine shaft. The coupling is done by means of the dog clutch members L and M, which are carried on squared (or splined) portions of the mainshaft. They are free to slide on those squared portions, but have to revolve with the shaft. If the member M is slid to the left it will couple the wheel I to the mainshaft giving the first gear. The drive is then through the wheels B, C, F and I and the dog clutch M. The other dog clutch is meanwhile in its neutral position as shown. If, with the member M in its neutral position, the member L is slid to the right, it will couple the wheel H to the mainshaft and give second gear, the drive being through the wheels B, C, E and H and the dog clutch L. If the member L is slid to the left it will couple the mainshaft directly to the pinion B and give a direct drive, as in a sliding-mesh gear box. The reverse gear is engaged by sliding the member M to the right when it will couple the wheel J to the mainshaft. The drive is then through the wheels B, C, G, the idler, J and the dog clutch M.

This type of gear box has several advantages over the ordinary form of sliding-mesh box. It facilitates the use of helical or double helical gear teeth which are quieter than straight teeth; it lends itself to the incorporation of synchronizing devices more readily than the sliding-mesh box; the dog clutch teeth can be made so that they are easier to engage than the teeth of gear wheels, and any damage that results from faulty manipulation occurs to the dog clutch teeth and not to the teeth of the gear wheels. Now, when once the dog clutches are engaged, there is no motion between their teeth, whereas when gear teeth are engaged the power is transmitted through the sliding action of the teeth of one wheel on those of the other. The teeth have to be suitably shaped to be able to transmit the motion properly, and if they are damaged the motion will be imperfect and noise will result. Damage is, however, less likely to occur to the teeth of the dog clutches, since all

462

engage at once, whereas in sliding a pair of gears into mesh the engagement is between two or three teeth.

On the other hand, the wheels on the mainshaft must be free to revolve so that they must either be bushed or be carried on ball or roller bearings. If bushes are used lubrication is difficult, wear will occur and noise will arise. If ordinary ball or roller bearings are used wear is avoided but the gear box becomes bulky and heavy.

The use of needle roller bearings overcomes both difficulties.

21.13 A Five-speed Gear Box

The gear box shown in Fig. 21-14 is an example of a mixed type of box, the first and second speeds being by sliding-mesh gears and the others by constant-mesh gears. The shaft A is coupled to the driven shaft of the clutch and has the pinion B formed integral with it. This pinion drives the layshaft to which the gears C, D, E and F are splined. The mainshaft G is supported at the left in a roller spigot bearing housed inside the pinion B, in the centre by a ball bearing carried in an intermediate wall of the gear box casing and at the right in a combined roller and ball bearing assembly.

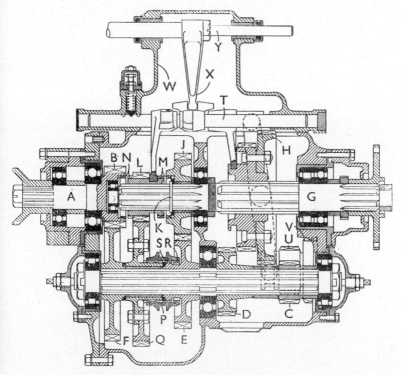

Fig. 21-14: Five-speed gear box

The ball bearing part of this assembly is used to position the main-shaft axially and to take any thrust that may come on it while the roller bearing takes the greater part of the journal loads. The double gear H is free to slide on splines on the mainshaft and gives first and second speeds when slid to right or left so as to mesh with C or D respectively. The gear J is free to rotate on a bush on the mainshaft and is kept in place by the split ring K which fits in a groove turned in the mainshaft. The split ring itself is kept in place by the overlapping portion of the washer (sectioned in full black) between it and the gear J. The latter is in permanent mesh with the gear E of the layshaft, and when coupled to the mainshaft by sliding the gear L to the right so as to engage the dog clutch teeth M, gives third speed. Fourth speed is a direct drive and is obtained by sliding L to the left so as to engage the dog clutch teeth N. Fifth speed is an overdrive, the ratio being less than unity, and is given by sliding the sleeve P (which is splined to the boss of the gear Q) to the left. The dog clutch teeth R of the sleeve P then engage the teeth S formed on the boss of the gear E and thus the gear Q is coupled to the layshaft, on which it has hitherto been free to revolve on the sleeve provided for it. The drive is then from B to F, through the teeth S and R to the gear Q, thence to the gear L and the mainshaft. Since the gear Q is larger than the gear F the mainshaft goes faster than the engine shaft A. Reverse is obtained by sliding the reverse idler UV to the left so that the teeth U engage those of the gear H and the teeth V those of the gear C.

The layshaft is carried in a ball bearing in the intermediate wall of the gear box casing and in roller bearings at the ends. It is positioned axially by the screwed studs shown in the end covers.

The selector forks, by which the various members are slid in order to engage the various gears, are fixed to rods T free to slide in the cover casing W. The selector rods are positioned by spring-loaded plungers as shown. The reverse idler is operated from its selector rod through a rocking lever (shown dotted) pivoted on the wall of the casing. The striking arm X turns about the axis of the shaft Y, to which it is fixed, in order to select the appropriate selector rod and then slides axially in order to slide that rod. The connection between the shaft Y and the change gear lever will be on the lines of that shown in Fig. 21-8. Packing rings are provided in the ends of the bushes carrying the shaft Y and special sealing devices (not shown) are provided where the engine and mainshafts pass through the cover plates in order to prevent the leakage of oil.

21.14 Another Example of a Constant-mesh Gear Box

A modern design of five-speed gear box in which all the gears except those giving first gear are in constant mesh is shown in Fig. 21-15. The shaft A, which is coupled to the clutch shaft, is supported in two ball bearings the right-hand one of which positions the shaft axially. The pinion B is integral with the shaft A and

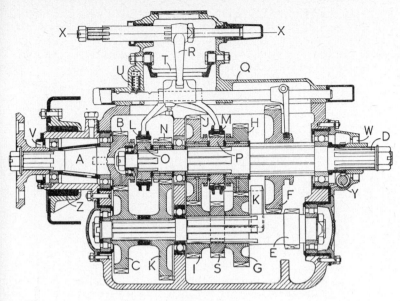

Fig. 21-15

meshes with the layshaft gear C. The layshaft consists of a splined shaft having an integral pinion E and on which are mounted the gears G, S, I, K and C. It is carried in roller bearings at the ends and a ball bearing in the middle; the left-hand roller bearing positions the shaft axially, both its races being provided with lips for that purpose. The outer races for the roller bearings are mounted in steel shells that are held in the cast aluminium casing of the gear box by the studs and nuts that secure the end covers.

The gears G, I and K mesh with the gears H, J and N which are free to revolve on the mainshaft D on needle roller bearings, hardened steel sleeves being provided on the shaft for these bearings to run on. The bearings and gears are secured axially by hardened steel washers fixed on the shaft by reason of the nut at the left-hand end. The gears H, J, N and B are coupled to the mainshaft, when required, by the dog clutches L and M; these take the form of sleeves having internal teeth to fit the external teeth of the members O and P which are splined to the mainshaft. The teeth of the sleeves L and M fit the small diameter toothed portions of the gears H, J, N and B to enable the different ratios to be obtained.

Reverse gear is obtained by sliding the gear F to the left to mesh with the portion K of the compound reverse idler; the other toothed portion of this idler meshes permanently with the pinion S of the layshaft.

The gear F and the sleeves M and L are actuated by striking forks carried by rods that are free to slide in the cover casting Q and

465

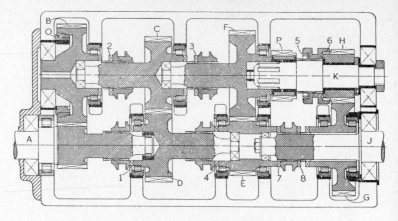

Fig. 21-16: Maybach gear box

which are moved by the motion of the striking arm R along the axis XX. Selection is done by the rotation of the arm R about the axis XX and a pivoted interlocking member T, similar in principle to that shown in Fig. 21-9 and described previously, prevents two gears from being engaged at once. The selector forks are held in their various positions by the spring-loaded plungers, one of which is seen at U.

Oil seals are housed in the recesses V and W and a speedometer drive is provided at Y.

The box is supported at the front by a rubber bushing Z carried by a cross member of the frame and at the back on two lugs (not shown) which also seat on rubber pads.

21.15 Maybach Gear Box

This is an exceedingly compact design and although it is now obsolete merits a brief description. The model shown in Fig. 21-16 gives seven forward and one reverse ratio. Four pairs of gears are used to obtain these ratios, each pair being in constant mesh. The pinion A is coupled through the main clutch to the engine and J is the output shaft. The pinion A is supported in a bearing in the casing at one end (this bearing being arranged close to the pinion so as to take the greater part of the load) and in a spigot bearing inside the gear D at the other end. Similar bearing arrangements are adopted for the gears C, D and F, while B, E and G are each carried in two bearings housed in the casing, and H and P are carried on bushes on the shaft K. The latter is splined into the boss of the gear F. The wheel G is free to rotate relatively to the shaft J which passes through it. Sliding dog clutch members are used to engage the gears as required.

466

Fig. 21-17

GEAR	DOG TEETH ENGAGED	DRIVE
1	2,4,6,8.	
2	2,3,6,8.	
3	1,4,6,8.	
4	1,3,6,8.	
5	2,3,7.	
6	1,4,7.	
7	1,3,7.	

The manner in which the seven ratios are obtained is shown in Fig. 21-17.

21.16 Synchromesh Devices

These are used to simplify the operation of changing gear, so that this can be done by unskilled drivers without the occurrence of clashes and consequent damage. The principle of all the devices is that the members which ultimately are to be engaged positively are first brought into frictional contact and then when the friction has equalized their speeds the positive connection is made. The devices can be applied to sliding-mesh boxes, but are almost always used with constant-mesh boxes.

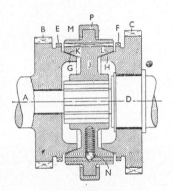

Fig. 21-18

The five constructional arrangements described below cover practically all the different arrangements commonly used.

In Fig. 21-18 the mechanism is shown applied to the direct drive and the next lower gear of an ordinary constant-mesh box whose general arrangement is as shown in Fig. 21-13. Thus A is the engine shaft and the integral gear B meshes with a wheel fixed to the layshaft (not shown) while the gear C is free to rotate on the mainshaft D and is permanently meshed with another wheel fixed to the layshaft. Both B and C are formed with integral dog tooth portions E and F and conical portions G and H. The member J, which is free to slide on splines on the mainshaft, has conical portions K and L to correspond with G and H. Thus if J is slid sideways to the left the cones K and G will come into contact and the friction between them will tend to equalize their speeds. The outside of the member J is formed with teeth which are exactly

467

similar to the teeth E and F and the member M is free to slide on these teeth except that spring-loaded balls N engaging recesses in M tend to prevent such sliding. There are usually six of these balls. If the balls N are overcome, however, and M is slid to the left along the outside of J, the teeth on the inside of M will engage the teeth E and there will be a positive drive between A and D through the teeth E, and the members M and J. The member M is actuated by the selector fork P and thus by the gear lever. In changing gear the gear lever is brought to the neutral position in the ordinary way but is immediately pressed in the direction it has to go to engage the required gear; supposing this to be top gear the effect is to press M to the left. The spring-loaded balls N however cause J to move with M and thus the cones K and L are brought into frictional contact. When the speeds of G and J have become equal a slightly greater pressure on the gear lever overcomes the resistance of the balls N, and M slides along J so that its teeth engage the teeth E, thus establishing the positive connection. Unless the gear lever is pressed so as to force the cones G and K together there will be no synchronizing action. If the member M is slid along J before synchronization has been effected a clash will result. This may occur if the gear lever is moved too rapidly and will tend to occur if the springs beneath the balls N are too weak.

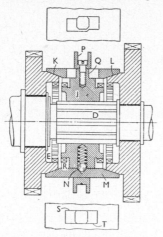

Fig. 21-19

The construction shown in Fig. 21-19 is that of Fig. 21-18 turned inside out. Thus the cones K and L are formed in the ends of a sleeve M free to slide on a member J which is splined to the main-shaft. The sleeve M must, however, rotate with J because of the projecting pieces Q which engage slots cut in M. The selector fork engages the ring P which is secured to the projecting pieces Q. Spring-loaded balls N again tend to make M move with J. The action is very much as before, thus pressure on the gear lever tends to slide J to the left, say, and the balls N cause M to move with J, thus bringing the cone K into contact. The resulting friction will, given time, produce synchronization and then an increased pressure on the gear lever will slide J along inside M and the dog teeth E and R will engage, thus establishing the positive connection.

The construction of Fig. 21-18 is rather more convenient where the wheels B and C are small.

When the member M is slowing the wheel B down (as it is in all the early stages of a change " up ") there will be a pressure between

468

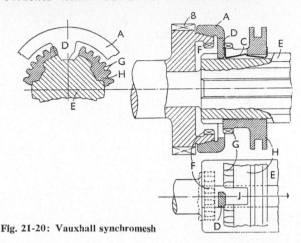

Fig. 21-20: Vauxhall synchromesh

the sides of the projections Q and the sides S of the slots as shown in the part plan. At the moment of synchronization the pressure will become zero and after synchronization (supposing the dog clutches are not engaged) the pressure would be between the other sides of the projection Q and the side T of the slot. The friction consequent on these pressures will help in preventing J from being slid along before synchronization has occurred and this latter occurrence can be almost entirely prevented by shaping the slots as shown in the part view at the top of Fig. 21-19.

21.17 Another Type of Synchromesh

The mechanism used by Vauxhall Motors (and other General Motors concerns) works on a different principle from that used in the types described previously. It is shown as applied to the direct-drive engagement in Fig. 21-20. The cone A is loosely carried on the male cone of the gear B and has three fingers D whose ends engage the spaces between the splines of the mainshaft E but with considerable clearance as shown in the end view and plan. Thus while A has to rotate at the same speed as the shaft E it can move relatively to that shaft through a small angle. The gear B has internal dog clutch F which can engage the external teeth G on the member H, which is splined to the mainshaft and which has three slots J cut in it. These slots are just a little wider than the fingers D. Springs C are carried by the member H as shown.

The action will be described as it occurs when top gear is being engaged. Because of the small amount of friction always present between the cones in A and B there will be a drag on the former member which will keep the fingers D up against one side of the space between the splines of the shaft E, as shown in the plan and end view. This drag will be accentuated as soon as an attempt is made to move the member H along so as to engage the teeth G

469

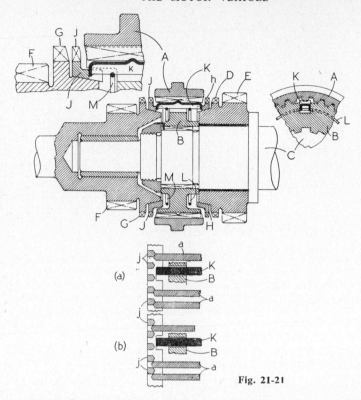

Fig. 21-21

and F, because firstly the springs C will press against the fingers D and secondly the corners of the slots J will bear against the corners of the fingers D. Thus the cones will be pressed together and the friction between them will tend to bring about synchronism. The clutch being disengaged, synchronism will in due course come about and, if the dog clutch teeth were not then engaged, the speed of B, which has up to now been higher than that of E, would become lower. The fingers D would then be pressed against the opposite sides of the spaces between the splines of the shaft E. Consequently at about the moment of synchronization the fingers will be about to leave one side of the spaces between the splines and pass over to the other side. The pressure on the sides of the fingers D is thus, at about the moment of synchronization, quite small and so the force acting on the member H, in conjunction with the bevelled corners of the fingers D and slots J, can move the fingers slightly so that they come opposite the slots J. The member H can then be slid over so as to engage the teeth G and F, the spring C being slightly depressed as this is done. Clearly until synchronization is almost effected the greater the force that is applied to the member H the greater will be the force pressing the cones together and the

470

greater will be the friction between them and the sooner will synchronization be brought about. This is an advantage over the first type above, where the maximum force that can be used to press the cones together is limited by the strength of the springs pressing the retaining balls into contact with the cone members.

21.18 Another Example

A further example of a synchromesh mechanism, that used in the Hillman " Minx," is shown in Fig. 21-21. The dog clutch sleeve A is free to slide on splines on the hub B, which is fixed to the mainshaft C, and is controlled by the striking fork of the gear change mechanism. When moved to the right its internal splines *a* ultimately engage the dog teeth D to give third gear and when moved to the left they engage the dog teeth G to give fourth gear, The synchronizing action is provided by the baulk rings H and J. which are coned internally to engage the cones formed on the gears E and F and which have external teeth *h* and *j* similar in form to the dog teeth D and G and are therefore the counterpart of the internal splines *a* of the sleeve A.

The hub B has three grooves formed in it, as shown in the upper part of the elevation and in the scrap plan and end views, and fitting freely in these grooves are three fingers K. At their ends these fingers engage grooves in the baulk rings H and J but these grooves are wider than the fingers K so that although the baulk rings are constrained to rotate at the same speed as the hub they can rotate slightly relative to that hub. The fingers K are pressed outwards by circlip springs L and M and thus the ridge in the middle of the fingers is kept in engagement with a groove formed in the middle of the splines of the sleeve A.

Consider the action when a change from third to fourth gear is being made. At the beginning of the change the gear F will be rotating at a higher speed than the mainshaft, hub B and the baulk rings. When the gear lever is pushed so as to try to engage fourth gear it tries to press the sleeve A to the left but this merely causes the fingers K to push the baulk ring J against the cone of the gear F. Friction between the cones then tries to speed up the baulk ring and, conversely, to slow down the gear F. The baulk ring is thus forced into the position shown in the scrap plan view (*a*). In this position the teeth *j* are half opposite the splines *a* of the sleeve A. Thus even if the pressure applied to the sleeve A by the striking fork is sufficient to depress the fingers K against the force of the spring M the sleeve cannot move to the left and the pressure will merely be transferred to the baulk ring by the contact between the ends of the splines *a* and the teeth *j*. Thus the harder the gear lever is pressed the greater will be the friction, between the baulk ring and the cone of the gear F, which is tending to synchronize those members.

When synchronism is attained the frictional drag between the baulk ring and the gear F is reduced to zero and the pressure applied

471

to the sleeve A is able, in conjunction with the inclined ends of the teeth *j* and splines *a*, to rotate the baulk ring slightly to its central position as shown in the lower plan view (*b*) and the sleeve A can then move across so that the splines engage the dog teeth G thus clutching the gear F to the hub B and mainshaft.

21.19 The " Smith " Synchromesh Mechanism

The firm of Smiths (Motor Accessories) Ltd., have brought out a new design of synchromesh which, while basically similar in principle and arrangement to the mechanism described above, differs in that it employs multiple cones and thus increases the frictional torque tending to produce synchronization, other factors being the same. This reduces the time required to bring about synchronism and makes gear changes faster. The arrangement of the mechanism is shown in Fig. 21-22, in which the parts have been annotated with the same letters as the corresponding parts in Fig. 21-21. The important difference is that the cones J and H are now made in two parts J_1 and J_2 and H_1 and H_2 and between these parts there are intermediate cones P and Q. The outer cone J_1 is driven by the member K as in Fig. 21-21 and the inner one by the projection S which engages a

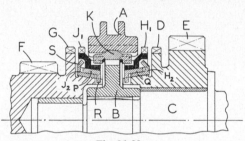

Fig. 21-22

recess formed in J_1. The intermediate member P is driven by the projection R which engages a slot formed in the cone of the member F. When the shaft C is rotating relative to F there are now three slipping surfaces in the cone assembly whereas in Fig. 21-21 there is only one and hence for a given axial force on the sleeve A and with the same dimensions the synchronizing torque will be approximately three times as great.

21.20 " Porsche " Synchromesh

The principle of this will be explained with reference to Fig. 21-23 which shows a design used by Henry Meadows, Ltd., of Wolverhampton, in some of their gear boxes. The gear G is on the end of the clutch shaft and drives the layshaft; H is the mainshaft of the gearbox. When changing up to the direct drive, the sleeve A, which is splined to the three-armed spider K, is moved to the left by the gear lever, and the conical inner surfaces of its splines make

472

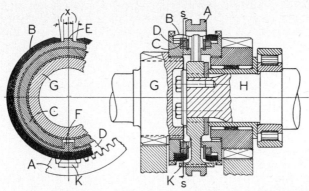

Fig. 21-23

contact with the conical outer surface of the ring B.   Friction then causes the latter to move relative to the member C so that the clearance at X is taken up and the end of the ring bears against the key E.   The friction on the ring then tends to expand it and this increases the pressure between the ring and the sleeve A and makes it virtually impossible to move the latter any further to the left. When synchronism is achieved, the frictional force on the ring B is reduced to zero and it becomes easy to move the sleeve A over so that its internal splines engage the splines or teeth formed on the member D, which is itself splined to the gear G.   This provides a positive drive between the gear G and the shaft H.   The ring B is thicker at its centre, opposite to the key E, than at its ends though this is not very apparent from the drawing.   This tapering is designed to obtain a uniform pressure between the ring B and the sleeve A, and to accommodate it, the outer surface of the ring C is made eccentric to the inner surface.   The key F compels the ring C, and thus the ring B, to rotate with the gear G.

21.21 Lubrication of the Gear Box

The lubrication of gear boxes, other than epicyclic types, which will be considered later, is usually effected by putting enough oil into the box to ensure that at least one gear will dip into the lubricant. When the gears are rotating the oil will be thrown about all over the box, thus lubricating the various parts.   Dip-rods are usually provided; by suitably positioning the filler spout overfilling can be prevented.

The oil required is different from that suitable for an engine, the conditions being quite different.   Temperatures are much lower and carbonization has not to be considered.   On the other hand, the pressures to which the oil films may be subjected may be much heavier than in an engine.   The instructions of makers and the advice of reputable oil companies should always be followed.

It should not be thought that filling a gearbox to a higher level than that recommended will reduce the frictional losses in the box. On the contrary, the loss due to the churning of the oil will be greatly increased. Tests made by several authorities, including the National Physical Laboratory, have shown that several horse power may be used simply in churning the oil in a gear box which is filled too full. Also it is wrong to suppose that a very thick oil is better able to withstand heavy pressures than is a thin oil. Except on the direct advice of a competent authority grease should never be put into a gear box.

Special oil seals of various patterns are fitted where the gear box shafts pass through the casing and these usually give no trouble, but leakages might be caused by the expansion of the air enclosed in the box, and a vent should always be provided. Large washers are sometimes fitted on the inside of the ball bearings supporting the shafts of gear boxes to keep any particles of grit or chips from the gear teeth, from the bearings. The oil used must be such as will not have any bad effect on the races or balls of the bearings or the latter will have their life greatly reduced.

Some of the exterior parts of the selector and gate change mechanisms are best lubricated with a thin " machine " oil, but an engine oil will generally do; gear box oil is usually too thick.

21.22 Free-wheel Devices

These are simply one-way clutches, usually of the roller type, that are occasionally fitted in the transmission line, just behind the gear box; they will transmit torque in one direction only (like the claws of a starting handle), and the transmission parts behind the device can therefore overrun the parts in front of it. Thus the engine can be allowed to idle simply by closing the throttle, without having to disengage the gears, and by coasting down hills an improved petrol consumption is obtained. This is perhaps the chief advantage of these devices, a secondary one being that gear changing is made easier, since if the device is placed behind the gear box, then on closing the throttle, the engine and the gear box shafts will slow down and a change of gear can be effected without serious clashing occurring. A positive clutch is always provided so that the device can be put out of action when necessary.

21.23 Auxiliary Gear Boxes and Overdrives

The gear ratios adopted in all vehicles have to be a compromise since the factors concerned in their choice are conflicting. Thus for good acceleration in top gear, a ratio that is low in comparison with that which would give the best top speed on a good level road would be used. Again for the best fuel economy higher ratios would be used than if a lively performance was the chief requirement.

The provision of a large number of ratios reduces the element of compromise and so there is a tendency to employ gear boxes giving a large number. This can be done in two ways; one is to provide the large number of ratios in a single box of more or less conventional form and the other is to use an auxiliary gear box in tandem with a main gearbox giving only three or four ratios. The first method complicates the construction of the box and may make gear-changing a difficult operation but gearboxes giving up to ten ratios are now being used.

If an auxiliary gearbox is used, it may be an entirely separate unit or it may be built on or attached to the main gearbox so as to form a single constructional unit. The auxiliary box usually is behind the main box and provides only two ratios, one of which is a direct drive. In vehicles for use " off the road," the second ratio is a reduction and its use lowers all the ratios of the main box and makes them suitable for cross-country use. The vehicle is then virtually provided with two sets of ratios, one for use on roads and the other for cross-country work, and this is how the auxiliary box is generally used. The change from the direct drive to the low ratio will only be made when the vehicle is at rest or is moving at a very low speed, while with either of these the ratios available in the main box will be used as required by the prevailing conditions. Auxiliary gear boxes of this type are usually constant mesh boxes employing a layshaft but are sometimes of epicyclic type.

21.24　A Leyland Ten-ratio Gear Box

This provides a good example of the first of the above methods. It will be seen from Fig. 21-24 that the shaft arrangement is conventional, the mainshaft being in line with the clutch shaft and the layshaft below on a parallel axis. Two pairs of gears AB and CD provide alternative drives to the layshaft, the gears B and D being

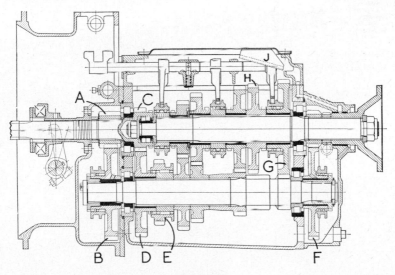

Fig. 21-24

475

connected to it as required by muff type dog clutches. The muff E of the dog clutch for coupling the gear D has gear teeth on its exterior and provides a power take-off, the drive for which goes from A to B and thence to E which will be in its neutral position as shown. As there are two alternative drives to the layshaft the four pinions on it, which mesh directly with gears on the mainshaft, will provide eight ratios; the direct drive between the clutch shaft and the main shaft gives the ninth ratio while the tenth is an overdrive and is obtained by clutching the gear F to the layshaft. It should perhaps be pointed out that the drive from the gear G to the mainshaft is obtained by clutching it to the gear H which is splined to the mainshaft. The reverse ratios are given by sliding a reverse idler into mesh with the gear H. The ratios are

Low 1st	9·352	1st	6·988
Low 2nd	5·764	2nd	4·308
Low 3rd	3·552	3rd	2·655
Low 4th	2·147	4th	1·605
Top	1·0	Overdrive	0·76

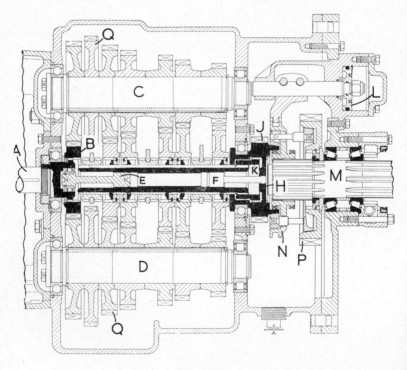

Fig. 21-25

The gear box is lubricated by splash provided by partly immersing the layshaft and reverse idler in oil. A trough J catches and feeds oil to the plain bearing on the outside of the hub of the output coupling.

21.25 The Fuller Twin-countershaft Gear Box

This provides an example of the second method of obtaining a multiplicity of ratios but also embodies a principle which enables the size of the box to be reduced. By using two layshafts (or countershafts) the tooth loads are halved and so the gears can be made only a little more than half as wide as they would have to be if only one layshaft were used. This will, however, be successful only if the torque is in fact equally divided between the two layshafts and the way in which this is ensured is described later.

The gear box shown in Fig. 21-25 comprises a five-speed and reverse box followed by a two-speed one, the combination thus providing ten forward and two reverse ratios. The input shaft A ends at the right in a narrow splined portion which engages splines inside the pinion B but enough clearance is provided between the splines to allow the pinion to float radially by several thousandths of an inch. The pinion meshes with gears on the two layshafts C and D which are identical and are carried in ball and roller bearings in the casing so that they rotate about fixed axes. The gears are driven by keys which ensure that they are assembled in the correct relative positions to enable them to mesh correctly with the mainshaft gears. The latter are free radially of the shaft and are positioned axially in pairs by collars, the inner ones being fixed inside the gears and the outer ones to the shaft and whose faces abut. The mainshaft is supported at each end by relatively flexible dumb-bell shaped members E and F; one end of each of these is fixed inside the mainshaft and the other ends are supported respectively in the spigot bearing inside the shaft A and in the boss H which is, in effect, part of the gear J. The latter is carried in the casing in a large ball bearing. The mainshaft gears are coupled to the shaft when required by sliding dog clutches. Because the mainshaft is free to float radially it will move slightly, if the tooth loads are unbalanced, until the upward tooth load at one side of the gear which is clutched to it is balanced by the downward tooth load at the other side. The torques transmitted by the layshafts are thus equalized. In order not to compromise the freedom of the mainshaft to move in this way it is connected to the output member J through an intermediate member K which is splined on the inside to the mainshaft and on the outside to the member J; both sets of splines are made with sufficient clearance to allow the freedom desired. The reverse ratio pinions on the layshaft (at the right) engage idlers which are carried on roller bearings and which mesh with the reverse gear on the mainshaft. The gears QQ are for a power take-off.

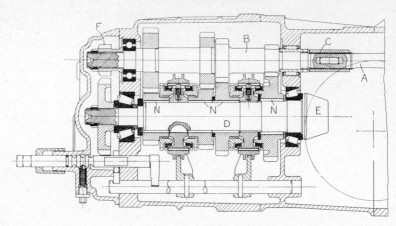

Fig. 21-26

The auxiliary gear box is housed in the right-hand part of the casing and a direct drive by clutching the member J to the output shaft M by means of the dog clutch N which is operated by air pressure applied to the piston L. The low gear is obtained by engaging the dog clutch with the gear P, the drive then going from the member J through the two layshafts (not shown in the view because they do not lie in the plane of the drawing) to the gear P. The layshafts are carried in the casing on ball and roller bearings and rotate about fixed axes. The gear P, however, is free radially and can thus float sufficiently to enable the layshaft tooth loads to balance each other. The dog clutch N is provided with synchromesh for both its engagements.

21.26 An " All Indirect " Gear Box

Fig. 21-26 shows the gear box of the Hillman " Imp " and is a good example of this type of box, which is particularly useful in cars having rear-wheel drive with the engine at the rear as in the " Imp " or having front-wheel drive with the engine at the front, the engine axis being longitudinal in both cases. The clutch shaft A is coupled to the input or driving shaft B by a splined muff C. Five pinions are either integral or fixed to the shaft B and four of these pinions mesh with gears that are carried on the driven or output shaft D on needle roller bearings N. The driven shaft is made integral with the pinion E of the hypoid final drive and is carried in the casing on taper roller bearings. The input shaft is carried at the right in a needle roller bearing and at the left in a ball bearing. The gears on the driven shaft are coupled to that shaft when required by dog-clutches and synchromesh is provided. Reverse is obtained by sliding a reverse idler (not seen in the view)

478

into mesh with the pinion F, which is fixed to the tail of the shaft B, and the corresponding gear fixed on the end of the driven shaft; both these gears are outside the end wall of the gear box casing and are housed in the end cover. Now that gears can be made with sufficient accuracy to ensure reasonable silence in operation there is no real objection to the absence of a direct drive and the convenience of the all indirect design is very great.

CHAPTER 22

Epicyclic and Pre-selector Gear Boxes

Types of epicyclic gearing. Gear ratios. Wilson and Cotal gear boxes

HITHERTO we have dealt only with what is termed " ordinary "
gearing, the characteristic feature of which is that the axes
of the various gears are fixed axes, the motions of the gears being
simply rotations about their own axes. The characteristic feature
of " epicyclic " gearing is that at least one gear not only rotates
about its own axis but also rotates bodily about some other axis.
An example of epicyclic gearing is shown in Fig. 22-1. A spur
pinion A, integral with its shaft, is free to rotate about its own
axis XX, being carried in bearings in the frame E. A cranked
shaft or arm C is also free to rotate about the same axis XX and
carries on its crank pin a spur pinion B. The latter is free to
rotate about its own axis YY but must also rotate bodily about
the axis XX when the arm C is rotated in its bearings. The pinion B
meshes with the pinion A and also with an internally toothed ring
or annulus D which forms part of the frame E and is therefore fixed.
The annulus D is, of course, circular and is concentric with the
axis XX. This arrangement is an epicyclic train of gearing providing
a definite and fixed speed or gear ratio, between the shaft A and
the shaft of the arm C; it is *not* a gear box.

The action of this gear train will be understood on reference to
Figs. 22-2 (*a*) and (*b*), in which the " business " portion of the
pinion B, the only part which for the moment is useful, has been
blacked in. It will be seen that this portion constitutes a lever,
one end P of which fits in a tooth space of the annulus D, the other
end fitting in a tooth space of the pinion A. At its centre R the

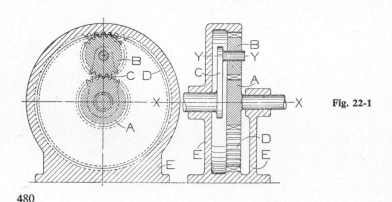

Fig. 22-1

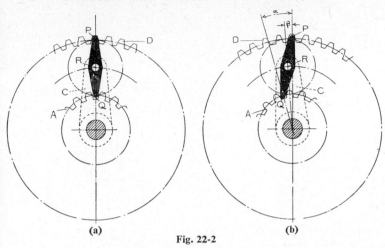

(a)   (b)

Fig. 22-2

lever is pivoted on the pin of the arm C. Now suppose the pinion A
to be turned through a small angle as shown at (b). The tooth
space of A moves round to the left slightly, taking with it the end Q
of the lever. Since the other end P of the lever is in a tooth space
of the fixed annulus D the lever has to pivot about that point P
as fulcrum. In so doing the centre R of the lever will move to the
left, but since R is nearer than Q to the fulcrum P the point R will
not move as far as Q. Now the lever PQ is attached at R to the
arm C, hence the end of that arm moves round to the left a smaller
distance than did the tooth space of A, and since the point R is
farther from the axis XX than is the tooth space of A the angular
movement of the arm C will be still smaller than that of the pinion A.

The above action can only be supposed to take place for very
small movements of the pinion A because obviously for large
movements the lever PQ will go out of engagement with the pinion A
and the annulus D. But we have in reality not a lever such as PQ
but a complete pinion which acts as a succession of such levers so
that the action is kept up, and as the pinion A is turned so the arm C
is turned at a slower speed in the same direction.

22.1   Another Epicyclic Train of Gearing

The arrangement of gears just described is only one of many
different forms of epicyclic gearing; different, that is, in their
mechanical arrangement. Fig. 22-3 shows a second arrangement.

The wheel A, integral with its shaft, is free to rotate about its
axis XX in the frame E. It meshes with the teeth B_1 of a compound
pinion which is free to revolve on the pin of the arm C. The latter
is carried in the frame, being free to revolve about the axis XX.
The portion B_2 of the pinion meshes with a wheel whose axis is XX
but which, being part of the frame, is fixed. When the arm C is

481

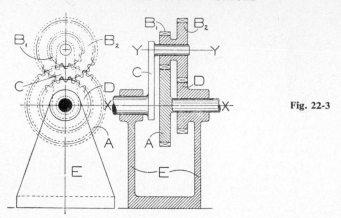

Fig. 22-3

turned the wheel A is driven round in the same direction as the arm but at a lower speed.

To illustrate the action Fig. 22-4 (*a*) and (*b*) has been drawn, in which the " business " portion of the pinion is blacked and shaded, and, again, it can be regarded as a lever, although the resemblance is not so easily seen as in the previous example. One end P of this lever engages a tooth space of the wheel D which is a fixture, the other end Q engages a tooth space of the wheel A, while at R the lever is pivoted to the arm C. Imagine the arm C to be turned through a small angle, as shown at (*b*). The point R of the lever is moved slightly to the left and, as the only motion possible to the lever PQ is to pivot about the point P, it turns about that point as a fulcrum. The end Q will, therefore, move in the same direction as the point R but, being nearer to the fulcrum, it will move a shorter distance. Thus the wheel A will be moved,

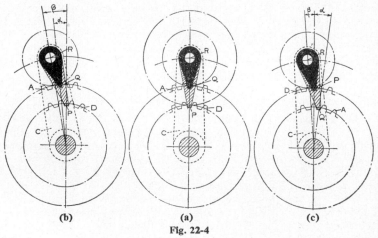

(b) (a) (c)

Fig. 22-4

as shown, in the same direction as the arm C, but through a smaller angle. As there is actually a complete pinion B instead of a lever PQ the action can be sustained.

It will be noticed that the fixed wheel D is smaller in diameter than the driven wheel A. When the fixed wheel is larger than the driven one the latter will be driven in the opposite direction to the arm. This is shown at (c). As before, when the arm C is turned through a small angle the point R of lever PQ is moved a small amount to the left, and the lever turns about the point P as fulcrum. Now the end Q of the lever is on the opposite side of the fulcrum P to the point R which moves to the left. The end Q of the lever, therefore, moves to the right taking with it the wheel A with which it engages. Thus the driven wheel A moves in the opposite direction to the arm C.

The wheels that are carried on the rotating arm in epicyclic gearing are generally called planet wheels, while the wheels at the centre about which the planet wheels roll are called sun wheels by analogy with the solar system. Epicyclic gearing is sometimes referred to as " planetary " gearing.

22.2   Other Forms of Epicyclic Gearing

There are many other forms of epicyclic gearing using both spur and bevel gears, but the two forms described are the most important as regards motor vehicles. If the working of these is thoroughly understood no difficulty should be experienced in following the working of other forms. In the next paragraphs it is shown how the gear ratio of an epicyclic train may be worked out, and the method is applicable to all the various forms of epicyclic gearing.

22.3   Gear Ratio of Epicyclic Gearing

Consider the epicyclic train shown in Fig. 22-1. The gear ratio of the train is the ratio between the number of turns made by the arm and the (consequent) number of turns made by the sun wheel. If the arm C is turned once round (keeping the annulus D fixed) then the sun A will be turned a certain definite amount. Now, provided that in the end we arrive at the result that the annulus D has not moved and that the arm C has made one turn, the number of turns made by the sun A will be the same however we arrive at that result. This may be seen by considering as an analogy a wheel rolling on a board, as shown in Fig. 22-5. If the wheel is rolled one half turn (the board being fixed) it will move along by the amount S (half the

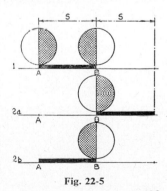

Fig. 22-5

483

circumference of the wheel). The result of the operation is that the wheel has turned half a turn about its axis and has moved bodily the distance S, while the board has not moved at all. Suppose now that from the original position the board and the wheel are moved solidly, both together, the distance S. The position will then be as at 2a. Now, keeping the wheel at B, let the board be moved back under the wheel to its original position. The board must, therefore, be moved back the distance S under the wheel, and in so doing it will turn the wheel half a turn.

It should be clear that when the board has arrived back in its original position the result is the same as before. The board (having arrived back into its original position) has not moved. The wheel has moved bodily the distance S and has made half a turn about its axis. We have arrived at the same result in two steps instead of in a single step. By adopting a similar procedure with epicyclic gearing the motions of the various members are easily found. We arrive at the desired result in two steps instead of in one and we so arrange the steps that in one of them we *turn every member the same amount*, and that in the other step we *keep the arm of the train fixed*, so that for that step the train works as ordinary gearing, which can easily be dealt with. An example will make the process clear, especially if the steps are recorded in tabular form.

Thus, considering the gear shown in Fig. 22-1, suppose the wheels to have the following numbers of teeth: A, 40; B, 20; D, 80. We are concerned with the motions of the various wheels and the arm and our table will have four columns:

	Arm C	Annulus D	Sun Wheel A
First step			
Second step			
Desired result	+1	0	?

Now when we have arrived at the desired result the arm C must have made one turn and the annulus D no turns. These figures may, therefore, be inserted as shown. Secondly, it is required that in the second step the arm of the train shall be fixed, hence we must have zero for the arm in the second step, thus:

	Arm C	Annulus D	Sun Wheel A
First step			
Second step	0		
Desired result	+1	0	?

It follows that the motion of the arm in the first step must be $+1$, and since we want all the members to have the same motion in the first step all the members must receive $+1$ turn, thus:

	Arm C	Annulus D	Sun Wheel A
First step	$+1$	$+1$	$+1$
Second step	0		
Desired result	$+1$	0	?

Again, it follows that the motion of the annulus D in the second step must be -1 in order that the two steps shall add up to zero. The minus sign indicates that in this step the annulus is to be turned *backwards*. Now, considering the second step, the arm is going to be fixed and the annulus is going to be turned backwards one turn. The wheel B will then turn in the same direction as the annulus, that is, backwards, while the sun wheel A will turn in the opposite direction to B and hence in the opposite direction to the annulus. In the second step, therefore, the sun wheel moves forward so that whatever the amount of the motion the sign is $+$. Care must be taken to get the sign of the motion right. The amount of the motion is given by the rules of ordinary gearing as—

$$1 \times \frac{\text{No. teeth in annulus}}{\text{No. teeth in pinion B}} \times \frac{\text{No. teeth in B}}{\text{No. teeth in A}}.$$

This becomes—

$$1 \times \frac{80}{20} \times \frac{20}{40} = 2.$$

Our table now appears as under, and on adding up the motions of the sun wheel in the two steps its resultant motion is found:

	Arm C	Annulus D	Sun Wheel A
First step	$+1$	$+1$	$+1$
Second step	0	-1	$+2$
Desired result	$+1$	0	$+3$

Since the sign of the resultant motion of the sun wheel A is positive, that wheel moves in the same direction as the arm, so that the gear is a " forward " one. The gear ratio $\dfrac{\text{Arm C}}{\text{Wheel A}} = \dfrac{1}{3}$ so that the sun wheel A goes three times as fast as the arm. If an epicyclic train of this type is to be used in a motor car it will have to be with the engine driving the sun wheel A and with the arm C coupled to the driving wheels. As will be seen later, a train of this type is used in the Wilson epicyclic gear box.

22.4 " Clutch " Action of Epicyclic Gearing

In the train of gearing shown in Figs. 22-1 and 2, when the pinion A was turned the lever PQ pivoted about the point P and thus caused the arm C to turn. Now suppose that the annulus D is made a separate member from the frame E, free to revolve about the axis XX, then when the pinion A is turned, instead of the lever PQ pivoting about the point P and thus moving the arm C, the latter will remain stationary and the lever PQ will pivot about its centre R and cause the annulus D to revolve in the opposite direction to the pinion A. If now a brake is applied to the annulus D so as to slow it down and finally bring it to rest, then the arm C will be gradually speeded up and will finally rotate as it would do if D were part of the frame E. Therefore, by making what will ultimately be the fixed member of the train free, and by gradually bringing that member to rest, the driven member will gradually be speeded up and there is no longer any necessity for a separate clutch such as is required with ordinary gear boxes. The clutch action by which the engine is gradually coupled to the driving wheels is obtained in the epicyclic gearing itself. Hence cars employing epicyclic gear boxes have no " clutch " in the ordinary sense of the word.

22.5 Epicyclic Gear Boxes

So far we have dealt only with epicyclic trains of gearing giving a single ratio between two shafts. We will proceed to the consideration of epicyclic gear boxes giving a number of different gear ratios. Two different methods are employed.

In the first separate trains of epicyclic gearing are provided, each giving a certain gear ratio; in these trains what will be the fixed members when the trains are in use are arranged to be free and brakes are provided so that any one of those members may be brought to rest as required. The train to which that member belongs then comes into operation. If that member is released and another one brought to rest by means of its brake another train will be brought into operation. The top gear is usually obtained by clutching the driving member direct to the driven member by means of an ordinary cone or plate clutch, or by locking any two members together in which case all the wheels and arms will revolve as one solid mass thus giving a direct drive. On top gear all the planet gears will be at rest relatively to their pins, that is, although they will be rotating bodily with the arms they will not be turning on the pins of the arms.

Generally, some of the wheels are common to all the epicyclic trains.

An example of this type of gear box is shown in Fig. 22-6. The casing A forms the common arm of all the trains and carries the compound planet gears $D_1 D_2 D_3$, made out of a solid piece of metal, on pins as shown. The casing is connected to the flywheel by a

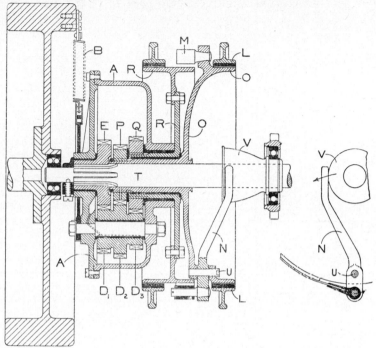

Fig. 22-6: An epicyclic gear box

number of springs B which give a cushioned drive which smooths out some of the torque fluctuations of the engine. The planet D_1 meshes with the sun wheel E, which is splined to the driven shaft T. The latter is permanently connected to the driving road wheels. The planets D_2 and D_3 are in mesh with suns P and Q which are fixed to sleeves integral with brake drums O and R respectively. If the brake L is applied to the drum O then the sun P will be held at rest and P D_2 D_1 and E will constitute a train of the type shown in Fig. 22-3, the fixed sun being smaller than the driven sun. Hence a forward gear will be obtained, T turning in the same direction as the engine but at a lower speed. If the brake is applied to the drum R then Q will be held fixed and Q D_3 D_1 and E will constitute a train of the type shown in Fig. 22-4 (c), and a reverse gear is obtained.

To obtain a direct drive the drums O and R are locked together and the whole gear rotates " solid." This is done by means of a brake whose parts are anchored to the drum O on pins M and encircle a portion of the drum R. The brake is operated by levers N pivoted on pins U carried by the drum O, the levers being moved outwards, so as to apply the brake, by sliding the cone member V along to the right. The action is indicated in the part end view.

487

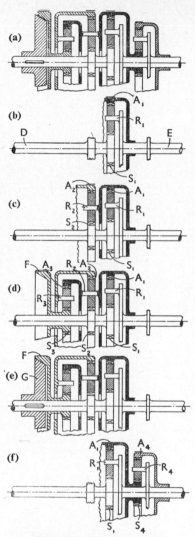

Fig. 22-7: Wilson gear ratios

The gear is lubricated by oil which is introduced into the casing A through a plug, not shown.

The second method, an example of the use of which is afforded by the Wilson box which will be described, is as follows.

One train of epicyclic gearing is used for all the various ratios, its sun S_1 (Fig. 22-7 (*b*)), being secured to a shaft D coupled permanently to the engine and its arm R_1 to the shaft E which is coupled permanently to the driving road wheels and the various ratios are obtained by driving the annulus A_1 at different speeds in relation to the engine speed. Supposing the latter to be constant at say 1,000 r.p.m., then if the speed of the annulus A is zero (that is, it is held at rest), then the speed of the arm R_1 would be 1,000 $S/(A+S)$, where A and S represent the number of teeth in the annulus and sun respectively. Taking a numerical example, suppose $A = 100$ and $S = 25$ then the speed of R will be 200 r.p.m. and the gear ratio is 1,000 to 200 or 5 to 1. Suppose now that the annulus instead of being held at rest is driven in the same direction as the engine at, say, 100 r.p.m., then (the engine speed being 1,000 r.p.m. as before), the speed of the arm R will be 280 r.p.m, instead of 200 r.p.m.

Thus a higher gear is obtained. Similarly, if the speed of the annulus was made 200 r.p.m., then the speed of the arm would be 360 r.p.m. If the annulus were driven in the opposite direction to the engine then the arm would rotate slower than when the annulus was fixed. Thus, if the speed of the annulus were, say, 400 r.p.m. backwards, then the speed of the arm (engine speed still 1,000 r.p.m.) would be −120, that is, backwards, thus giving a reverse gear. Thus, by driving the annulus at different speeds (in relation to engine speed), the driven shaft is driven at different speeds, that is, different gear ratios are obtained.

To enable the annulus of the main train to be driven at these different speeds, auxiliary epicyclic trains are used. Thus, for second gear the train S_2 R_2 A_2 (Fig. 22-7 (c)) is utilized. In this train the sun S_2 is fixed to the engine shaft D, the annulus can be held at rest by a brake and the arm R_2 is coupled to the annulus A_1. If the annulus A_2 is held at rest and the engine drives the suns S_1 and S_2 then, considering train S_2 R_2 A_2 it should be clear that R_2 will rotate in the same direction as the engine but at a lower speed. But R_2 is secured to A_1 and so A_1 is rotated in the same direction as the engine and R_1 will rotate at a higher speed than it did on first gear when A_1 was fixed.

To get third gear, the arm R_1 has to be made to rotate faster than on second gear and to do this the annulus A_1 and thus the

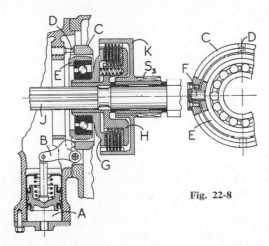

Fig. 22-8

arm R_2 must be made to rotate faster. To do this the annulus A_2 is now caused to rotate in the same direction as the engine. This is brought about by the train S_3 R_3 A_3, of which the sun S_3 is held at rest by the brake on its brake drum F, while the arm R_3 is coupled to the annulus A_2 and the annulus A_3 is coupled to the arm R_2. Considering the train S_3 R_3 A_3 if S_3 is fixed and A_3 is rotating in the same direction as the engine then the arm R_3 will also be rotating in the same direction as the engine. But R_3 is coupled to A_2 and so in the train S_2 R_2 A_2 both the sun S_2 and the annulus A_2 are rotating in the same direction as the engine and thus the speed of the arm R_2 must be greater than when A_2 was fixed. The speed of the annulus A_1 is thus greater than on second gear, that is, a higher gear is obtained.

The direct drive for top gear is obtained by locking S_3 to the engine shaft D by sliding the male cone G, which is splined to D,

489

along so as to engage the female cone formed in the drum F which is fixed to S_3. This has the effect of locking the gear so that it must all revolve " solid."

In recent designs the direct drive clutches are of multi-plate form; an example is given in Fig. 22-8.

To obtain a reverse gear the auxiliary train S_4 R_4 A_4 is brought into action. The sun S_4 of this train is secured to the annulus A_1, the arm R_4 is fixed to the driven shaft D and the annulus A_4 can be held at rest by a brake.

Considering train S_4 A_4 R_4 if A_4 is fixed and R_4 is rotating backwards then S_4 will be rotating backwards at a higher speed than the arm and thus in train S_1 R_1 A_1 although the sun S_1 is rotating forwards the annulus A_1 is rotating backwards at such a speed that R_1 goes backwards also. This explanation can only be made convincing by working out the gear ratio as follows.

Suppose the numbers of teeth $S_1=25$, $A_1=100$, $S_4=40$, $A_4=80$. Keeping A_4 fixed, let R_4 be rotated backwards one turn, the motions of the members of train S_4 R_4 A_4 may be obtained by the method previously described and as shown in the table Fig. 22-9. Now con-considering train S_1 R_1 A_1 since A_1 is secured to S_1 it has received -3

R_4	A_4	S_4
-1	-1	-1
0	$+1$	-2
-1	0	-3

Fig. 22-9

R_1	A_1	S_1
-1	-1	-1
0	-2	$+8$
-1	-3	$+7$

Fig. 22-10

turns and since R_1 and R_4 are both fixed to the driven shaft D the arm R_1 has received -1 turn the same as R_4. Hence in train S_1 R_1 A_1 the motions of R_1 and A_1 are settled and the consequent motion of S_1 may be found as shown in the table Fig. 22-10.

Thus the engine shaft has turned $+7$ turns and the driven shaft has turned -1 turn and a reverse gear ratio of 7 to 1 is obtained.

22.6 Brakes and Selector Mechanism

The brakes used in the Wilson box consist of two parts, an outer band and an inner one. The cross section of the outer band is shown inset in Fig. 22-11. C is the metal part of the band and D is the Ferodo lining; this is in contact with the drum over only half the width of the drum, the inner band occupying the space E. By this means the outer band is made to operate the inner band and duplication of the operating mechanism is obviated. The bands are anchored to the gear box casing at points diametrically opposite each other (Fig. 22-11, opposite): the outer band by the hook link D and the inner band by the strut E which is pinned to a lug F

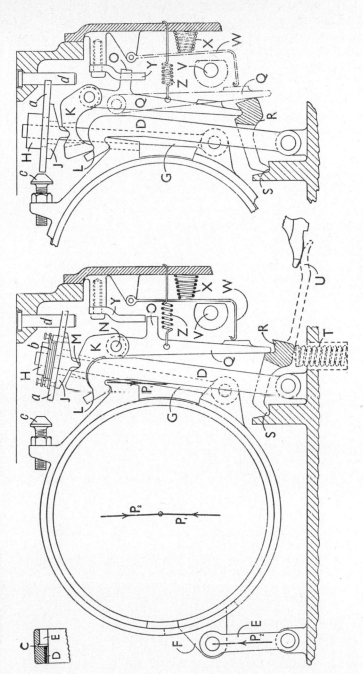

Fig. 22-11: Wilson selector and brake mechanism

integral with the inner band and passing through a slot in the outer band.

The reason for employing two bands on each drum is to make the force P_2 applied by the strut E, balance and cancel the force P_1 applied by the link D so that a pure couple is applied to the drum and there will be no large reaction forces on the bearings of the drum. If the outer band alone were used there would be a force P_1 as shown by the arrow, acting on the bearings of the drum; if the inner band alone were used there would be a force P_2 on the bearings; when both bands are used these reaction forces P_2 and P_1 cancel each other.

The hook links D are made in two parts and in between them lies a pull rod G, pinned to a lug on the outer band. At its upper end this pull rod carries a nut H which rests on a plate J which in turn has a knife edge bearing M on the lever K. The latter is fulcrumed on the top of the hook link at L and when it is pushed upwards by a force acting at N the pull rod is pulled upwards and the outer band is closed on to the drum, thereby closing the inner band on to the drum also. Fig. 22-12 shows diagrammatically the lever K in the off and on positions. In the former the leverage is x/y and in the later x_1/y_1. Owing to the placing of the points M

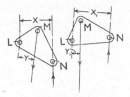

Fig. 22-12

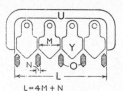

L = 4 M + N

Fig. 22-13

and N in relation to the fulcrum L the distance x_1 is greater than x and y_1 is less than y, hence the leverage in the " on " position is several times as great as in the " off " position. The importance of this will be seen later. Pivoted to the lever K is a strut Q attached to which is a light spring Z which tends to draw the strut to the right.

There is a strut Q, a lever K, a nut and a pull rod for each of the four brakes and for the top gear clutch and the arrangement is such that all five struts lie side by side along one side of the gear box. (For convenience these parts will be given suffixes corresponding to the gear to which they belong, that is, Q_1 is the strut belonging to the first gear.) Running along that side of the box and being thus common to all the struts is a " bus-bar " R pivoted on a knife-edge pivot at S. A powerful spring, T (shown only diagrammatically) urges the bus-bar upwards unless it is prevented from so doing by means of the pedal U (also shown diagrammatically). It should now be clear that if the bus-bar is depressed by the pedal and one of the struts is moved so that its end comes over the edge of the bus-bar then when the latter is allowed to rise it will push that strut upwards and thus apply its brake.

To enable the gears to be pre-selected the struts are controlled by means of a camshaft V and levers W which are placed so that they are exactly opposite the struts and on which bear fairly strong springs X. The camshaft V has a cam opposite each lever W and is coupled to the pre-selector lever which may be situated just beneath the steering wheel or in any desired position. The cams have flats on them, these flats being in different angular positions and arranged so that normally the flat on only one cam can be brought opposite any lever W, letting it move forward.

Let us now suppose that first gear is engaged so that strut Q_1 is in engagement with, and is being held up by the bus-bar and let us suppose that the pre-selector lever is turned to the second gear position. The effect is to rotate the camshaft to a new position in which lever W_1 is pressed back against the pressure of its spring X_1 and spring X_2 is allowed to press its strut Q_2 forward. However, since the bus-bar is " up," the strut Q_2 merely comes up against the face of the bus-bar as shown on the right. Nothing more happens now until the pedal U is depressed *fully* thus depressing the bus-bar fully. When the latter is *fully* depressed, the spring Z_1 is able to pull the strut Q_1 away from the bus-bar and the spring X_2 is able to push the strut Q_2 over a little more so that it engages the bus-bar. When the " clutch " pedal is allowed to rise the bus-bar rises also and now pushes up strut Q_2 thus braking the annulus A_2 and engaging second gear.

22.7   Interlocking Mechanism

It is possible, should the spring Z_1 be broken, that when the second gear has been selected and the pedal is depressed the strut Q_1 may fail to be disengaged from the bus-bar, and, the strut Q_2 having been moved over by its lever, when the bus-bar is allowed to rise both struts Q_1 and Q_2 would be pushed up and an attempt would be made to engage two gears simultaneously. While this might not result in any serious damage it is altogether prevented from occurring by the interlocking mechanism. This consists of a number of swinging pieces Y, pivoted on pins on the side of the gear box casing and lying between the jaws of a U-shaped piece of metal (as shown in Fig. 22-13). When the struts are pushed up by the bus-bar the projecting " tails " O have to pass between the swinging pieces Y. The width of the jaw in the U-shaped piece of metal is made equal to the combined width of all four swinging pieces plus the width of only one tail O, thus it is impossible for two struts to move upwards simultaneously. If, as supposed above, two struts are engaged by the bus-bar, when the latter tries to rise the tails on the two struts will jam on the swinging pieces and the struts and bus-bar will be held down so that no brake at all will be applied and the gear will be in neutral. This is, in fact, how neutral is obtained. When the pre-selector lever is turned to the neutral position the camshaft is turned to a position such that two levers W are allowed to move forward and the action described above then occurs.

22.8 Top-gear Engagement

The mechanism for engaging the clutch giving the direct drive is

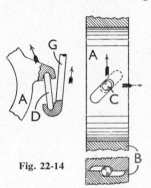

Fig. 22-14

shown in Fig. 22-14. The ring A is free to rotate and to slide in part of the casing B and a number of balls C fit in grooves cut on the slant as shown, half in A and half in B. The pull rod G is provided with a cup at its lower end and a rod D engages this cup and a second cup formed in a lug integral with the ring A. Thus when the pull rod G is pulled upwards the ring A is rotated and, because of the balls C in the inclined slots this rotation produces an axial motion which is communicated to the male cone of the clutch through a large ball bearing, thus engaging the clutch. A spring returns the ring A when the pull rod is released.

22.9 Automatic Adjusters

These are seen in Fig. 22-11 but their action will be made clear by reference to Fig. 22-15. Surrounding the nut H on the top of the pull rod is a coil spring b one end of which is secured to a pin fixed in a plate a which is free to turn round the nut H. The spring is coiled round the nut a few turns, is looped round the pin in the plate a again and finally is secured to a pin passing through a slot in the plate a and fixed in the knife edge plate J. When the pull rod is moved upwards by the bus-bar its upper end moves over and the plate a approaches the stop c fixed to the brake band (to the gear box casing for top gear). When the brake is in proper adjustment it comes on fully just as the plate a touches the stop c, but if wear has occurred the plate hits the stop and is rotated about the nut H in an anticlockwise direction. This rotation does not

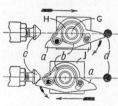

Fig. 22-15

turn the nut however, because the spring b uncoils and becomes free on the nut. When the pull rod is released its upper end moves back and the plate a hits the stop pin D, fixed in the casing. This causes the plate to rotate in a clockwise direction and this rotation *is* communicated to the nut H because for this direction of rotation the spring b coils up and grips the nut. The

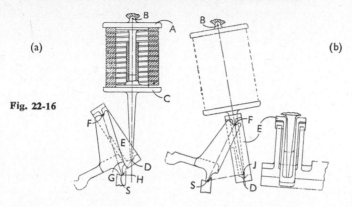

(a)

(b)

Fig. 22-16

nut being turned slightly the brake is tightened up slightly. The action described occurs every time the brake is applied and released, until the nut has been tightened up so much that when the brake is fully on the plate *a* only just reaches the stop *c*; the brakes are then in proper adjustment. Thus provided the stops *c* are positioned properly and that the automatic adjusters work regularly the brakes will be maintained always in the proper adjustment.

22.10   Spring Compensator Mechanism

The device which is used to keep the pedal pressure necessary to hold the bus-bar right down (when the spring is fully compressed) at a reasonable figure while enabling the required force to be applied to the struts when a brake is applied and the bus-bar is up (when the spring will have extended somewhat and be exerting a smaller force) is shown in Fig. 22-16. The upper spring sleeve A abuts on a spherical seating B on part of the casing and the finger of the lower sleeve C bears in a cup D formed in the " bucket " E. The latter is pivoted on a knife edge bearing F on a projecting arm of the bus-bar which is pivoted at S. At (*a*) the bus-bar is depressed fully and the line of action of the spring force BD passes to the right of the knife-edge F; the spring force consequently keeps the bucket hard up against the abutment G on the bus-bar. In this position the bucket is in effect solid with the bus-bar and the arm on which the spring force acts is the distance SD, the effective arm being the perpendicular distance SH which is quite small. Thus, although the spring is fully compressed and is exerting its maximum force the couple tending to lift the bus-bar is not very great and the pedal pressure required to balance it is also not excessive.

As the bus-bar rises, the point F moves over and gets nearer and nearer to the line BD, the pressure of the bucket on the abutment G becomes less and less and, since the spring extends, the spring force becomes less. In the very early stages the increase in the effective arm SH, due to the arm SD becoming more nearly perpendicular

495

to the line of action BD, more than compensates for the decrease in the spring force but this does not last long and then the couple acting on the bus-bar begins to fall off. At about this moment the point F comes to lie on the line BD and from thence onwards the bucket swings away from the abutment G as shown at (b). The line of action of the spring force must then always pass through the knife edge F and the arm against which the spring works is now in effect SF, the effective arm being SJ. As the bus-bar continues to rise this arm (SJ) increases in length because the arm SF comes to be more nearly perpendicular to the line BFD. This increase more than compensates for the reduction in spring force due to the extension of the spring and thus the couple tending to make the bus-bar rise increases and with it the force applied to the struts so that, in conjunction with the toggle action of the lever K (Fig. 22-11), sufficient force is applied to the end of the brake band to apply the brake.

22.11 Other Forms of Wilson Gear Box

Wilson gear boxes are extensively used in public service vehicles and lorries, but in a variety of forms which differ in some respects from that described in the previous articles, although most of the important principles outlined are used in these other forms, some of which will now be described.

One variation is to employ power to depress the bus-bar when a gear change is to be effected. This is done by fitting an air pressure or a vacuum cylinder and enables " two-pedal control " to be achieved. When this is done it is also frequently convenient to employ electromagnetic selection of the gears. In this the camshaft V of Fig. 22-11 is eliminated and the struts Q are operated directly by solenoids. Selection then becomes a matter of switching in the appropriate solenoid. Current is not passed to the solenoid until the bus-bar is operated and this is done by a secondary movement of the selector lever when the selected gear is actually required.

In vehicles where compressed air is available for brake operation, etc., full power operation is commonly used. The bus-bar is eliminated and each brake is provided with its own air cylinder; an example is shown in Fig. 22-17. When air pressure acts on the piston A the strut Q lifts the lever B and the roller lifts the lever K. An increasing leverage is obtained partly because the point P approaches a " dead-centre " position above the axis O and partly by the toggle action of the lever K as described in Section 22.6. The direct drive clutch also has its own cylinder as shown in Fig. 22-8. The force acting on the piston is transmitted through the lever B and the lever C to the thrust race housing E, and hence to the pressure plate G. The hub H, which carries the inner plates of the clutch, is splined to the input shaft J; and the drum K, which carries the outer plates, is splined to the sun S_3 of the third auxiliary epicyclic train. The lever C takes the form of a ring surrounding the housing

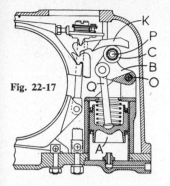

Fig. 22-17

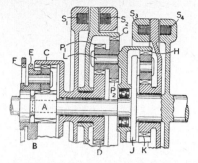

Fig. 22-18: Cotal epicyclic gear box

E, to which it is pivoted on pivots F; a fixed pin D forms the fulcrum for this lever.

When air power is not available and power operation of the gear box is required, oil pressure is usually employed. Two oil pumps are fitted, one driven off the input shaft and the other off the output shaft, and these pumps supply the pressure oil for the brake-actuating cylinders which are substantially of the same form as shown in Figs. 22-8 and 22-17.

22.12 Cotal Epicyclic Gear

This is shown in Fig. 22-18; the wheel A is integral with the engine shaft and meshes with pinions carried by a spider B which is free to slide along the outside of the engine shaft. When the spider B is slid to the left its teeth E mesh with teeth F of an annulus which is fixed to the gear box casing. The pins of the spider then form fixed bearings for the pinions, and so the annulus C with which the latter mesh is driven in the opposite direction to the wheel A. This gives the reverse drives. When the spider B is slid to the right its teeth E engage the teeth of the annulus C and then the wheel A, pinions, spider B and annulus C revolve " solid." This gives the forward drives.

The four forward ratios are obtained by means of two epicyclic trains arranged in tandem. One consists of the sun D (fixed to the annulus C), the compound planets $P_1 P_2$ (carried on the pins L of the arm which is integral with the annulus H of the second train) and the annulus G which can be held fixed.

When this is done the annulus H is driven in the same direction as the sun D but at a lower speed. The second train consists of the annulus H, the sun K and the arm J which is fixed on the output shaft. The sun K can be held at rest so that the train gives a reduction between the annulus H and the arm J and it can also be locked to the output shaft so that the train must revolve " solid." The annulus G can also be locked to the sun D so that the first train must revolve " solid."

The fixing and locking of the members is done by electromagnets

497

whose windings S_1 S_2 S_3 S_4 are energized as may be required. For first gear S_2 and S_3 are energized and both epicyclic trains provide a reduction since both annulus G and sun K are fixed. For second gear, S_2 and S_4 are energized and the second train revolves solid, the only reduction being in the first train. For third gear, S_1 and S_3 are energized, the first train is locked solid and the only reduction occurs in the second train. For fourth gear S_1 and S_4 are energized and both trains revolve solid so that a direct drive is obtained.

The windings S_1 and S_4 are carried by parts that sometimes rotate and so these windings are connected to slip rings on which brushes bear. The current for energizing the windings is supplied by the battery or generator of the car and is between two and three ampères.

The gear is extensively used on the Continent of Europe and has been used on both cars and lorries in England but not to any great extent.

The control is extremely simple consisting merely of a switch which connects the appropriate winding to the battery. This switch is usually mounted at the centre of the steering wheel.

CHAPTER 23

Torque Converters and Automatic Gear Boxes

Torque converters.   Chevrolet " Turboglide" transmission.   Automatic gear
boxes.   Hydramatic transmissions.

A TORQUE converter is a device which performs a function
similar to that of a gear box, namely, to increase the torque
while reducing the speed, but whereas a gear box provides only a
small number of fixed ratios the torque converter provides a continuous variation of ratio from the lowest to the highest.

Constructionally, a torque converter is somewhat similar to a
fluid flywheel from which it differs in one important aspect, namely,
in having *three* principal components instead of only *two*. Torque
converters all consist of (*a*) the driving element or *impeller* which
is connected to the engine, (*b*) the driven element or *rotor* which is
connected to the propeller shaft, and (*c*) the fixed element or *reaction
member* which is fixed to the frame. It is the last element which
makes it possible to obtain a change of torque between input and
output shafts and, as has been seen, the fluid flywheel, which does
not have any fixed member, cannot produce any change of torque.

A three-stage torque converter is shown in the several views of
Fig. 23-1.   The impeller, shown in sectional perspective at (*d*), is a
" conical " disc provided with blades A the outer ends of which
are tied together by a ring *u*.   If this impeller is immersed in fluid
and rotated then the fluid between the blades will be flung out more
or less tangentially and a flow will be established from the centre
or " eye " of the impeller to the periphery.   The velocity of a particle
of fluid on leaving the impeller is indicated by the line V_a in the
view (*a*); this velocity may be resolved into a purely tangential
component V_t and a purely radial component V_r.

The rotor or driven element is sectioned in black in the views (*a*),
(*b*) and (*c*) and is shown in sectional perspective at (*f*).   It consists
of a portion similar to the impeller, comprising the disc member *b*,
which carries the blades F, and the hollow annular member *g* which
is carried by the blades F and which in turn carries blades B and D;
these latter blades are tied together at their outer ends by rings
as shown.

The fixed, or reaction, member consists of a drumlike casing *h*
fitting the shaft portions of the impeller and rotor at the centre
and thus enclosing those members.   The reaction member carries
blades C all round its periphery and blades E project, in a
ring, from the right-hand end wall.

The action of the converter is as follows—the fluid flung out at
the periphery of the impeller impinges on the blades B of the rotor
and is deflected by those blades, the tangential component of the

499

velocity of any particle, for example, V_t (view (a)) being abstracted, more or less completely, so that the velocity of the particle on leaving the blades B is more or less radial as indicated by the arrow V_b. The particle being considered has therefore lost momentum in the tangential direction and this momentum has been gained by the blades B, that is, by the rotor. In being deflected backwards by the blades the fluid applies a pressure forwards on the blades. On leaving the blades B the fluid is guided round by the fixed casing and enters the blades C. In passing through these blades the velocity of the particle is changed from a more or less purely axial velocity (V_b^1 in views (b) and (e)) into a velocity having a considerable tangential component V_t (view (e)). In deflecting the fluid in this way the blades C, and thus the fixed casing, receive

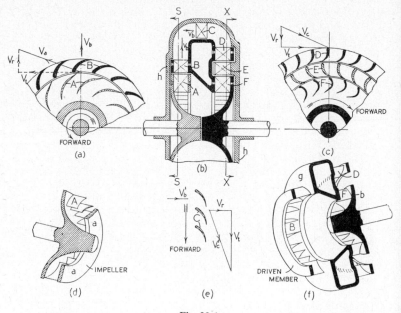

Fig. 23-1

a backwards thrust and unless the reaction member were fixed these thrusts would make it rotate backwards. The particle of fluid is now guided round by the fixed casing and enters the blades D of the rotor with a velocity V_c (view (c)) which again has a considerable tangential component V_t and again on passing through the blades this tangential component is abstracted and the momentum associated with it is acquired by the rotor. The particle of fluid now enters the blades E which restore the tangential component of velocity once more and finally it enters blades F which finally abstract the tangential momentum, which is acquired by the rotor.

500

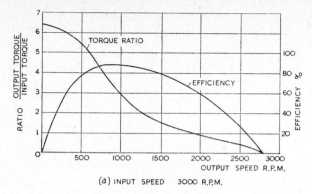

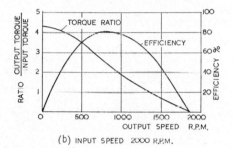

(a) INPUT SPEED 3000 R.P.M.

(b) INPUT SPEED 2000 R.P.M.

Fig. 23-2

The particle of fluid has now found its way back to the eye of the impeller and the cycle commences all over again.

The rotor or driven element thus receives three driving impulses, one from the blades B, one from the blades D and one from the blades F, and this converter is consequently called a " three-stage " converter.

The characteristics of a torque converter of this kind are shown by the graphs Fig. 23-2 (a) and (b).

The graphs (a) show the manner in which the torque-increase and efficiency vary when the rotor speed varies from zero to the maximum value (2,700 r.p.m.), the impeller speed being constant at 3,000 r.p.m. When the rotor speed is zero (because the resistance opposing its motion is large enough to hold it fixed) the torque tending to rotate it will be nearly 6½ times the torque developed by the engine at its speed of 3,000 r.p.m. If the resistance to the motion of the rotor now decreases so that the rotor starts to rotate, then as it gathers speed so the driving torque acting on it falls off. At a rotor speed of 1,000, for example, the driving torque would have fallen off to about three times engine torque, at 1,900 r.p.m. the driving torque would be only just equal to engine torque, while at 2,700 r.p.m. the driving torque would have fallen to zero. The efficiency on the other hand starts at zero when the rotor speed is

501

zero, because although the driving torque acting on the rotor is
then large no rotation occurs and the torque does no work; thus
no work is being got out of the converter but a lot of work is
being put in by the engine and so the efficiency is zero. As the rotor
speed increases so does the efficiency and a peak efficiency of 86 to 90
per cent is reached at a rotor speed of about 1,000 r.p.m. As the
rotor speed continues to increase the efficiency falls off again
and at 2,700 r.p.m. becomes zero once more, this time because
although the rotor is revolving rapidly the driving torque on it is
zero and no work can be got out of it.

The graphs (b) show the same things but for an impeller speed
of 2,000 r.p.m. instead of 3,000 r.p.m. It will be seen that the
driving torque acting on the rotor when it is " stalled," that is, held
at rest, is now only 4½ times engine torque and it falls off to zero
at a rotor speed of 1,800 r.p.m. The efficiency only reaches a
maximum value of about 80 per cent instead of 85 to 90 per cent.

It is thus seen that only over a rather narrow range of rotor
speeds is the efficiency reasonably good and it must be borne in
mind that if the efficiency is, say, 60 per cent, then 40 per cent of
the power developed by the engine is wasted, being converted into
heat which raises the temperature of the torque converter fluid and
which has to be dissipated by some means, commonly a radiator.
The fall off of efficiency at the low speed end of the range can be
tolerated because those speeds are normally used only for short
periods when starting and climbing severe hills, but the fall off at

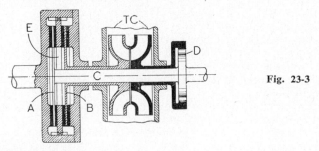

Fig. 23-3

high speeds cannot be tolerated and must be circumvented. There
are two principal ways in which this can be done, (a) by substituting
a direct drive for the torque converter at high speeds and (b) by
making the torque converter function as a fluid flywheel at the
higher speeds. These will now be considered in detail.

23.1 Torque Converter with Direct Drive

Referring to Fig. 23-3, a double clutch, provided with two
separate driven plates A and B, is situated between the engine and
the torque converter (TC), only the impeller and part of the rotor
of which are shown. The plate A is connected to the shaft C
which is permanently coupled to the propeller shaft while the

plate B is connected to the impeller of the torque converter. The rotor of the latter is connected through the free-wheel D to the shaft C and thus to the output shaft. The intermediate plate E of the clutch can be pressed either to the left or to the right. When pressed to the right it grips the plate B and thus drives the impeller of the torque converter and the drive passes through the torque converter and the free-wheel D to the output. If now the plate E is pressed to the left the plate B (and torque converter) will no longer be driven but the drive will pass direct through plate A to the

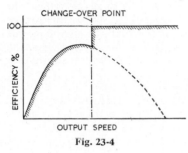

Fig. 23-4

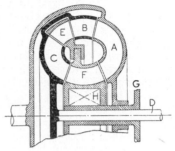

Fig. 23-5

shaft C and output which will override the rollers of the free-wheel D; the rotor of the torque converter will thus come to rest. The efficiency of the direct drive is 100 per cent and the combined efficiency curve will be as shown in Fig. 23-4. The change-over from converter to direct drive is done by the operation of a lever or pedal by the driver. This arrangement and the torque converter as described above, was developed by Leyland Motors, Ltd., but has subsequently been used by firms in many countries, particularly the United States of America. In some applications the change-over has been made automatic, being controlled by a governor driven from the output side of the converter.

23.2 Turbo-Transmitters Converter

The second method of obviating the fall off in efficiency at the higher output speeds is used in the Turbo-Transmitters converter unit shown diagrammatically in Fig. 23-5.

The impeller is seen at A and is permanently connected to the engine crankshaft; it differs from the impeller of the Leyland converter in having blades that extend over nearly half of the complete fluid circuit instead of over only about a quarter of that circuit. The impeller thus more nearly resembles the impeller of a fluid flywheel from which it differs chiefly in having blades that are curved in the end view whereas the blades of a fluid flywheel impeller are straight. The driven member, shown sectioned in solid black, has two sets of blades B and C and is fixed to the output shaft D. The reaction member also has two sets of blades E and F. The blade unit E is carried on the unit F on which it is free to rotate

503

in the forwards direction but is prevented from rotating backwards by pawls that engage ratchet teeth on F. The member F in turn is free to rotate on the fixed member G but again only in the forwards direction. Backwards rotation is prevented by a multi-plate clutch, situated at H, which engages and locks F to G whenever the member F tries to rotate backwards but which disengages when F tries to go forwards, which motion is thus allowed. This clutch is described later (see page 505). The converter is a two-stage one, two driving impulses being given to the driven member, one when the direction of the fluid is changed in the blades B and a second when the direction of the fluid is changed in the blades C. When the torque acting on the driven member BCD is greater than the engine torque applied to the driving member A, there will be a reaction torque acting on the blades E and F; this will be transmitted by the pawls and ratchet teeth from E to F and by the clutch at H to the member G. Whenever the torque acting on the blades B and C tends to fall below the torque applied to A, a forwards torque will be applied to the blades E and F; this will merely cause those blades to rotate forwards and the converter will then function as a fluid flywheel; the percentage slip will then be quite small, say about 5 or 6 per cent, and will decrease as the speed of the driven member increases.

The characteristics of this converter will thus be somewhat as shown in Fig. 23-6, which shows torque increase and efficiency curves for an input speed of 3,500 r.p.m. The converter being

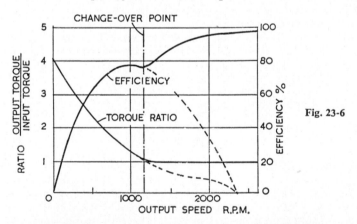

Fig. 23-6

only a two-stage one, the maximum torque is only about 4 times engine torque as compared with $6\frac{1}{2}$ to 7 in the Leyland converter, but otherwise the curves are very similar in general shape. The change-over point, at which the reaction members E and F begin to rotate forwards, and the unit commences to function as a fluid flywheel, is at 1,200 r.p.m., and from that speed onwards the output torque will be approximately equal to the input torque and the output speed will be only some 5 or 6 per cent less than engine speed.

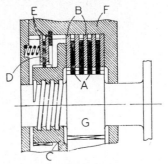

Fig. 23-7

When the engine speed is less than the maximum 3,500 r.p.m. assumed above, and when the throttle opening is reduced so that the engine torque is less than the maximum, then the change-over speed will be lower than the 1,200 r.p.m. corresponding to maximum engine speed and torque.

The fact that the change-over is quite automatic is important and is responsible for the good performance of this type of converter at part throttle loads and medium engine speeds.

Details of the automatic multi-plate clutch which locks the reaction member F to the fixed member G, for backwards rotation, are given in Fig. 23-7. The clutch proper consists of a set of inner plates A splined to the member G, and a set of outer plates B splined to the hub of the member F. These plates are squeezed together by the nut C which engages a left-handed screw formed on the end of G. On the outside of the nut C is a single plate D which engages spring-loaded plates E carried by the hub of F. Thus there is always a small frictional torque tending to lock F to the nut C and when F tends to go backwards the nut is rotated on its thread and moves to the right, thus engaging the clutch plates A and B. Friction between the left-hand plate B and the end of the nut increases the engaging forces and the clutch locks F to G. When the member F tends to rotate forwards the nut C is rotated forwards and screws to the left, thus disengaging the plates A and B. The only frictional drag on the member F is then that due to the plate D.

This torque converter was developed and is manufactured by Turbo-Transmitters Limited of Southport, England.

23.3 Other Arrangements of Torque Converters

Four arrangements of single-stage converters are shown in Figs. 23-8 to 23-11.

In Fig. 23-8 the reaction member R is permanently fixed, which makes it unsuitable for use in motor vehicles unless some form of direct drive is provided and the converter is emptied when the direct drive is engaged.

The design shown in Fig. 23-9 is widely used, being simple constructionally; the one-way clutch S is sometimes placed outside the casing by providing the reaction member with a sleeve which passes through the cover of the impeller member.

In Fig. 23-10 an auxiliary impeller I_2 is provided and is carried on a one-way clutch S_3 on the main impeller I_1; the reaction

505

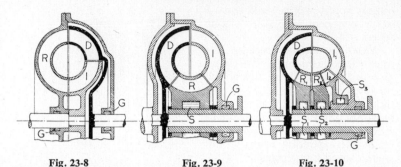

Fig. 23-8   Fig. 23-9   Fig. 23-10

member is also divided into two portions R_1 and R_2, each of which is anchored separately by the one-way clutches S_1 and S_2. This arrangement, which was introduced on Buick cars some years ago, is claimed to increase the efficiency of the converter and to make the change over to coupling action smoother.

In the Borgward converter shown in Fig. 23-11 the whole reaction member RR_1 and the impeller I on which the reaction member is mounted on ball bearings B, is moved to the left when converter action is required. This fixes the reaction member by engaging the cone clutch H and is done by the reaction of the pressure that exists inside the coupling at L and which acts on the exposed area of the driven member D. To obtain direct drive, oil under pressure from the gear box control unit is passed to the space K and moves the reaction member and impeller to the right so as to engage the cone clutch M. The one-way clutch S enables the output member E to drive the impeller, and thus the engine, in the forwards direction and so permits the engine to be used as a brake or to be started by towing the car.

The arrangement of a two-stage converter shown in Fig. 23-12 differs from that of Fig. 23-5 in that only a single reaction member

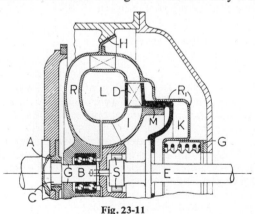

Fig. 23-11

is used and so the second driven member D_2, which is bolted up to the member D_1, discharges direct into the inlet of the impeller. The single plate clutch C gives a direct drive when it is required; the method of engaging this clutch is not shown but various means are used; a very convenient one when the converter is associated with an automatic gear box is to make the presser plate of the clutch function as a piston in a cylinder formed in the flywheel and to engage the clutch by admitting pressure oil to this cylinder.

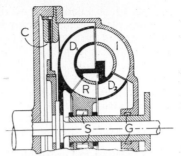

Fig. 23-12

In Fig. 23-13 is shown the two-stage or two " phase " converter used at one time on Buick cars. In this the first driven member D is made integral with the annulus of a sun and annulus epicyclic gear the sun S_1 of which is prevented from rotating backwards by the one-way clutches TT. The blading D is thus enabled to drive the output member L, which carries the planets of the epicyclic on the pins K. These pins also serve to secure the second driven member J to the output member which is thus driven direct by the second stage of blading. The first set of reaction blades F lies between the two driven members and is also anchored by the one-way clutches TT. The portion G of the assembly FGH does not carry any blading and G and H are connected only by three spokes. A second reaction member N is placed between the driven blading J and the impeller entry and the angular disposition of the blades Q of this member can be adjusted by means of cranked shafts S (one for each blade) which are actuated by the piston P. When the blades are at a large angle to the axis of the converter the torque ratio is greater than when they are approximately parallel to the axis and so when rapid acceleration is required and the accelerator pedal is pressed hard down it is made to admit pressure oil to the piston P and so bring the blades to the "high angle" position.

The whole of the reaction member N is free to rotate forwards on the fixed sleeve U but is anchored against backward rotation by the clutch V. At the change-over point the member N starts to rotate forwards and as the member FGHS will have previously started to rotate forwards the whole unit

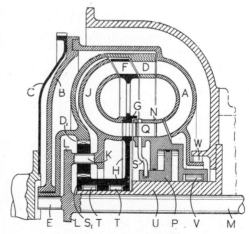

Fig. 23-13

will function as a coupling and the epicyclic will be rotating " solid."
The cover plate B closes the impeller casing at the front (engine) end
and is centred on the boss of the member DD_1 which in turn is
centred on the spigot E of the output shaft M. The latter is running
in bearings in the fixed sleeve U. A relatively flexible disc C
transmits the driving torque from the crankshaft to the impeller casing
and accommodates any slight misalignment that may exist between
the bell housing which carries the sleeve U and the crankshaft
which is carried in the crankcase. A seal W prevents egress of fluid
at the rear end of the converter.

23.4   Chevrolet " Turboglide " Transmission

In this transmission, which is shown in Fig. 23-14, the combination
of the hydraulic torque converter and the epicyclic gearing has been
carried further than in the Buick converter described earlier, and

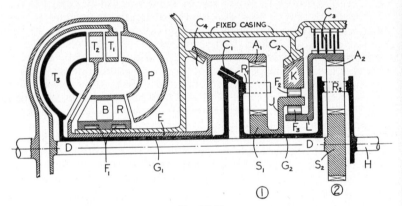

Fig. 23-14

each of the three driven members of the converter is connected
directly to one or more elements of the epicyclic gearing, and thus
to the output shaft.

The converter has five elements, the pump P, three " turbine " or
driven elements T_1, T_2 and T_3, and a reaction member R. The
latter is free to rotate in the forward direction on the freewheel F_1
and is provided with a set of blades B, whose angles are adjustable
as in the Buick converter; the mechanism for making the adjustment
is not indicated.

The first turbine element T_1 is coupled by the shaft D to the sun
S_2 of the second epicyclic train; the second turbine T_2 is coupled
through the sleeve E to the annulus A_1 of the first epicyclic train
and the third turbine T_3 is coupled to the output shaft H by the
sleeve G_1, the clutch C_1 (which is always engaged except when
neutral and reverse are selected), the sleeve G_2 and the planet
carrier R_2. The sun S_1 is normally prevented from rotating backwards by the freewheel F_2, since usually the clutch C_2 is engaged

508

and the member K is fixed so that the sleeve J cannot rotate backwards. The annulus A_2 is also prevented from rotating backwards by the freewheel F_3 which locks it for such rotation to the sleeve J. Engagement of the clutch C_3 fixes the annulus A_2 against forwards or backwards rotation, and this is done when " low " is selected so as to reduce the load on the freewheel F_3, when the engine is pulling hard under adverse road conditions, and to allow the engine to be used effectively as a brake on down gradients.

At low forward speeds of the output shaft H relative to the engine speed, the sun S_1 and annulus A_2 will be stationary because the torques on them will tend to make them rotate backwards and this motion is prevented by the freewheels F_2 and F_3. Both epicyclic trains then provide speed reductions and torque increases, and all three turbines will be driving.

As the output speed rises, the torque passing through the sun S_2 will fall and at some point will tend to become negative, and then the annulus A_2 will start to rotate forwards and the turbine T_1 will be effectively out of action. At a higher output shaft speed, the sun S_1 will start to rotate forwards and the turbine T_2 will go out of action. The drive will then be through T_3 direct to the output shaft, the only torque magnification then being that due to the torque converter itself. Finally, the reaction member R will start to rotate forwards and the torque converter will run as a fluid coupling. The speeds and torques at which these events occur will depend on the angle at which the blades B are set.

Reverse is obtained by engaging the clutch C_4 and disengaging C_1, C_2 and C_3. The trains 1 and 2 are then compounded and give a reverse ratio, the whole of the driving torque being transmitted by the turbine T_1 and sun S_2. Forward motion of S_2 tends to drive R_2 forwards and A_2 backwards; backward motion of A_2, however, results in backward motion of S_1 (through the freewheel F_3 and the sleeve J) and so in train 1, whose annulus is fixed, the sun tends to rotate the planet carrier R_1 backwards. The backward torque on R_1 is greater than the forward torque on R_2 (from S_2), and so R_1 and R_2 will move backwards.

23.5 The Perkins "DDT" Transmission

The fundamental basis of the Perkins differential diesel transmission has been mentioned in Chapter 13 and the general arrangement of the transmission is shown in the diagram Fig. 23-15. It consists of a single stage torque converter coupled to a two speed and reverse epicyclic gear. As mentioned in Chapter 13 the engine torque is shared in a fixed ratio between the impeller of the torque converter and the rotor of the engine supercharger. This is done by the epicyclic train BCH in which the annulus H is coupled to the impeller I of the torque converter and the sun C is connected through gears E and F to the supercharger. The engine torque is thus divided in the ratio *Torque converter/Supercharger* $= H/C$ where *H* and *C* are the numbers of teeth in the annulus and sun

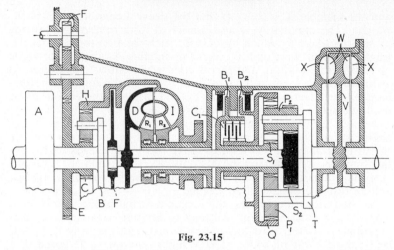

Fig. 23.15

respectively. The converter has a two-part reaction member R_1R_2 and its driven member D is connected to the sun S_2, it also carries a clutch plate F which enables the converter to be put out of action and the torque acting on the annulus H to be transmitted direct to the sun S_2. The epicyclic gear can be locked solid by engaging the clutch C_1 to give a direct drive and a low forward ratio is obtained by applying the brake B_1 so as to fix the sun S_1. The reverse ratio is given by applying the brake B_2. The assembly VWX at the right is a " hydraulic retarder " to provide braking torque, because with a torque converter the engine cannot be used effectively as a brake. The principle of this is dealt with in Section 29.4.

23.6 Automatic Transmissions

Transmission systems that will function purely automatically without any attention from the driver of the vehicle have been sought for many years by designers, but even to-day such systems have not been fully achieved since present-day automatic transmissions still include control levers or press buttons, which have to be operated by the driver to enable the transmission to cope with the widely varying driving conditions encountered. However, systems which need no attention under ordinary road conditions and which require only the selection of the appropriate operating range when heavy gradients or very difficult terrain are to be traversed are now in extensive use. The transmissions can be divided into those which employ mechanical gear boxes, usually epicyclic, to provide all the required variations of gear ratio, and those which use a torque converter in conjunction with a mechanical gear box.

It is very difficult to design an automatic control system for an ordinary gear box that will function as satisfactorily under all conditions as can a really competent driver, but present-day systems will give better results than the average driver can achieve. In general, the control must bring about changes from low to higher gears when the vehicle speed rises and from high to low gears when the vehicle speed falls. However, it is frequently possible to employ the higher gears even at low vehicle speeds, for example on level roads and with following winds, when the resistances to be overcome are low.

The control system must therefore take account of the engine load and, in general, produce changes up when the load is light and changes down when the load is heavy. There are, however, occasions, such as on descending hills, when it is desirable to employ a low gear although the load on the engine may be nil or the engine may be acting as a brake. It is under these diverse conditions that the human element has to be retained in the control.

The automatic systems now in use consequently all utilize the two factors mentioned above, namely vehicle speed and engine load, in their operation. The vehicle speed factor is dealt with by employing some form of speed-sensitive unit which is driven off the output side of the gear box and is thus responsive to vehicle speed. These units may be mechanical, hydraulic or electrical and examples of each of these are given in the descriptions which follow. The engine load factor is introduced at present only by indirect means; it is assumed that engine load is a function of the depression of the accelerator pedal and the latter supplies the corresponding control, the actual form of which will depend on whether the system is a mechanical, an hydraulic or an electrical one.

It is essential that the vehicle speed, at which any change from a lower gear to a higher one is produced when the vehicle speed is rising and the accelerator pedal position is constant, shall be higher than the speed at which, when the speed is falling and the accelerator pedal position is unchanged, the corresponding change down will occur. If this is not so, a change up is likely to be followed immediately by a change down, and this sequence may go on indefinitely. This phenomenon is known as "hunting." It is also generally desirable that in traffic, when the accelerator pedal is released and the vehicle comes to rest, the control system shall not produce all the changes down from top to bottom, but shall retain the gear that is in use when the accelerator pedal is released until the vehicle speed has fallen nearly to zero, and shall then engage the low gear ready for the ensuing acceleration. It is also desirable that it shall be possible to start off in first or in second gear according to the prevailing road conditions.

The above considerations should be borne in mind when reading the descriptions of the systems that follow since many of their apparent complications are due to the necessity to comply with the requirements outlined above.

23.7 The Borg Warner Type 35 Gear Box

This is shown in Figs. 23-16 and 17. It consists of a single stage torque converter IDR coupled to a three forward and one reverse

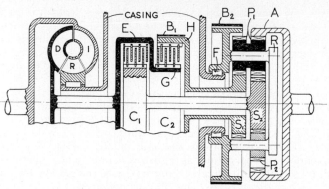

Fig. 23.16

ratio epicyclic gear. The driven member D of the converter is, in effect, integral with the drums E and G of the clutches C_1 and C_2. When C_1 is engaged the drive goes to the sun S_2 and if the brake B_1 is applied gives the low forward ratio while if the brake B_2 is applied instead of B_1 then the intermediate ratio is obtained. The one-way sprag clutch F prevents the planet carrier R from rotating backwards but allows it to rotate forwards. By engaging both clutches C_1 and C_2 simultaneously the gear is locked solid and the direct drive is obtained. To get reverse the clutch C_2 is engaged and the brake B_2 is applied, the drive then goes from S_1 to P_1

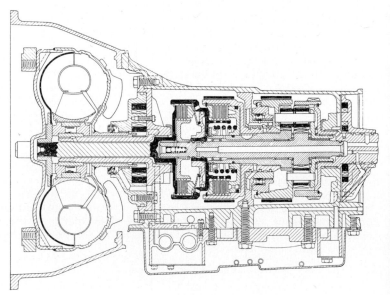

Fig. 23.17

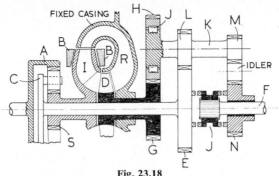

Fig. 23.18

and thence to the annulus A, the planet carrier being fixed.

The teeth seen on the outside of the annulus in Fig. 23-17 are engaged by a detent when the control lever is put into the " Parking " position and this holds the car stationary. Two oil pumps provide the oil pressures required to engage the clutches and apply the brakes. One is housed in the left-hand end wall of the box and is driven off the sleeve of the impeller so that it is working whenever the engine is running while the other is seen at the right-hand side and is driven off the output shaft of the box so that it will be running when the car is in motion. The principle underlying the action of the control system is similar to that of the Hydramatic boxes which are described in detail below.

23.8   The Voith " Diwamatic " Transmission

This is shown in Fig. 23-18 and is an example of a " split-torque " transmission, the engine power being transmitted partly by a single-stage torque converter and partly by direct mechanical action through an epicyclic gear. A forward and reverse gear box of conventional form is also employed. The converter is somewhat different from the usual arrangement in that the impeller I discharges directly into the fixed casing R whose passages lead the fluid into the driven member D. The division of the engine torque is done by the epicyclic train ACS in which the annulus is driven by the engine. When the vehicle is at rest and the planet carrier C is therefore stationary (assuming the dog-clutch J to be engaged with the gear E) the impeller I will be driven at a relatively high speed in the opposite sense to the rotation of the annulus A. The fluid will then develop a high torque on the driven member D and this will begin to rotate (in the same sense as the annulus) and will apply a torque to the gear E through the gears G and H, the one way clutch J and the pinion L. A driving torque will also be applied to E direct through the planet carrier C. As the speed of the vehicle increases so the speed at which the impeller is driven will fall and the torque acting on the member D will also fall. At a speed determined by a governor driven from the output gear E

513

the brake BB will be applied and the impeller brought to rest. The whole of the engine torque and power will then be transmitted mechanically through the planet carrier C and the dog-clutch J. The reverse drive is obtained by engaging the dog-clutch with the gear F and as this is done a cam operates a valve which empties the torque converter. The brake BB has therefore to be applied in order to obtain a drive and the application of this brake will also give the clutch action which is normally obtained from the torque converter.

23.9   Hydramatic Transmissions

These fully automatic transmissions were developed by General Motors Corporation and used in many of their American-built cars. Transmissions similar in principle but differing in constructional arrangement are being fitted in several of the Corporation's European-built products and variants are being made by Rolls-

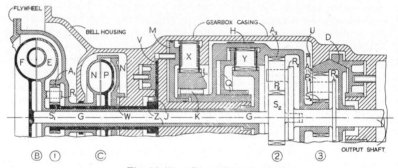

Fig. 23-19: " Strato-flight " gear box

Royce and Mercedes-Benz.   They are essentially three or four speed and reverse epicyclic gear boxes having brakes and clutches operated by oil pressure and which are controlled by the joint action of a governor, whose speed is proportional to that of the car, and of a valve actuated by the accelerator pedal.

The speeds at which the changes up will occur, supposing the accelerator to be pressed hard down, are, usually, as follows: First to second, 19–23 m.p.h.; second to third, 37–40 m.p.h.; third to fourth, 70–74 m.p.h.   At low throttle openings these changes will occur 7–9, 14–16 and 19–22 m.p.h.   The changes down are arranged to occur at lower speeds than the corresponding changes up in order to prevent " hunting."   Thus at full throttle the down change speeds are fourth to third, 38–17 m.p.h.; third to second, 13–10 m.p.h.; second to first, 8–6 m.p.h.

The gear box was originally produced in 1938 and was redesigned in 1956; the constructional arrangement of the " Strato-flight " model is indicated in Fig. 23-19.   It comprises three sun-and-annulus type epicyclic trains 1, 2 and 3, two multi-plate clutches X and Y,

EPICYCLIC COMBINATIONS AND GEAR RATIOS IN HYDRAMATIC GEARBOX

Gear	Train No. 1	Coupling C	Sun S_1	Brake V	Train No. 2	Brake X	Annulus A_2	Clutch Y	Brake D	Ratio
1	In reduction Ratio 1·55 : 1	Empty	Fixed	On	In reduction Ratio 2·55 : 1	On	Fixed	Disengaged	Off	1·55 × 2·55 = 3·966 : 1
2	In direct drive Ratio 1 : 1	Full	Rotating	Off	In reduction Ratio 2·55 : 1	On	Fixed	Disengaged	Off	1 × 2·55 = 2·55 : 1
3	In reduction Ratio 1·55 :	Empty	Fixed	On	In direct drive Ratio 1 : 1	On	Rotating	Engaged	Off	1·55 × 1 = 1·55 : 1
4	In direct drive Ratio 1 : 1	Full	Rotating	Off	In direct drive Ratio 1 : 1	On	Rotating	Engaged	Off	1 × 1 = 1 : 1
Reverse	In reduction Ratio 1·55 : 1	Empty	Fixed	On	Compounded with train No. 3	Off	Rotating backwards	Disengaged	On	4·31 : 1

of which the former functions as a brake, a double-cone brake D, two fluid couplings B and C and two one-way clutches or sprags. J and K. The coupling B is always filled with oil and transmits power on all the gears but the coupling C can be filled or emptied as required and is used for second and fourth gears only.

The epicyclic train 3 provides the reverse gear only and will be dealt with later on; the trains 1 and 2 together provide the four forward ratios. Each of these trains can be used so as to provide either a reduction or a direct drive; thus train 1 gives a reduction of $1 \cdot 55 : 1$ when its sun S_1 is fixed and the annulus A_1, which is permanently coupled to the flywheel, drives the planet carrier R_1. The latter is integral with the driving member E of the fluid coupling B and thereby drives the member F which is coupled by the shaft G to the sun S_2 of the second epicyclic train. If the annulus of the train 2 is fixed then the sun S_2 will drive the planet carrier R_2, which is the output member of the box, with a reduction of $2 \cdot 55$ to 1. The four forward gear ratios are therefore obtained as shown in the table on page 515.

Because some slip will occur in the coupling B the sun S_2 will be driven at a lower speed than that of the planet carrier R_1 and this slip will modify the numerical values quoted above and will make all the reductions slightly greater.

The epicyclic trains of the gear box are essentially the same as in the models produced prior to 1956 but the methods used to control the elements of the trains in order to give either a reduction or a direct drive are different. Whereas in the earlier models the sun S_1 was fixed by the application of a band brake it is now fixed by a " sprag " or one-way roller clutch J which prevents the inner member of the unit, which is integral with the sun S_1, from rotating backwards. Similarly the annulus A_2 of the second train was fixed by a band brake in the earlier models and is now fixed, when necessary, by the sprag K (or the band brake H or by both together) which prevents it from rotating backwards provided the outer member L of the sprag itself is prevented from rotating by the engagement of the multi-plate " neutral " clutch X which locks it to the casing of the gear box. This is done by admitting pressure oil behind the piston M. To obtain first gear the clutch X is engaged, the clutch Y is disengaged and the sun S_1 and annulus A_2 are fixed by the sprags J and K respectively. To obtain second gear the epicyclic train 1 has to be put into direct drive. In the earlier models this was done by engaging a multi-plate clutch that was arranged between the planet carrier member R_1 and the sun S_1, and this method is used in the " Dual-Range " model, but in the " Strato-flight " model it is done by filling the coupling C, which in first gear was empty, so that the driving member N, which is permanently coupled to the flywheel, drives the member P which is permanently attached to the sun S_1. If no slip occurred in the coupling C then the train 1 would give a 1 : 1 ratio since the sun and the annulus would be running at the same speed. Because some slip must occur in the coupling C the sun S_1 will run slightly slower than the annulus A_1 and the train will give a reduction slightly greater than unity. This slip will also modify the ratios quoted above for second and fourth gears. This use of a fluid coupling instead of a multi-plate clutch is to provide a much smoother take-up of the drive than was previously obtainable.

Third gear is obtained by emptying the coupling C so that train 1 goes back into reduction and by engaging the clutch Y so that train 2 goes into direct drive. This is done by admitting pressure oil behind the piston Q; this is the same as in earlier models.

To obtain reverse the clutch Y is disengaged and the coupling C is emptied while the annulus A_3 is fixed by admitting oil behind the piston D. Train 1 then provides a reduction, its sun being fixed by the sprag J, and the trains 2 and 3 function as a compound train to give a reversal of direction and a reduction in speed between the sun S_2 and the output member R_2. This action is precisely as in the reverse gear of the Wilson gear box (see Section 22.5 p. 486). During reverse the sun S_3 and hence the annulus A_2 will be rotating backwards and to permit this rotation to take place the sprag K must be made inoperative; this is done by disengaging the clutch X so that the outer member L of the sprag is free to rotate; the band brake H must also be free.

When the train 1 is being used to provide a reduction and the sun S_1 is prevented from rotating backwards by the sprag J the single-disc brake V may be employed to hold the sun against any tendency to rotate *forwards*, which tendency would arise if the car over-ran the engine: this enables the engine to be used as a brake.

The coupling C is filled by means of a large capacity vane-type pump and the emptying is done by opening a valve provided in the cover N^1 of the coupling which will permit the oil to be discharged by the action of centrifugal force. The operation of this "dumping" valve is by means of oil pressure which is admitted to the space W and thence through passages in the cover N^1 to the valve.

When the clutch Y is engaged the engine torque is divided at train 1; part of the torque is transmitted direct from the arm R_1 through the sleeve Z and the clutch Y to the annulus A_2 while the remainder is transmitted through the coupling B and the shaft G to the sun S_2. Approximately 40 per cent of the engine torque goes through the coupling B.

Because the coupling C runs at engine speed and has to transmit only just over one-third of engine torque it can be made smaller in size than the coupling B which has to transmit slightly over one and a half times engine torque on the first and second gears (when the clutch Y is disengaged) and which runs at a lower speed than the engine.

23.10 Hydramatic " Strato-flight " Gear Box Controls

The steering column control lever has six positions, Parking (P), Neutral (N), Normal driving ($\triangle$ Dr), Fast accelerating, driving

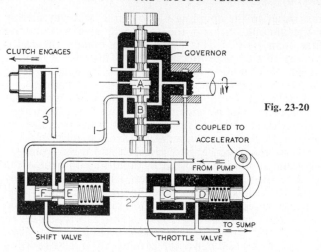

Fig. 23-20

(Dr △), Low range (Lo) and Reverse (Rev.). Parking differs from neutral in that a positive lock engages the teeth U (Fig. 23-19) to lock the output shaft of the gear box when (P) is selected.

At the rear end of the gear box there is a governor which is driven by the output shaft and whose speed is thus proportional to the road speed of the vehicle. The governor is actually two governors in one assembly and is shown diagrammatically in Fig. 23-20. Since both governors function in the same manner only one need be described. Considering the valve B and assuming that the pump that supplies the system with pressure oil is operating, the action is as follows. The valve is shown in the equilibrium position. the upper end of the portion B is just closing the port by which pressure oil is introduced while the lower end of B seals the pipe line 1 from the exhaust port. The pressure in line 1 will be lower than the pump pressure and, as will be seen shortly, will be proportional to the rotational speed of the governor. The position is that the centrifugal force acting on the valve and tending to make it move outwards (downwards in the figure) is just balanced by the force due to the oil pressure acting on the under side of the piston A and which tends to move the valve inwards. Suppose now that the governor speed increases a little, then the centrifugal force will increase and will overcome the oil pressure so that the valve will move outwards; this will open the pressure oil inlet from the pump and the pressure in the line 1 will rise until the increased pressure acting on A is sufficient to balance the centrifugal force when the valve will move into the equilibrium position again. Thus the oil pressure in line 1 will always be proportional (up to the limit of the pump pressure) to the centrifugal force acting on the valve and thus proportional to the square of the governor speed. The reason for using two valves is that a single valve that provided

518

sufficient pressure to control the changes at low car speed would give pressures that would be much too great at the higher speeds while if a valve suitable for the high speed changes were used it would give insufficient pressure for the low speed changes.

The governor valve B thus gives a pressure in line 1 which is dependent on the road speed of the vehicle. This pressure will be referred to as G1 governor pressure, that from the other valve will be called G2 governor pressure.

The throttle valve acts in a similar manner to the governor valve and is also shown in the equilibrium position, the pressure of the spring towards the left being balanced by the oil pressure in line 2 which acts on the left-hand end of the valve and tends to move it to the right. If the accelerator pedal is further depressed the balance will be upset and the valve will move to the left, the part C will then uncover the inlet port from the pump and the pressure in the space between the parts C and D will increase and this increase will be communicated by the by-pass to the left-hand end of the valve and by the pipe line 2 to the right-hand end of the shift valve. The increase of pressure will continue until the force exerted by the oil on the left hand of the throttle valve moves that valve back to the equilibrium position. The spring is now compressed a little more and the pressure in line 2 is a little higher than before. On the other hand if the accelerator pedal is released a little then the oil pressure on the left-hand end of the valve will move the valve to the right, thus uncovering the exhaust port. The pressure in the line 2 will then fall until the spring force moves the valve back to the equilibrium position again.

The throttle valve thus gives a pressure that is dependent on the throttle opening. This pressure will be referred to as throttle valve (TV) pressure.

The shift valve shown in Fig. 23-20 is a simplified version of the actual shift valves but enables the fundamental action to be explained easily. In the position shown the governor pressure in line 1 which acts on the left-hand end F of the valve has overcome the combined force of the spring and the throttle-valve pressure acting on the right-hand end E and the valve is in its extreme right-hand position in which the pipe coming from the pump is connected to line 3 which goes to an operating member of one of the epicyclic trains, say the clutch Y of Fig. 23-19. That clutch will therefore be engaged so as to give the direct drive in the train and this corresponds to the change up from first to second or from third to fourth gear.

If the speed of the car decreases or the accelerator is depressed further, then the shift valve will be moved to the left and will cut off line 3 from the pump line 1 and open it to exhaust so that the change down would occur.

The motion of the valve is made a " snap " motion by reason of the difference in diameter of the ends E and F and this also imparts a delay action so that the valve will not move back so as to change

519

down again unless the car speed decreases appreciably or unless the throttle is opened considerably. These actions are obtained as follows. In the position shown the forces acting on the valve to the right are due to governor pressure acting on the end F and pump pressure acting on the difference in area of E and F, whereas when the valve started to move to the right the latter pressure was absent. Hence as the part E uncovers the inlet port an additional force urges the valve to the right and makes the valve motion rapid. Again before the valve can move back to the left the force on F due to the governor pressure must fall below the force on E due to the throttle valve (or the latter must rise above the former) by an amount corresponding to pump pressure multiplied by the difference in area of E and F. The valve cannot move back, therefore, unless an appreciable fall of car speed, or an appreciable increase in throttle opening occurs and thus " hunting " is prevented. The snap action of the valve when moving to the left occurs because as soon as the part E covers the inlet port and the part F uncovers the exhaust port the force due to pump pressure acting on the difference in areas of E and F disappears and the valve moves across rapidly to its extreme left position.

The complete control system is shown in Fig. 23-21, in which the manual valve is shown in the △ Dr (Drive left) position, corresponding to normal driving, and the shift and coupling valves are shown in the position corresponding to low gear; the car speed and governor pressure being assumed to be low. The main pump supplies oil to the governor which gives G1 pressure in line 9 and thus on the left-hand end of the boost valve. The latter acts in a manner similar to the throttle valve to give a pressure in line 12 which is proportional to, but higher than, the governor G1 pressure. This boosted governor pressure is passed via line 12 to the transition valve and then by line 13 to the left-hand end of the coupling valve. The latter, in the position shown, opens the line 15, which controls the emptying valve of the coupling C (Fig. 23-19), to exhaust so that the emptying valve is open and the coupling C is empty. The epicyclic train 1 is thus in reduction. Since pump pressure via lines 2, 6, 8 and 10 is applied to the neutral clutch (X, Fig. 23-19) the latter is engaged, thereby enabling the freewheel unit (Fig. 23-19) to anchor the annulus of the rear epicyclic which is thus also in reduction, giving first gear. For the moment it will be assumed that the throttle opening is kept constant and at a moderate value, then as the speed of the car rises the G1 pressure acting on the coupling valve will rise and will eventually move the coupling valve to the right. This will cut off line 15 from exhaust and open it to line 14 so that pump pressure via line 1 will be applied to the coupling-emptying valve so as to close it. At the same time the coupling valve will open line 3 to line 16 so that pump oil will be supplied to the coupling C so as to fill it. As the coupling fills so the first epicyclic will go into direct drive, thus giving second gear. Further increase in car speed and governor pressure, which acts via

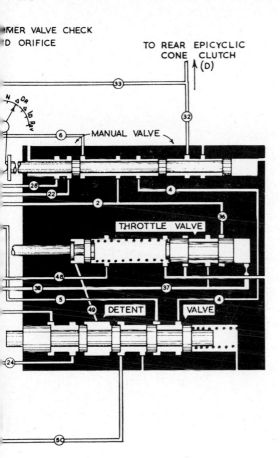

VALVE

MER VALVE CHECK
D ORIFICE

TO REAR EPICYCLIC
CONE CLUTCH
(D)

MANUAL VALVE

THROTTLE VALVE

DETENT   VALVE

UTCH

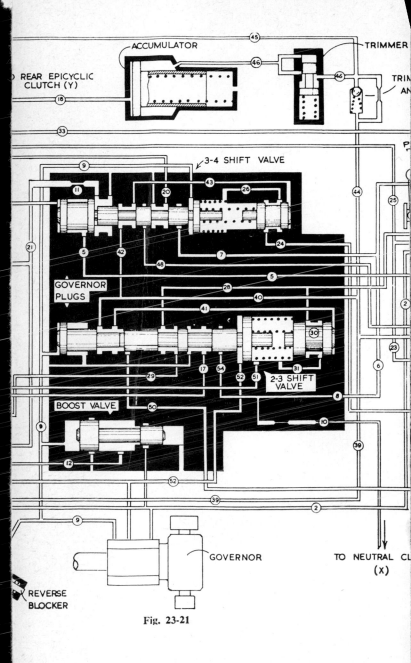

Fig. 23-21

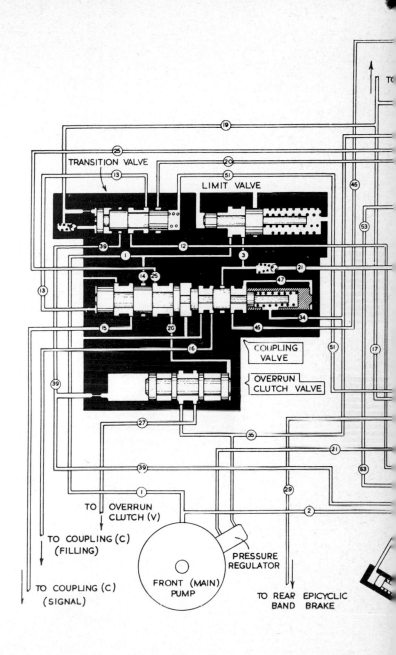

TRANSITION VALVE

LIMIT VALVE

COUPLING
VALVE

OVERRUN
CLUTCH VALVE

TO OVERRUN
CLUTCH (V)

TO COUPLING (C)
(FILLING)

TO COUPLING (C)
(SIGNAL)

FRONT (MAIN)
PUMP

PRESSURE
REGULATOR

TO REAR EPICYCLIC
BAND BRAKE

line 9 on the left-hand end of the 2–3 shift valve will cause the latter to move to the right and bring about the change up from second to third gear as follows. Pump pressure via line 6 from the manual valve will be passed via lines 8 and 54 to line 17, which has hitherto been opened to exhaust; thus pump pressure will be passed to the rear epicyclic clutch (Y) so as to engage it and via line 19 to the left-hand end of the transition valve. The latter will consequently move to the right, thus cutting off line 12 from line 13 and opening the latter to line 20 and thus to exhaust. The oil pressure on the left-hand end of the coupling valve will thus be released and the coupling valve will move back to the left, thereby opening lines 15 and 16 to exhaust. The coupling C will thus empty and the first epicyclic will go back into reduction. Since the rear epicyclic is now in direct drive third gear is obtained. This action is controlled by the orifice which restricts the entry of oil into the transition valve and by the accumulator whose piston will have to be moved to the right before pressure can build up in the line going to the clutch Y.

The change up from third to fourth will follow if the car speed and governor pressure continue to increase, the action being that governor (G_1 and G_2) pressures which act, via lines 9 and 53, on the 3–4 shift valve, will move that valve to the right, producing the following results. Line 20 will be cut off from exhaust and be opened via lines 7 and 6 to pump pressure from the manual valve, and this pressure will be passed via the transition valve (which is to the right) and line 13 to the coupling valve, thereby moving that valve to the right and opening lines 15 and 16 to pump pressure; the coupling C will thus be filled and the first epicyclic will go into direct drive, thus giving fourth gear. At the same time pump pressure from the manual valve via lines 4, 5 will be passed to line 21 and thus to the inner end of the pressure regulator of the pump where it will act so as to reduce the maximum pressure produced by the pump. This is desirable since it reduces the power consumption of the pump, and permissible since at all except large throttle openings, the torques in fourth gear are not heavy.

If the car speed and governor pressure fall the above changes will occur in the reverse order and the changes down will occur successively.

The effect of varying the throttle opening will now be considered. Throttle valve pressure via lines 36, 37, 38, 40, 41, 42 and 43 is applied to the right-hand ends of the 2–3 and 3–4 shift valves and via lines 44, 45 and 47 to the right-hand end of the coupling valve, and so increasing TV pressure will necessitate higher governor pressures in order that these valves may be shifted to produce the changes up and these changes will consequently occur at higher car speeds. The TV pressure also acts via line 46 on the annular area of the accumulator piston so as to tend to hold that piston down; this tends to speed up the engagement of the rear epicyclic Y on a 2–3 change as the throttle opening is increased. The TV pressure that

521

can be applied to the accumulator is limited by the trimmer valve to 75 lb/sq. in. in order that the clutch engagement shall not be made unduly harsh. It will be noticed that when the coupling and shift valves move to the right the TV pressure acting on the right-hand ends of those valves is cut off; this produces the difference in the car speeds at which the changes down will occur and also provides some of the " snap " action of the valves.

A " part-throttle " change down from fourth to third can be produced, provided the car speed is not too high, by depressing the accelerator about half-way to the bottom position. This opens line 48 to TV pressure which is thus passed via line 43 (the 3–4 shift valve being to the right) to the right-hand end of the 3–4 shift valve regulator plug which is accordingly forced to the left and thereby opens line 26 to TV pressure which is enabled to act on the large area of the shift valve and move it to the left, so producing a change down from fourth to third. A forced change from third to second can be produced by pressing the accelerator to the floor; this moves the detent valve to the right and passes TV pressure via lines 49, 50 and 41 (the 2–3 shift valve being to the right) to the right-hand end of the 2–3 shift valve regulator plug, forcing it to the left so that TV pressure is caused to act via line 31 on the large end of the shift valve and move it to the left to produce the change down. When this occurs the coupling C has to be filled and the rear epicyclic clutch Y has to be released and it is necessary to ensure rapid movement of the transition valve to the left and of the coupling valve to the right as soon as the 2–3 shift valve moves to the left. The transition valve is moved rapidly by passing TV pressure via the detent valve to line 50 and hence as soon as the 2–3 shift valve opens line 40, to line 39 and thus to the right-hand side of the large left-hand end of the transition valve (which is to the right), rapid movement of which is allowed by the lifting of the ball valve and by-passing of the restricting orifice. The moving of the transition valve passes governor boost pressure via lines 12 and 13 to the end of the coupling valve (which in third gear is to the left) and moves it to the right. To speed up this motion a momentary reduction of the TV pressure acting on the right-hand end of the coupling valve is produced as follows. The movement of the 2–3 shift valve to the left opens line 17 and thus lines 18 and 19 to exhaust so that the accumulator piston moves rapidly to the left (in the diagram); this produces a sudden lowering of pressure in line 46 and, because of the trimmer valve check and orifice, in line 45 also and hence via line 47 behind the right-hand end of the coupling valve. As soon as the latter moves to the right the line 45 will be closed so that although the pressure in line 45 will build up slowly through the trimmer valve orifice it will not act to move the coupling valve back to the left again.

When the manual valve is moved to the Dr △ (Drive Right) position it opens line 22 to pump pressure and hence pump pressure is applied via lines 23, 24 and 26 to the right-hand end of the 3–4 shift valve; this has the effect of preventing governor pressure via lines 9 and 53 from moving the shift valve to the right except at very high car speeds so that the gear box is virtually reduced to a three-speed box and the increased acceleration of third gear is retained. Pump oil is also passed via lines 25 and 26 to the over-run clutch valve and moves that valve to the left so that line 26 is opened to line 27 and pump pressure is applied to engage the over-run clutch. The engagement of the over-run clutch is delayed until the sprag has engaged because the volume of oil trapped in the left-hand end of the over-run clutch valve has to be discharged through a restricted orifice. This enables the engine to be used as a brake in third gear if required since the over-run clutch will prevent forward rotation of the sun of the front epicyclic whereas the sprag will not do so. The line 25 is cut off from line 26 whenever the coupling valve moves to the right, as it does for second gear, so that the over-run clutch valve is moved back to the right-hand position and the over-run clutch is released as is necessary to enable the front epicyclic to go into direct drive.

When the manual valve is moved into the Lo position pump pressure is passed to line 28 and thus via line 30 and 31 to the right-hand end of the 2–3 shift valve so as to prevent that valve from moving to the right except at very high car speeds. The gear box is thus restricted to first and second gears. This is intended to enable very heavy going, such as in sand, to be negotiated. Since under these conditions torques will be high, oil from line 28 is passed via line 29 to the rear epicyclic band brake which thus assists the rear sprag in holding the annulus of the rear epicyclic and also holds that annulus against forward motion so that the engine can also be used as a brake in second gear if required. If the car speed should increase sufficiently to enable governor pressure to move the 2–3 shift valve to the right so as to produce a change up to third the shift valve will cut off line 28 from line 29 and thus release the band brake. In this position of the manual valve the line 4 is cut off from pump pressure so that pressure is not applied to the pump pressure regulator and the maximum pump pressure is not reduced.

When the manual valve is moved to the Rev. position pump pressure is applied direct via line 32 to the rear epicyclic cone clutch (D) and via line 33 and 34 to the inside of the coupling valve regulator plug. The coupling valve is thus prevented from moving to the right and the front epicyclic is kept in reduction. It will be noticed that governor pressure is always applied to the reverse blocker so that if the forward speed of the car is higher than about 10 m.p.h. the blocker will be held out against spring pressure and will prevent the selector and manual valve from being moved to the Rev. position. Line 33 is also connected via line 35 to the outer end of the pump pressure regulator so as to increase pump pressure in order to provide ample holding power to the cone clutch D. There is also a connection via line 27 to the over-run clutch so that the engine can be used as a brake in reverse.

The action of the limit valve, which has not yet been dealt with, is that it acts as an excess pressure safety valve since if the pump pressure via line 1 exceeds the maximum safe value the valve will move sufficiently far to the right to open line 1 to exhaust. The valve also acts to prevent the pressure falling below a value of about 55 pounds per square inch, as it might do if a leak developed in coupling C, because at lower pressures it will not move far enough to uncover line 3. Under these conditions the filling of coupling C will be done by oil from the manual valve via lines 4, 5, 11, 21 and the non-return valve into line 3.

23.11 "Wilson" Automatic Gear Box

Wilson epicyclic gear boxes, such as have been described in the previous chapter, are produced in a fully automatic form. The author is indebted to Self Changing Gears, Ltd., of Coventry, for information and drawings. The gear box itself is as described in Section 22.5, but direct air or oil operation of the brake bands as described in Section 22.11 is always used and the valves controlling the flow of air or oil to the operating cylinders are themselves operated by solenoids or electro-magnets.

The vehicle speed factor in the control is obtained by driving a small electrical generator off the output shaft of the gear box. The voltage developed by this generator is then proportional to the vehicle speed and can be used to control the gear changes. The basic principle of the control is that the generator voltage is opposed by a constant voltage derived from the vehicle battery and that, when the generator voltage exceeds this battery voltage, it passes current through a relay which closes or opens contacts so as to produce the appropriate gear changes.

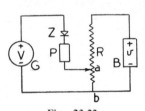

Fig. 23-22

The basic circuit is shown in Fig. 23-22. The battery B is connected across a potentiometer winding R, while the generator G and relay P are connected across a portion ab of this winding. If the voltage across ab due to the battery is greater than that due to the generator, then the battery tends to pass current from a through the relay P and the generator G, but this is prevented by the inclusion of a rectifier Z, which will permit current to flow only in one way, i.e. from the generator to the relay and thence to a. When the generator voltage rises and becomes higher than the battery voltage across ab, the generator will pass a current through the relay and the relay will be operated. A number of relays is used and they are connected to different tapping points a on the potentiometer so that they operate at different generator voltages and hence at different vehicle speeds.

The engine load factor is obtained from the accelerator pedal which operates a "throttle switch" which, in effect, varies the resistance of the potentiometer R (Fig. 23-22) and thus varies the voltages opposing the generator voltage; and this varies the vehicle speeds at which the relays will be operated.

The complete electrical circuit (with some simplifications) is shown in Fig. 23-23, where the various contacts that are controlled by the relays corresponding to P are shown in the positions they occupy when the vehicle is stationary. The control can be operated manually, by moving the selector from one position to another, or automatically by putting it in the position A. Manual control will first be dealt with.

With the selector in position 1 and with the main switch closed, current can flow from the battery to the magnet valve 1 and thus first gear will be engaged. Current will also flow through the selector to the generator field winding (XX) so that the generator will be excited and will generate a voltage as soon as its armature is rotated. Then, as the engine is speeded up, the vehicle will move off in first gear. At a very low vehicle speed the generator voltage will become high enough to operate the relay I and this will close the contacts i_1 and i_2 and open the contacts i_3. The closing of i_1 will connect the generator field winding direct to the battery so that the generator signal will not be interrupted when the selector is moved from position to position.

The closing of contacts i_2 enables second gear to be obtained by moving the selector to position 2, and the opening of contacts i_3 will prevent reverse gear from being obtained at too high a forward speed. Third and fourth gears cannot, however, be obtained at the low vehicle speed assumed since the contacts 3sa and 5sa are open. As the speed rises the relay 3P will be operated and will close the contacts 3p. This will energize the secondary relay 3S and this in turn will operate all the contacts 3s (thus 3sa, b and c will be closed and 3sd will be opened). Thus third gear can now be obtained when it is selected. At a higher vehicle speed the relay 4P will be operated and will energize the relay 4S, thus operating all the 4s contacts; 4sa, b and d will be closed and 4sc and e will be opened. The only effect of this will be that the opening of 4se will prevent first gear from being obtained even if it should be selected. At a still higher speed the relay 5P will be operated and the contacts 5S will be closed so as to energize the relay 5S and operate all the 5s contacts; 5sa, b and d being closed and 5sc and e being opened. The opening of 5se will prevent second gear from being obtained, and the closing of 5sb will enable fourth gear to be obtained whenever it may be selected.

If the throttle is opened beyond the idling position, then, when the vehicle speed falls, the actions described above will occur in reverse order and the various changes down may be obtained whenever the vehicle speed is suitable for the gear selected. If a gear is selected which is too low in relation to the vehicle speed, the next higher gear will be obtained.

525

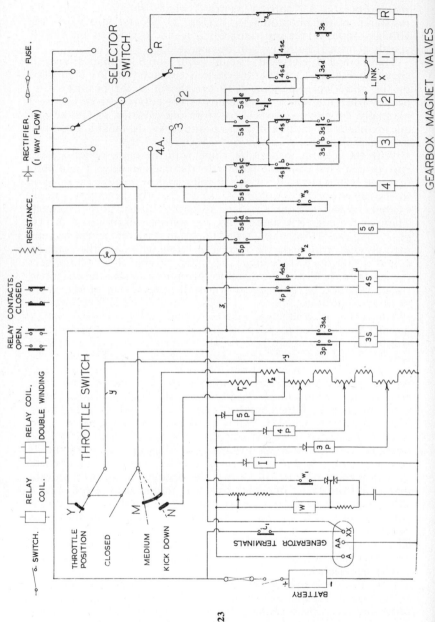

Fig. 23-23

23.12 Automatic Control

If the vehicle is at rest with the engine idling and the selector in the A position, the battery will be connected through the contacts 5sc, 4sc and 3sd to magnet valve 1 so that first gear will be engaged. (If the link X is changed so as to connect with magnet valve 2, starting will be in second gear.) As the vehicle gathers speed, the relay I will operate with the same results as in manual operation. Relay 3P will next operate so that all the 3s contacts will be operated. The opening of 3sd will cut off the current to magnet valve 1, and the closing of 3sc will pass current to magnet valve 2 so that second gear will be engaged. Rising vehicle speed will then cause the relay 4P to operate and the contacts 4s will be operated. The opening of 4sc disengages second gear and the closing of 4sb gives third gear. Finally relay 5P will be energized and the contacts 5s will be operated. The opening of 5sc will disengage third gear and the closing of 5sb will give fourth gear. As the vehicle speed falls, the above actions will occur in the opposite sense and the gears will change down in sequence until the starting gear is reached.

The vehicle speeds at which the various relays will be energized will be increased if the throttle is opened sufficiently to cause the contact M to be closed, since this will short-circuit the resistance r_1 and increase the battery voltage which the generator has to overcome. This effect will be enhanced if the throttle is opened wide so that the contact N is closed, thus short-circuiting the resistance r_2.

If the vehicle is moving at a speed such that the higher gears have been engaged and then the accelerator pedal is suddenly released as, for example, might be done to bring the vehicle to a standstill in traffic, then the closing of the contact Y will prevent all the various gears from being obtained one after the other until the starting gear is reached. Instead the gear actually engaged at the moment when the accelerator pedal is released will be retained until the vehicle speed has fallen to a value such that the engagement of the starting gear would be imperative, and then that gear would be engaged. This action is brought about as follows. The closing of the contact Y passes current via the line y to the line z and thus through the contacts 5sa and 4sa to the relays 5S and 4S so that, even if the relays 5P and 4P are de-energized, the secondary relays will still be energized and the gear in engagement will be retained. However, when the vehicle speed falls low enough to bring about the de-energizing of the relay 3P and the contact 3p opens, then the circuit through the contact Y will be broken and the relays 5S and 4S will be de-energized and the starting gear will be obtained.

The relay W is a safety device and operates only when the generator voltage falls very suddenly, as would happen if any failure occurred. When the relay W does operate, the contacts w_1, w_2 and w_3 are closed. The contact w_1 keeps the relay W energized, while the contact w_3 maintains the current supply to the relays 5S, 4S and 3S, and thus retains the gear that is in use in engagement. Contact w_2 lights a warning lamp to draw attention to the failure.

CHAPTER 24

Universal Joints

Principle of operation.   Constructional forms.   Flexible-ring joints.   Constant-velocity joints.

A UNIVERSAL joint is a form of connection between two shafts, whose axes intersect, whereby the rotation of one shaft about its own axis results in the rotation of the other shaft about its axis.

The principle on which the Hookes type of universal joint works is illustrated in Fig. 24-1.   The shaft A is formed into a fork at its end and pivoted between the prongs of this fork is a cross-piece C. The cross C can therefore pivot about the axis XX relatively to the shaft A.   The other shaft B is similarly forked and the other arms of the cross are pivoted between the prongs of this fork.   The shaft B can therefore pivot about the axis YY relatively to the cross C and, since the latter can pivot about the axis XX relatively to the shaft A the shaft B can assume any angular position relatively to shaft A.   Or from another point of view, if the shafts A and B are supported in bearings with their axes at an angle, then when the shaft A is turned about its axis the motion is communicated to the shaft B and it turns about its axis; the arms of the cross meanwhile oscillating in the prongs of the forks.

The axes XX and YY intersect at O and are perpendicular one to the other.   The axes of the arms of the cross C are also perpendicular to their respective shafts.   The axes of the shafts intersect at O, which point is the " centre " of the joint.

It does not matter how the pivoting action is obtained; all that is required is that the shaft B shall be able to pivot independently about two intersecting perpendicular axes such as XX and YY, relatively to the shaft A.

24.1   Constructional Forms of Universal Joints

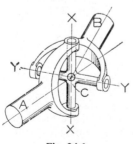

Fig. 24-1

There are several types of universal joint all working on the principle outlined above, but in motor cars and lorries the joints are of two principal forms. These may be called—

(1) " Cross " type.
(2) " Ring " type.

Examples of these are shown in Figs. 24-2 and 3.

A proprietary design of cross type joint is shown in Fig. 24-2.   The yoke members A are secured to the shafts that are connected by the joint and carry bushes B. These are positioned by the projecting lips C of the yokes, which fit machined portions of the bushes and by the keys D integral with the bushes and which fit in keyways formed in the yokes. The keys D transmit the drive and relieve the set screws E of all shearing stresses. The two yokes

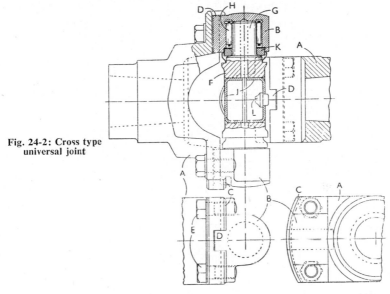

Fig. 24-2: Cross type universal joint

are coupled by the cross member F which consists of a central ring portion and four integral pins G. The ends of the latter bear on the bottoms of the bushes B thus centring the joint. Between the pins G and the bushes B are needle roller bearings H. The hole in the centre of the cross member F is closed by two pressings J and forms a reservoir for lubricant which reaches the bearings through holes drilled in the pins G. The cork washers K form a seal at the inner ends of the pins and also serve to retain the needle rollers when the joint is taken apart. A single filling of oil suffices for practically the whole life of the joint. Any excessive pressure in the reservoir which might lead to oil being forced out past the seals K is prevented by the relief valve L.

Fig. 24-3 shows a ring type joint. The member A is bolted to one shaft by its flange and the fork B is secured to the other shaft by splines. The two members are coupled by the ring C. This ring is made of two steel pressings each forming half the ring and being bolted together by the nuts on the trunnion portions of the four bushes D whose shape is clearly seen in the separate plan view. The pins of the fork member B fit in two of the bushes and the ends of the pin E, which is fixed in member A, fit in the other two

529

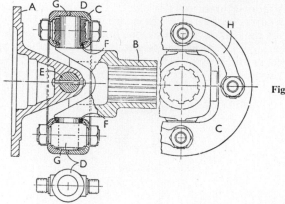

Fig. 24-3: " Ring " type
universal joint

bushes.   The space inside the ring forms a reservoir for oil which
may be introduced through a nipple not shown.   The joint between
the two halves of the ring is ground to form an oil-tight joint and
escape of oil at the points of entry of the pins is prevented by the
compressed cork washers F.   The shafts are centred relatively to
the ring by reason of the fitting of the pins on faces G accurately
machined inside the ring, and not by the cork washers.   The nuts
securing the ring are locked by a pair of tab washers H.

Another universal joint construction is shown in Fig. 24-4.   It
consists of a ball A having two grooves formed round it at right
angles.   In these grooves the forked ends of the shafts E and F fit.
Obviously when the joint is put together the shaft E can slide round
in its groove, thus turning about the axis XX.   Similarly the shaft F
can slide round in its groove, thus turning about the axis YY.
This type of joint was used at one time in front wheel brake linkages.
The arrangement of the shaft bearings has to be such that the shafts
cannot move away from the centre of the ball, otherwise the joint
would come apart.   It is not suitable for use in the transmission.

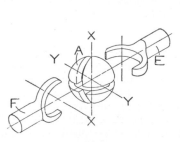

Fig. 24-4

Fig. 24-5

24.2 Flexible-ring Joints

A joint that acts by the flexure of a flexible ring is much used to connect shafts between which the angular displacement will not be very great. Such a joint is shown in Fig. 24-5. The shafts are provided with three-armed spiders, the arms of which are bolted to the opposite faces of a flexible ring, the arms of one spider being arranged mid-way between the arms of the other. The flexible ring is usually made of one or more rings of rubberized fabric made in a special way so as to provide the necessary strength. A number of thin steel discs is sometimes used instead of the fabric rings. When the shafts are revolving about axes which are not coincident there is a continuous flexing of the ring. This type of joint has several advantages over the universal joints described above, the principal of which are the elimination of the need for lubrication and cheapness of manufacture. The joint cannot cope with such large angular displacements as the universal joints and when the torque to be transmitted is large it becomes very bulky.

Care has to be taken in assembling the joint to ensure that the shafts shall run truly without wobble. Practically the only attention required by these joints is periodical inspection to see that the bolts have not become slack.

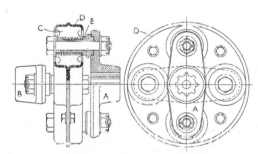

Fig. 24-6: Layrub flexible joint

24.3 Rubber-bushed Flexible Joints

Joints of this kind are now widely used and there are several forms of them, three being shown in Figs. 24-6, 7 and 8. The first of these is the original Layrub; it is basically a " ring " type of joint. The shafts that are connected by the joint carry the two-armed spiders A and B projecting from which are bolts carrying special rubber bushes C. These bushes are housed inside the coupling ring D which is made of two exactly similar steel pressings bolted together. The rubber bushes by distorting slightly enable any misalignment of the shafts to be accommodated. Angular misalignments up to 15° can be allowed for but generally the misalignment is limited to about half that amount. The joint can also accommodate a considerable amount (up to $\frac{1}{2}$ in) of axial movement of the one shaft relative to the other and when two of them are used, one at each end of a propeller shaft, it is usually

531

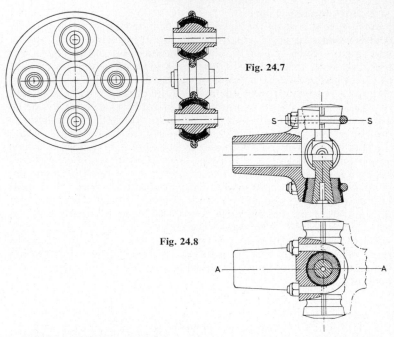

Fig. 24.7

Fig. 24.8

possible to dispense with the sliding joint that is essential when all-metal joints are used.

Since the only connection between the shafts is through the rubber bushes, the joints also assist in smoothing out vibrations; this property has been used to give a flexible clutch plate in a single-plate clutch the driven plate being connected to the clutch centre by four Layrub bushes.

The bushes are made with concave ends as shown in order to keep the internal stresses in them approximately uniform and to increase their flexibility. They are made with a metallic gauze insert on their insides and are forced on to the sleeves E which are made somewhat larger than the holes in the bushes. The outside diameters of the bushes are also greater than the diameters of the pockets in the ring D in which the bushes are housed and so when the coupling is assembled the bushes are compressed to such an extent that although when the joint flexes the distance between the sleeve E and the ring D may increase on one side the rubber remains in compression and is never in tension. The sleeves E have spigots which fit into holes in the spiders so that the bolts are not called upon to transmit the torque and are not subjected to any shearing.

Fig. 24-7 shows a design of the Metalastik company in which the rubber bushes are bonded to the spherical pins and are compressed when the two metal pressings which form the ring of the

532

joint are assembled together. These pressings are held together by spinning the lips of one of them over those of the other. The design in Fig. 24-8 is basically a " cross " type of joint and is made by the Moulton company. The rubber bushes are bonded on the inside to the tapered portions of the arms of the cross and on the outside to steel shells. The latter fit into depressions formed in the flanges of the joint and are held in place by stirrups which are bolted up to the flanges.

24.4 Constant Velocity Joints

The Hookes type of universal joint suffers from a disadvantage which is obviated in some other types of joint. It is that supposing one of the shafts connected by a Hookes joint is revolving at an absolutely constant speed then the other shaft will not revolve at a constant speed but with a speed that is, during two parts of each revolution, slightly greater and, during the other two parts of the revolution, slightly less than the constant speed of the first shaft. The magnitude of this fluctuation in speed depends on the angle between the axes of the two shafts, being zero when that angle is zero but becoming considerable when the angle is large. This disadvantage becomes of practical importance in front wheel driven vehicles and in the drives to independently sprung wheels where the angle between the shafts may be as large as 40°. It can be obviated by using two Hookes joints arranged as shown in Fig. 24-9 (a) and (b), the intermediate shaft being arranged so that it makes

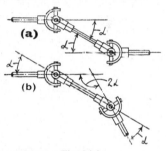

Fig. 24-9

equal angles with the first and third shafts and the fork pin axes of the intermediate shaft being placed parallel to each other. The irregularity introduced by one joint is then cancelled out by the equal and opposite irregularity introduced by the second joint. Examples of front wheel drives using this arrangement are shown in Figs. 31–30 and 31–32. A slightly different arrangement using the same principle is given in Fig. 34–11.

Constant velocity joints are joints which do not suffer from the above disadvantage but in which the speeds of the shafts connected by the joint are absolutely equal at every instant throughout each revolution. Although such joints have been known for very many years they have not been used to any extent until recently. Several are now, however, being manufactured in quantities and are being increasingly used in motor vehicles.

The Tracta joint which is manufactured in England by Bendix Ltd., is shown in Fig. 24-10, from which the construction will be clear. The joint is a true constant velocity joint but the theory of it is beyond the scope of this book and those who are interested in this

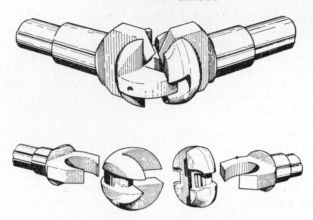

Fig. 24-10: Bendix "Tracta" universal joint

theory and in those of the other joints described below, are referred to an article by one of the authors in *Automobile Engineer*, Vol. 37, No. 1. Another true constant velocity joint, the Weiss, which is used to a considerable extent in America, where it is manufactured by the Bendix Products Corporation, is shown in Fig. 24-11. It consists of two members each with two fingers or arms in the sides of which are formed semi-circular grooves. When the two members are assembled the fingers of the one fit in between the fingers of the

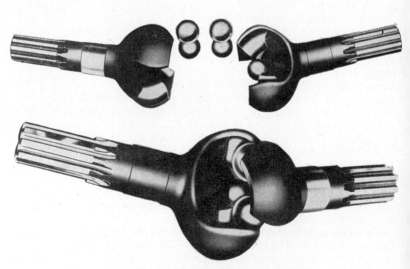

Fig. 24-11: Bendix "Weiss" universal joint

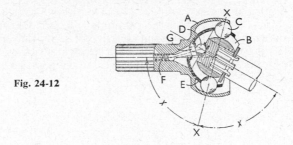

Fig. 24-12

other and balls are inserted in the grooves of the fingers and form the driving connection between them. The formation of the grooves is such that the balls lie always in a plane making equal angles with the axes of the shafts connected by the joint, this being a fundamental condition that must be satisfied if the drive is to be a constant velocity drive. This joint has the property that the shafts connected by it may be moved apart axially slightly without affecting the action of the joint and this axial motion is accommodated by a rolling of the balls along the grooves in the fingers of the joint members and so takes place with the minimum of friction.

A third example is shown in Fig. 24-12. It is the Rzeppa (pronounced Sheppa) and it consists of a cup member A with a number of semi-circular grooves formed inside it and a ball member B with similar grooves formed on the outside. Balls C fit half in the grooves A and half in B and provide the driving connection. For true constant velocity operation the balls must be arranged to lie always in a plane making equal angles with the axes of rotation of the members A and B. This is ensured by the control link D and the cage E. The former has spherical ends one of which engages a recess in the end of the member B while the other is free to slide along a hole formed inside A; the link is kept in place by the spring F. The spherical enlargement G of the link engages a hole formed in the cage E which has other holes in which the balls C fit. When the shaft B swings through an angle relatively to A the link D causes the cage E and the plane XX of the balls C to swing through half that angle and thus the balls are caused to occupy the required positions for the correct functioning of the joint.

24.5 Garrington Joint

A new design of constant-velocity universal joint has been produced by Messrs. Garringtons, Ltd., of Bromsgrove, Worcestershire, and is shown in Fig. 24-13. The construction comprises two forked members, somewhat resembling the forks of the Weiss joint, but instead of employing balls to connect the arms of these forks, use is made of semi-cylindrical pads which are free to pivot in seats formed in the arms. The pads of one arm slide relative to the pads

535

of the mating arm; they are held in place during assembly by spring clips. The joint will accommodate axial movement between the shafts it connects without detriment to its universal action. It is claimed that the joint will work at greater angles than other forms of joint and that, size for size, it will transmit greater torques.

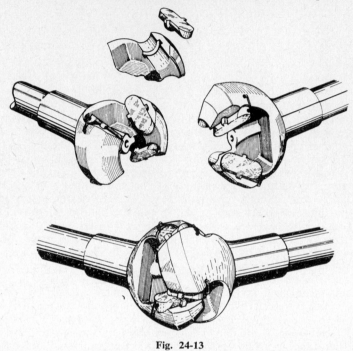

Fig. 24-13

CHAPTER 25

The Back Axle

Live rear axles.   The final drive.   Torque reaction and thrust systems.

IT has been seen in Chapter 18 that the mechanical transmissions in present-day use are of three main types.   The systems are similar up to the rear of the gear box, so that the clutches and gear boxes described in the previous pages could be used equally well in each system.   It now becomes necessary, however, to consider the systems separately, and we shall take the most important one, the " live " axle system, first.

25.1   Live Back Axles

A live axle is one that rotates or houses shafts that rotate, while a dead axle is one that does not rotate or house rotating shafts. The live axles used in motor cars have two distinct functions to fulfil, namely—

(1) To act as an axle beam upon the ends of which the road wheels can revolve and through which the weight of the body and load can be transmitted, via the springs and the road wheels, to the ground.

(2) To act as a housing and support for the final drive, the differential and the shafts that transmit the drive to the road wheels.

In view of this last function it will be found that the majority of live axles are of hollow or tubular construction.

25.2   Final Drive

It has been mentioned that at some point in the transmission the drive has to be turned round through 90° and also reduced in speed in the ratio of from 4 to 1 in cars up to 10 to 1 in lorries. These two functions are performed by gearing in the back axle. When the reduction in speed is not very great, say, up to about 7 to 1, it is usually obtained in one step.   The axle is then a " single reduction " axle.   When the speed reduction is large it is usually performed in two or more steps giving " double " and " triple " reductions.   The first step of the reduction almost always consists of either a bevel pinion and wheel, or a worm and worm-wheel, so that in either case the drive is turned round through 90° as is required.   We will consider the construction of double reduction axles later on, confining our attention at first to single reduction types.   All the remarks that will be made about " torque reaction " and " thrust," however, apply just as much to the double reduction axle as to the single reduction one, in fact, they apply to every form of live axle.

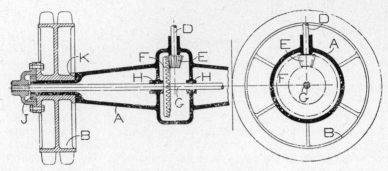

Fig. 25-1 : Single reduction axle

25.3 Single Reduction Live Axles

The general arrangement of the single reduction live axle is shown in Fig. 25-1. A hollow casing A carries on its ends the road wheels B. The weight of the body and load is supported by the casing A through the springs which are attached to the body and to the axle in a manner which will be described later. The casing in turn is supported at its ends by the road wheels. It therefore acts as a beam and is subjected to a bending action as is shown in Fig. 25-2, where the forces P are the supporting forces supplied by the road wheels, and the forces W are the body load, applied to the casing through the springs. The casing has to be stiff enough to withstand this bending action without undue flexure.

Supported in bearings in the casing A is a short shaft D integral with which is a bevel pinion E. The shaft D is coupled by means of a universal or flexible joint, outside the casing, to the propeller shaft and hence to the mainshaft of the gear box. Inside the casing the bevel pinion E meshes with, and drives, a bevel wheel F which is fixed to a transverse shaft G. This shaft is supported in bearings HH in the casing and is bolted to the hubs of the road wheels B at its outer ends. Obviously, when the pinion shaft D is turned by the propeller shaft the drive is transmitted through the bevel wheel to the transverse shaft G and hence to the road wheels. The road wheels are kept in place on the casing A in the end direction by nuts J and the shoulders K of the casing. The final drive shown is a bevel one, but worm gearing is also used, as will be seen later. The differential has been omitted, as it sometimes actually is, to simplify the construction, in order to bring out the principles involved.

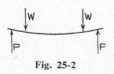

Fig. 25-2

25.4 Torque Reaction

In Fig. 25-1 the propeller shaft applies a torque to the shaft D and this torque, increased in the same ratio as the speed is reduced, is transmitted to the shaft G. Now it should be clear that if the road wheels B are fixed, then on turning the shaft D the pinion E will have to roll round the bevel wheel F taking with it the casing. There is a tendency for the same action to occur when the road wheels are being driven by the shaft D. The torque producing this action is the equal and opposite reaction to the driving torque which is applied to the road wheels. This phenomenon is called torque reaction, and the tendency of the axle casing to turn in the opposite direction to that in which the road wheels are being driven has to be opposed; otherwise, of course, the propeller shaft, which connects the shaft D to the gear box shaft, would be subjected to a heavy bending action which it could not support.

Now, we can overcome this tendency of the axle casing to turn by attaching an arm to the casing and securing the front end of this arm to the frame of the car; and in all cars there is some member which acts in this manner. The actual arrangements used will be described later, after another phenomenon has been dealt with.

25.5 Driving Thrust

The action of the driving wheels has been considered previously, and the way in which the driving thrust or tractive effort arises has been explained. This tractive effort, driving the road wheels and axle casing forwards, has to be communicated to the frame and body of the vehicle. The axle has, as it were, to push the frame and body along and so must be connected to the frame by a connection that can transmit the forward thrust. Again, the most convenient construction is some form of arm attached to the axle casing and to the frame, and there will always be a member or members acting in this way. These members are known as thrust members or radius rods.

25.6 Torque and Thrust Member Arrangements

In addition to the torque reaction and the driving thrust, there will frequently be sideways forces which have to be transmitted from the body to the wheels. The connections between the axle and the frame must therefore be capable of dealing with four separate actions, namely:

(i) the weight of the body;
(ii) the torque reaction;
(iii) the driving thrust;
(iv) the sideways forces.

It has been pointed out that arms attached to the axle casing and anchored to the frame form a convenient method of dealing with the torque reaction and the thrust, and the springs are, of course, expressly designed to take the weight of the body. Certain forms of spring, however, can also be made to deal with the other actions so that separate members may not be needed for them. Numerous arrangements of the connections between the axle and the frame have been employed at various times but only four of them are now used at all extensively. They are as follows:

(1) The springs act also as torque members, and as thrust members, and transmit the sideways forces.

(2) The springs act also as thrust members and deal with the sideways forces, but a separate torque member is used.

(3) The springs deal also with the sideways forces, but the torque reaction and driving thrust are dealt with by separate members.

(4) The springs transmit only the weight of the body and the torque reaction, driving thrust and the sideways forces are dealt with by separate members.

In considering these arrangements it must be borne in mind that the axle will rarely move up and down parallel to the frame. Generally one wheel will be going over a bump or into a hole while the other remains on the level. The axle then assumes an angular position relatively to the frame, and the connection between the various torque members, thrust members and springs, and the frame must be such that this will not involve undue stresses in the various components.

25.7 Springs Act Also as Torque and Thrust Members

This system, which is known as the " Hotchkiss drive," is the simplest of the systems and is the most widely used. The arrangement of the parts is shown in Fig. 25-3. The springs A are bolted rigidly to the axle casing B and at their front ends are pivoted on pins which, being carried in brackets bolted to the frame, are part of it. At their rear ends the springs are connected to the frame by

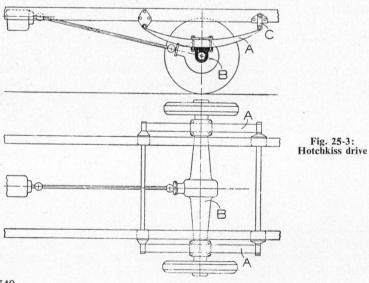

Fig. 25-3:
Hotchkiss drive

swinging links or shackles C. It should be clear that the axle casing cannot turn under the torque reaction without causing the springs to flex in the manner shown (exaggerated) in Fig. 25-4. Since the springs offer considerable resistance to this kind of deformation the torque reaction is overcome. It should also be clear that the front half of the spring will transmit the driving thrust to the frame.

Fig. 25-4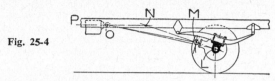

Now although the springs are able to deal with the torque reaction in the manner indicated they cannot do so without flexing to a slight extent, and this necessitates the employment of two universal joints in the propeller shaft. Referring to Fig. 25-4, when the axle casing turns slightly the axis of the bevel pinion shaft moves to LN and no longer passes through the centre of the front universal joint O. As the propeller shaft is attached to that joint it would be bent unless a second joint were provided at M, when it could assume the position OM and remain straight.

Again, when the axle moves upward relatively to the frame it has to move in a circle (approximately) whose centre is the pivot pin at the front end of the spring. The propeller shaft, however, must move in a circle whose centre is the front universal joint. Since these two centres do not coincide the distance between the front universal joint and the pinion shaft of the axle will alter as the axle moves up or down, and to accommodate this a sliding joint has to be provided somewhere in the propeller shaft. Usually one of the universal joint forks is left free to slide on its splined shaft or a universal joint of the " pot " type is used.

Some difficulty may be experienced in seeing how the axle can assume an angular position relatively to the frame (in the end view), since the springs are pivoted on pins at their ends and bolted rigidly to the axle at the centre. As a fact, if the various members were rigid the axle could not assume such a position. Those members, however, are by no means rigid and small deflections take place in the springs and in the frame. which in conjunction with the clearances which necessarily exist in the spring pivots, allow the axle to assume angular positions to the extent ordinarily necessary; the arrangement is not suitable for vehicles that have to operate on very rough ground. Special forms of spring to frame connections are sometimes used to eliminate the twisting of the springs.

25.8 The Hotchkiss Drive Plus Torque Member

One disadvantage of the Hotchkiss drive is that if the springs are made sufficiently stiff to take the torque reaction without undue flexure they will generally be somewhat too stiff to give the best

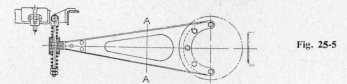

Fig. 25-5

springing action. The springing qualities have, to some extent, to
be sacrificed to simplicity of construction. This sacrifice need not
be made if a separate torque member is used, although some of the
simplicity of construction is then lost.

The system is now used very little; it is similar to the Hotchkiss
drive, but since the springs are no longer required to take the torque
reaction they no longer need to be bolted rigidly to the axle casing
at their centres. Instead they are bolted to separate spring seats
which are free to turn on the axle casing. The springs are pivoted
to the frame at their front ends and shackled to the frame at their
rear ends, and the propeller shaft requires two universal joints and
a sliding joint as before.

The torque member takes various forms, the commonest of
which is a triangular shaped steel pressing such as is shown in
Fig. 25-5. Whatever its form it is bolted rigidly to the axle casing
at the rear and is prevented from moving up or down at the front
usually by means of a shackle which couples it to the frame. The
shackle permits the front end of the torque member to move slightly
in the fore and aft direction, which is necessary because the axle
does not move up and down in a true circle when the springs flex,
and so the front end of the torque member cannot be made a
fixed pivot.

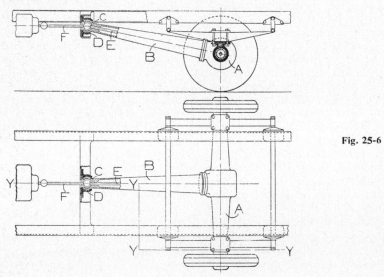

Fig. 25-6

Occasionally, two such torque members are used. Also, in order to reduce the shocks that would otherwise be felt when, for example, the clutch is engaged too rapidly, the front end of the torque member is often allowed to have small vertical movements by using a spring anchorage such as is shown.

Torque members are sometimes made tubular and then usually surround the propeller shaft. They may then be shackled to the frame in the ordinary way, but occasionally they are allowed to bear on the propeller shaft near to the front universal joint, a ball bearing being provided. The vertical force which has to be applied to the torque member to prevent the axle casing from turning now has to be taken by the front universal joint.

Although strictly the spring seats should be pivotally mounted on the axle casing as stated above, some makers consider it better to bolt the springs rigidly to the axle casing, thereby avoiding an awkward lubricating point and cheapening the construction slightly.

25.9 Single Torque-Thrust Member, the Springs Being Separate Members

This construction, which is still occasionally used, is shown in Fig. 25-6. Bolted to the axle casing A and surrounding the propeller shaft is a tubular member B, the front end C of which is spherical and fits in a cup D bolted to a cross member of the frame (or to

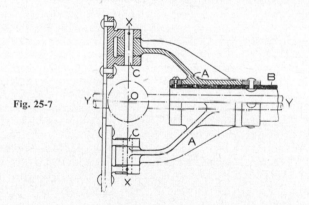

Fig. 25-7

the back of the gear box). The springs are bolted to spring seats that are pivoted on the axle casing, and at each end are shackled to the frame. Clearly the member B will transmit the thrust from the axle to the frame and will also take the torque reaction. Since the centre line of the bevel pinion shaft will always pass through the centre of the spherical cup, if the propeller shaft E is connected to the gear box shaft F by a universal joint situated exactly at the centre of that cup, no other universal joint will be needed and no sliding joint will be necessary, since both pinion shaft and propeller shaft will move about the same centre, namely, that of the spherical cup, when the axle moves up or down. The springs now have to be shackled at each end instead of at their rear ends only, because since the axle has to move about the centre of the spherical cup, if the front ends of the springs were merely pivoted to the frame then the front halves of the springs would not be able to flatten out when the axle moved upwards.

An alternative to the ball and cup construction is shown in Fig. 25-7. The tubular member B is again bolted to the axle casing at its rear end, but at the front it has pivoted on it a forked member A which is pivoted on pins C carried by brackets riveted to a cross member of the frame. By pivoting on the pins C the axle can move about the axis XX, both rear wheels moving up or down together, while by the tube B turning in the bracket A about the axis YY one rear wheel can move up without the other. The universal joint must have its centre at O, the intersection of the axes XX, YY.

In this system the spring seats are sometimes pivoted to the axle casing by means of *spherical* pivots. This relieves the springs of twisting stresses when the axle assumes angular positions relatively to the frame. The same advantage was sought in some early designs by attaching the spring shackles to the frame on a pivot whose axis was parallel to the centre line of the frame.

25.10 Transverse Radius Rods

In the system described in the previous article the sideways forces are transmitted to the axle from the frame by the springs, but when it is desired to use coil springs or torsion springs or air bellows as springs, this is no longer feasible, since such springs cannot deal with these forces. In such cases it is usual to employ a transverse radius rod which is arranged to lie approximately parallel to the wheel axis and which is pivoted at one end to the axle and at the other end to the frame or body structure. Such rods are sometimes called " Panhard rods " and two common arrangements are shown in Figs. 25-8 and 25-9. In the first of these the rod A is placed above the axle to which it is pivoted at the middle, while in the second the rod is placed behind (sometimes in front of) the axle and the connection with the axle is near the road wheel. This

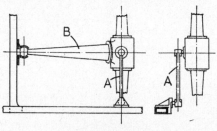

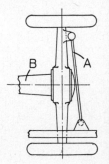

Fig. 25-8 (*above*)

Fig. 25-9 (*right*)

enables a longer rod to be used, but it is not usually feasible to place the rod exactly parallel to the wheel axis as can be done in the first arrangement. The joints at the ends of the rod should be ball and socket joints to allow for the relative motions that occur, but when the axle motions are not large, rubber bushes can often provide the necessary freedom. In the figures it has been assumed that a torque-thrust member B is provided, but occasionally transverse-radius rods are used with other methods of dealing with the torque and thrust.

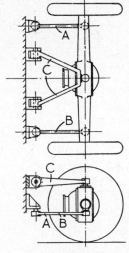

Fig. 25-10

25.11   Use of Three Radius Rods

The principle of a system which is sometimes used is shown in Fig. 25-10. Radius rods A and B are placed parallel to the centre line of the vehicle and at the ends of the axle, while a wishbone-shaped member C is placed at the centre.   The rods A and B are provided with ball and socket joints at both ends, while the wishbone member is pivoted to the frame on a transverse pin joint and to the axle by a ball and socket joint.   The wishbone member deals with all the sideways forces, while all three rods between them deal with the driving and braking thrusts and torques.   The torques are transmitted to the frame by tension and compression forces in the rods.   Thus the driving torque reaction (which would act in a clockwise direction as seen in the end view) produces a tension force in the member C and compressive forces in the rods A and B, while the brake torque produces a compressive force in the wishbone and tension forces in the rods A and B.   The functions performed by these rods are sometimes performed by the springs, for example, when quarter elliptic springs are used; but, since the springs cannot be pivoted to the frame by ball and socket joints, they may take some of the side forces even though ball and socket joints are used to connect their ends to the axle.

If the upper radius rod of Fig. 25-10 is made a simple link with a single pivot connection to the frame, then a transverse radius rod must be provided to position the axle sideways.   These arrangements are fairly common when air or coil springs are used.

In the Mk. II Jaguar cars full-cantilever springs pivoted at their rear ends to the axle are used.   These deal with the thrust and in conjunction with longitudinally disposed radius rods placed above the axle deal also with the torque reactions.   A short transverse radius rod positions the axle sideways.   Rubber bushes are used at the pivots and connections.   The arrangement is similar in principle to the Scammell suspension shown in Fig. 34-19.

545

CHAPTER 26

The Differential

Its object and principle of operation.   Bevel and spur wheel types.   Differential locks.   Z-F differential.

THE differential is an arrangement that enables one shaft to drive two other shafts with equal efforts, that is, torques, although those other shafts may be revolving at unequal speeds. The principle of the differential is really very simple, being that of the ordinary weighing beam.   If a scale-beam is fulcrumed at its centre and loads are applied at its ends, then if the beam remains stationary or swings with uniform velocity the loads applied to its ends must be equal.

In Fig. 26-1 is shown a differential in place in the back axle of a car.   It consists of a drum-shaped casing A which is carried in ball bearings BB in the axle casing so that it is free to revolve about the axis XX, which is the axis of the road wheels.   Fixed to the casing A is a crown wheel C which is driven by the bevel pinion D.

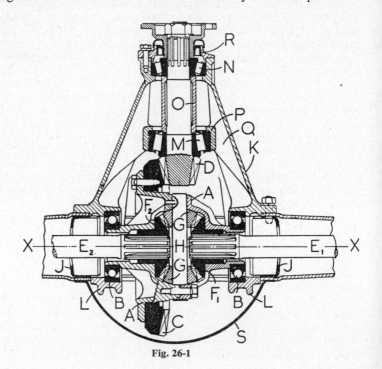

Fig. 26-1

The arrangement is similar to that of Fig. 25-1, except that the crown wheel is fixed to the casing A instead of to a cross shaft connected to the road wheels. In place of that cross shaft there are now two " differential " or " drive " shafts E_1 E_2, which are connected at their outer ends to the road wheels. At their inner ends they pass through the bosses of the differential case A in which they are quite free to turn. Inside the differential case the shafts E_1 E_2 carry the bevel wheels F_1 F_2 with which the bevel pinions GG mesh. The pinions G

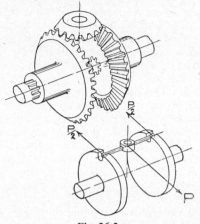

Fig. 26-2

are free to turn on the pin H fixed in the differential case. The arrangement of the gears F_1 F_2 and G is shown in perspective in Fig. 26-2.

It should be clear that if the differential case is held fixed and the wheel F_1 is turned in the forwards direction at, say, 2 r.p.m. then the wheel F_2 will be turned backwards at 2 r.p.m., since it is equal in size to F_1.

These motions are relative to the differential case and they will not be affected by any motion of that case.

If, therefore, the differential case is revolving at, say, 200 r.p.m. in the forwards direction and the wheel F_1 is still turning at 2 r.p.m. forwards relatively to the differential case, the wheel F_2 will still be turning at 2 r.p.m. backwards relatively to the differential case.

The actual speed of the wheel F_1 will then be 202 r.p.m. because its forward motion of 2 r.p.m. relatively to the differential case is added to the forwards motion of 200 r.p.m. of that case. The actual speed of the wheel F_2 will be 198 r.p.m. because its backwards motion of 2 r.p.m. relatively to the differential case is subtracted from the forwards motion of 200 r.p.m. of that case.

This is the action that occurs when a car moves in a circle; the road wheels are constrained to move at different speeds and do so by virtue of one wheel speeding up and going faster than the differential case while the other slows down and goes an equal amount slower than the differential case. The speed of the differential case is thus the mean of the road wheel speeds. When the car moves in a straight line the road wheels turn at the same speed as the differential case, and the differential pinions do not have to turn on their pins at all.

The above description should make it clear how the road wheels can turn at different speeds; it remains to show that when so doing

547

they are driven with equal torques. In Fig. 26-2 the bevel wheels are shown replaced by discs having notches in their peripheries. Lying with its ends in these notches is a beam. If a force P is applied to the centre of the beam in a direction tangential to the discs as shown, then if the beam does not turn about the vertical axis, or if it turns about that axis with uniform velocity, the forces at the ends of the beam must be equal and each will be equal to $P/2$. The reactions of the forces acting on the ends of the beam act on the discs, hence equal forces are applied to the discs at equal distances from their axes, and therefore the twisting moments or torques acting on the discs are equal.

It should readily be seen that the bevel pinion acts in a manner precisely similar to the beam. Hence the torques transmitted to the drive shafts are equal and each will be equal to half the torque applied to the differential case by the final drive. In the actual differential the force P appears as a pressure between the bevel pinion and its pin while the forces $P/2$ appear as pressures between the teeth of the bevel pinion and the bevel wheels.

26.1 Spur Differential

The differential described above is called a bevel differential, because it uses bevel wheels. There is another form which utilizes spur wheels. Such a differential is shown in Fig. 26-3. The wheels A, B are splined to the drive shafts that drive the road wheels. Meshing with the wheel A is a spur pinion E_1, whose teeth extend nearly across the gap between the wheels A and B. The spur pinion F_1 meshes in a similar way with the wheel B, and at the centre the two pinions mesh together. The pinions are carried

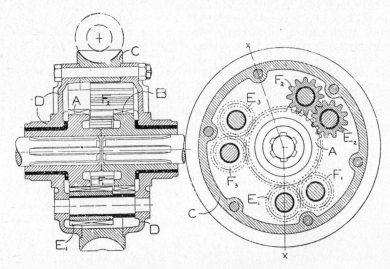

Fig. 26-3: Spur type differential

on pins which are supported by the ends of the differential case, which in this design is formed of the worm wheel C of the final drive and two end cover plates DD. It should be clear that if the differential case is held fixed and the wheel A is turned in, say, the clockwise direction, then the pinion E_1 will be turned in a counter-clockwise direction, the pinion F_1 in a clockwise direction and the wheel B in the counter-clockwise direction. Hence, if one of the differential wheels goes faster than the differential case, the other differential wheel will go an equal amount slower, just as in the bevel type.

As regards the equality of the torques, the torque on the wheel A is due to the pressure of the teeth of the pinion E_1. This pressure tends to make the pinion E_1 revolve on its pin, and this tendency is opposed by a pressure between the teeth of the two pinions at the centre. This last pressure tends to make the pinion F_1 revolve on its pin, and this tendency is opposed by the pressure between the teeth of the pinion F_1 and the wheel B. If the pinion E_1 (and therefore the pinion F_1 also) is at rest relatively to, or if it is revolving uniformly on, its pin then the two pressures acting on it must be equal. Hence, all the pressures between the teeth of the wheels A and B and the pinions E_1 and F_1 are the same, and hence the torques acting on the wheels A and B are equal. Three pairs of pinions are provided as shown.

26.2 Friction in Differentials

In the consideration given to the torques transmitted to the two drive shafts it has been assumed that the various wheels and pinions can revolve without any friction on their pins, but this is neither possible nor desirable. The friction that is present may destroy the equality of the torques transmitted to the drive shafts, and the greater the friction the greater the possible inequality of the torques. Now, if one of the road wheels gets on to a patch of greasy road it may lose its grip, and any torque that is applied to it will simply cause it to spin round. Under these conditions the only torque that can be transmitted to that wheel without causing it to spin is the small torque required to overcome the friction in the wheel bearings, and the small friction between the wheel and the ground. But since the differential equalizes the torques transmitted it follows that only the same small torque can be transmitted to the other road wheel, and although that wheel may have a perfect grip of the road, the grip cannot be utilized. If, however, a large amount of friction is present in the differential, then a larger torque could be transmitted to the gripping wheel than to the slipping wheel, and the grip of that wheel could be utilized. With this object differentials are sometimes made intentionally with a large amount of friction.

The other method of overcoming the difficulty of a slipping wheel is the provision of a differential lock. This puts the differential out of action altogether, and then the whole torque applied

549

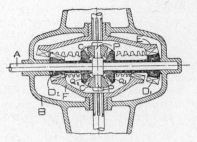

Fig. 26-4

to the crown wheel by the bevel pinion can be transmitted to the wheel that retains its grip of the ground. Differential locks act either by clutching one or both of the differential wheels to the differential case by means of dog-tooth clutches, or by locking the differential pinions so that they cannot revolve on their pins. Differential locks are not used on passenger cars or light lorries, but a number of makes of heavy lorry fit them and they are generally fitted to half-track machines.

Instead of using a differential the drive shafts are occasionally driven through one-way ratchets and when the vehicle moves in a circle the outer ratchet is overridden. This arrangement avoids any trouble from a slipping wheel but does not give equality of drive between the wheels. For driving in reverse, means of putting the ratchets out of action must be provided.

26.3   Another Arrangement of the Bevel Final Drive

The bevel final drive is sometimes arranged in a different manner from that described previously, generally because some other difference in axle construction necessitates the change. The principle of this other method is shown in Fig. 26-4. The propeller shaft is coupled to the shaft A which passes right across the centre portion of the axle casing B in which it is supported. At the centre of the axle the shaft A is enlarged and formed into pins PP to carry the differential pinions CC. These mesh with the differential wheels $Q_1 Q_2$, which are integral with the bevel pinions $D_1 D_2$, of which D_1 meshes with the large bevel wheel E and D_2 with the smaller bevel wheel F. The bevel wheels E and F are supported in the axle casing and are splined on to the shafts which drive the road wheels.

Of course, the gear ratio between D_1 and E is the same as the ratio between D_2 and F. The action of the differential is just the same as in the conventional axle, but the reduction of speed now occurs between the differential and the road wheels instead of between the propeller shaft and the differential case. The differential therefore runs at a higher speed than the road wheels, enabling smaller wheels to be used in it.

It should also be clear that it is quite possible to have the axes of the shafts inclined to each other in the end view, and advantage has been taken of this feature to arch the back axle casing and to tilt the rear wheels in order to reduce the overhang on the axle and to bring the road wheels perpendicular to the curved surface of a cambered road. Arched back axles are not now used, and the form of final drive described is uncommon.

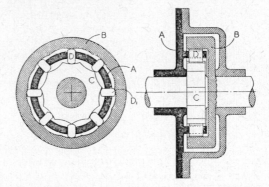

Fig. 26-5

26.4 Z-F Differential

This device is designed to permit the half-shafts to rotate at different speeds when the adhesion of the road wheels forces them to do so but to transmit torque to one wheel only if the adhesion of the other wheel should be unduly low. Tests have shown that it is effective to some extent and it has been fairly widely used by German designers and by one American maker. It is made in two forms which are shown diagrammatically in Figs. 26-5 and 6. It consists of four main elements, the driving member A to which is fixed the crown wheel of the final drive and which corresponds to the case of an ordinary differential, two cam members B and C fixed respectively to the right- and left-hand half-shafts and which correspond to the differential wheels, and of a set of plungers D free to slide in slots machined in the member A and which correspond to the differential pinions. Supposing the member A to be fixed and the member B to be rotated slowly clockwise then the cam surfaces of B will force the plungers D to slide to and fro in their slots but because the cam member B has a different number of cam surfaces from C the latter will be forced to revolve in the opposite direction to B. This will be seen by considering the plunger D_1, clearly clockwise rotation of B will force this plunger inwards and this will clearly force the cam C anti-clockwise. If now all three members are given an additional clockwise rotation then it will be seen that the members B and C will be rotating respectively faster and slower than the member A as in a true differential. The difference in speeds between the members B and C and the member A will not be equal in magnitude however.

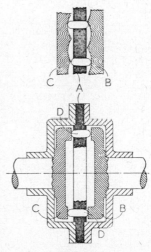

Fig. 26-6

When the member B makes one revolution relative to A the member C will make 13/11 revolution since B has 13 lobes and C only 11. There is, however, considerable friction between the plungers D and the member A and cam surfaces so that while the device gives the difference in speed necessary for cornering it enables a torque to be transmitted to one cam member even though the resistance to the other cam member is very low.

26.5 Thornton Powr-Lok Differential

This is manufactured by the Dana Corporation of Toledo, Ohio, U.S.A., and its construction is shown in Fig. 26-7. The crown wheel of the final drive is fixed to a flange of the differential case A, which is carried in bearings in the axle case in the usual manner. Differential wheels are splined to the ends D of the half-shafts and mesh with four differential pinions as usual. The pinions, however, are now carried on two separate cross-pins B and C, instead of on a four-armed spider, and the cross-pins are not fixed in the differential case at their ends, but are merely located in Vee-shaped grooves, as shown in the view at the top of the figure. The grooves for locating the cross-pin C face the opposite way to the grooves that locate the cross-pin B.

The differential pinions are formed with cylindrical necks which bear against disc-shaped members F and H; between these and the ends of the differential case the plates of clutches G and J are situated. The outer plates of these clutches are provided with projections, or splines, which engage with the differential case, and the inner plates are splined to the hubs of the discs F and H, which themselves are splined to the half-shafts.

Considering the pin B, the driving forces between it and the differential case are exerted between the faces E, and thus have components which tend to push the pin to the left. This, in turn, causes the necks of the pinions to bear on the face of the disc F and

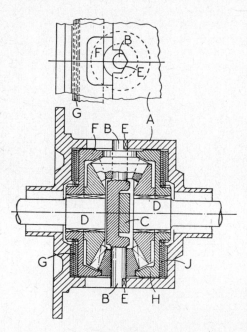

Fig. 26-7

thus to lock the clutch G. Similarly, the pin C is pushed to the right and locks the clutch J.

Thus under normal, straight-ahead driving conditions, the clutches G and J transmit a considerable part of the driving torques applied to the half-shafts, and this action also occurs even if one of the wheels slips on the ground. Thus this differential overcomes to a considerable extent the chief disadvantage of the conventional type. When rounding a corner the outer (say, left-hand) wheel tends to overrun the differential case and this results in one of the pins (say, B) moving forwards relative to the differential case. This reduces the forces between the faces E, and thus the clutch G is freed and the differential can function in the ordinary way.

CHAPTER 27

Axle Constructions

Bevel-pinion shaft and worm-shaft mountings.   Wheel bearings.   Axle casing constructions.

THE pinion shaft of a bevel final drive and the worm shaft of a worm drive must be supported in journal bearings at two, or more, points and must be held axially.   The latter can be done by using separate thrust bearings, or by means of the journal bearings.

In Fig. 26-1 is shown a differential and final drive such as might be used in a car or medium weight lorry.   The differential case A is made in two halves which are bolted together and thus secure the pins H on which the differential pinions G are free to revolve.   The tubular extensions of the differential case carry the inner races of ball bearings B so that the case is free to rotate about the axis XX. The outer races of the bearings B are carried in the cover plate casting K, caps L being provided so that the differential case, complete with its bearings, may be placed into position.   The cover plate bolts up to the front face of the circular centre-portion of the axle casing while the rear face is closed by a pressed steel cover S. In cars this cover is frequently welded in place because the petrol tank makes it inaccessible but in lorries it is usually removable so as to give access to the final drive and differential.   The centre portion of the axle casing, which is formed of steel pressings, is stiffened by pressings J and the caps L are machined so as to bear against the machined opening in the axle casing in order to give them the maximum support.   The bevel pinion D is carried in two taper roller bearings M and N.   The inner races are fixed to the pinion shaft by the nut at the outer end, a spacer O being provided, and the outer races are carried in the cover plate casting K.   The housing P for the outer race of the bearing M is supported by several webs Q that connect it to the body of the casting K.   By the proper machining of the spacer O the bearings M and N are " pre-loaded," that is, there is a load on them when the pinion is free of all load; this enables the axial deflection of the bearings due to the load applied to the pinion when driving, to be reduced in magnitude and helps in maintaining the proper contact between the teeth of the pinion and crown wheel.   Similarly the bearings B are also pre-loaded.   An oil seal is provided at R.

Ball journal bearings are often used for the pinion shaft instead of taper roller bearings.   The outer ball bearing is then commonly used to position the pinion shaft axially, its races being fixed respectively to the shaft and the cover casting.   The bearings are frequently pre-loaded.   Taper roller bearings are frequently used to support the differential case instead of ball bearings.

554

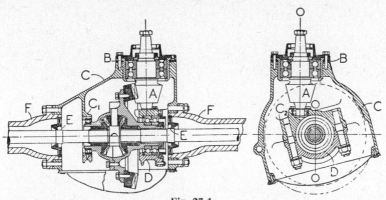

Fig. 27-1

A hypoid gear final drive assembly is shown in Fig. 27-1. The pinion A, integral with its shaft, is now supported in two large ball bearings at its outer end and in a parallel roller bearing at its inner end. The ball bearings take the axial loads and position the shaft axially, a selected washer B being used between the flange of the sleeve carrying the bearings and the neck of the casting C in order to give the correct adjustment. The roller bearing is carried in the web C_2 of the casting C and this web also houses two angular contact bearings which support one side of the differential case, the other side being supported by a parallel roller bearing housed in the web C_1. Both webs are provided with caps. The axial position of the differential case and crown wheel is determined by a selected washer interposed between the bearings and a flange of the web C_2 and cap D. Tubular arms F are bolted up to the central portion C of the axle to complete the axle structure and oil seals are provided at E.

An underhung worm-drive axle is shown in Fig. 27-2. The worm A, which is integral with its shaft, is supported by parallel roller bearings B and positioned axially by the dual purpose bearing C. As the latter is being used as a thrust bearing its outer race is an easy fit in the bore in which it is housed but is held securely against axial movement. This type of bearing is now regarded as superior to an ordinary thrust bearing of the type shown in Fig. 2-8. The bearings of the worm are carried in the cover plate casting D which bolts up to the underside of the axle casing K. In an overhead worm drive the cover plate would be bolted to the top of the axle casing. An oil seal is provided at J. The differential case is formed of the worm wheel itself and of two end plates that are bolted up to it at each side. Ball bearings which fit on the bosses of the end plates and are carried in the cover plate casting D serve to support the differential case. Bearing caps E enable the differential assembly to be placed in position and these caps are arranged to bear against machined faces G on the axle casing so as to get the

555

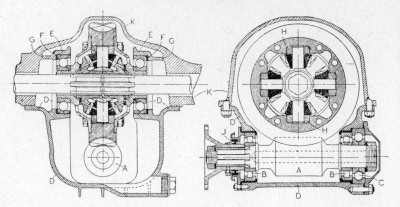

Fig. 27-2

maximum lateral support. Washers F, which are selected of suitable thicknesses during assembly, enable the lateral position of the worm wheel in relation to the worm to be adjusted. A bevel type differential is used, four pinions being provided and carried on the arms of a cross-shaped spider; these arms fit into four rectangular blocks H that in turn fit into slots formed in the bore of the worm wheel, thus enabling the spider and pinions to be assembled, and driven by the worm wheel. The blocks H are held sideways by the end plates of the differential case. The axle casing is a forging and is like an inverted pot at the centre; it has tubular arms which carry the spring seats and wheel bearings.

27.1 Wheel Bearings

In the axle shown in Fig. 25-1, where the road wheels have plain bearings on the axle casing, the differential shafts play no part in transmitting the weight of the body, which comes upon the axle casing through the springs, to the wheels and thus to the ground. The shafts merely transmit the driving torque from the differential to the wheels. This is not always so; the shafts sometimes play an essential part in the support of the axle casing, and thus of the body. In the arrangement shown in Fig. 27-3, for example, the road wheels are fixed to the ends of the differential shafts, which are supported in journal bearings in the axle casing. The vertical load, which comes on to the axle casing through the springs, is transmitted through these bearings to the shafts and thence through the wheels to the ground. The reaction of the force W acting between the wheel and the ground acts upward on the wheel as shown.

Now it should be clear that this force has a tendency to bend the overhanging part of the shaft as shown in Fig. 27-4 (*a*). Thus, that part of the differential shaft is subjected to a bending action, or " bending moment," due simply to the vertical load carried by the

556

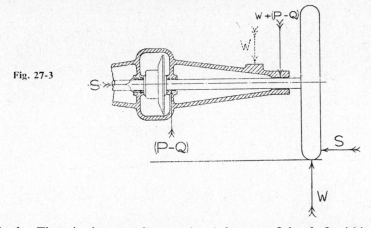

Fig. 27-3

wheel. There is also a tendency to bend the part of the shaft within the axle casing, but this need not be considered. It should also be clear that there is a tendency for the overhanging part of the shaft to be sheared off as shown at (*b*). This tendency is the same at all points of the overhanging end of the shaft, and this portion of the shaft is said to be subjected to a " shearing force."

Again, if from any cause a side force *S* acts upon the wheel, it will tend to push the differential shaft into the axle casing. This tendency is resisted by a thrust bearing situated at the centre of the axle and it should be obvious, therefore, that the shaft has to transmit an end thrust. If the force *S* acts outwards the end thrust becomes a pull. It should also be clear that the force *S* tends to bend the overhanging part of the shaft as shown at (*c*). It also tends to bend the portion of the shaft within the casing, but again this need not be considered. Finally the shaft has to transmit the driving torque. Summing up, the shaft has to withstand the following actions—

    (1) A bending action due to the vertical load carried by the wheel.

    (2) A shearing action due to the vertical load carried by the wheel.

    (3) A bending action due to any side load which may act upon the wheel.

    (4) An end thrust or pull due to any side load upon the wheel.

    (5) The driving torque.

This arrangement of the differential shaft is called a " non-floating " one, while the arrangement of Fig. 25-1, where the shaft transmits only the driving torque, is called a " full-floating " one. These two arrangements stand at the opposite ends of a variety of arrangements of which

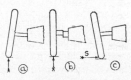

Fig. 27-4

557

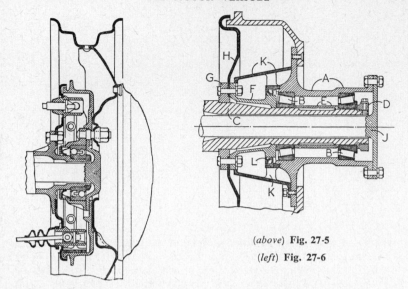

(*above*) **Fig. 27-5**

(*left*) **Fig. 27-6**

the intermediate ones are such that the differential shafts are subjected to one, two, three, or four of the loads listed above, in addition to the driving torque, which, of course, has always to be transmitted.

Some typical road wheel bearings are shown in Figs. 27-5, 6, 7 and 8. The first of these is a full-floating bearing for a lorry; the hub A of the road wheel is carried on two taper roller bearings B whose inner races fit on the end of the axle casing C. One of these bearings will take any end thrust to the right while the other will take any thrust to the left. The inner races are pulled up against the spacer F by the nut D which is screwed to the end of the axle casing and locked by a bolt whose head enters a hole in the casing. The spacer E prevents excessive loads being applied to the bearing by tightening the nut too much and also enables the left-hand race to be firmly held. The spacer F is bolted up to the flange G, the back plate H of the brake assembly being placed between these two members. The flange G is welded to the axle casing. The casting K which is bolted up to the hub A and which houses the oil seal L serves to keep oil or grease from getting through on to the brake shoes or mud from getting into the wheel bearings. The wheel hub is driven by the half shaft J whose end is formed into a flange that is bolted to the hub. The brake drum is bolted to the outer side of the flange of the hub and so can be removed without disturbing the bearings.

In the bearing assembly shown in Fig. 27-6 a double row ball bearing is used, its inner race being held on to the outer end of the axle casing by a nut and its outer race being held between the flange of the half shaft and a member which is bolted to the flange. The pressed steel wheel centre and the brake drum are also bolted to this flange. The bearing thus takes end thrusts in both directions while the half shaft takes only the driving torque although it also assists the bearing in taking the tilting actions due to end loads acting on the wheel. The back plate of the brake assembly is bolted up to a flange that is integral with the end of the axle casing.

In the assembly shown in Fig. 27-7 the half shaft A is formed with a flange at its end to which is bolted the brake drum E and also the road wheel (not shown). The half shaft is supported by a single

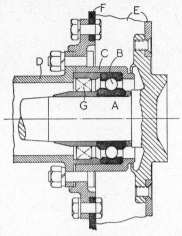

Fig. 27-7

row ball bearing B whose outer race is housed in the cup C which is bolted up to the flanged end of the axle casing D. The back plate F of the brake assembly is also bolted to a flange of the member C. The outer race of the bearing B is thus held so that it can take end thrusts in both directions while the inner race abuts up against the shoulder of the half shaft on the right-hand side and is held by the collar G, which is a force fit on the shaft, at the left.

The bearing thus takes all the end thrusts but the half shaft is subject to shearing force and bending moments. An oil seal, indicated at G, prevents the egress of oil from the axle casing.

In Fig. 27-8 the end of the half shaft A is tapered and the brake

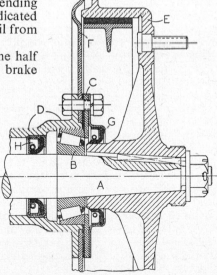

Fig. 27-8

559

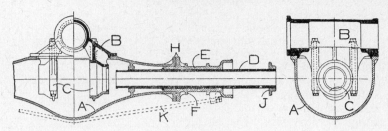

Fig. 27-9: Worm drive axle casing

drum E is bolted to it, a key serving to transmit the drive. A single taper roller bearing B supports the half shaft, its inner race fitting the taper on that shaft while its outer race fits in the end of the axle casing and is held in by the plate C which, together with the oil seal housing G and the brake back plate F is bolted up to the flange of the axle casing. The bearing B can thus take end loads acting to the right but loads to the left have to be carried through the half shaft to the bearing at the other side of the axle. The half shafts therefore abut at the centre of the axle. An oil seal H serves to prevent oil from escaping from the axle.

27.2   Axle Casing Constructions

Space is not available to allow all the axle constructions that are used to be described; only the most important types can be dealt with.

A common type when a worm final drive is used is shown in Fig. 27-9. The central portion A is a hollow iron or steel casting open at the top and having tapering extensions at each side. Bolted to the top of this member is a cover plate B in which are arranged the bearings for the worm and for the differential case. The latter is carried in ball or roller bearings housed in the cups CC, the upper halves of which are integral with the cover plate, the lower halves being separate caps in order that the differential case may be got into position. The caps are secured by the nuts and bolts shown, but studs screwed into the cover plate are sometimes used instead of bolts.

By supporting the differential case in this way the worm and worm wheel can be adjusted to the correct relationship on the bench, and then the whole assembly can be bolted to the axle casing A. The gearing can also be easily withdrawn for inspection.

Pressed into the extensions of the central casting are two steel tubes D, which at their outer ends carry the bearings for the road wheels, ball or roller bearings being arranged between them and the inside of the wheel hubs. The springs are bolted to spring seats pivotally mounted on the cylindrical portions of the extension castings E, the latter being bolted by flanges H to the central casting. The wheels are kept on by nuts J screwed to the ends of the tubes D, while side thrusts towards the centre of the axle are taken on the ends of the members E.

This construction provides a strong and rigid axle, but to make it more rigid a tie-rod was occasionally provided as shown by the dotted lines at K.

A construction for a bevel final drive is shown in Fig. 27-10. The central portion A is roughly a ring, but at one point there is a neck B to take one of the bevel-pinion shaft bearings. The left-hand side of the ring is quite open, but the right-hand side is closed by the web of metal C in which is formed a cup D to house the other pinion-shaft bearing. The toothed part of the pinion occupies the position shown at E, so that there is a bearing on each side of it. This makes the loads on the bearings more nearly equal and reduces the overhang of the adjacent universal joint.

Bolted up to the sides of the central ring are two tubular extensions F. These are almost identical, and at their outer ends carry the wheel bearings, spring seats and brake anchorage brackets. The differential case is carried in bearings which are housed at one side in the cup J and at the other side in the recess K.

Another construction is shown in Fig. 27-11 which is almost self-explanatory. The axle is formed of two halves A and B, bolted together by a number of bolts C. To register one half relatively to

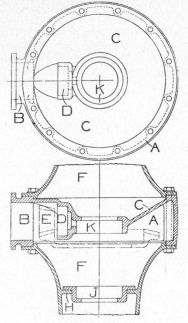

Fig. 27-10

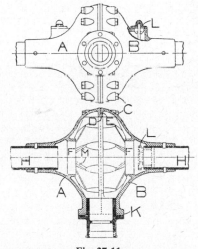

Fig. 27-11

the other the half A has a projecting lip D which fits in the machined flange E of the other half. Holes F are arranged to carry the differential case bearings. Steel tubes H, forced into and riveted in

561

the halves A and B, carry the wheel bearings, spring seats, etc., at their outer ends. The axial position of the differential case and crown wheel may be adjusted by means of the sleeves L which are screwed into the ends of the tubes. Access to these sleeves is provided by the caps L which also carry pins for locking the sleeves.

As shown, the axle is for a bevel final drive, but a similar construction is sometimes used for worm drives. The construction has the disadvantage that adjustment of the gearing in assembly is difficult, and that for inspection the complete axle has to be dismantled.

The halves A and B are usually made of malleable cast iron or cast aluminium alloy, but steel pressings are sometimes used. When castings are employed, stiffening webs M are usually provided, but with steel pressings the webs are omitted.

The tubular extensions H are sometimes made integral with the halves A and B, the material used being cast aluminium alloy.

The bevel pinion is carried in a steel sleeve (sectioned in black) and its axial position can be adjusted by substituting washers of different thicknesses at K.

27.3 " Banjo " Axle

The most popular modern axle casing construction is that known by the above name. In its most usual form it consists of two steel pressings of the shape shown in Fig. 27-12 placed face to face and welded and riveted together, thus forming a casing resembling a banjo with two necks. The ring portion of this casing usually lies

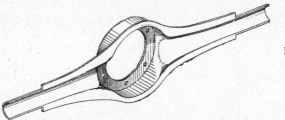

Fig. 27-12: Banjo
back axle casing

in a vertical plane; a bevel final drive being used. The arrangement of the final drive and differential is as described in Section 26.1. At its ends the axle casing is stiffened by suitable steel sleeves and is arranged to carry the road wheel bearings, spring seats and brake anchorage brackets.

The banjo is sometimes built up from two halves joined on a horizontal plane instead of on the vertical plane as shown, it is sometimes made all in one piece without any joint, and it is sometimes made a solid forging. The latter gives a very strong axle and is used in heavy lorries. With a forged steel axle the ring portion of the banjo may be placed horizontally, instead of vertically, thus enabling a worm final drive to be used. The worm and wheel are mounted in a cover plate, similar to that shown in Fig. 27-2, which is bolted to the top or bottom face of the banjo ring according to whether an overhead or an underneath position is required for the worm.

CHAPTER 28

The Double Reduction Axle

Principal methods employed on heavy commercial vehicles

IN this type of axle the permanent reduction of speed between the engine and road wheels is obtained in two separate steps. Double reduction axles are used chiefly on heavy lorries, buses, etc., for the following reasons: such vehicles run at low speeds in comparison with passenger cars; thus, while cars run at speeds up to 80 m.p.h., lorries are limited to between 20 and 30 m.p.h.; they also have larger diameter wheels. Thus, although lorry engines run at much slower speeds than car engines, the reduction of speed between the engine and the road wheels is a good deal larger, being from 5 to 1 up to 10 to 1, as against $3\frac{1}{2}$ to 1 up to 6 to 1.

If these large reductions were obtained in a single step, using, say, bevel gearing, then either the bevel pinion would have to be made very small with few teeth, when it would be both weak and inefficient, or the crown wheel would have to be made very large, which would result in a heavy and expensive axle, and would reduce the clearance between the axle and the ground too much. Similar conditions are found, to a lesser degree, with worm final drives, and so the double reduction axle is adopted when the final drive ratio has to be large. On some vehicles they are used to enable a very low body position to be obtained.

28.1 Both Steps at the Centre of the Axle

This type of double reduction final drive is shown in Figs. 28-1, 2, 3 and 4. Referring to Fig. 28-1, the bevel pinion A is driven by the propeller shaft and gears with a small crown wheel B. The latter is fixed to a layshaft C, to which is also fixed a spur pinion D. The layshaft is carried in ball or roller bearings at its ends in the axle casing, suitable thrust bearings being provided to take the thrust of the bevel gears. The spur pinion D meshes with a large spur wheel E which is bolted to the differential casing F just as the crown wheel of a single reduction axle is bolted. The differential case is carried in ball or roller bearings in the axle casing in the usual way.

The arrangement of the gearing in Fig. 28-2 is slightly different from the above. The differential is here situated between the two halves of the layshaft instead of between the two drive shafts. The propeller shaft drives the bevel pinion A, which gears with a small crown wheel B that is

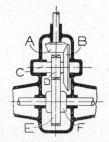

Fig. 28-1

563

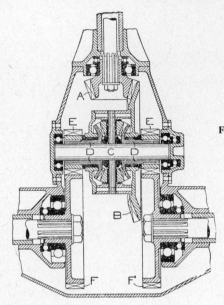

Fig. 28-2: Axle with double reduction at centre

bolted to the differential case. The latter is supported by the shaft C which is carried in ball bearings in the axle casing. The differential wheels DD are now integral with short sleeves free to rotate on the shaft C, and which carry spur pinions EE at their outer ends, outside the differential casing. The pinions EE mesh with spur wheels FF fixed to the drive shafts. Thus the differential action is obtained between the pinions EE instead of between the drive shafts themselves. The chief advantage of this arrangement is that the differential now revolves at a higher speed than the road wheels, and so, for a given torque on the latter, the forces on the differential wheel teeth are smaller, enabling smaller wheels to be used. To set against this advantage, two spur pinions and wheels are required for the second reduction, thus increasing the cost.

A third arrangement is shown in Fig. 28-3. The spur pinion A driven by the propeller shaft, drives a wheel B fixed to the layshaft C, to which is also fixed the bevel pinion of the bevel drive. The arrangement of the latter is normal. It will be observed that the axis of the propeller shaft is higher than it would be with a single reduction bevel gear axle, and can thus be brought more nearly into line with the mainshaft of the gear box, so that the work put upon the universal joints is reduced. This advantage is also obtained with the other types of double reduction axle and with the overhead worm driven axle.

With single reduction bevel axles and with underhung worm drives the engine and gear box are sometimes inclined in the frame in order to obtain this advantage.

564

An arrangement in which the second reduction is by an epicyclic gear is used by Messrs. Scammel on some of their lorries and is shown diagrammatically in Fig. 28-4. A bevel first reduction and a normal bevel type differential are used, the differential case being carried in bearings in the end plates A which are bolted up to flanges on the central drum-shaped portion of the axle casing. The differential shafts carry pinions B which form the sun wheels of epicyclic gears of the sun and annulus type. The annuli C are

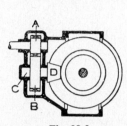

Fig. 28-3

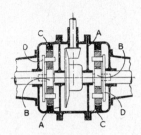

Fig. 28-4

fixed, being formed integral with the end covers which are bolted up to the central casing on the same flanges as the plates A. The arms D which carry the planet pinions are made integral with the drive shafts and are supported in bearings in the end covers C. The tubular end portions of the axle casing are bolted up to the end covers C on flanges as shown.

28.2 Kirkstall Double-reduction Axle

An interesting and original design by the Kirkstall Forge Engineering Company, of Leeds, who manufacture axles for all kinds of vehicles, is shown in Fig. 28-5.

The first reduction occurs betwen the worm and worm-wheel, the latter being fixed to the annulus member A which is carried in bearings C and D in the axle casing; the second reduction is obtained from the epicyclic action of the train consisting of the annulus A and sun S, in conjunction with the concentric spur train (not epicyclic) consisting of the pinion H and the annulus J. The annulus A meshes with three planet pinions which are carried by the member E and the latter is splined to the left-hand half-shaft F. The pinions mesh at the centre with the sun S, which is integral with the pinion H. The latter drives the annulus J through three pinions K, which are carried on pins L supported by the member M which is fixed to the axle casing. The annulus J is splined to the right-hand half-shaft. The left-hand half-shaft is thus driven in the forward direction by forward motion of the annulus A, as it would be if the sun were fixed; but the sun, being free, will be driven in the backward direction so that the speed of the planet carrier E and its half-shaft will be lower than if the sun S were fixed. The backward motion of

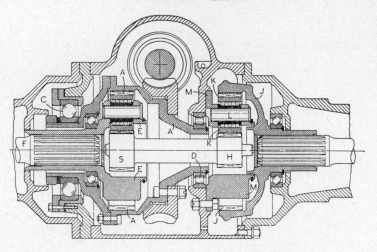

Fig. 28-5: Kirkstall double-reduction axle

the sun S and pinion H is converted to forward motion of the right-hand half-shaft by the pinions K, and some reduction of speed occurs in this train.

In order that equal torques shall be exerted on the two half-shafts, the gear train H, K, J must have a particular ratio in relation to that of the epicyclic train A, S. This particular ratio is found as follows. Let the torque imparted to the annulus A by the worm and wheel be T, and let the number of teeth in the annulus and sun be denoted respectively by s and a. Then the torques applied to the member E

will be $\dfrac{T \times (a + s)}{a}$ and the torque acting on the sun S will be

$T \times \dfrac{s}{a}$ (backwards). The torque applied to the annulus J is therefore

$T \times \dfrac{s}{a} \times \dfrac{j}{h}$ where j and h are the numbers of teeth in J and H respec-

tively. Hence if the torques applied to the two half-shafts are to be equal, we must have

$$T \times \frac{a + s}{a} = T \times \frac{s}{a} \times \frac{j}{h}$$

that is $\dfrac{a + s}{s}$ must equal $\dfrac{j}{h}$

The value of the second reduction produced by the trains A, S and H, J may now be found by using the tabular method described in Chapter 22. Let N_A, N_F and N_S be respectively the speeds of the annulus A, the left-hand half-shaft F and the sun S. Then we have the results shown on the page opposite:

566

Planet Carrier E or left-hand half-shaft F	Annulus A	Sun S
N_F	N_F	N_F
O	$N_A - N_F$	$(N_F - N_A)\dfrac{a}{s}$
N_F	N_A	$N_S = N_F(1 + \dfrac{a}{s}) - N_A \cdot \dfrac{a}{s}$

and the speed of the right-hand half-shaft will be $- N_S \times \dfrac{h}{j}$ or

$$N_R = \left[N_A \frac{a}{s} - N_F \left(1 + \frac{a}{s} \right) \right] \times \frac{h}{j}$$

the minus sign occurs because the annulus J goes in the opposite direction to the pinion H.

Since j/h is made equal to $(a + s)/s$, as stated above, we get

$$N_R = N_A \times \frac{a}{s} \times \frac{h}{j} - N_F$$

But in straight-ahead running $N_R = N_F$, hence

$$2 N_R = N_A \times \frac{a}{s} \times \frac{h}{j}$$

The second reduction is therefore

$$\frac{N_A}{N_R} = 2 \times \frac{s \times j}{a \times h}$$

It will be noticed that the shaft SH is supported solely by the contacts between the teeth of the gears S and H and the planets and pinions K. This ensures equal division of the torques acting on the pinions S and H between the three pairs of teeth of each pinion which transmit the torques.

28.3 One Step at Centre of Axle, the Other at Road Wheels

Double reduction axles of this type may be divided into two classes, those in which the second reduction is provided by a simple spur pinion and wheel, and those in which it is given by an epicyclic train. An example of the second type is given in Chapter 31, while an axle of the first type is shown in Fig. 28-6. It is a design of the Mercedes-Benz Company. It will be seen that the parts required to fulfil the two functions of a live axle are to a great extent independent members. A forging A, to the ends of which are bolted the members B, forms the axle beam and the road wheels, the hubs of which are seen at C, revolve on taper roller bearings on the ends of the members B. The springs are bolted to seats formed on the forging A, and the weight of the body is carried by this forging and the covers B. A separate casing D houses the first

567

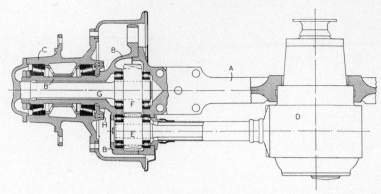

Fig. 28-6

reduction and differential, and light tubular covers protect the half-shafts. At their outer ends the latter are splined to pinions E, which are carried in roller bearings and which mesh with the gears F. The latter are also carried in roller bearings and are splined to the shafts G, which are integral with the hub-caps and by which the wheel hubs C are driven. Seals H serve to keep lubricant in and mud out.

This arrangement has the advantage that the half-shafts revolve at higher speeds than the road wheels so that the torques they have to transmit are correspondingly smaller than if they drove the road wheels direct. The system gives a very rigid construction, and by arranging the half-shafts below the axle beam, a very low body position can be obtained. Alternatively, by placing the half-shafts above the axle beam, a very high ground clearance could be achieved, but this would introduce certain difficulties and has not become widely used. In the axle shown the half-shafts are situated behind the axle beam and the only gain in road clearance is that, because of the second reduction, the crown wheel of the first reduction, and hence the casing, D, can be smaller than otherwise.

In some early axles of this type the gear F was replaced by an internally toothed ring with which the pinion E meshed. The drawback to this arrangement was the great difficulty in providing satisfactory seals.

CHAPTER 29

Brakes

Functions and methods of operation. **Types of brake.** **Semi-servo brakes.**
Compensating mechanisms. **Linkages and their adjustment.** **Hydraulic**
mechanisms.

THE operation performed in braking is the reverse of that carried out in accelerating. In the latter the heat energy of the fuel is converted into the kinetic energy of the car, whereas in the former the kinetic energy of the car is converted into heat. Again, just as when driving the car the torque of the engine produces a tractive effort at the peripheries of the driving wheels, so, when the brakes are applied the braking torque introduced at the brake drums produces a negative tractive effort or retarding effort at the peripheries of the braking wheels. As the acceleration possible is limited by the adhesion available between the driving wheels and the ground, so the deceleration possible is also limited.

When a brake is applied to a wheel of a car, a force is immediately introduced between the wheel and the road, tending to make the wheel keep on turning. In Fig. 29-1 this force is shown as the force F; it is this force which opposes the motion of the car and slows the latter down. The deceleration is proportional to the force F, the limiting value of which depends on the normal force between the wheel and the road, and on the coefficient of friction, or of adhesion, as it is called. Since the force F does not act along a line of action passing through the centre of gravity of the car, there is a tendency for the car to turn so that its back wheels rise into the air. The inertia of the car introduces an internal force F_1 acting at the centre of gravity in the opposite direction to the force F. The magnitude of the inertia force F_1 is equal to that of the force F. The two forces F and F_1 constitute a couple tending to make the back wheels rise as stated. Since actually the back wheels remain on the ground, an equal and opposite couple must act on the car somewhere so as to balance the overturning couple FF_1.

This righting couple is automatically introduced by the perpendicular force W_1 between the front wheels and the ground increasing by a small amount Q while the force W_2 between the back wheels and the ground decreases by an equal amount Q. The forces $+ Q$ and $- Q$ constitute a couple which balances

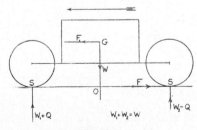

Fig. 29-1

569

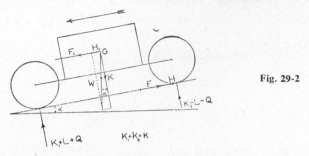

Fig. 29-2

the overturning couple FF_1. The magnitude of the latter is $F \times OG$, so that other things being equal the smaller the height OG the less the overturning couple. The magnitude of the righting couple QQ is $Q \times SS$, so that the greater the wheelbase SS the less the force Q, that is, the less the alteration in the perpendicular forces between the wheels and the ground.

When going down a hill the conditions are changed. From Fig. 29-2 it will be seen that the vertical force W, the weight of the car, can be resolved into two components H_1 and K. The component K is the only part of the weight of the car that produces any perpendicular force between the wheels and the ground, and is, therefore, the only part of the weight giving any adhesion. Thus, on a hill, the adhesion available is necessarily less than on the level. The component H_1, however, tends to make the car run down the hill, and if the car is merely to be kept stationary, a force H equal and opposite to H_1 must be introduced by applying the brakes. The forces H and H_1 constitute an overturning couple, which is balanced by an increase L in the perpendicular force between the front wheels and the ground, and an equal decrease in the rear.

If, instead of being merely held stationary, the car has to be slowed down, then an additional force F must be introduced between the wheels and the ground by applying the brakes harder. An equal inertia force F_1 is then introduced by the deceleration of the car. This inertia force acts at the centre of gravity of the car, and together with the force F constitutes an additional overturning couple, which is balanced by a further alteration Q in the perpendicular force between the wheels and the ground. The perpendicular force between the front wheels and the ground is thus increased by an amount $L + Q$, and that between the rear wheels and the ground is decreased by the same amount. Thus, on a hill, the deceleration possible is less than on the level for two reasons. First, the maximum perpendicular force between the wheels and the road is reduced from W to K, and secondly, part of the adhesion is neutralized by the component H_1 and is not available for deceleration.

If the rear wheels only are braked, the conditions are still worse, because the force producing adhesion is still further reduced by the amount $L + Q$.

570

A little consideration will show that the opposite action occurs when the car is being driven forward. The perpendicular force between the front wheels and the ground is then decreased, and that between the rear wheels and the ground is increased, so that from the point of view of adhesion the rear wheels are a better driving point than the front wheels. This is particularly so when accelerating up a hill.

The extent of this alteration in the weight distribution depends directly upon the magnitude of the deceleration, which, in turn, assuming the brakes are applied until the wheels are about to skid, depends upon the coefficient of adhesion between the wheels and the road. When that coefficient is low the maximum deceleration is low also, and the weight distribution is altered only slightly. Under these conditions the relative effectiveness of the front and rear wheels is in the ratio (approximately) of the weights carried by these wheels, and if the weight carried by the front wheels is only a small part of the total weight little will be gained by braking them.

When the coefficient of adhesion is high, the maximum deceleration possible is high also, and the alteration in the weight distribution may be considerable, depending on the relation between the length of wheelbase and the height of the centre of gravity. Under these circumstances it will probably be worth while to brake the front wheels, but each vehicle really needs to be considered separately, as it is not safe to generalize.

While introducing brakes on the front wheels always makes a greater deceleration possible, the extra complication is not always justified by the gain, which may be quite small. In most pleasure cars the gain is sufficient to justify the extra complication, but in some lorries where the wheelbase is long, the height of the centre of gravity small, and the weight carried by the front wheels only a small proportion of the total, this is not so.

However, there are other points of view besides that of maximum deceleration. In practice it is found that with front wheel brakes there is very much less danger of the rear of the vehicle swinging round when the brakes are applied on a greasy road and on corners. Also, since the total area of brake lining is usually greater, the brakes will not need adjusting or relining at such frequent intervals, and there is also the advantage that the wear of the tyres is more nearly equal, but here again the factors mentioned in the previous paragraphs have a bearing, and the gain, in some cases, may be small.

The present practice is to fit four-wheel brakes to practically every type of passenger vehicle and lorry.

29.1 Two Functions of Brakes

Two distinct demands are made upon the brakes of motor vehicles. First, in emergencies they must bring the vehicle to rest in the shortest possible distance, and secondly, they must enable control of the vehicle to be retained when descending long hills. The first demand calls for brakes which can apply large braking torques to the brake drums, while the second calls for brakes that can dissipate large quantities of heat without large temperature rises. It may be pointed out that the same amount of energy has to be dissipated as heat when a car descends only 400 yd of a 1 in 30 incline, as when the same car is brought to rest from a speed of 35 m.p.h. Thus heat dissipation hardly enters into the braking question when emergency stops are considered, but when descending long hills the problem is almost entirely one of heat dissipation.

29.2 Braking Systems

A driving wheel can be braked in two ways: directly, by means of brakes acting on a drum attached to it; or indirectly, through the transmission by a brake acting on a drum on the mainshaft of the gear box, or on the bevel pinion, or worm, shaft of the final drive. A brake in either of the latter positions, being geared down to the road wheels, can exert a larger braking torque on them than if it acted directly on them. If the final drive ratio is 4 to 1, then the braking torque exerted on each road wheel is twice the braking torque exerted on the brake drum by the brake, that is, the total braking torque is four times the torque on the brake drum. Thus, brakes acting on the engine side of the final drive are much more powerful than those acting on the wheels directly. A transmission brake, however, gives only a single drum to dissipate the heat generated, whereas when acting directly on the road wheels there are two or more drums. The single drum of the transmission brake is also badly situated from a heat dissipation point of view. Again, when the transmission brake is situated at the back of the gear box the braking torque has to be transmitted through the universal joints of the propeller shaft and the teeth of the final drive, which parts may have to be increased in size if they are not to be overloaded. The transmission brake, however, has the advantage that the braking is divided equally between the road wheels by the differential, and when it is situated at the back of the gear box its position relatively to the frame is fixed, and its action is not affected by the wheels going over bumps or by an alteration in the load carried, both of which occurrences tend to affect the action of wheel brakes unless the design of the connecting linkage is good. However, transmission brakes are now little used and when they are fitted they are frequently meant to be nothing more than " parking " brakes.

When all four road wheels are braked there are many combinations of arrangements available, but the most important are the following: Each road wheel is provided with a single brake drum having a single brake acting upon it, and all four of these wheel brakes are applied simultaneously by either the foot pedal or hand lever. The second arrangement is to have a single brake drum on each wheel, the front ones having a single brake acting on them while the rear ones have two brakes acting on each drum; all the wheels are braked by one pedal (or lever) and the second brake in each rear wheel is applied by the hand lever (or the pedal). The third arrangement is to have one brake drum on each wheel, each with a single brake, the foot pedal actuates all the brakes simultaneously while the hand lever actuates the rear wheel brakes alone through a separate connecting rod linkage.

29.3 Method of Actuating the Brakes

There are three ways of operating brakes. The first is by manual operation, which may call for considerable physical strength on the part of the operator; the second by some form of " Servo " system, in which the operator is assisted by external power, and the last is complete power operation. The first is the commonest system, although the second is used on a few large cars and to a considerable extent on lorries. The last system is confined to heavy lorries, especially those used with trailers.

Considering manually operated brakes, the brake pedal or lever may be connected to the actual brake either mechanically, by means of rods or wires, or hydraulically, by means of a fluid in a pipe; before considering these connections, however, we must deal with the brakes themselves.

29.4 Types of Brake

Brakes may be classified into three groups as follows—

(1) Friction brakes.
(2) Fluid brakes.
(3) Electric brakes.

The last two types are at present only in the development stage but may become of practical importance in connection with heavy, high-speed vehicles. The fluid brake can be made in two forms, in one of these there is a chamber, filled with fluid, inside which is a rotating member that is coupled to some part of the transmission so that it is rotated by the motion of the road wheels. The " churning " of the fluid by the blades or vanes of the rotor converts the kinetic energy of the vehicle into heat and thus provides a braking effort. Alternately the inner member may be held stationary and the chamber be rotated; this makes dissipation of the heat generated rather simpler, this dissipation may also be effected by passing the fluid through some form of radiator. The chief drawbacks of this type of brake are that it is difficult to control the braking effort precisely and that while it can provide large braking efforts at high vehicle speeds it can supply very little at low speeds and none at all when the road wheels are not rotating. Thus it can be used only to supplement a friction brake which must be used for low speeds and for holding the vehicle on gradients. In another form fluid is pumped by a positive displacement pump through restricted passages and energy is thereby converted into heat. The control of

573

this type is somewhat easier and it can be made to provide the necessary braking efforts at low speeds but it tends to be mechanically complicated and expensive.

The electric brake is in effect an electric generator which, being driven by the road wheels, converts kinetic energy into an electric current and thence, by passing the current through a resistance, into heat. In the "eddy current" brake the generator takes the form of an armature, provided with a winding, which can be energized by the passage of a small current from the battery of the vehicle. The armature thus produces a magnetic flux which passes through the metal parts of the rotor that surrounds the armature. The rotor is coupled to the road wheels and when it rotates eddy currents are produced in its metal parts. The energy represented by these currents is converted into heat because of the resistance to the passage of the currents. This type of brake suffers from the same drawback as the first type of fluid brake, namely, that it cannot provide any effort at zero speed and can be used only to supplement a friction brake. A fairly large number of such brakes are in use at the present time and have been quite successful.

The vast majority of brakes are friction brakes and these may be sub-divided into: (1) Drum brakes and (2) Disc brakes, according to whether the braked member is a drum or a disc. Disc brakes are only just coming into use but their advantages may bring them into extensive use particularly for special vehicles and tracked vehicles. Drum brakes are by far the most widely used type and are almost invariably internal expanding brakes in which the brake shoes are expanded into contact with the inside of the brake drum. The external contracting brake, in which the brake shoes or bands are contracted on to the outside of the drum are now used only in epicyclic gear boxes and in a few special cases, such as in tracked vehicles.

The principle of the internal expanding rigid-shoe brake is shown in Fig. 29-3. The brake drum A is fixed to the hub of the road

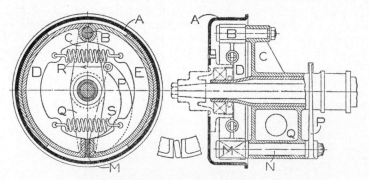

Fig. 29-3: Internal expanding rigid-shoe brake

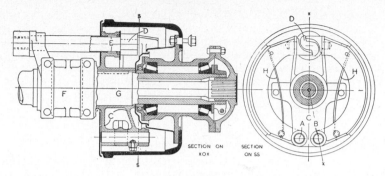

Fig. 29-4

wheel (shown in chain dotted lines) by bolts which pass through
its flange.   The inner side of the drum is open, and a pin B projects
into it.   This pin is carried in an arm C which is either integral
with, or secured to, the axle casing, a rear wheel brake being shown.
The brake shoes D and E are free to pivot on the pin B.   They are
roughly semicircular, and in between their lower ends is a cam M.
The latter is integral with, or is fixed to, a spindle N free to turn in
the arm Q of the axle casing.   A lever P is fixed to the end of the
cam spindle, and when this lever is pulled upon by a rod which is
coupled to its end, the cam spindle and cam are turned round
slightly, thus moving the ends of the brake shoes apart.   The
shoes are thus pressed against the inside of the brake drum, and
frictional forces act between them, tending to prevent any relative
motion.   The frictional force thus tends to slow down the drum,
but it also tends to make the shoes revolve with the drum.   The
latter action is prevented by the pin B and the cam M.   The pin B
is therefore called the "anchorage" pin.   The magnitude of the
frictional force, multiplied by the radius of the drum, gives the
torque tending to stop the drum, that is, the braking torque.

The reaction of this braking torque is the tendency for the shoes
to rotate with the drum, so that this reaction is taken by the pin B
and cam M, and ultimately by the axle casing and the members
which prevent the axle casing from revolving, that is, the torque
reaction system.   The shoes embrace rather less than half the
anchorage pin, hence a spring R is required to keep them in contact
with it, and a second spring S is provided to pull the shoes away
from the drum when the brake lever is released.   The brake shoes
are usually lined with some lining which will be considered later.

In lorries a separate anchorage pin is usually provided for each
shoe, as indicated in Fig. 29-4.   This shows a design of the Kirkstall
Forge Engineering Company.   The anchorage pins are seen at
A and B and are carried in the projecting arm C of the brake
anchorage bracket.   The latter is a force fit on the end G of the
axle case, and a key is provided to prevent any rotation.   The

575

actuating cam D is now of S-shape, which provides a greater amount of expansion of the shoes and a more constant leverage than is provided by the simple cam shown in Fig. 29-3. The cam D is integral with its shaft and is supported in needle roller bearings, one of which is seen at E. The pull-off springs H are now single-leaf springs, which are easier to remove and replace than coil springs. The seats F, to which the road springs are bolted, are formed integral with the brackets C.

29.5   Alternative Expanding Mechanisms

The cam expanding mechanism just described is simple in construction and fairly satisfactory in action, but others are used. Some alternatives are shown in Figs. 29-5 and 6.

In Fig. 29-5 (a) the spindle A corresponds to the cam spindle, but instead of a cam it carries two short arms B and C. These are coupled by short connecting rods D, E to the ends of the shoes. Obviously, when the spindle is turned, the shoes will be pressed into contact with the drum. The connecting rods may be made adjustable in length so that the shoes can be made to come into contact simultaneously. The shoes are withdrawn positively by the connecting rods when the brake is released, and so no return spring is needed between the shoes.

A " toggle " mechanism is shown in Fig. 29-5 (b), the rods A and B, pivoted to the brake shoes and to each other, constituting the toggle. A rod C enables the crank D, which is fixed to the operating spindle E, to depress the centre of the toggle, thus causing the shoes to be moved outwards.

29.6   Girling Roller Wedge Expander

Another design of expanding mechanism (that used with the Girling brake) is shown in Figs. 29-6, 13 and 28. The rod R (Fig. 29-6) is connected to the conical wedge member T and when this is pulled by the rod the plungers U and V are forced apart, thus forcing the ends of the brake shoes apart. The body W that carries the wedge and plungers is secured to the back plate of the

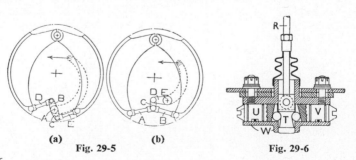

(a)   (b)
Fig. 29-5   Fig. 29-6

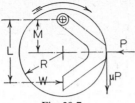

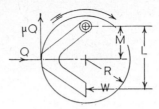

Fig. 29-7   Fig. 29-8

brake by studs, but not rigidly. It is free to slide sideways a little thus equalizing the forces applied to the brake shoes. Sliding friction between the wedge and the plungers is avoided by the interposition of rollers as shown.

In the design shown in Fig. 29-28 the housing carrying the plungers E and F is fixed to the back plate but the wedge member D has a transverse hole in which a pin H is free to slide and this equalizes the forces on the plungers. Thus, in both the Girling designs and the mechanism shown in Fig. 29-5 (b) the forces pressing the shoes outwards are always equal.

29.7 Elementary Theory of the Shoe Brake

Consider the simple shoe shown in Fig. 29-7. An actuating force W will give rise to a normal force P between the shoe and the drum (this force is shown as it acts on the shoe) and this normal force will produce a frictional force μP if the drum is rotating as shown. Now the shoe is in equilibrium under the action of the forces shown, together with the forces acting at the pivot, but the latter have no moment about the pivot and consequently the clockwise moments due to the forces P and μP must be balanced by the anti-clockwise moment due to W. Hence we get the relation –

$$W \times L = P \times M + \mu P \times R$$

and hence that—

$$P = \frac{WL}{M + \mu P}.$$

Now the braking torque acting on the drum is due entirely to the frictional force μP and is equal to $\mu P \times R$, or, substituting the expression obtained above for P, we get—

$$\text{Brake torque } T_t = \frac{\mu WLR}{M + \mu R}.$$

Considering the shoe shown in Fig. 29-8, the balance of moments about the pivot gives—

$$WL + \mu QR = QM$$

and hence—

$$Q = \frac{WL}{M - \mu R}$$

so that the expression for the braking torque is—

$$T_1 = \frac{\mu WLR}{M - \mu R}.$$

577

It is now easily seen that T_1 is greater than T_t, the other factors being equal. Let $\mu = 0.4$ in., $L = 6$ in., $M = 3$ in., $R = 4$ in. and $W = 100$ lb. Then—

$$T_1 = \frac{0.4 \times 100 \times 6 \times 4}{3 - 0.4 \times 4} = \frac{960}{1.4} = 685.6 \text{ lb-in.}$$

while—

$$T_t = \frac{960}{3 + 1.6} = 208.8 \text{ lb-in.}$$

Thus T_1 is 3·3 times T_t.

The shoe shown in Fig. 29-7 is called a "trailing" shoe while that shown in Fig. 29-8 is called a "leading" shoe. It should be clear, however, that in a conventional brake the leading shoe will become the trailing one if the direction of rotation of the brake drum is reversed and vice versa.

An actual brake shoe acts in a similar manner to the simple one considered above, the only difference being that the frictional force μP will act at a larger radius than the radius of the brake drum and this will accentuate the difference between the torques developed by the shoes.

In a brake of the type shown in Fig. 29-3, however, the expanding cam will not apply *equal* forces to the shoes but will apply a greater force to the trailing shoe. Taking the data assumed above and supposing that a total actuating force of 200 lb is available, then the cam would apply a force of 153·5 lb to the trailing shoe and only 46·5 lb to the leading shoe. The total braking torque would then be 651 lb-in. If, however, the whole 200 lb available for actuation had been applied to the leading shoe the brake torque would have been 1,371 lb-in, that is, more than twice as great and this result can be obtained by making both shoes leading shoes.

If the actuating mechanism were of the type that applies equal forces to the shoes then each actuating force would be 100 lb and the total brake torque developed by the two shoes would be 685·6 + 208·8 = 894·4 lb-in. Thus a floating or equalizing actuating mechanism gives an increase in brake torque for a given actuating force but it has the disadvantage that the wear of the leading shoe (assuming the shoes to have linings of the same material) would be 3·3 times that of the trailing shoe. The brake with two leading shoes would not suffer from this drawback and, as has been seen, gives an even greater brake torque. Such brakes are, therefore, becoming common. When hydraulic actuation is used it is a simple matter to make both shoes leading ones for the forward direction of rotation; the brake is arranged as shown in Fig. 29-9, two actuating cylinders, connected by a pipe, being used instead of one cylinder. For the reverse direction of rotation both shoes would be trailing shoes and the brake would be rather weak. For this reason it is usual to employ the two-leading shoe brake in the front wheels only, the rear brakes being the conventional leading and trailing shoe type.

578

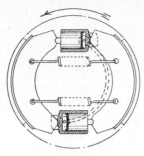

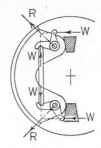

Fig. 29-9   Fig. 29-10

When the brake actuation is mechanical it is not so simple to make both shoes leading ones but a relatively simple mechanism has been developed by Messrs. Girling and the principle of this is shown in Fig. 29-10. The expanding mechanism, which is of the normal Girling type, does not act directly on the shoe but on one arm of a bell-crank which is freely pivoted on a pin carried by the shoe. The other arm of this bell-crank bears on a strut which connects it to an exactly similar bell-crank pivoted on a pin at the other end of the shoe. The other arm of this latter bell-crank bears against a fixed anchorage (shown cross-hatched) and the shoe itself can bear on this anchorage and on another one at the top, as shown. It should be clear that, supposing the arms of the bell-cranks to be all equal in length, the force in the strut will be equal to the actuating force W and this force will act on the bell-cranks as shown; also that the bell-crank at the bottom will press on the anchorage with a force W and the anchorage will press back equally on the bell-crank as shown. The resultant force on each bell-crank will thus be a force R as shown and these forces will press the shoe into contact with the drum. If the drum is turning clockwise the shoe will now move round clockwise very slightly until it bears on the anchorage at the top and is thus a leading shoe while if the drum is turning anti-clockwise the shoe will turn anti-clockwise and will bear on the anchorage at the bottom, being once again a leading shoe. Thus, by employing two shoes, each with the bell-crank and strut mechanism, a brake which is a two-leading shoe brake for either direction of rotation and which requires only one actuating mechanism is obtained.

29.8 Brake-shoe Adjustments

In order to take up the wear of the brake linings and to enable the clearance between the shoes and the drum to be adjusted the anchorages on which the shoes pivot are frequently made adjustable so that the shoes can be moved outwards. An example is shown in Fig. 29-11; it is the Girling design. The brake shoes pivot on the ends of plungers carried in a housing that is fixed to the back

579

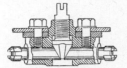

Fig. 29-11

Fig. 29-12

plate of the brake assembly. These plungers can be forced outwards by screwing in the adjusting wedge, thereby reducing the clearance between the brake shoes and drum. The adjusting wedge is roughly conical but the cone is actually a series of flats; this enables the pull-off springs to lock the adjustment positively.

An alternative point at which an adjustment can be made is between the actuating mechanism and the ends of the brake shoes. Thus the links A and B in Fig. 29-5 (*b*) may be made adjustable in length by forming them of two end portions screwed respectively right and left handed and of a centre portion or turnbuckle by turning which the effective length of the link may be varied.

A very simple but effective adjustment is the Lockheed " Micram " which is shown in Fig. 29-12. The brake shoe bears on the pin of the scroll member and the latter bears on a ridge of the member A which is fixed to the plunger of the actuating cylinder. By turning the scroll member with a screwdriver the brake shoe clearance may be reduced. The depressions formed in the surfaces of the scrolls provide a lock but necessitate the adjustment being made in steps of fixed magnitude.

29.9 Girling " Hydrastatic " Brake

In this brake, which is shown in Fig. 29-13, the clearance between the shoes and drum when the brake is off is reduced to negligible amounts and the shoes may actually be in contact with the drum. In an ordinary brake this would involve a drag that would affect the performance of the car and lead to excessive wear of the linings. These drawbacks are obviated in the Girling design by a careful balancing of the forces acting on the shoes. The adjustable anchorage A is of the usual Girling type and the shoes B and C are of simple T-section. A single spring D holds the shoes in contact with the anchorage plungers and the strength of this spring is carefully controlled. The expanding mechanism is arranged for both fluid and mechanical actuation, the former by a simple double acting cylinder whose pistons bear directly on the toes of the shoes and the latter by a wedge expander E which acts on the shoes through plungers FF of rectangular section. These plungers and the wedge E are free to slide in slots formed in the face of the

580

hydraulic cylinder casting and are held in position by a cover plate. Rollers G are provided to reduce friction and are left free to slide in the slot of the expander so as to equalize the forces applied to the shoes. The plungers F are retracted by the spring Q. The lining of the leading shoe is in two parts, J and K, and the trailing end of the latter is pressed outwards by a spring loaded plunger L so that when the brakes are off it stands a few thousandths of an inch higher than the remainder of the lining. Any contact between the lining and the drum is thus on this raised portion and this is well away from the leading edge of the shoe so that there is no tendency for the shoe to put itself on. The strength of the spring M is of great importance; it must be such that its moment about the anchorage just balances the moment due to the spring D. In order that the weight of the shoe shall not upset the balance of the forces acting on it the shoes are linked by a balance lever N and links PP so that the weight of the upper shoe balances that of the lower one. The lever N is pivoted on a post secured to the back plate and anti-rattle screws, which are adjusted so as just to bear on the webs of the shoes, are

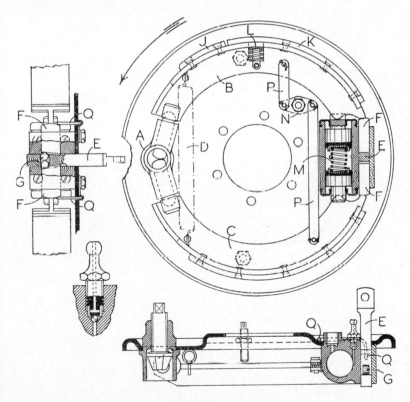

Fig. 29-13

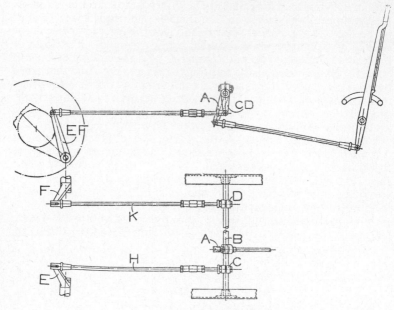

Fig. 29-14: Uncompensated brake linkage

also screwed into the back plate as shown in the plan view. The hydraulic cylinder is provided with a bleeder screw the arrangement of which is shown in the enlarged view inset.

29.10 Brake Linkages

By the phrase " brake linkage " is meant the arrangement of rods and levers by means of which the brake pedal or hand lever is connected to the actuating lever of the brakes themselves. These linkages may have to provide means of taking up the wear of the brake linings and they must be such that the up and down motions of the wheels do not affect the action of the brakes. The brakes have to be applied at least in pairs, because if a single brake were applied the car would skid sideways. The linkages in use are of two kinds—uncompensated and compensated.

An uncompensated linkage for rear brakes only is shown in Fig. 29-14. The hand lever is pivoted on a pin carried by a bracket attached to the frame member. The short arm of this lever is coupled by a rod to an arm A attached to a cross-shaft B. The latter is carried in bearings in brackets fixed to the frame members and, in addition to the arm A, carries two arms, C and D. These are situated in line with the brake actuating levers E and F, to which they are connected by rods H K. When the hand lever is pulled over, the levers E and F are turned through small angles,

582

thus expanding or contracting the brakes. Suppose now that the clearances between the shoes and drums of the two brakes are unequal. The levers E and F will then have to be turned through different angles in order to take up those clearances and bring the shoes into contact with the drums. The linkage, however, moves those levers through equal angles, and it follows that in this case the shoes of the brake having the greater clearance will not come into contact with the drum at all, and only the other brake will be applied. This defect can be remedied by shortening the rod (H or K) of the brake having the greater clearance until the clearances

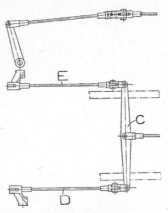

Fig. 29-15: Simple type of balanced linkage

are equal, when the brakes will be applied simultaneously. Even with correct adjustment, however, the pulls in the rods will be unequal if the shoe linings on one side compress more readily than those on the other side, and the brakes will be unequally applied.

In the linkage shown in Fig. 29-15, however, the pulls in the rods D, E must always be equal, because the rods are attached to a beam C pivoted at its centre like the beam of a pair of scales. With this linkage, if the clearances in the brakes are unequal, the brakes will still be applied simultaneously, the action being as follows: Suppose the clearances in the off-side brake are greater than those in the near-side one. At first the beam C will move parallel to itself until the time arrives when the near-side clearances are taken up and the shoes come into contact with the drum. The near-side end of the beam will then become a fulcrum, and the beam will tilt slightly, thus continuing to pull the off-side rod and the remaining clearance in the off-side brake will be taken up. The forces in the rods have up to now been small, just enough to overcome friction and the forces of the pull-off springs of the brake shoes. Both brakes being now in contact with their drums, the forces in the rods increase and the brakes are applied. Since the pulls in the rods D, E must be equal, the brakes must be applied approximately equally.

This type of linkage is called a compensated or balanced linkage, and the beam C is called a compensating or balance beam.

29.11 Compensating Mechanisms

The construction described above is somewhat crude, and although almost identical constructions are used on some lorries, more compact and neater constructions are adopted on cars. The principle of these other arrangements is still that of the balance beam, however. On cars the beam is usually made quite short, being only some 6 to 12 inches long, and is often arranged to lie vertically, the rod from one end then going direct to one brake while the other end of the beam is attached to the arm of a cross-shaft having a second arm on its other end connected to the other brake.

Another construction employs a pulley, the pivot of which is pulled by the rod connected to the brake pedal or hand lever. A flexible wire cable passes round the pulley and the ends of the cable are connected to the actuating levers of the brakes. Obviously the pulls in the two parts of the cable must be approximately equal. This construction is unsatisfactory if the pulleys are small in diameter.

A very good, but rather expensive, construction used on some high-class cars is similar to a bevel differential. The brake pedal or hand lever is coupled by a rod to an arm on the differential casing which carries a single planet bevel pinion. This meshes with two bevel wheels fixed to shafts that at their outer ends carry arms connected by rods to the brakes. The shafts are carried in suitable bearings in the frame, and their common axis is, of course, perpendicular to the centre line of the car. As in the differential the torques applied to the cross-shafts are equal, and hence the forces applied to the brakes.

29.12 Girling Brake Linkage

In this the forces for expanding the brake shoes are transmitted from the pedal to the shoes almost entirely by rods in tension, that is, rods subjected to pulls in the direction of their length and there is an almost complete absence of shafts subject to twisting and bending actions and having to be carried in bearings. The linkage is fully compensated, three compensating levers being used, one between front and back, one between near and off side at the front and the third between near and off side at the rear. One design of the compensator between front and back is shown in Fig. 29-16. The brake pedal A is pivoted on a short shaft at B and a lever C, fixed to the shaft, carries the compensating lever D on a pin at E. The upper end of the lever D is coupled by a short rod F (subject to a compression) to a lever G pivoted on a pin carried by any convenient part of the frame and thence by a rod in tension to the front compensator. The lower end of the lever D is coupled by a rod H, acting in tension, to the rear compensator. The effect of the arrangement is that, provided the arms of the levers D and G are equal, the forces P and Q transmitted to the front and back brakes are equalized.

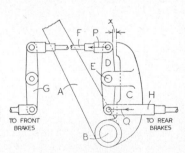

Fig. 29-16

584

As a safeguard against the breakage of either of the rods going to the front and rear compensators, stops are arranged for the ends of the lever D, small clearances being provided when the brakes are properly adjusted. Supposing the rod H should break then the lever D would pivot on its pin until the clearance " x " was taken up and then the front brakes would be applied. Similarly if the rod to the front brakes were to fracture the lever D would pivot until its lower end came up against the stop and then the rear brakes would be applied. In either case the travel of the brake pedal would be increased somewhat but the stops make it a practical certainty that one pair of brakes will always be available. The equality of the forces applied to the front and rear brakes will be upset if the lever D is not free to pivot on its pin, hence it is important that when the linkage is adjusted the lever D should be examined to see that the clearances at its ends are approximately equal. By making the arms of the lever D unequal in length a greater proportion of the pedal force can be transmitted to the front (or rear) brakes if that is desirable because of the weight distribution between the axles. The same result can also be obtained by using additional levers at other points of the linkage.

The compensators between the sides are of two kinds, shown in Figs. 29-17 and 18, but the principle of both is the same and the same description will apply. The rod from the brake pedal is coupled to the arm M of a three-armed member L whose other arms N and R are coupled to the brake shoe expanding wedges. The member L is pivoted on the stem of a member S which in turn is pivoted on a pin carried by a bracket on any convenient part of the axle casing (for the rear brakes) or frame (for the front brakes) when independent suspension is used. The assembly consisting of S and L is thus free to pivot about the axis XX and hence the forces P and Q applied to the brakes and which are the only forces having any moments about the axis XX, must be equal.

The shoe expanding mechanism used with the Girling linkage has been described previously.

The mechanical efficiency of this expanding mechanism is far

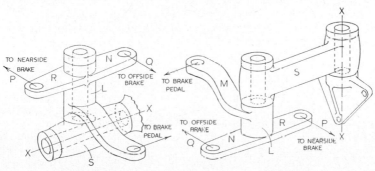

Fig. 29-17   Fig. 29-18

THE MOTOR VEHICLE

higher than is that of the ordinary cam mechanism and the mechanical efficiency of the Girling linkage is also higher than that of conventional linkages which contain numerous shafts carried in bearings that are usually badly lubricated. This enables a lower leverage between pedal and brake shoes to be used and that in turn makes the intervals between necessary adjustments longer.

29.13   Leverage and Adjustment of the Brake Linkage

The forces that have to be applied to the brake shoes in order to produce the maximum deceleration of the vehicle in an emergency stop are very large, approximating to the weight of the vehicle, and to enable the driver to produce these forces with an effort which cannot exceed about 150 lb and which is normally kept down to about one-third of that amount, the brake linkage has to provide a considerable leverage.   The leverage that can be provided, however, is strictly limited by several factors.   Firstly, a definite clearance has usually to be maintained between the brake shoes and drum; supposing this to be only 0·01 in. then, with a leverage between the shoes and brake pedal of 100 to 1, one inch of pedal travel would be required merely to take up the clearance.   Secondly, the brake linkage cannot be made rigid and so when the brake pedal force is applied the parts of the linkage stretch and give slightly and to take up this stretch may use up another inch of pedal travel.   Now the total travel that can be conveniently accommodated is limited to about 4 in. and so only 2 in. is available to take up the wear of the linings and this corresponds, with the leverage assumed above, to only 0·02 in.   It will thus be seen that it is important to keep the leverage provided down to the lowest value consistent with reasonable pedal pressures and to keep the " stretch " of the brake linkage (including deformation of the brake drums themselves) as low as possible.   But even when this has been done the brakes will still have to be adjusted at intervals.   The best place for this adjustment is as close to the brake shoes as possible and in cars nowadays the adjustment is always either at the anchorage or between the actuating mechanism and the shoes.   The reasons for this will be seen from the following considerations.

When a rod pulls on a lever as shown in Fig. 29-19 (1) the torque on the lever is the pull P multiplied by the perpendicular distance OA. In order to get the maximum torque on the lever the latter should, therefore, be perpendicular to the brake when the brake is " on." When a lever pulls on a rod, however, a different adjustment is required.   The first part of the movement goes to take up the clearance between the brake shoes and drum and the adjustment required is such as will bring this about for the smallest movement of the lever.   This is obtained when the movement of the lever is equal on either side of the position in which it is square with the rod, as shown at (2), since the horizontal movement x for a given angular movement θ is then greatest.   As soon as the clearances have been taken up, however, an adjustment is required that will

586

give the maximum pull in the rod for a given torque on the lever. This requires the lever to be in the position shown at (3) rather than in that shown at (4) since then the pull in the rod has a smaller turning moment on the lever and conversely a given turning moment on the lever produces a greater pull in the rod. It will be seen that these two adjustments are mutually incompatible and so a compromise has to be made. The lever is therefore put at or near

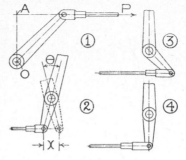

Fig. 29-19

the square position when the brake is " off," and the initial adjustment is as shown in Fig. 29-20.

As the brake linings wear the levers will move away from the best positions and if the adjustment to take up the wear were placed at the pedal end of the linkage this deterioration would continue and the effectiveness of the linkage would become progressively less. If, however, the adjustment is made at the brake shoes then after the adjustment has been made the linkage will be restored to its initial condition.

When adjustments are made with no load on the vehicle a check should be made with a load on, to determine that the brake shoes are clear of the drums when the brake is " off." This is because the flexing of the springs sometimes pulls the brakes on slightly, and if the clearance is small when the vehicle is unloaded the brakes may rub when a load is on. Such rubbing will cause overheating and possibly seizure of the brakes. For the same reason, when a lorry is being unloaded on an incline the wheels should be " chocked," in case the brakes should be released when the load is removed.

After the adjustment of a compensated linkage the compensating beam should lie square with the rods attached to it. An uncompensated linkage should be adjusted with the wheels jacked up so

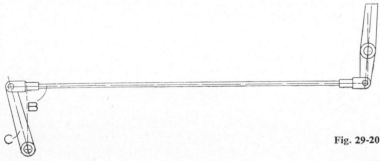

Fig. 29-20

587

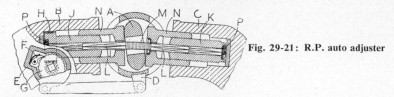

Fig. 29-21: R.P. auto adjuster

that it can be felt that all the brakes go on together. After this adjustment has been made, it is advisable to run the car down a fairly long hill with the brakes applied and at the bottom to feel the brake drums. If one drum feels much cooler than the others that brake is not doing its share of the work and it should be adjusted and another trial made. If such a trial is not made, then, until the brakes have worn themselves in, the danger of sideslip on greasy roads will be increased.

29.14 Auto Adjusters

Several devices for automatically adjusting the brakes so as to maintain approximately constant clearance between the brake shoes and drum are in use and one example is given in Fig. 29-21; it is the R.P. mechanism made by Clayton Dewandre, Ltd.

As the cam A is turned anticlockwise so as to expand the shoes B and C the arm D, which is fixed to the cam, causes the pawl casing E to rotate in an anticlockwise direction also. If the clearance between the shoes and drum is normal the shoes will come into contact with the drum before the pawl F rides over a tooth of the ratchet wheel G and when the brake is released no adjusting action will occur but if the clearance is greater than the normal by a pre-determined amount the pawl will ride over a tooth of the ratchet wheel and then when the brake is released the pawl will turn the ratchet wheel. The latter is fixed on the end of a shaft having an integral worm which meshes with teeth H formed on a screw J The latter is consequently rotated slightly and this rotation is com-municated to the screw K of the other shoe by the square rods LL which are connected together by the flexible shaft M. The screws J and K are thus screwed out of the nuts NN slightly and the clearance between the shoes and drum is reduced slightly. This action will occur every time the brakes are operated until the clearance has been reduced to the normal amount. The actual clearance maintained by the mechanism can be altered by altering the angle through which the pawl casing is rotated by the cam and this can be done by altering the length of the arm D. The nuts N are prevented from rotating by flanges formed on the cam and which embrace flats formed on the nuts. Hardened pads P are provided to transmit the thrust of the cam to the shoes.

In the latest design of this mechanism the casing E is not coupled to the cam A but to a pin fixed in the back plate of the brake. The action is the same as before except that the rotations of the casing E are now due solely to the motion of the brake shoe whereas in the design shown they are due to both the motion of the cam and that of the brake shoe. The later design has been found a little more reliable than the earlier one in which trouble sometimes arose from wear of the camshaft bearings.

Mechanisms of this kind can maintain the brake shoe clearances within a range of about 0·010 in. If attempts at maintaining very small clearances are made trouble may arise from the expansion of the brake drums due to temperature rises and to the stresses set up by the pressure of the brake shoes; the automatic adjuster may be operated by movement of the brake shoes consequent on these drum expansions and then when the expansions disappear the shoes may rub on the drum.

By using three separate pawls F whose lengths differ by one-third of the pitch of the ratchet teeth the effect of a ratchet having very fine teeth is obtained at the same time as the strength of much coarser teeth.

29.15 Hydraulic Systems

A fluid enclosed in a pipe may be used instead of rods or cables to connect the operating lever to the brake actuating levers. The general arrangement of such a system is as follows: The foot pedal actuates the piston in a " master " cylinder and forces fluid along a piping system to operating cylinders situated in the wheel brakes. The pistons of the operating cylinders are forced out and thus operate the brake shoes. Since all the operating cylinders are connected to the one master cylinder, it follows that the pressure in all the cylinders is the same, and hence compensation is automatically obtained. It is important that all air should be eliminated from the piping system and cylinders, because if air is present then, when the piston of the master cylinder is depressed, instead of fluid being forced along the pipes into the operating cylinders the air in the piping will be compressed, and since air is readily compressible the pressure in the system may not rise sufficiently to actuate the brakes. Of course, if enough travel could be given to the master piston the presence of air would not matter, because the air could be compressed sufficiently to raise the pressure until the brakes were operated; it is not possible to do this, however. Arrangements are therefore made to keep air out of the system.

A Lockheed master cylinder is shown in Fig. 29-22. It is integral with a reservoir which should always contain a reserve of fluid in order to keep the cylinder submerged and thus keep air out of the system. The piston is fitted with a rubber sealing cup and when pressed in by the brake pedal forces fluid into the piping system connecting the master cylinder to the operating cylinders in the brakes. The fluid passes through the holes A in the valve at the end of the cylinder by depressing the lip of the rubber cup B. When the brake pedal is released the returning fluid has to lift the whole valve against the pressure of the piston return spring and this

589

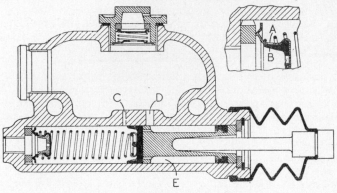

Fig. 29-22

ensures the maintenance of a slight pressure in the piping system
when the brakes are off so that fluid will tend to leak out rather
than air to leak in. The hole C which is uncovered by the piston
when in the off position enables fluid to enter the cylinder from the
reservoir if necessary. The hole D allows fluid to fill the annular
space E and this forms a safeguard against the leakage of air past
the piston. The valve in the filler cap keeps the reservoir sealed but
will allow air to enter if the pressure inside the reservoir should
fall below atmospheric pressure.

A Girling direct operating master cylinder is shown in Fig. 29-23.
It consists of two main castings A and B which are held together by
three studs and nuts. A metal disc C ensures the concentricity of
the two parts and forms the inner bearing for the plunger D, which
has an outer bearing in the bush E. The plunger carries the pedal
pad and is protected by the volute return spring F; a key L fitting
in a groove in the member B prevents the plunger and pedal pad
from turning. The pressure chamber G is connected by the piping
system to the operating cylinders and is sealed by the cup rubber H.
Another cup rubber is provided behind the bush E. The inner
bore of the cup rubber H is stepped so that when the plunger is

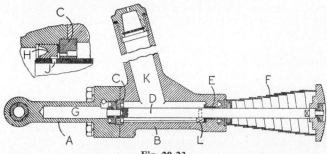

Fig. 29-23

fully out the small holes J are uncovered on the outside and fluid from the reserve tank K can, if necessary, pass through the holes in the disc C and into the pressure chamber G. When the brakes are off there is no pressure in the piping system.

A Girling " tension " type master cylinder is shown in Fig. 29-24. This is used in a " hydro-mechanical " brake system in which the front wheel brakes are operated by fluid and the rear wheel brakes by a mechanical linkage. The two main castings forming the master cylinder are held together by studs and nuts and are centred by the disc A which forms a bearing for the piston B. The piston rod also has a bearing in the left-hand casting and is coupled to the brake pedal and to the hand brake. A rod screwed into the right-hand casting connects the cylinder to the rear brake linkage. The pressure chamber is connected by a flexible hose to the pipe leading to the front brakes and is sealed by the cup rubbers C and D. The latter is expanded by a metal expander and the light spring shown. The cup rubber C is stepped in its bore so that fluid may enter the pressure chamber from the reservoir when the piston B is fully retracted. The reservoir is a separate tank and is connected to

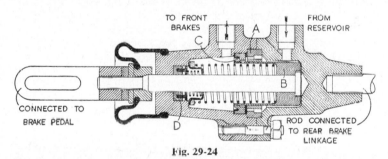

Fig. 29-24

he master cylinder by a flexible hose. When the brake pedal is depressed a pressure is set up in the pressure chamber and this pressure is communicated to the front wheel brakes by the fluid in the piping system and applies the front brakes. The pull applied to the piston rod is also transmitted direct through the master cylinder body and the rod to the rear brake linkage and applies the rear brakes. This system gives automatic compensation between the front and rear brakes, makes the use of two leading shoe brakes simple at the front wheels and complies with the law regarding the independence of the hand and foot brakes.

29.16   Lockheed Tandem Master Cylinder

This was devised to avoid the possibility of all the brakes of a vehicle being put out of action by a fracture in the pipe line leading to one brake cylinder. The master cylinder (Fig. 29-25) is provided with two pistons A and B the former being operated directly by the brake pedal. The space between the pistons is connected

591

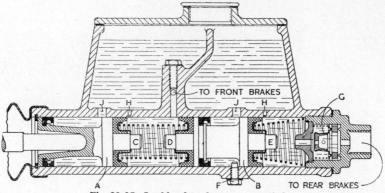

TO FRONT BRAKES

TO REAR BRAKES

Fig. 29-25: Lockheed tandem master cylinder

(through a non-return valve not shown, but similar to that seen at G) to the front brakes while the space between the piston B and the end of the cylinder is connected to the rear brakes. If the piping system is in order then when the brake pedal is depressed a pressure will be set up in the space between the pistons and hence in the operating cylinders of the front brakes. Since the piston B is free to move along the cylinder an equal pressure will be set up in the operating cylinders of the rear brakes. Thus, full compensation is still obtained. If, however, there is a fault in the piping system to the front brakes then no pressure will be set up in the space between the pistons and the piston B will not move until the projections C and D come into contact. When this occurs, however, the piston B will be moved directly by the brake pedal and the rear brakes will be operated. If a fault exists in the piping system to the rear brakes the piston B will move along the cylinder until the projection E strikes the end of the cylinder and until then no pressure will be generated. After the projection E has come into contact, however, further motion of the brake pedal will actuate the front brakes. Clearly the adjustments of the brakes must be attended to carefully so as to avoid the possibility of the available stroke of one of the pistons being used up before the brakes it operates are applied.

The return motion of the piston B is limited by the stop screw F.

29.17 Operating Cylinders

Various types of operating cylinders are used according to circumstances; one type is open at both ends and is fitted with two pistons which bear, either directly or through simple struts, on the brake shoes which are operated when fluid is forced in between the pistons. This type must clearly be situated inside the brake drum and this is sometimes a drawback since the space available is very limited and also the temperature may rise considerably and thus lead to vaporization of the brake fluid. An example is seen in Fig. 29-13. A second type of operating cylinder is closed at one end and has a single piston; this type may be placed either inside or outside the brake drum and may be used to operate a single brake shoe or a pair of shoes. For the latter purpose the operating cylinder is sometimes pivoted to one of the shoes and has its piston pivoted to the other shoe and is connected to the piping system by a flexible pipe. Alternatively the cylinder may be carried by the back plate of the brake but be free to slide, parallel to the cylinder axis, on that back plate; the piston then bears on one brake shoe and the cylinder on the other shoe. When only one shoe has to be operated the cylinder will be fixed to the back plate and the piston will bear on the shoe. A " bleeder " screw is usually incorporated in the operating cylinders so that the piping system may be bled until it is free of air. This is done as follows. A piece of rubber pipe is connected to the nipple of the bleeder screw (see, for example, Fig. 29-13) and its end is kept submerged below the level of some brake fluid contained in a glass jar. The reservoir of the master cylinder is filled with fluid and is kept full during the bleeding operation. The bleeder screw is then loosened a turn or two and the brake pedal is pushed down and allowed to come *right* up several times so that fluid is pumped through the piping system and out through the bleeder screw into the glass jar and pumping is continued until the fluid coming out is seen to be free of air. The bleeder screw is then tightened. Each bleeder screw throughout the system is treated in this way.

A single acting Lockheed operating cylinder that incorporates provision for the mechanical operation of the brake shoes is shown in Fig. 29-26. The body A is carried by the back plate B but is free to slide parallel to the cylinder axis. The piston is made in two parts C and D and bears, through a *Micram* adjuster, on the leading shoe of the brake. The cylinder body bears on the trailing shoe at E. When fluid enters the cylinder a force is exerted on the piston and thus on the leading shoe; the reaction of this force acts on the cylinder body and is transmitted to the trailing shoe, because, as mentioned above, the body is free to slide on the back plate. Mechanical operation is through the lever F which is pivoted on the pin G carried by the cylinder body. When the lever is pulled inwards (towards the centre of the car or upwards in the figure) it applies a force to the piston member D and thus to the leading shoe. The reaction of this force acts on the pin G and is

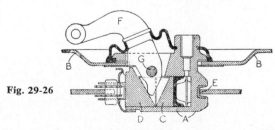

Fig. 29-26

593

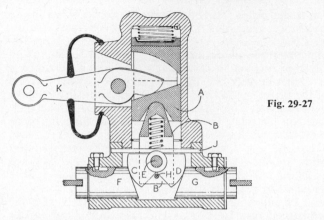

Fig. 29-27

transmitted by the cylinder body to the trailing shoe. A rubber filling piece is provided in the cylinder in order to reduce the volume of fluid enclosed inside the brake drum where it is subject to any temperature rise that may occur.

An external operating cylinder of Lockheed design is shown in Fig. 29-27. The piston is again in two parts and bears on a strut B which carries the members C and D on a pin E. The members C and D bear on the plungers F and G which, in turn, bear on the brake shoes. When fluid enters the cylinder the piston and strut are forced down and the plungers F and G are forced apart, thus applying the brake shoes. The sectors C and D provide a rolling action so that friction is eliminated and also provide a toggle action so that an increasing leverage is obtained. Also since the strut B has a spherical seating in the piston A it can move sideways at its bottom end and thus equalize the forces applied to the two plungers. The pin J serves as an anchorage for the return spring of the strut B and the pin H holds the sectors C and D in place during assembly of the mechanism. For mechanical actuation the lever K is pulled upwards so as to force the piston A downwards and apply the brake shoes as before.

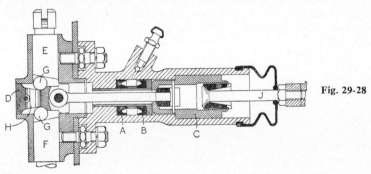

Fig. 29-28

594

A Girling external operating cylinder arranged for mechanical operation is shown in Fig. 29-28. Fluid from the master cylinder enters between the cup rubbers A and B and forces the piston C to the right. The wedge D is thereby pulled to the right and actuates the plungers E and F through the rollers G which eliminate sliding friction. Since the member H is free to slide in the wedge D it follows that the forces applied to the brake shoes are equalized. Mechanical operation is by the rod J and does not involve movement of the cup rubber B, neither is the rod J moved when the brake is applied by the fluid.

29.18 Disc Brakes

Brakes using flat discs as the friction elements have been used at various times during the last forty years and one make, the Tru-Stop brake, has been used extensively as a transmission brake. In recent years the disc brake has become the principal type for use on the front wheels of cars and on some classes of commercial vehicle. In high performance cars they are used almost exclusively and on all four wheels.

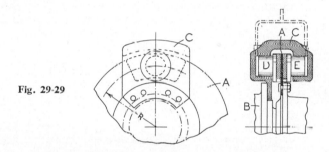

Fig. 29-29

The earliest disc brakes were made on the same lines as a multiple disc clutch but as they were not successful they need not be mentioned further. Those now in use may be classified as

(*a*) Non-self-energizing brakes.

(*b*) Self-energizing brakes.

In the latter the frictional forces are used to assist in the application of the brake whereas in the former they are not so used.

Modern brakes of the first type all use a single disc which is part of the wheel assembly and rotates with it while the friction elements are small pads which can be pressed against the faces of the disc. The simplest constructional arrangement is indicated in Fig. 29-29. The disc A is secured to the wheel hub which rotates on bearings on the stub axle B or on the axle casing for a rear wheel brake. The stub axle carries a calliper member C in which are formed two actuating cylinders which accommodate pistons D and E. The outer ends of the pistons are fixed to the pads which carry the

595

friction linings. Since the pressures set up in the two cylinders will be equal the axial forces applied to the disc are balanced. The brake torque is given by

$$T = 2\mu p a R$$

where μ is the coefficient of friction, p is the fluid pressure, a is the area of each cylinder and R is the distance from the wheel axis to the effective centre of the friction pads, which may be taken to be as shown. Although the axial forces on the disc are balanced there will be an unbalanced radial force equal to $2\mu p a$ acting on the disc and this force will have to be supported by the wheel bearings. By using two callipers placed diametrically opposite, the brake torque can be doubled and the radial forces on the disc be made to balance. This simple construction has two disadvantages: it is difficult to support the pistons adequately and to prevent the frictional forces from producing undue wear of the cylinders, and it is difficult to find the necessary space to house the actuating cylinder which lies on the wheel side of the disc. The first difficulty can be overcome by a slight increase in the complexity of the construction but the second one remains.

An alternative arrangement is shown in Fig. 29-30. In this there is only one piston and the calliper C is carried on links FF so that it can float sideways. This floating freedom is essential in order to

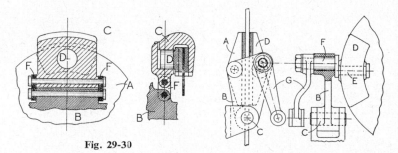

Fig. 29-30

Fig. 29-31

ensure equality between the forces acting between the friction linings and the disc. The freedom could also be provided by leaving the disc free to slide axially on splines but this is not usually satisfactory.

In the Tru-Stop brake which is shown in Fig. 29-31, equality between the forces acting between the friction linings and the disc is obtained by leaving the link B, which carries the two shoes, free to pivot on the fixed pin C which is carried by a part of the gear box casing. The shoe A is pivoted on a pin which is fixed in the link B while the shoe D is pivoted on the pin E of a crank or eccentric F, which is carried in bearings in the link B and to which the actuating lever G is fixed. When a pull is applied to the lever G the shoes are drawn together and grip the disc.

596

Clearly these forms of disc brake provide much smaller areas of friction lining than an ordinary shoe brake of the same overall dimensions and it might be supposed that the wear of the linings would be excessive but in practice this is not found to be so. The explanation appears to be that the cooling of the brake is improved because most of the disc area is exposed and so the temperature of the linings is kept down; it is well known that the rate of wear of brake linings for a given rate of energy dissipation increases rapidly when the temperature goes up.

An example of the self-energizing type of disc brake is shown in Fig. 29-32, which indicates a recent design of the Argus brake which was developed in Germany just before 1939. The brake drum is made in two parts A and B and is bolted up to the wheel hub so that it is the rotating member. The friction linings CC are complete rings and are carried by the discs D and E. These are centred on the axle casing F and a key G prevents the disc D from rotating. One disc has an annular cylinder J formed in it and the other has a corresponding annular piston. The brake is applied by admitting fluid into the cylinder J which thus forces the discs apart axially and brings the friction linings into contact with the faces of the drum. As soon as the disc E makes contact the friction will tend to rotate it and so the balls H (of which there are usually six) are made to ride up the sloping sides of the conical recesses in which they are housed and thus to increase the axial force between the discs and the drum. The extent to which the fluid pressure actuating force is thus augmented depends on the angle of the conical recesses, the shallower the recesses the greater the augmentation.

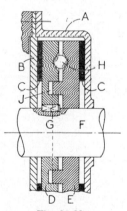

Fig. 29-32

In an actual example of this construction the cylinder J and its piston are made separate from the discs to which they are attached in order that they may be insulated from the discs. If this is not done the actuating fluid in the cylinder is likely to become over-heated.

Purely mechanical methods of forcing the discs apart are sometimes used.

An alternative construction is shown in Fig. 29-33, in which the discs D and E are both anchored by the key G but, because the keyways in them are wider than the key, only for rotation in one direction: disc D against clockwise and E against anti-clockwise motion. The brake is applied by admitting fluid to the actuating cylinder J which bears on a lug K of the disc D while the piston L bears on a lug M of the disc E. The fluid pressure thus forces the discs to rotate slightly in opposite directions and the balls H then produce the axial displacement to bring the friction linings into contact with the drum. When contact is made the friction on the linings will tend to rotate the discs and,

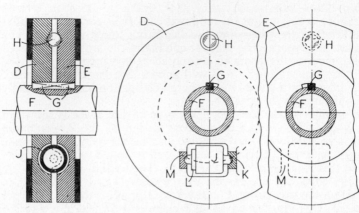

Fig. 29-33

depending on the direction of rotation of the brake drum, one or other of the discs will come up against the key G and be anchored by it while the other disc will be anchored only by the balls H which will therefore provide the self-energizing action. The brake torque can be shown to be given by the expression

$$T = \frac{2\mu p a R R_c}{R_b \cos \alpha - \mu R \sin \alpha}$$

where p is the pressure in the actuating cylinder, a is the piston area R the mean radius of the friction rings, R_b the radius of the circle on which the balls H are situated, R_c the distance between the axis of the discs and the axis of the actuating cylinder, and 2α is the included angle of the conical recesses. As α is made larger so the denominator of the expression giving the brake torque gets smaller and so the brake torque becomes greater. The angle α thus controls the self-energizing action and there is a limiting value for it beyond which the brake will lock itself on as soon as contact is made between the friction linings and the drum. This value must not be approached too closely. This arrangement of the disc brake will require a lower actuating pressure p for a given brake torque, all other factors being the same, than will be needed in the arrangement of Fig. 29-32. This is because in the former the actuating force itself is magnified by the wedging action of the balls. On the other hand the design of Fig. 29-32 makes it easier to provide a larger cylinder area. The self-energizing disc brake will require smaller actuating forces at the brakes than the non-self-energizing types. With the latter servo systems may have to be used to keep the brake pedal efforts down to reasonable values or the leverage of the brake actuating linkage may have to be higher than with other types of brake. If extra high leverages are used then it becomes imperative to use automatic brake clearance adjusters.

CHAPTER 30

Servo- and Power-operated Brake Systems

AS the weight of a vehicle goes up the force that must be exerted on the pedal of a simple brake system in order to produce the maximum deceleration permitted by the state of the road also goes up and when the weight exceeds 2 to 3 tons may become greater than a man can exert. The driver must then be given some assistance in applying the brakes. This can be done in two ways, (a) by using a " servo " mechanism which adds to the driver's effort although that effort remains a considerable part of the total effort applied to the brakes, or (b) by using " power operation " in which case the effort of the driver is a controlling effort only and is not transmitted to the brakes at all.

Servo systems are usually lower in cost than power-operated systems and can frequently be fitted as an addition to a vehicle having an ordinary brake system. They are widely used on vehicles coming within the medium weight range, say, 2 to 6 tons, whereas power operation is used for heavy vehicles where the weight exceeds 6 tons or so and for vehicles used with trailers.

There are two essential features of both servo and power brake systems; these are (1) the " time-lag " of the system, that is the time interval between the moment when the brake pedal is depressed and the moment when the brakes come on, must be very small and (2) the system must be such that the driver can judge the intensity of application of the brakes fairly accurately. The second feature usually requires that the force applying the brakes shall be closely proportional to the force exerted by the driver on the brake pedal.

The source of the additional effort supplied by a servo system may be (a) the momentum of the vehicle itself; (b) vacuum in a reservoir, obtained by connecting the reservoir through a non-return valve either to the induction manifold of the engine or to a separately driven exhauster; (c) oil under pressure supplied by a pump driven by the engine or some part of the transmission system; (d) air under pressure supplied by an air compressor driven by the engine.

Mechanical servo mechanisms are the only ones that use the momentum of the vehicle and they are now very rarely used. It has, however, been thought advisable to retain the description of one as an example of the type.

30.1 Principle of the Mechanical Servo

The principle of the mechanical servo mechanism is shown in Fig. 30-1. The disc A is geared permanently to some member of the transmission, such as the gear box mainshaft or the propeller

599

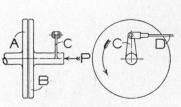

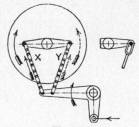

Fig. 30-1   Fig. 30-2

shaft, and is thus always revolving whenever the road wheels are revolving. A second disc B is arranged so as to be capable of being pressed against the disc A as in a single plate clutch. The shaft of the disc B has fixed to it a lever C that is coupled by a rod D to the brake linkage.

Supposing the car to be moving forwards so that the disc A is turning in the direction shown, then if the disc B is pressed into contact with the disc A with a force P a driving torque will act upon B tending to make it rotate in the same direction. The magnitude of this torque will depend upon the force P, the coefficient of friction between the discs and their dimensions. The disc B will turn slightly under the action of this torque, thereby pulling up the rod D and applying the brakes to such an extent that the pull in the rod D exerts a torque equal and opposite to the driving torque between the discs. When this condition is reached there will be no further motion of the disc B and slip will take place between the discs.

The above is the principle of most mechanical servo mechanisms. Differences between individual designs are in the arrangement of the " clutch " AB and in the arrangements adopted to overcome the following difficulty.

The disc A being in permanent connection with the driving wheels, if the latter are turning backwards the disc A will be turning backwards also, and instead of the brakes being applied they would be taken off. This difficulty has to be circumvented, and this may be done in several ways, two of which will be described.

The principle of the first method is shown in Fig. 30-2. Instead of carrying the operating arm C directly on the shaft of the disc B it is now made in the form of a bell-crank pivoted on a fixed pin somewhat below the discs. The short arm of the bell-crank is coupled by the rod D to the brake linkage, while the longer arm is coupled by short lengths of chain X and Y to points on the disc B diametrically opposite each other. If the disc B is turning in the clockwise direction, then the chain Y, being flexible and unable to transmit any force in compression, cannot cause the bell-crank to move. But the chain X can act in tension so as to pull the arm of the bell-crank up and thus apply the brakes. Similarly, if the disc B turns in the counter-clockwise direction the chain X is inoperative, but the chain Y can pull the arm of the bell-crank up and thus apply the brakes as before.

The second method of allowing for the reversing of the car consists of providing alternative drives to the disc A. Each of these drives incorporates a one-way ratchet, and one of them contains some form of reverse gear. Thus, when the car moves forward one ratchet is inoperative and the drive goes through the other, and the disc A is driven in the forwards direction. When the car reverses the last mentioned ratchet becomes inoperative and the drive goes through the first. But since there is a reverse gear between the driven member of this ratchet and the disc A the latter is still driven in the forwards direction.

30.2 Renault Servo Brake

The construction of a mechanical servo mechanism designed by the Renault Company is shown in Fig. 30-3. The disc A is in permanent driving connection with the mainshaft of the gear box, and, therefore, with the road wheels, through the worm C and worm wheel D, the latter being splined to the shaft carrying the disc A. The driven disc B is mounted on a sleeve to which is keyed the hub E, and a short length of chain connects a pin of that sleeve to a lever of the brake linkage. Between the two discs is a friction-fabric ring.

The brake pedal is coupled to the lever F, while lever H is coupled to the brake linkage; the bosses of these levers have inclined faces (similar to the claws of a starting handle), between which are situated steel balls K. When the brake pedal is depressed the levers F and H move round together until the clearances in the brake linkage are taken up, when further motion of the lever H is opposed. Lever F then moves on ahead of lever H and the balls K, riding up

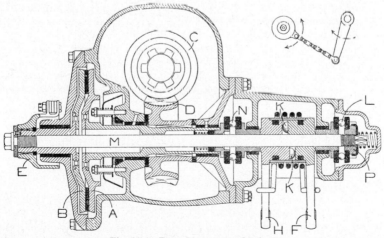

Fig. 30-3: Renault servo mechanism

the inclined faces of the lever bosses, cause the levers to move apart axially. Now the lever F bears through the thrust bearing L, nut P and rod M, against disc B, and lever H bears, through the bearing N, against the shaft carrying the disc A. Hence the discs A and B are pressed together, and a frictional torque then acts between them, tending to turn the disc B and to apply an additional force to the brake linkage through the chain connecting the boss E to that linkage. The use of this length of chain ensures that the brakes are applied whichever way the disc A may turn, that is, whether the car goes forwards or backwards, as will be seen by considering the end view inset in the corner of the figure. The relative position of the discs A and B, axially, can be adjusted by means of the nut P.

30.3 Vacuum Brake Operation

Vacuum may be used in two ways in the application of brakes. In each method a cylinder fitted with a piston, or diaphragm, is used and the piston is coupled to the mechanical brake linkage. In one method the cylinder is permanently open to the atmosphere at one end and is open to the atmosphere at the other end also when the brakes are off. The brakes are applied by exhausting the latter end of the cylinder to the desired degree thus setting up a force on the piston equal to the pressure difference on its two sides multiplied by its area. In the other system the cylinder is closed at both ends and when the brakes are off the same degree of vacuum exists in both ends. To apply the brakes one end is opened to the atmosphere so that the pressure in that end rises and gives a force on the piston which applies the brakes. The second system is commonly referred to as a " suspended vacuum " system. Its chief advantages over the first system are that it is slightly more rapid in action and that there is a smaller amount of air that has to be exhausted either by the engine through the induction manifold, or by the exhauster, if a separate one is used. Both of these advantages arise from the fact that under the second system vacuum has to be destroyed in a volume equal to the piston area multiplied merely by the piston travel necessary to apply the brakes; whereas in the first system the volume that has to be filled, and subsequently exhausted, is equal to the piston area multiplied by the maximum piston travel possible, plus any clearance which may then remain between the piston and the end of the cylinder. By increasing this clearance volume in a suspended vacuum system, the servo cylinder can be made to function as a vacuum tank and a separate tank can therefore be dispensed with. This is done in many light commercial vehicles.

30.4 Clayton Dewandre Master Servo Unit

The constructional form of this which is shown in Fig. 30-4 is in use in an immense number of vehicles but it is gradually being displaced by units employing the same principle but which are cheaper to produce. It consists of a drawn-steel cylinder A fitted

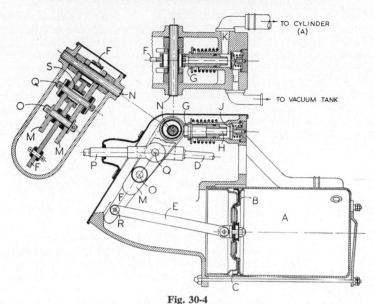

Fig. 30-4

with a piston B sealed by a cup-leather C. The piston is connected by a link E to the lower end R of a " balance " lever F, the upper end of which bears against the valve G. In the position shown, the right-hand end of this valve is clear of the face of the valve J so that the port H through the centre of the valve G opens the passage K and the cylinder A to the atmosphere. The balance lever F is pivoted on the pin O, which is carried by the support levers MM. The latter are pivoted on the fixed pin N. The brake pedal is coupled by the rod D to the balance lever at the point Q, but the connecting pivot pin S is hollow and there is ample clearance between it and the pin Q. The latter serves to couple the support levers MM to the brake linkage through the rod P. The arrangement is shown in perspective in Fig. 30-5.

When the brake pedal is depressed the balance lever is rotated clockwise about the pivot pin O, and its upper end pushes the valve G to the right. This seats on the valve J and thus closes the vent H to the atmosphere. It then pushes the valve J off its seat, so that the vacuum tank is put into communication with the cylinder A via the passages L and K. The pressure in the cylinder A starts

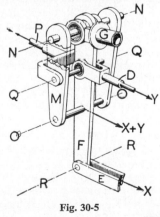

Fig. 30-5

to fall so that a force, X, is exerted, which tends to pull the lower end of the balance lever to the right. When this force reaches a value sufficient to balance the force applied by the rod D, the balance lever will be rotated slightly anti-clockwise, and this will bring the valve G to the " lap " or " brake applied " position, the valve J being seated but the vent H being still closed. In this position the cylinder A is isolated. The force X is now balancing the force Y applied by the brake pedal, and the relation of these forces is determined by the ratio of the lever arms of the balance lever. Thus

$$X \times RO = Y \times QO \text{ so that } X = Y \times \frac{QO}{RO}.$$

The resultant of the forces X and Y applied to the balance lever $\left[\text{equal approximately to } Y\left(1 + \frac{QO}{RO}\right)\right]$ is applied to the pin O and through the support levers and the rod P to the brake linkage. As the brakes come on, the support levers may rotate slightly, but this will not upset the balance of forces since in the " lap " position the upper end of the balance lever is concentric with the pivot N, about which the movement will be occurring.

The force transmitted to the brake linkage is thus seen to be proportional to the force applied by the driver to the brake pedal, and the degree to which the latter will be augmented by the servo is determined by the ratio of the lever arms of the balance lever.

If for any reason the vacuum formed in the cylinder A is insufficient, the brakes may be applied purely by the force Y, the action being as follows. The depression of the brake lever rotates the balance lever clockwise about the pin O until the clearance betwen the eye of the balance lever and the pin N is taken up. The pin N then becomes a fulcrum for the balance lever and the force Y can be transmitted through the pin O and the levers MM to the rod P. Since the rods D and P are approximately in line, the force in the rod P will then be equal to the force in the rod D.

When hydraulic actuation of the vehicle brakes is adopted, the master cylinder of the system is bolted up to the vacuum servo unit, but the latter is rearranged slightly. The rod D is now coupled to the support levers and operates the piston of the master cylinder, while the rod P is pivoted to the balance lever and connected to the brake pedal. The forces in the rods D and P will now be compressive forces instead of tension forces.

30.5 " Three Unit " System

In this system, which is much used, the vacuum master servo actuates the rear brakes direct, the rod P of the servo being coupled to the rear brake linkage. Each front brake, however, is provided with an operating cylinder mounted on the stub axle and the pistons of these cylinders are coupled to the camshaft levers of the brakes.

The cylinders are connected by pipes to the master servo cylinder. Thus the same degree of vacuum is set up in the front brake actuating cylinders as in the master servo cylinder and the intensity of the application of the front brakes, like that of the rear ones, is proportional to the brake pedal force.

This system is a power-operated system so far as the front brakes are concerned because none of the force applied by the driver to the brake pedal is transmitted to the front brakes.

30.6 Vacuum Trailer Brake Operation

Vacuum-operated brakes for trailers can be divided into two groups, (a) those in which a vacuum has to be set up in the trailer connecting pipe in order to operate the brakes and (b) those in which a vacuum exists in the trailer pipe when the brakes are off and the brakes are applied by reducing this vacuum.

A simple arrangement of the first kind is to provide the trailer with brake-operating cylinders whose pistons are coupled by simple linkages to the brakes and to connect those cylinders by pipes to the cylinder of the master servo of the tractor. The drawback of this simple arrangement is that a lengthy pipe has to be exhausted before the trailer brakes are applied and the time lag may be excessive so that there would be a danger of the trailer over-running the tractor.

When the tractor is not fitted with a master servo the trailer brakes may be controlled independently by means of a reaction valve such as is shown in Fig. 30-6. This uses a balance lever F pivoted on a pin O carried by support levers MM which are pivoted on a fixed pin N. The brake pedal rod is pivoted to the upper eye of the balance lever which encircles the pin Q carried by the support levers MM and to which the brake actuating rod P is pivoted. The lower eye of the balance lever surrounds the pin N and is connected

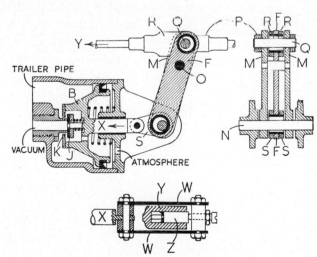

Fig. 30-6

to the piston B. When a force, Y, is applied by the brake pedal the balance lever turns about the pin O and the piston B is moved to the right ; this first seats the valve K, thus blanking off the trailer pipe from the atmosphere and then unseats the valve J, thus opening the trailer pipe to the vacuum reservoir. The vacuum set up in the cylinder A produces a force X acting to the left on the piston B and when this is sufficient to balance the force Y the piston will move slightly to the left, thus seating the valve J but not unseating K. The valve is then in equilibrium and the degree of vacuum in the trailer pipe is seen to be proportional to the force applied by the brake pedal rod since the forces X and Y are in the inverse ratio of the lever arms of the balance lever. The resultant of the forces X and Y (approximately equal to $X + Y$) is applied to the pin O and hence to the rod P. Thus the valve acts in a similar manner to the master servo unit but the brake pedal force is not increased so much.

When the tractor brake actuation is hydraulic the reaction valve for controlling the trailer brakes is slightly different from that described above, the difference being shown in the scrap plan view in Fig. 30-6. A small cylinder Y is connected to the hydraulic system of the tractor and its plunger Z is coupled by links W to the plunger X of the valve. When the valve is in the equilibrium position the force acting on the plunger Z is balanced by the force, due to the vacuum, acting on the piston B. The system is now, however, a power system so far as the trailer brakes are concerned since none of the effort of the driver is transmitted direct to the trailer brakes.

An example of the second type of system is shown in Fig. 30-7. The tractor vehicle incorporates a master servo whose cylinder is connected by a pipe to the control valve B which is also connected to the tractor reservoir and the trailer pipe line. The arrangement of the valve B is shown in Fig. 30-8. The trailer also has a valve exactly similar to the valve B and the illustration is annotated to show both these valves; the captions in brackets refer to the trailer valve. Considering the tractor valve, when the brakes are off the double

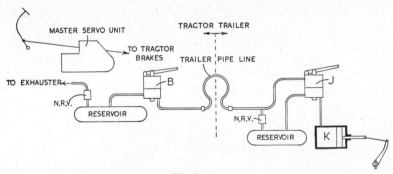

Fig. 30-7

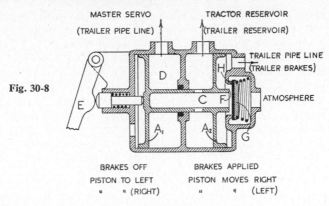

Fig. 30-8

piston $A_1 A_2$ is in the position shown and the trailer pipe is connected via the hollow stem C to the tractor reservoir. When the brake pedal is depressed a vacuum is set up in the master servo cylinder and thus in the left-hand side D of the valve B. Thus, a force will act on the piston A_1 which will move to the right. The face F will seat on the valve G and that valve will be forced off its seat H, thus opening the trailer pipe to the atmosphere. The pressure in the trailer pipe will rise and a force to the left will act on piston A_2. The rise of pressure (or reduction in vacuum) in the trailer pipe line will be just sufficient to make the forces on the pistons A_1 and A_2 balance and when this occurs the valve G will re-seat on the face H but the face F will still be seated on the valve G. The piston $A_1 A_2$ is now in equilibrium and the trailer pipe is isolated, the pressure in it being proportional to the degree of vacuum set up in the master servo cylinder and thus proportional to the brake pedal force. Since this valve sets up a pressure that is proportional to a vacuum it is sometimes called an *inverting* valve.

Turning now to the trailer it will be seen that there is a vacuum reservoir connected through a non-return valve (n.r.v.) to the trailer pipe line, a valve J (identical in construction to the valve B) and brake-operating cylinders K. When the brakes are off and the trailer pipe line is connected via the valve B to the tractor reservoir the trailer reservoir will be exhausted through the non-return valve and so the trailer reservoir vacuum will be the same as the tractor reservoir vacuum; hence the piston of the valve J (Fig. 30-8, with captions in brackets) will be in equilibrium with the valve G pushed off its seating H so that the trailer brake cylinders are open to the atmosphere. When the brake pedal is depressed and the pressure in the trailer pipe line rises the force acting to the left on piston A_1 will increase and the pistons will move to the left, thus seating valve G on the face H and unseating the face F. The trailer brakes will thus be connected to the trailer reservoir and the degree of vacuum set up in the brake cylinders will be such that the resulting force to the right on piston A_2 will just balance the force, to the left,

607

on A_1. The face F will then re-seat and the trailer brake cylinders will be isolated with a degree of vacuum in them which is proportional to the tractor brake pedal force.

30.7 Reservoirs

The reservoirs used with vacuum brake systems are usually simple cylindrical (sometimes spherical) vessels fitted with a non-return valve in the pipes connecting them with the induction manifold or the exhauster, as the case may be. A drain plug or cock is usually fitted at the lowest point. To give a sufficient reserve to enable several brake applications to be made even though the engine has stopped requires a large reservoir; but a large reservoir takes a long time to evacuate and this is a drawback. To overcome this difficulty dual reservoirs are sometimes used. These comprise

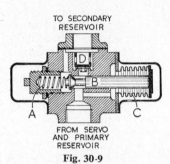

TO SECONDARY
RESERVOIR

FROM SERVO
AND PRIMARY
RESERVOIR

Fig. 30-9

a small tank which can be quickly evacuated and a large one which provides a suitable reserve but which does not begin to be evacuated until the small one has been completely evacuated. The diverter valve which governs this action is shown in Fig. 30-9. Until the small or primary tank is exhausted the spring A keeps the valve B on its seat and the large or secondary tank is blanked off. As the small tank is evacuated and the pressure in it falls a force acting to the left will be set up on the bellows C, which is subject to atmospheric pressure externally and to the pressure in the small tank internally. When the pressure in the small tank is reduced to the designed value the valve B will be unseated and the large tank will begin to be evacuated. The large tank supplements the small one when necessary because if the pressure in the small tank rises above that in the large tank the valve D will open and put the two tanks into communication.

30.8 Bendix " Hydrovac "

This comprises a vacuum servo combined with the master cylinder of an hydraulic brake actuation system. It is shown diagrammatically in Fig. 30-10, in which the sizes of the master cylinder and the vacuum valve system have been exaggerated relative to the other units in order to make the details clear. When the brake pedal is in the off position the valve A will be off its seat and so both sides of the piston B will be subject to vacuum and there will be no force acting on the piston. The plunger C, which is integral with the piston rod, will be off its seating in the piston H so that the hydraulic piping system leading to the brakes will be open to the master cylinder D and thus to the brake fluid reservoir. When the

608

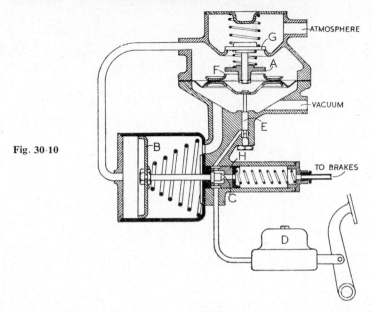

Fig. 30·10

brake pedal is depressed a pressure will be set up in the master cylinder and this pressure will act on the plunger E of the vacuum valve. The diaphragm F will be pushed up until it seats on the valve A and then the valve G will be pushed off its seat. The left-hand end of the vacuum cylinder will thus be opened to atmosphere and the pressure in it will rise so that a force will act on the piston B to push it to the right. The movement of the piston B will first seat the plunger C on to the piston H and then will force the latter into its cylinder so as to apply the brakes. The force due to the oil pressure acting on the left-hand side of the piston H will be added to the force due to the piston B so that the system is a servo system. The pressure in the left-hand end of the vacuum cylinder also acts on the top of the diaphragm F and when the pressure reaches a value sufficient to balance the hydraulic force applied to the plunger E the diaphragm will be depressed slightly and the valve G will be seated again. The left-hand end of the vacuum cylinder will then be isolated and the pressure in it will be proportional to the hydraulic pressure acting on the plunger E, that is, proportional to the brake pedal force. If for any reason no vacuum is available then the pressure set up in the master cylinder D will be transmitted direct to the brake cylinders because the plunger C will remain off its seat.

30.9   Hydraulic Servo Systems

As examples of hydraulic servos two systems produced by the Lockheed company will be described. The first of these is shown

609

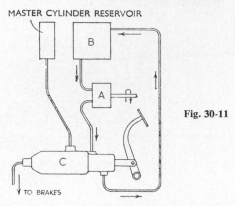

Fig. 30-11

in Fig. 30-11, and consists of a pump A which draws fluid from a tank B and circulates it through the servo unit C back to the tank, until the brake pedal is depressed. This closes the passage for the fluid because the plunger D (Fig. 30-12) seats on the end of the master cylinder piston E. Pressure therefore builds up in the space F and is exerted to the left on the annular area a of the master cylinder piston and to the right on the annular area b of the plunger D thus tending to separate those members. The pressure on the master cylinder piston will move it to the left, thus applying the brakes, the pedal and plunger D following up this motion. The magnitude of the pressure built up, and therefore the magnitude of the braking effort, will be proportional to the force applied by the driver to the brake pedal because when the pressure reaches a value such that the fluid force acting to the right on the plunger D just overbalances the force to the left applied by the brake pedal the plunger D will be forced slightly to the right, thus opening a passage for the fluid from the pump to flow back to the tank and the pressure will not increase further. When the brake pedal is released the plunger D will move to the right, thus causing the pressure in the space F to fall to zero and the brakes to be released.

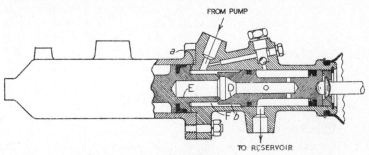

Fig. 30-12

The pump is driven by the engine or off any convenient point of the transmission and thus will not be operative when the engine or vehicle is at rest, and in this case the brakes can only be applied direct, the brake pedal force being transmitted direct from the plunger D to the master cylinder piston. The use of an accumulator enables power operation to be obtained at all times and a system of this kind is shown in Figs. 30-13 and 30-14.

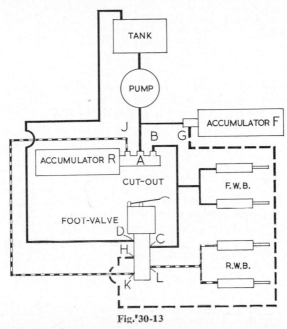

Fig. 30-13

In Fig. 30-13 the pump supplies fluid to the cut-out valve and in normal operation when the pump is running and the accumulators are charged up this fluid flows from A to B and thence from C to D through the driver's foot valve and so back to the supply tank. The pressure in the pipe line BC is then only a little above atmospheric and so the pump is running light. When the foot valve is depressed the flow from C to D is restricted and a pressure builds up in the pipe line BC and as this is connected to the actuating cylinders of the front brakes these are applied. As will be seen later the pressure that is set up will be proportional to the force applied by the driver to the brake pedal. If the pump is not running then the front brakes will be operated by the accumulator F which is coupled by the pipe GH to the foot valve and the flow will then be from H to C. The rear brakes are normally operated direct from the accumulator R via the pipe JK and so through the foot valve to L. Again, the pressure set up in the brake-actuating cylinders will be proportional to the force applied by the driver.

611

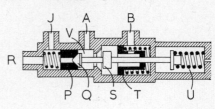

Fig. 30-14

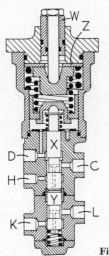

Fig. 30-15

The operation of the cut-out valve is shown by the diagram, Fig. 30-14; it regulates to pressures in the accumulator, cutting off the pump supply when the pressure reaches the upper limit and bringing it in again when the pressure falls to the lower limit. In the diagram the valve is shown in the position it occupies when the accumulator pressure is above the lower limit and is able to keep the sliding seat P seated on the end Q of the valve QS. The pump is assumed to be running and it will keep the valve S off its seat in the casing and will also press back the sliding member T so that fluid can flow from A to B. As the pressure in the accumulator falls so the valve QS and the sliding seat P (still in contact) will move to the left and when the lower limit for the accumulator pressure is reached the valve S will seat on the casing. The pressure in the space V will then force the sliding seat P away from the valve Q and fluid will flow into the accumulator. The pressure in the pipe line connecting the pump and the space V also acts on the non-return valve of the accumulator F (Fig. 30-13) and so if the accumulator pressure is low it also will be charged up.

The construction of the driver's foot valve is shown in Fig. 30-15. Its operation is as follows. In the position shown there is a passage from C to D and the fluid from the pump via the cut-out valve will flow without any great pressure drop. But when the brake pedal is depressed the valve spool X will be depressed through the inner spring and this will reduce the area for the flow of fluid from C to D and so the pressure in the space C and the reduced part of the valve X will rise and, as explained above, the increased pressure will apply the front brakes. The pressure in the space C is transmitted through the holes (shown dotted) in the lower end of the valve X and will act in the space between X and Y.

612

This pressure will tend to push the valve X upwards and that valve will consequently reach an equilibrium position in which the fluid pressure acting on its bottom end balances the force exerted on its upper end by the inner spring and thus by the brake pedal. Thus the pressure in the brake-actuating cylinders is made proportional to the force applied to the brake pedal. Returning now to the lower spool Y, this has been pushed down a little by the valve X but not enough to open the passage from K to L. However, as the pressure in the space between X and Y increases the valve Y will be pushed further down and the passage from K to L will be opened. Fluid will then flow from the accumulator R (Fig. 30-13) to K and L and thus to the rear-brake-actuating cylinders. The pressure set up in the latter will be transmitted through the holes drilled in the lower part of the valve Y and will act in the space at the bottom of that valve. The valve will thus reach an equilibrium position in which the fluid pressure on the bottom end balances that on the top end and as the latter is proportional to the pedal force so the pressure in the rear brake actuating cylinders is also kept proportional to the pedal force. Clearly, the front brakes are independent of the rear ones and vice versa.

The purpose of the outer spring at the top of the assembly is to limit the normal vehicle deceleration to a value which will not be objectionable to passengers while still permitting greater decelerations in emergencies. The compression of the inner spring is normally limited by the plunger W coming into contact with the plate Z which is held up by the pre-compressed outer spring. But extra force applied by the driver in an emergency will compress the outer spring further and thus increase the force applied to the valve spool X and thus will increase the brake-actuating pressures.

30.10 Compressed Air Systems

Most of the compressed air brake systems in use are power systems although there is no reason why compressed air should not

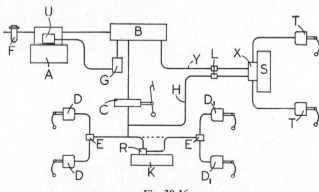

Fig. 30-16

be used in servo systems, in fact most of the units described above for vacuum could be modified so as to work equally well with compressed air.

A complete system suitable for a vehicle having a trailer is shown in Fig. 30-16. The compressor A may be driven off the engine or, in electrically propelled vehicles, by a separate electric motor. The compressor charges a reservoir B to a pressure which is regulated by the governor valve G. When this pressure is reached, the unloading valve U lifts the inlet valves of the compressor so that the latter runs " light." The air supply to the brake cylinders DD of the tractor vehicle is supplied direct from the reservoir through the brake valve C, which controls the pressure in the brake cylinders to a value proportional to the force exerted on the brake pedal. The brake cylinders D_1D_1 may be supplied in the same way if the dotted pipe line replaces the units R and K.

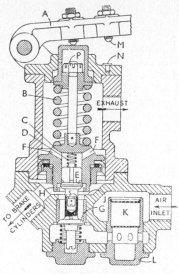

Fig. 30-17

When the brake cylinders are at some distance from the brake valve, however, they may be operated indirectly from an auxiliary reservoir K situated close to them. In this case, the air from the brake pedal valve operates a relay valve R which passes air from the reservoir K to the brake cylinders D_1D_1 and regulates the pressure to the same value as determined by the brake valve. The reservoir K is charged from the main reservoir when the brake valve is in the " off " position.

The trailer brakes are operated by air from the trailer reservoir S by means of an emergency relay valve X. The reservoir S is charged direct from the main reservoir on the tractor, through the emergency pipe line Y, and the brake operation is controlled by the air supply coming from the brake pedal valve via the pipe line H through the medium of the valve X.

A filter F is usually fitted, and sometimes an anti-freeze device as well. The latter feeds small amounts of methanol (methyl alcohol) into the air drawn into the compressor and this lowers the freezing point of any moisture that is in the air and prevents the system from frosting up.

Dual reservoirs are used as in vacuum systems, the smaller reservoir being charged up to full pressure very rapidly and before the larger one. The actuating cylinders employed are similar to those used with vacuum brakes but are smaller in size because of

614

the higher pressures that can be used. Pressures of the order of 80 to 100 lb/sq. in. are usual.

Some of the components mentioned above will be described in greater detail.

A brake pedal reaction valve is shown in Fig. 30-17. It is the design of G. D. Peters, Ltd., of Slough. When the pedal A is depressed the spring B and piston C move downwards, the only force resisting this motion being that of the small spring D. The first small downward movement of the piston brings the valve E on to its seat and closes the passage through that valve and the ports F to the exhaust. The downward movement of the piston and valve E is then communicated by the shoulder S to the valve G, which is pushed off its seat. Air is then passed through the valve G to the brake cylinders. The pressure built up in the latter is also exerted on the underside of the piston C, and when the pressure reaches a value depending on the force applied to the pedal A it forces the piston up slightly which brings the valve G on to its seat again so that no further rise of pressure occurs. The upward pressure of the air on the piston is now balancing the downward force applied to the latter by the pedal A through the spring B, thus the pressure in the brake cylinders is made proportional to the force applied to the pedal. When the pedal is released the air pressure on the piston forces it upwards and the valve E is unseated, thus allowing the air to pass from the brake cylinders to the exhaust and releasing the brakes.

The nut P maintains a small amount of precompression in the spring B so that initially that spring moves " solid." The downward movement of the piston is limited by the projecting stop lip H, which comes into contact with the face J of the body casting. The lip H has slots cut through it to allow the passage of air from the valve G to the brake cylinders.

The maximum force that can be applied to the piston C (and thus the maximum pressure that can be built up in the brake cylinders) is limited by the adjustable stop screw M, which comes into contact with the peg N.

Both the valves E and G are provided with " wings " to guide them and a non-ferrous sleeve is inserted for the valve G to slide in. The small spigot on the end of E is a loose fit inside the hole in G to allow for any slight misalignment between the upper and

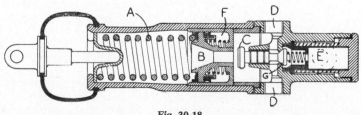

Fig. 30-18

lower body castings. These castings are spigoted together and are secured by four bolts. The piston is sealed by the cup leather shown. The air passing through the valve is filtered by the pack of horse-hair K contained in the easily removable pot L.

Another brake pedal valve is shown in Fig. 30-18. It is made by Clayton Dewandre, Ltd. The force applied by the driver to the brake pedal compresses the spring A and causes the piston B to move to the right so that the portion C of the valve CG seals off from the atmosphere the pipes DD, which come from the brake cylinders. The valve G is then pushed off its seat and passes air from the reservoir via the filter E to the brake cylinder pipes DD. The pressure that builds up in the latter also acts on the piston B, being admitted to the space F, and the force that is exerted on the piston moves it slightly to the left so that the valve G seats, but the

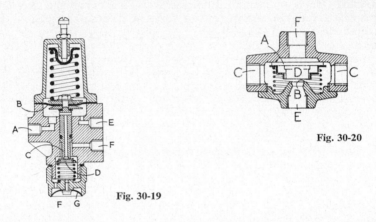

Fig. 30-19

Fig. 30-20

valve C does not open, i.e. the valve reaches a " lap " position. The pressure set up in the pipes DD is therefore proportional to the forces exerted by the spring A and thus to the force exerted on the brake pedal by the driver.

The principle of the governor valve made by Clayton Dewandre is shown in Fig. 30-19. The port A is connected to the reservoir whose pressure thus always acts on the lower side of the diaphragm B. This pressure is also transmitted to the driver's pressure gauge by a pipe connected to the port E. The valve is shown in the position corresponding to the lower limit of the air pressure. The spring has overcome the air pressure acting on the lower side of the diaphragm and has pushed the valve D off its seat, thereby opening the port F to the atmosphere through the dust protecting valve G. The port F is connecting to the unloading mechanism of the compressor and with only atmospheric pressure applied to it the compressor will be functioning and passing air to the reservoir so that the pressure in the latter will rise. It will be noted that the hole down the centre of the valve C is closed by the contact with

616

the valve D. The diaphragm is in equilibrium under the action of the spring force downwards and the air pressure upwards. This pressure acts on the area of the diaphragm minus the area of the valve C but plus the area of the hole in the latter. As the reservoir pressure increases the diaphragm will gradually move upwards until when the upper pressure limit is reached the valve D will seat on the casing and contact between it and the end of the valve C will be broken. Immediately this occurs the force tending to push the diaphragm upwards will increase by the amount due to the air pressure acting on the annular area of the valve C and so the diaphragm and valve will move up with a " snap " action. Air from the reservoir can now pass through the valve C and the port F to the unloading gear and unload the compressor by holding its inlet valve up. As the reservoir pressure gradually falls the valve C will move downwards until it contacts the valve D, thereby shutting off the air passage from the reservoir to the port F and pushing the valve D off its seat. This opens the port F to atmosphere so that the unloading mechanism will bring the compressor into action again. This action will also be a " snap " action because when the valve D is pushed off its seat the air pressure will no longer act on the annular area of the valve C and so the upward force on the diaphragm will be suddenly decreased.

A quick release valve is shown in Fig. 30-20. The port F is connected to the brake pedal valve, the port E to atmosphere, and the ports CC to the brake cylinders. In the " off " position shown, the brake cylinders are open to the atmosphere through the port E. When pressure air enters the port F, the diaphragm A will be moved downwards and its stem D will meet the seat B and seal off the exhaust port E. Pressure air will pass round the periphery of the diaphragm to the ports CC and the brake cylinders. When the pressure in the latter equals that in the port F, the diaphragm will reseat on the upper seating, but the stem D will remain seated on the seat B. This is the " brake holding " position of the unit. As soon as the pressure in the port F falls below that in the ports CC, the stem D will lift off the seat B and the air in the brake cylinders will escape to the atmosphere without having to pass along the pipe from F to the brake pedal valve.

The Bendix emergency relay valve is shown in Fig. 30-21. When the trailer reservoir pressure is low, air will pass from the tractor reservoir along the emergency pipe line (Y of Fig. 30-16) and through the non-return valve C and the space B to the trailer reservoir. The emergency line pressure is also exerted on the top of the diaphragm E and the latter will be depressed and the valve G will open, as shown. Air to the trailer reservoir can thus pass also via the space A and the valve G. If, however, the pressure in the emergency pipe line should fall below that in the trailer reservoir, the valves C and G will close and the trailer reservoir pressure will be maintained. The pressure below the diaphragm D will keep the valve N off its seat and the diaphragm itself in contact with the

617

face X so that air from the trailer reservoir can reach the trailer brake cylinders only via the valve K.

In the ordinary way the brakes will be applied by the admission of pressure air from the brake pedal valve to the upper side of the diaphragm J. This will seat that diaphragm on to the seating L and will seal off the brake cylinders and the space M from the exhaust port O. The piston R will also be depressed, and the valve K will be unseated so that air from the trailer reservoir can pass to the trailer brake cylinders. The pressure set up in the latter will be such that the force exerted on the underside of the diaphragm J just balances the force applied to the top side, and so the trailer

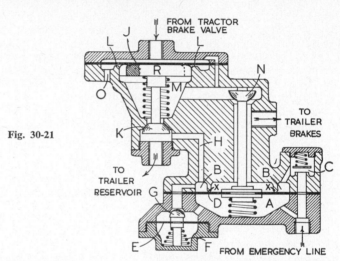

Fig. 30-21

brake pressure will be equal to the pressure set up in the service pipe by the brake pedal valve, and will be proportional to the force exerted on the brake pedal.

If the trailer is disconnected or breaks away from the tractor, the pressure in the emergency pipe line will fall to atmospheric and the trailer reservoir pressure in the space B will depress the diaphragm D and seat the valve N. Air will then pass from the trailer reservoir via the space B and round the stem of the valve N to the trailer brake cylinders, and the pressure set up in these will be approximately equal to the trailer reservoir pressure, so that a full application of the trailer brakes will result.

Power operation is especially suitable when a large number of brakes have to be operated, as, for example, on eight-wheeled vehicles and when trailers are used, because although the driver's valve proportions the intensity of the braking to the force exerted by the driver, this latter force does not increase with an increase in the number of brakes operated as it would do in a mechanically-operated system. The connection between a tractor and trailer

618

is simpler with air operation, relative movement between the two being allowed for by the use of a flexible hose connection and having no effect on the brake operation, a condition that is not easily obtained with mechanical linkages. The trailer brakes can also be arranged to come on automatically should the trailer break away from the tractor.

30.11 Actuating Cylinders for Air Brakes

Air pressure brakes are usually actuated by diaphragm cylinders in which the diaphragm acts as a piston but has the advantage that no sliding air-tight joints are necessary. In order to enable a single cylinder to be used for both the foot-pedal and hand-lever operation the Dewandre Company have introduced the triple diaphragm cylinder shown in Fig. 30-22. When the brake pedal

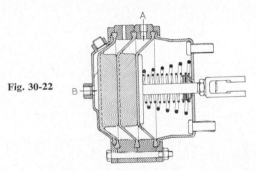

Fig. 30-22

is depressed air is admitted to the space A while operation of the hand-brake admits air to the space B. The space between A and B is open to atmosphere. For both forms of braking the force applied to the brakes will be regulated by a brake valve so that it is proportional to the force exerted by the driver. Although air pressure is used for the application of the hand brake the brake will be held on by the usual ratchet even if the air pressure should fall after the brakes have been applied.

CHAPTER 31

Front Axle and Steering Mechanism

Primary considerations. The Ackerman linkage. Centre point steering. Castor action. Axle construction. Steering mechanisms. Alignment of front wheels.

THE steering of multi-wheeled vehicles is, as far as possible, arranged so that all the wheels will roll truly without any lateral slip, and to understand the principles involved the reader must have a clear idea of what constitutes true rolling action.

In Fig. 31-1 is shown a cylindrical wheel in contact with the ground. If this wheel is rolled along it will move in the direction YY, perpendicular to the axis XX, and the action will be a purely rolling action. If, however, the wheel is made to move in the direction XX the action is wholly a sliding one, since obviously no rolling can occur in that direction. If, now, the wheel is made to move in some intermediate direction ZZ, the action will be compounded of a rolling action in the direction YY and a sliding action in the direction XX. Hence, if a wheel is desired to roll without lateral slip the direction of its motion must be perpendicular to its axis.

It should easily be realized, therefore, that to obtain true rolling of the wheels of a multi-wheeled vehicle when moving in a curved path it is necessary to arrange that the axes of all the wheels shall intersect in one point, which will be the centre about which the vehicle for the instant will be turning. This may be done by turning all the wheels of the vehicle, but usually only the front wheels are steered, the rear ones being carried on bearings on the axle casing and having a common axis which always remains perpendicular to the centre line of the vehicle. In the latter case it is obvious that, if lateral slip of the wheels is to be avoided, the centre about which the vehicle turns must be a point on the produced axis of the rear wheels, and the front wheels must be turned until their axes intersect at that point. This can be done by pivoting the whole front axle at its mid-point on a vertical axis, the wheels being left free to revolve on the ends of the axle beam and thus having a common axis. When the axle is turned about its central pivot this common axis will intersect the axis of the rear wheels in some point and true rolling of the wheels will be obtained. This arrangement is used for heavy slow-speed steam wagons and tractors, but is not suitable for high-speed vehicles, for which the following method is used.

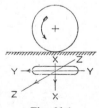

Fig. 31-1

The front wheels are free to revolve on one

arm of L-shaped "stub axles" A, B
(Fig. 31-2), which are pivoted at their
corners on vertical pivot pins on the
ends of the axle beam C. The latter
is connected to the frame of the
vehicle by the road springs and remains approximately parallel to the
rear axle in plan. The other arms D,
E of the stub axles are coupled together by a "track" rod F which is
pivoted to their ends; these arms are
generally known as "track arms."
The stub axles together with the front
wheels can, therefore, be turned
round so that their axes intersect at
some point O on the axis of the
rear wheels. It should be observed
that the angle β through which the
outer stub axle has to be turned is
smaller than the angle α through
which the inner one is turned.
This, as will be explained in the
next paragraph, is brought about by
a suitable arrangement of the track
arms and track rod.

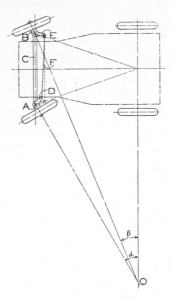

Fig. 31-2: Principle of the
Ackerman system of steering

31.1 Ackerman Linkage

The required movement of the stub axles through the angles α and
β as described above, is obtained, approximately, by suitably
inclining the track arms D and E towards each other, so that in the
straight-ahead position, shown in the dotted lines, their centre
lines if produced as shown would intersect on the centre line of the
car at a point whose exact position depends on the relation between
the wheelbase and track of the car and other factors, but which will
be near to the axis of the rear wheels.

The way in which this inclination of the track arms causes the
stub axles to move through different angles is shown in Fig. 31-3.
The full lines show the straight-ahead position and the dotted
lines the position when the vehicle is turning towards the left.
The stub axle B has been turned through the angle β by the movement of the steering wheel and the end D of its track arm has
moved to D^1 a distance x parallel to the axle beam. Since the

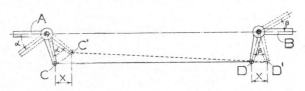

Fig. 31-3

621

track arms are connected by the track rod it follows that (neglecting the slight inclination of the track rod) the end C of the other track arm has to move the same distance x parallel to the axle beam. But the point D is moving near to the bottom of its circle, while the point C is moving towards the side, and so a given movement x parallel to the axle beam results in a greater angular movement of the track arm A.

The actual track arms may be curved, but the effective arm is, of course, the line joining the centre of the stub axle pivot pin to the centre of the pivot connecting the track arm to the track rod.

In the figure the track rod is placed behind the axle beam, and this is the more usual position, but frequently it is placed in front of the axle beam. Provided the track arms are suitably inclined to each other a similar action again occurs. The rear position has the advantage that the track rod is protected by the axle beam, but the track rod has to work in compression, whereas when placed in front of the axle beam it works in tension, which is a more favourable condition.

The linkage described above is known (in England) by the name "Ackerman linkage," and it gives true rolling of the wheels in only three positions of the stub axles. One is when the wheels are parallel and the vehicle travelling in a straight line, and the other positions are when the vehicle is turning either to the right or to the left and the inner track arm has been turned through a certain angle depending on the design. In any other position the axes of the front wheels do not intersect on the axis of the back wheels and a certain amount of lateral slip must occur between some of the wheels and the ground. Except when turning in a circle of very small radius the error is small and may possibly be neutralized by the lateral flexibility of the tyres.

There are several linkages which give perfect steering at all locks, but they are all somewhat complicated, and although they have been used they have not proved satisfactory in practice, so that the Ackerman linkage is almost universal.

31.2   The Steering of Multi-wheeled Vehicles

In rigid six-wheeled lorries the axes of the two rear axles remain always approximately parallel and perfect steering cannot theoretically be obtained for, referring to Fig. 31-4, if the centre of rotation is some point O_1 lying on the axis of the middle axle then the wheels of the rear axle must slip laterally, and similarly if the steering centre is O_3 on the axis of the rear axle then the wheels of the middle axle must slip laterally. The probability is that steering occurs about some point such as O_2 on a line mid-way between the axes of the two axles and the steering linkage of the front axle is usually laid out on this assumption, that is, for a wheelbase W measured to the mid-point between the two axles.

Four wheels are sometimes used at the front end of large lorries, all four wheels being steered, the arrangement being as shown in

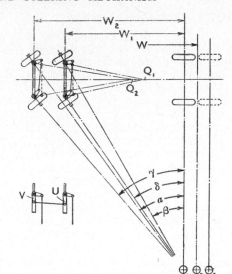

Fig. 31-4

Fig. 31-4. Each axle has an Ackerman linkage to connect the nearside to the offside wheel and these linkages make the nearside wheels swing through the correct angles γ and δ, provided the offside wheels are turned through the correct angles α and β. These linkages should theoretically be designed for different wheelbases, that of the first axle for the wheelbase W_2 and that for the second axle for the wheelbase W_1 (in an eight-wheeled vehicle these wheelbases would both be measured to the mid-point between the two rear axles). The two offside wheels must however be swung through the different angles α and β by the steering wheel and this may be done in two or three ways. One is indicated in the inset view. The steering arms of the two axles are connected together by a link, but the arm U of the second axle is made a little longer than that, V, of the first axle. One of the arms is operated in the usual way by the drag link which connects it to the drop arm of the steering box. A second, and more usual, method is shown in Fig. 31-5. Two drop arms OB and PD are used, one for each axle, the former being carried on the spindle of the steering box in the usual manner while the latter is pivoted on a bracket on the frame. The arm PD is operated from OB by a coupling link E and it is always moved through smaller angles because the length PD is greater than the length OA. In addition, the length PC is less than the length OB and so the stub axle of the second axle is moved through smaller angles than that of the first axle as is required.

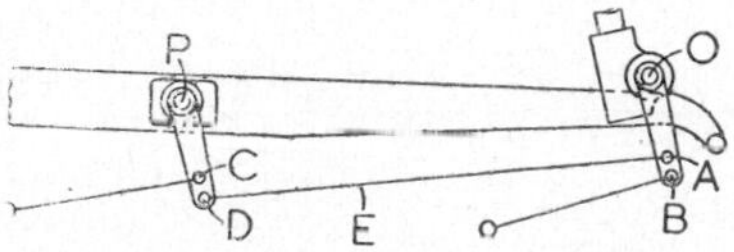

Fig. 31-5

31.3   Centre-point Steering

In Fig. 31-6 it will be noticed that the axis about which the stub axle (with its road wheel) turns when steering is effected intersects the ground at the point O, while the road wheel makes contact with the ground at the point P.   Now when a car is travelling along a road there is a force acting between the front wheels and the road in a direction opposite to that of the motion.   On a good road this force may be small, but on a bad road, and when the front wheels are braked hard, it may be considerable.   This force acts perpendicular to the line OP (in plan) and hence has a moment, about the axis XX, which tends to turn the stub axle about its pivot pin.   This tendency has, of course, to be resisted.   Now the stub axle on the other side tends to turn in the opposite direction, and since the two stub axles are connected together by the track rod the two tendencies towards rotation will, if they are equal, neutralize each other, and the only result will be a stress in the track arms and the track rod.   If, however, the two tendencies are not equal, then the difference between them has to be resisted by the friction in the steering mechanism or by the driver.

In order to reduce to the minimum the moment of the force tending to turn the stub axles the point P is brought as close to the point O as is conveniently possible, and very often the points are made to coincide.   When such coincidence is obtained the construction is said to give centre-point steering, and it can be obtained or approximated to in three ways—

(1) Keeping the swivel pin axes vertical the wheels can be inclined so as to bring the point P nearer to the point O.
(2) Both the wheels and the swivel pins can be inclined.
(3) A construction can be adopted that enables the swivel pin to be situated in the plane of the wheel.

Method three is adopted by a few makers and method two by a much larger number, but the first method is now used very rarely. Centre-point steering is, however, only approximated to and not actually obtained on most cars.   It should be mentioned that

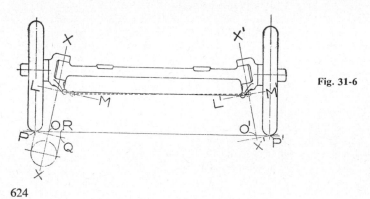

Fig. 31-6

designers are by no means in agreement as to whether true centre-point steering is desirable, although a fairly close approximation to it is admitted to be desirable when the front wheels are braked.

Inclination of the wheels is generally referred to as " camber " and the angle between the plane of the wheel and the vertical is called the " camber angle."

There are one or two points which should perhaps be mentioned in connection with the use of inclined swivel pins. Firstly, the connections between the track arms and the track rod can no longer be simple pivots, but must be ball and socket joints because, as will be seen from Fig. 31-6, when the stub axles are turned the end of one track arm moves up and the end of the other one down, so that the track rod assumes an angular position in a vertical plane as well as in the horizontal plane. Secondly, unless true centre-point steering is obtained the front of the vehicle will have to be lifted slightly when steering is effected. This can be seen from the same figure. The point of contact of the wheel with the ground moves in a circle whose plane is perpendicular to the swivel pin axis. This plane is seen in the figure as the line PQ. If the stub axle were turned through half a turn (which, of course, is not actually possible) then the point of contact of wheel and ground would move from P to Q, and if the vehicle did not lift slightly the wheel would have to penetrate the ground to the depth QR. Actually, of course, the vehicle would be lifted the amount QR, and a similar action occurs when the stub axle is turned through smaller angles. This action tends to make the steering self-righting, so that after a turn the car automatically comes back to a straight path. This is due to the weight of the car, which tends to turn the wheels until they are in the position where the centre of gravity of the car is lowest, and this position is with the wheels set parallel.

31.4 Castoring or Trailing Action

The axes of the front wheels are sometimes arranged to be slightly behind the axes of the swivel pins, as shown in Fig. 31-7. The wheel then tends to behave in a similar manner to the castors used on furniture, and to set itself so as to be always behind the swivel pin axis in the direction of motion. This again results in the steering being self-righting. The amount by which the point of contact of wheel and ground lies behind the intersection of the swivel pin axis with the ground is called the amount of " trail." It is always quite a small amount, being generally not more than about one inch. Castoring action is usually obtained by inclining the swivel pins in a fore and aft

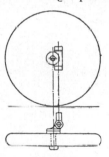

Fig. 31-7

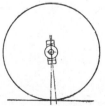

Fig. 31-8

625

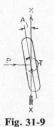

Fig. 31-9

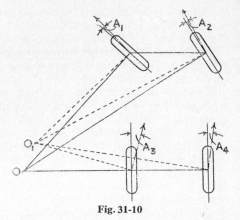

Fig. 31-10

direction, as shown in Fig. 31-8. The angle through which the swivel pins are tilted from the vertical in this way is called the "castor angle." This tilting is very easily done by putting wedges between the spring seats of the main axle beam and the springs, or by inclining the springs. Consideration will show that a front-wheel-driven car requires negative trail.

In practice the steering of a wheeled vehicle is not quite such a simple matter as these considerations would imply, because it has been found by experiment that a wheel which is rolling along a road cannot sustain any side force unless it is held so that its plane makes an angle with the direction of motion. Thus in Fig. 31-9 if the wheel is required to travel in the direction XX while a side force P is applied to it the wheel must be held so that its plane makes an angle A (called the " slip angle ") with XX, as shown. It has been found that the side force that can be sustained is proportional to the magnitude of the slip angle for values of the latter up to about 6°. The ratio *Side force sustained/Slip angle* has been taken as a measure of the cornering ability of a tyre and has been called the " cornering power," being usually measured in pounds per degree.

31.5 Cornering Power

The cornering power of tyres has been found to depend on many factors such as the construction of the tyre itself, the value of the vertical force between the tyre and the road (referred to in what follows as the load on the tyre), the inflation pressure, the size of the tyre and the extent of any tilting of the wheel. Thus the cornering power of a tyre falls off as the load on the tyre departs from the normal load for the tyre, but the extent of this falling off is small provided the variation in the load does not exceed plus or minus about 50 per cent of the normal load. The cornering power increases as the inflation pressure is increased, but is smaller for large tyres than for small ones of the same type of construction.

As regards camber the cornering power falls off as the top of the wheel in Fig. 31-9 is moved in the direction of the force P (this being called positive camber) and increases with the amount of negative camber. The cornering power has been found to be independent of the speed.

31.6 Self-righting Torque

When a wheel is travelling along the line XX as in Fig. 31-9 there will be a torque T acting between it and the road which will tend to turn the wheel so that its plane becomes parallel to the direction of motion, and in order to keep the wheel travelling as shown an equal and opposite torque must be applied to the axle carrying the wheel. The torque T may be called the " self-righting torque " and it has been found to increase in direct proportion to the load on the wheel and to be greater for wheels with positive camber than for vertical wheels.

31.7 Steering Characteristics

The result of the above actions is that when a vehicle moves in a circular path the centre of that path does not coincide with the point of intersection of the wheel axes. This is indicated in Fig. 31-10, where O is the intersection of the wheel axes and O_1 is the actual centre of rotation. The slip angles for the wheels (A_1, A_2, A_3 and A_4) will in general all have different magnitudes.

If a side force P acts on a car that is travelling in a straight line XX (Fig. 31-11), that force must be balanced by side forces acting between the road and the wheels and the wheels must be set at the appropriate slip angles to the direction of motion. If the slip angles for all the wheels were equal then the car would continue to move in a straight line but inclined at that slip angle to the original path, but if the slip angles of the wheels are not equal then the car will generally move in some curve. If, for example, the slip angles of the back wheels are a little greater than those for the front wheels, the car will begin to move about some centre O as shown. This would introduce a centrifugal force which in effect would increase the magnitude of the side force P and would thus accentuate the action. The car will tend to move in a curve such as YY, veering towards

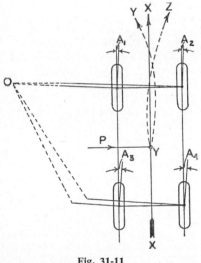

Fig. 31-11

627

the side force P. This action has been called "oversteer" and tends to increase with any increase in the speed, because the centrifugal force increases as the square of the speed, while the side forces between the wheels and the road do not increase with the speed but only as the result of an increase in the slip angles. A car with this steering characteristic when going round a corner may require the steering wheel to be turned back towards the straight ahead position in order to keep it from turning too sharply and is generally less stable and more difficult to handle than a car with an "understeer" characteristic. The latter would be obtained if the slip angles of the front wheels were greater than those of the back wheels, for then the centre of rotation would lie on the opposite side of the line XX and the car would tend to move in a curve such as YZ. The centrifugal force due to this motion opposes the side force P and the action will tend to decrease with any increase in the speed. A car with an understeer characteristic when turning a corner will tend to straighten out and the steering wheel will generally have to be turned a little more to counteract this tendency. Such a car is more stable and easier to handle. An oversteer characteristic can sometimes be corrected by decreasing the slip angles of the rear tyres and increasing those of the front tyres by increasing the inflation pressure of the rear tyres and decreasing that of the front tyres or by altering the weight distribution so that a smaller proportion of both the load and the side force comes on to the rear wheels.

Since both the slip angle and the self-righting torque are affected by alteration of camber the steering characteristic can be controlled to some extent by controlling the change of camber of the wheels due to a tilt of the body of the car relative to the ground. This can be done with independent suspensions of the double arm type (see Chapter 33).

31.8 Axle Beam

When the front wheels are not braked the axle beam is usually a simple forging of I section with suitable seats for the attachment of the springs and with the ends suitably shaped to carry the stub axles. The I section is adopted because it is the best adapted to withstand the bending action to which the beam is subjected. This action arises, as in the back axle, because the axle beam is supported at its ends, while the loads are transmitted to it at the spring seats which are situated nearer to its centre. The action tends to bend the beam in a vertical plane.

Simple rectangular and tubular sections are also sometimes used.

The axle beam is also subjected to a bending action in the horizontal plane, but usually this action is small compared with that in the vertical plane. But when the front wheels are braked the horizontal bending action becomes considerable. In this case a rectangular or a circular section may be more suitable than an I section. Again, when the front wheels are braked the portions of

628

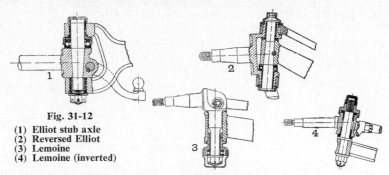

Fig. 31-12
(1) Elliot stub axle
(2) Reversed Elliot
(3) Lemoine
(4) Lemoine (inverted)

the axle beam between the stub axles and the spring seats (and possibly the rest of the axle also) are subjected to a twisting action, the torque reaction of the braking torque applied to the brake drums. A circular section is best adapted to withstand this twisting action. Hence, when front wheel brakes are fitted, circular sections are often used.

31.9 Stub-axle Construction

The principal methods of pivoting the stub axles on the ends of the axle beam are shown in Fig. 31-12. The first goes by the name of the Elliot stub axle, the second is called the Reversed Elliot, the third is sometimes called the Lemoine. The third and fourth methods are sometimes used upside down, that is, with the wheel axis below the axle beam instead of above it.

In the Elliot construction the swivel pin is usually fixed in the stub-axle forging and its ends therefore turn in the forked end of the axle beam. In the Reversed Elliot construction the swivel pin is usually fixed in the axle beam, so that in each construction the bearing surfaces are situated as far apart as possible and when wear occurs on those surfaces the resulting angular shake or play is as small as possible.

31.10 Steering Column

The motion of the stub axles is controlled by the steering wheel, which is situated at the top of the steering column. The motion of the steering wheel is not, however, transmitted direct to the stub axles. At the bottom of the column (occasionally at the middle or top) mechanism is situated that introduces a leverage between the steering wheel and the stub axles, and so reduces the effort that has to be applied to the steering wheel in order to overcome the frictional forces opposing the turning of the stub axles. It follows, of course, that the steering wheel has to be turned through larger angles than the stub axles, thus while the latter may turn through an angle of about 50° from the straight position to the position of full lock, the steering wheel will have to be turned through from 4 to 9 or 10 times that angle to effect the motion.

629

The amount of leverage depends upon several factors, of which, perhaps, the chief are the weight of the vehicle and the type of tyre used; lorries are provided with greater leverage than cars.

31.11 Reversible and Irreversible Steering

In most steering gears it is possible to grip the stub axles and to turn them round, thus turning the steering wheel round also; but this is not always possible. Sometimes when the operation is attempted the frictional forces called into play are equal to the forces tending to produce motion, so that no motion can occur. When this is so the steering is said to be irreversible, but modern steering gears are always reversible.

The steering mechanism which provides the necessary leverage may be of several forms, of which the following are the principal—

    (1) Toothed gearing—

        (a) Spur gears. Ordinary and epicyclic.
        (b) Pinion and rack.
        (c) Bevel gears.
        (d) Worm gears.

    (2) Screw and nut.
    (3) Left- and right-hand screw.
    (4) Double screw.
    (5) Cam.

An example of type (1) (a) is shown in Fig. 31-13. The pinion A is integral with the steering wheel shaft and is carried in the bracket B fixed to the frame. The shaft A is positioned axially by an integral flange that is held between the bracket B and the end of the steering column C. The only forces that this flange has to take are those applied to the steering wheel by the driver. The pinion A meshes with the internal teeth of the sector D, the latter is fixed to the member EF whose stem E pivots in the bracket B and whose arm F is coupled by links to the steering arms of the stub axles.

31.12 Rack and Pinion Steering Mechanism

This is now a very common type of mechanism and, like the spur gear type, gives a very direct action. It also fits in very well with

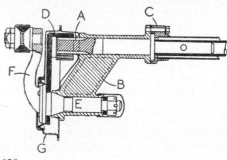

Fig. 31-13

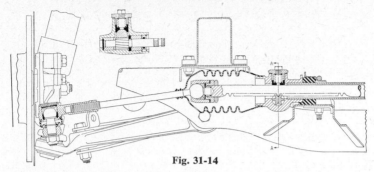

Fig. 31-14

many types of independent suspension. An example is shown
in Fig. 31-14: it is the design used by the Standard Motor Co.
in their Triumph 2000. The rack is housed in a tubular casing
which is supported on the frame near its ends in rubber bushes.
A spring loaded pad presses the rack into contact with the pinion
which is made integral with a short shaft that is coupled to the
steering wheel shaft by splines. The pinion shaft is carried in the
end casing in plain bearings. The ends of the rack are connected
to the track rods by ball and socket joints, the centres of which lie
close to the axes about which road wheels will move during spring
action. This enables undesirable steering motions of the wheels
to be avoided.

In certain types of suspension the axes about which the road
wheels move lie close to the centre line of the car and in such cases
the ball joints by which the rack is connected to the track rods may
be placed at the centre of the rack instead of at its ends.

Fig. 31-15

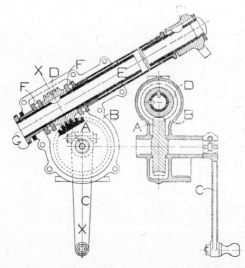

631

31.13   Worm and Wheel Steering

A worm and wheel steering mechanism is shown in Fig. 31-15. A worm wheel A, made in this design of steel, is carried in bearings in a cast iron case B which is made in halves. The outer end of the worm wheel spindle is squared to receive the " drop arm " C which is provided with a ball end. The end of the drop arm is connected by a rod, known as the " side rod " or " drag link," to a " steering arm " fixed to one of the stub axles, so that motion of the worm wheel results in motion of the stub axles. The worm wheel meshes with a case-hardened steel worm D keyed on to a tubular shaft E which is carried in bearings in the casing, and which at its upper end carries the steering wheel. To position the worm in the axial direction thrust bearings FF are provided. The upper thrust bearing abuts against the casing, but the lower one against the nut G, which is screwed into the casing and locked by a lock-nut. An adjustment is thereby provided so that end play of the worm can be eliminated.

This type of mechanism is now hardly ever used.

31.14   Screw and Nut Mechanism

An example of this type of steering gear is shown in Fig. 31-16. A multiple-threaded screw B is free to rotate in bearings in a cast iron casing C. Axial motion is prevented by thrust bearings DD and the screw is connected by the shaft A to the steering wheel. A nut H fits on the screw and is prevented from rotating. Hence, if the screw is turned the nut must move axially up or down the

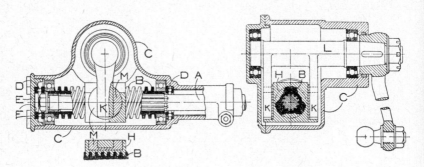

Fig. 31-16: Screw and nut steering mechanism

screw. This motion is caused to rotate the drop arm through the medium of a two-armed spindle L, which is carried in ball bearings in the casing and which carries the drop arm at its outer end. The two arms KK of the spindle L straddle the nut, to which they are connected by the bronze pads MM. These pads are free to turn in cylindrical recesses formed in the sides of the nut, and they are provided with parallel grooves to receive the arms of the spindle L. The pads are necessary because the nut moves in a straight line while the arms of the spindle L move in circular paths.

In this design the nut is prevented from rotating by the arms K of the spindle L. In some designs this is done by guiding the nut in guides in the casing. In some designs also short connecting rods are used, instead of the pads, to connect the nut with the arms of the spindle L.

Backlash in the above mechanism can arise from end play of the screw and from wear of the threads of the screw and nut, etc. End play of the screw is eliminated in assembly by means of the selected washer F. Wear of the threads cannot usually be remedied except by replacement, but in view of the large area of contact between the nut and the screw the wear should be small provided lubrication is attended to.

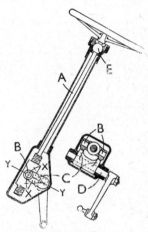

Fig. 31-17

This type of mechanism has the advantage that the leverage provided increases as the steering approaches full lock.

A slightly different form of screw and nut mechanism is shown in Fig. 31-17. The screw is formed on the end of the shaft A to which the steering wheel is fixed. The nut is formed with integral trunnions BB which pivot in holes in the ends of arms CC of the fork member, which is splined to the drop arm shaft D. At its upper end the shaft A is supported in the steering column in a ball and socket joint E which secures it against axial motion but allows it to turn about its axis and also to swing slightly about an axis perpendicular to the axis of the shaft itself. This last freedom is required because the trunnions BB must move in the arc XX as the nut moves to and fro along the screw, and so the lower end of the shaft A is moved slightly in the direction YY. Actually, instead of a plain ball and socket joint at E, a self-aligning ball bearing is used. Alternatively an ordinary journal bearing supported in a rubber bush may be used, the rubber bush accommodating the rocking of the shaft A. This arrangement eliminates the pads M of the mechanism of Fig. 31-16, reduces the number of bearings required and so cheapens the construction. The fixing of the nut against rotation is also more easily done by the arms CC than by the arms KK of Fig. 31-16.

31.15 Cam Steering Mechanisms

Many cam steering mechanisms have been invented but few have been commercially successful. One example which is used by many makers is shown in Fig. 31-19. It is the Marles steering gear. Carried by the drop arm spindle A on the ball bearings shown is a Vee-shaped roller B which engages a groove cut in the member C. The latter is keyed to the steering wheel shaft but is fixed axially. When the steering wheel is turned the spiral groove in the member C constrains the roller B to move to the right or left from the position shown, thus turning the drop arm. End play of the member C can be eliminated by screwing the casing E farther into the steering box, a clamping screw F being provided for locking purposes. Proper meshing of the roller with the groove in the member C may be obtained by turning the pin D. The centre portion of this pin, which carries the races that support the roller, is eccentric to the end portions, hence when the pin is turned the roller is moved into closer mesh with the member C.

31.16 Screw and Lever Mechanism

This mechanism is a form of cam mechanism and an example is shown in Fig. 31-19. At the bottom end of the steering wheel

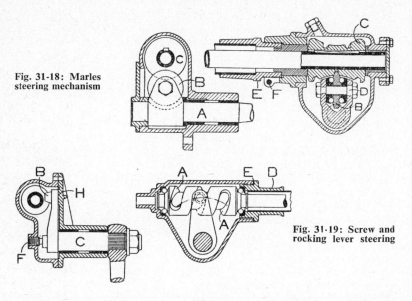

Fig. 31-18: Marles steering mechanism

Fig. 31-19: Screw and rocking lever steering

shaft a helical groove A is formed, and this engages the projection B of the drop arm spindle lever. When the steering wheel shaft is turned the drop arm is rocked to and fro. End play of the steering wheel shaft is eliminated by putting in a suitable washer at E. The drop arm spindle lever is supported by bearing on the cover plate at H, and a screw F prevents it from meshing too deeply with the groove A. The pin B is sometimes made in the form of a roller, being carried in bearings in the drop arm spindle lever. A recent modification is to provide the lever with two pins which, in the central position of the gear, engage the screw near its ends. This enables increased leverage to be obtained when the steering is locked hard over.

In the Marles Weller steering gear, whose general arrangement is similar to that of Fig. 31-19, the pin B is formed with two hemispherical recesses one on each side and half-balls fit in these recesses. The approximately flat faces of the half balls engage the sides of the screw thread.

31.17   Steering Connections

The drop arm, or rack, of the steering mechanism is connected to the steering arm of the stub axle and the connections must be such as will allow of angular motion in two planes. Ball and socket joints are now used almost always but at one time universal joints were used. An example of modern ball and socket joint construction is shown in Fig. 31-20; it is the design of Automotive Products Ltd. The bush A is split on a vertical diameter and can thus be made to contact the ball member both above and below the central horizontal plane and so this bush carries all the actual steering loads, the lower member B being spring loaded to eliminate backlash and rattle. The bushes are moulded in a composition

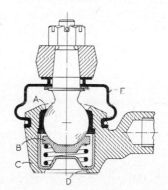

Fig. 31-20

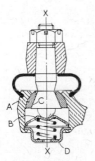

Fig. 31.21

which contains a lubricant and the joint requires no other lubrication throughout its life. The ball and bush assembly is retained in the solid eye of the link C by rolling the lip of the eye over, as seen at D. Dust and water are excluded by the rubber boot E. The surface of the ball is plated to give protection against corrosion and to provide a fine surface finish. Joints of this kind can provide considerable angular freedom in all directions.

In the joint of Fig. 31-21 the upper, load bearing, surface is formed on a bush A which is free to rotate on the conical end of the pin C.

This enables a large spherical surface to be provided while at the same time reducing the relative motion between that surface and the eye of the rod. This is because motions about the axis XX

will occur at the surface C. A spring-loaded cup B holds the parts in contact and limits any separation to the amount of the clearance between the bottom of the cup and the cap D. When the angular motions about XX are not large the member A is usually made integral with the pin.

A Thompson self-adjusting ball joint is shown in Fig. 31-22; the wedge-shaped half bushes are acted upon by the spring which tends to force them apart so as to take up any clearance

Fig. 31-22

that may develop from wear. The "angle" of the wedges is made such that the forces applied by the ball to the wedges cannot move the wedges back. In a variation of this design the wedge members are forced apart by a taper-ended pin which is pressed in radially between their ends by a spring. This type is particularly suitable for tractors.

31.18 Alignment of the Front Wheels

When a vehicle is moving in a straight line all its wheels should be parallel to the direction of motion. Unless the back axle has been badly damaged the back wheels will be so, but proper adjustment is necessary if the front wheels are to be so. In order that the front wheels shall be parallel when the vehicle is moving they must usually be set slightly out of parallel when the vehicle is stationary, the distance between the wheels in the plan view being made slightly less at the front than at the back. Then, when the vehicle is moving along the road the forces acting on the wheels will cause small deflections in the steering connections, which will bring the wheels into parallelism. This setting of the wheels is known as " toe-in " and the difference between the " track " of the wheel rims at the front and back varies with different makers from almost nothing up to as much as $\frac{1}{4}$ in. Modern practice is to keep it as small as possible.

31.19 Power Steering

It has been seen that when the size and weight of a vehicle become large it may be necessary to have servo assisted or power-operated brakes and, for the same reasons, it may also become necessary to employ power steering. Several systems have been developed by various makers and three will be described. They are all similar in principle and are all operated by oil under pressure. This oil is supplied by a pump driven off the engine, or sometimes off the rear end of the gear box. An accumulator or reservoir is usually provided. The pressures used are fairly high, reaching 1,000 lb/sq. in. Systems using compressed air have also been developed but the principle of operation is the same as that of the systems about to be described. This is that the first slight movement of the steering wheel operates a valve so as to open up a passage for pressure oil from the pump and accumulator to the appropriate end of a " slave " cylinder whose piston is connected to the steering linkage. A pressure difference is thus built up across the sides of the piston which therefore moves and actuates the steering. The movement of the piston is arranged to " re-set " the valve, that is, to bring it back to the equilibrium position and so the movement of the piston and steering linkage is made proportional to the movement of the steering wheel. The systems are always arranged so that the steering linkage can be actuated direct by the steering wheel if the oil pressure should not be available. They are also sometimes arranged so that some appreciable effort must be applied to the steering wheel before the valve of the system is operated; this effort is transmitted direct to the steering linkage and, if the forces and moments opposing motion of the road wheels are small, this direct effort may be sufficient to overcome them and the steering is then done direct without any power assistance. This is claimed to give a good " feel " to the steering. When the resistances are larger then the valve is moved and the power effort is added to the direct manual effort.

31.20 Vickers System

The principal features of the system developed by Vickers Incorporated of Detroit are shown in Figs. 31-23 and 24. The slave cylinder A (Fig. 31-23) takes the place of the drag link of the steering linkage being connected by a ball and socket joint B to the steering arm of the stub axle while the piston rod is coupled by the ball and socket joint C to the frame. The drop arm D of the steering box is arranged to actuate the valve of the system, as will be seen from Fig. 31-24. Supposing the steering wheel to be turned so that the drop arm turns clockwise then the valve E will be moved to the left, thus opening the port x to the pressure supply and the port y

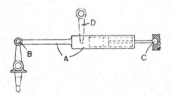

Fig. 31-23

to the exhaust. The pressure in the end F of the slave cylinder will therefore rise while that in the end G will fall. The cylinder will therefore move bodily to the left, thus actuating the steering. The movement of the cylinder brings the valve E back to the equilibrium position and the desired movement of the steering will have been

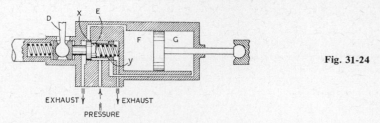

Fig. 31-24

effected, chiefly by the oil pressure but partly by the direct pressure of the drop arm on the left-hand spring of the valve. The movement of the valve is limited to a very small amount either way and if the oil pressure should not be available then the drop arm can actuate the steering direct as soon as the valve comes up against its stop. There is therefore some backlash, the amount depending on the free movement allowed to the valve, when the steering is being operated manually. In order that the slave cylinder shall not exert any drag on the system when it is being operated manually a valve is provided which opens a direct passage between the ends of the cylinder if the oil pressure fails and the movement of the control valve exceeds the normal amount.

31.21 Ross System

This is shown in Figs. 31-25, 26 and 27. The steering wheel is fixed to the shaft A which at its lower end is provided with a screw or cam B, the groove of which is engaged by the pin C. The latter is carried in taper roller bearings in an arm secured to the drop arm shaft D, the drop arm E is also fixed to this shaft and is actuated by the piston of the slave cylinder through a yoke member that engages a sliding block carried on the pin G of the arm F. The latter arm is also fixed to the drop arm shaft. The shaft A and cam B are, in effect, integral with the valve of the system which is situated at H and is shown in more detail in Figs. 31-26 and 27. Supposing the steering wheel to be turned clockwise then for the first slight movement the pin C will remain fixed and the cam B,

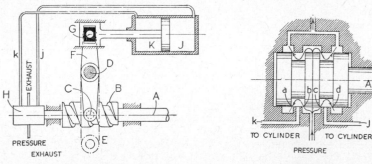

Fig. 31-25

Fig. 31-26

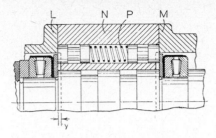

Fig. 31-27

shaft A and valve will move to the left. The detailed action of the valve will be described later but when it moves to the left the pressure in the pipe *j* will rise and that in *k* will fall and so the piston of the slave cylinder will be urged to the left thereby rotating the drop arm anti-clockwise and actuating the steering. The anti-clockwise movement of the lever and pin C will move the valve back to its equilibrium position. The action of the valve is as follows. Referring to Fig. 31-26, the valve position, when the system is in equilibrium, will be such that the areas of the passages *a*, *b*, *c* and *d* will be equal (neglecting for the moment the effect of the piston rod of the slave cylinder), the pressure drops across the passages *b* and *c* will be equal and the pressure drops across the passages *a* and *d* will also be equal. The pressures in the recesses of the valve will therefore also be equal and these pressures are transmitted by the pipes *j* and *k* to the ends of the slave cylinder. If now the valve is moved to the left the passages *b* and *d* will be reduced in size while the passages *a* and *c* will be increased. The pressure drop across *b* will increase while that across *c* will decrease, the pressure drop across *a* will decrease while that across *d* will increase. Hence the pressure in the left-hand recess and pipe *k* will fall and the pressure in the right-hand recess and pipe *j* will rise as described above. The effect of the piston rod of the slave cylinder is to reduce the effective area of the end K of the cylinder and as the forces acting on the piston must be balanced in the equilibrium position the pressure in the end K must be a little higher than in the end J. This is obtained automatically, the valve setting itself so that the area *c* is slightly larger than *b* and the area *d* slightly smaller than *a*. The valve is provided with a number of centring springs P (Fig. 31-27), in the equilibrium position these springs exert no force on the valve because the plungers against which the springs act abut against the end covers L and M. Before the valve can move from the equilibrium position a torque must be exerted on the steering wheel which is sufficient to produce a force equal to the spring force. The reaction of this force acts on the pin C (Fig. 31-25) and is transmitted to the steering linkage. If the forces opposing the motion of the road wheels are small steering may be effected without any movement of the valve and purely by the manual effort of the driver. Under these conditions there will be no backlash in the steering. If the forces opposing the motion of the road wheels are

639

large then the valve will be moved and the steering will be done mainly by the slave cylinder. If no oil pressure is available the motion of the valve is limited to the amount y (shown exaggerated), the depth of the recess in the end of the body N of the valve housing, and the backlash is limited accordingly. The space between the plungers acted on by the centring springs is connected to the pressure side of the system and consequently when oil pressure is available the force of the centring springs is supplemented by the force exerted on the plungers by the oil.

31.22   The Marles-Bendix " Varamatic " System

This is shown in Figs. 31-28 and 29. The mechanical part of the system is based on the Marles mechanism which is described in Section 31.15 while the servo part is basically the same as that of the Ross system described in Section 31.21. There are, however, some important differences. The cam A (Fig. 31-28) now has a variable pitch so that when the roller follower B is in the central position shown the ratio *Angular motion of cam/Angular motion of droparm* (*C*), for a very small motion, is about 21/1 but when the drop arm and follower have moved about 12 degrees away from the central position that ratio has fallen to 13/1 and thereafter it remains constant at that value. The valve which controls the servo action now operates by the rotational displacement of its two main components instead by their axial displacement as in the Ross system.

The cam is carried in the casing on two angular contact ball bearings and is coupled at the left-hand side to the torsion bar D by a cross-pin. At the right-hand end the torsion bar is coupled, also by a cross-pin, to the sleeve E which is splined to the steering-wheel shaft and which forms the inner member of the valve. The left-hand end of the sleeve E is formed with splines F which engage splines formed in the right-hand end of the cam A but these splines are machined so as to allow 7 degrees of freedom of rotation and are only to provide a safeguard against over-stressing of the torsion bar when the steering is operated without servo assistance. Pipes connect the pump, which is driven by the engine, to the valve and the latter to the outer end of the servo cylinder; the inner end of the servo cylinder forms the casing which houses the cam A and follower assembly and the valve is directly connected to that space. The outer member G of the valve is coupled by the ball-ended pin H to the right-hand end of the cam A. The servo piston J is integral with a stem on which rack teeth are formed and these teeth engage teeth machined on the end of the drop arm forging C.

The principle of operation of the valve is shown by the diagrams Fig. 31-29 (*a*) and (*b*). It is really three valves in parallel and these are denoted by suffixes 1, 2 and 3 but the action will be described in relation to one of them. The ports P are connected to the delivery of the pump and when the valve sleeve E is centrally placed as shown at (*a*) fluid flows equally to each of the pockets S_1 and

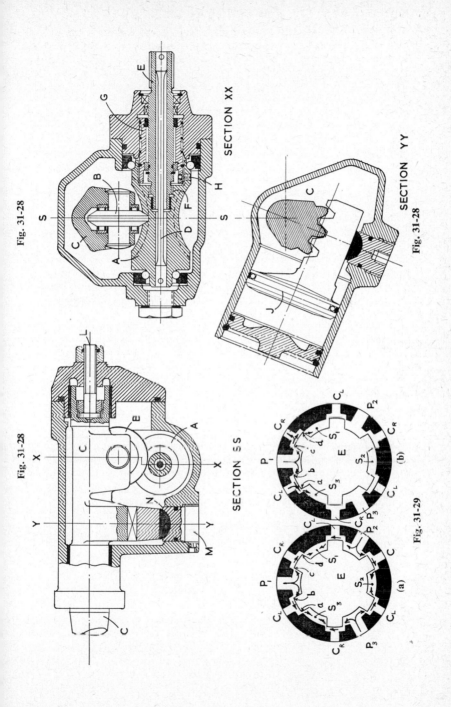

Fig. 31-28

SECTION XX

Fig. 31-28

SECTION YY

Fig. 31-28

SECTION SS

Fig. 31-29

S_2 which are connected at their ends to the return pipe to the pump. The pressure drops across the apertures b and a are equal to those across the apertures c and d and so there is no pressure difference between the spaces C_L and C_R which are connected to the ends of the servo cylinder. Hence there is no net hydraulic force acting on the servo piston. But when a torque is applied to the steering wheel to overcome a resistance to a steering motion of the road wheels the torsion bar is twisted and relative motion occurs between the inner valve sleeve E and the outer one G, as is shown at (b). The passage c is thereby increased while the passage d is decreased and so the pressure in the space C_R is raised. Conversely, the passage b is decreased and a is increased so that the pressure in the space C_L is lowered. A pressure difference is thus established across the servo piston and the drop arm is rotated. As this occurs the cam and outer sleeve of the valve rotate so as to follow up the inner valve sleeve and bring the valve to a central position. The drop arm having thus been rotated the required amount the servo action ceases and the system remains in equilibrium. The use of three sets of ports provides a valve in which the radial hydraulic pressures are balanced and the required port areas are obtained with a valve only one-third the length that would be needed if only one set was provided.

Provision is made for adjusting the mesh of the roller B with the cam A; this is done by means of the screw L which, when turned, will move the drop arm shaft C in or out and thus bring the roller into closer or looser mesh. Similarly, the mesh of the rack teeth on the servo piston stem can be adjusted by means of the screwed plug M which bears on the underside of the stem through the spherically seated pad N.

31.23 Driving and Braking of Steered Wheels

Various methods of driving a steered wheel are shown in Fig. 31-30. In the examples (a) and (b) a conventional axle is assumed, but in the others independent suspensions are shown. The arrangement

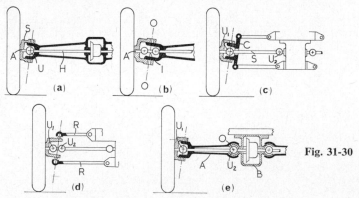

Fig. 31-30

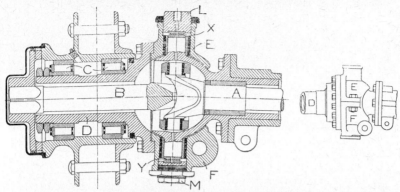

Fig. 31-31: Details of the F.W.D. stub axle

at (*a*) is the simplest, a single universal joint U being provided to accommodate the steering motion of the stub axle S. Unless this joint is of the constant velocity type, there will be an irregularity in the drive to the wheel whenever the stub axle is turned for steering purposes while, if the wheel is given any camber and the wheel shaft A is inclined to the half-shaft H, the irregularity will always be present. This constructional arrangement was adopted by the Four Wheel Drive Company in their lorries, which were amongst the earliest four wheel driven vehicles, and although the details of this arrangement are obsolete the general arrangement still represents current practice. An ordinary live axle is used so far as the final drive, differential and axle casing surrounding those components are concerned, but at their outer ends the drive shafts are carried in bushed bearings at A and are forked to form one member of a Hookes type universal joint. The other shaft of this joint is seen at B and conveys the drive to the hub cap of the road wheel. The latter is carried on bearings on the stub-axle member, which is made in three pieces D, E and F bolted together as shown in the right-hand view. The inner spherical surfaces of the portions E and F touch the corresponding surfaces of the end of the axle casing in order to make the housing oil-tight and to exclude mud and dust, but those surfaces do not carry any loads. The latter are carried on the projecting swivel pins of the axle casing.

In the arrangement shown in Fig. 31-30 (*b*), two universal joints are used and are symmetrically disposed relative to the king-pin axis OO. When the stub axle is turned about that axis for steering purposes, the angles between the intermediate shaft I and the wheel shaft A and half-shaft H respectively will be maintained equal as in Fig. 24-7, page 532, and so a constant velocity drive will be obtained. An example of this construction is shown in detail in Fig. 31-32. It is the design of the Kirkstall Forge Engineering Company and incorporates a second reduction gear which is housed in the wheel hub. This second reduction is between the pinion which is splined

643

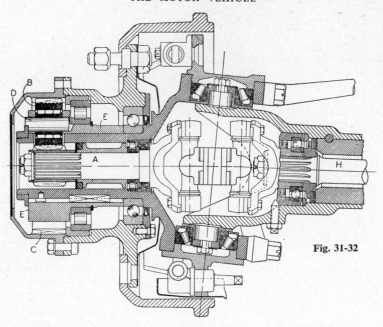

Fig. 31-32

to the end of the shaft A and the annulus C which forms the hub
cap of the road wheel and is bolted to the hub of the latter. The
intermediate pinions B are carried on pins D, which are supported
in the member E. The latter fits the cylindrical extension of the
stub axle and a key prevents rotation. Because the intermediate
member coupling the two universal joints is rigid, and the forks of
the joints are rigidly attached to the half-shaft H and wheel shaft A
respectively, one of these shafts must be left free to float axially.
This will be seen from Fig. 31-35, in which the full lines show the
position when the wheels are in the straight-ahead position, and
the dotted lines the position when the stub axle is turned for steering.
It is clear that the distance X_1Y_1 is less than the distance XY. This
variation is accommodated by leaving the shaft A (Fig. 31-32) free
to float. It is therefore carried in a parallel roller bearing at the
right end and is supported by the contacts with the three pinions B
at the left end. The omission of a bearing at the left end ensures
equal division of the driving torque between the three pinions.

The example shown in Fig. 31-30 (c) is a conventional double-
arm type of suspension, in which a stub axle carrier C connects the
two arms. The drive shaft S is provided with universal joints U_1
and U_2. The first of these accommodates the steering motion of
the stub axle and, in conjunction with the second, allows for the
vertical motion of the wheel assembly. Because the distance
between the centres of the universal joints cannot be kept constant,
the shaft S must be provided with some axial freedom. This is

usually done by leaving one of the universal joint forks free to slide on the splines of its shaft.

In the example shown in Fig. 31-30 (*d*), the stub axle carrier is omitted and the stub axle is carried directly by the arms RR, to which it is connected by ball and socket joints which accommodate the steering motion as well as the vertical motion of the road wheel. The joint U_2 now has to be supported from the stub axle through the joint U_1, and the construction of a joint which provides this support is shown in Fig. 31-33. The joint is made by the Glaenzer Spicer Company, of Poissy, France, to whom the author is indebted for drawings. The forks A and B are integral with the shafts A and B of Fig. 31-30 (*d*), and are coupled by four-armed spiders and an intermediate member C. The shaft B is supported relative to A by the ball and socket DE. The ball D is free to slide along the spigot shaft F, and the socket E is integral with the spigot G. The connection keeps the two universal joints and the intermediate member in the correct relationships to provide a constant-velocity drive, as described above.

Fig. 31-30 (e) shows a " swinging arm " type of independent suspension, in which the arm A which carries the stub axle is pivoted to the final drive casing B on the axis O. Two universal joints are necessary; one (U_1) to accommodate the steering motion and the other to allow for the swinging of the arm. The arrangement does not provide a constant velocity drive unless both the joints are of the constant velocity type. The casing B is carried by the frame of the vehicle.

In the arrangement shown in Fig. 31-34 there is a gear reduction between the drive shaft and the road wheel. This makes the speed of rotation of the drive shaft higher than that of the wheel and reduces the torque the universal joint has to transmit. The drive shafts are more exposed and difficult to protect from mud and dust but, being higher than the axle, are more out of the way of damage from the striking of obstacles.

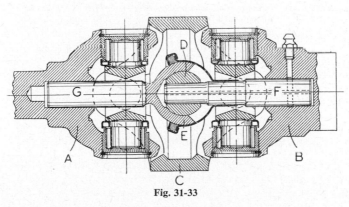

Fig. 31-33

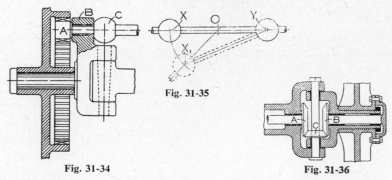

Fig. 31-35

Fig. 31-34

Fig. 31-36

The use of a universal joint can be avoided by using the arrangement shown in Fig. 31-36, where the half shaft carries a bevel gear A which drives a second bevel gear B fixed to the road wheel shaft through the intermediate wheel C. The latter is free to rotate on bearings on the swivel pin. The turning of the stub axle for steering purposes is accommodated by the rolling of the wheel B round the wheel C, and although this introduces an epicyclic action which causes an acceleration or deceleration of the road wheel this action only occurs during the time the stub axle is actually being turned. The arrangement can be made somewhat more robust than the universal joint drive, but is rather clumsy and is very little used.

31.24 Braking of Steered Wheels

The arrangements of the actual brakes are similar to those used with unsteered wheels, internal expanding rigid shoe brakes being used. The shoes are anchored to a back plate which is fixed to or is made integral with the stub-axle forging. The only difficulty that arises is in the connection of the brake linkage carried on the frame to the expanding mechanism of the brake, which turns with the stub axle about the swivel pin when the wheels are steered. The difficulty is avoided by the use of Bowden cable or fluid (including vacuum or air) operation of the brakes, in which the connection between the brake and the frame takes the form either of a flexible cable inside a semi-flexible sheath or of a flexible tube. These methods are consequently very commonly used.

In the Girling linkage the turning of the stub axle is accommodated by the pin joint between the pull rod (Fig. 29-6) and the expander wedge, the axis of this pin being made to coincide approximately with the swivel pin axis. Any slight geometrical errors that arise because exact coincidence of the axes cannot be always obtained are accommodated by slight movements of the compensating beams in the linkage.

CHAPTER 32

The Carriage Unit

Frame design.   Types and action of springs.   Chassis lubrication.

IN this chapter the carriage unit, which was mentioned at the beginning of Chapter 18, will be considered in greater detail.

32.1   The Frame

The general design of the frame is shown by Fig. 32-1.   It consists of two longitudinal or side members A and B, which are usually made in the form of pressings of channel section, as shown at *a*, but may be made of plates welded together.   In lorries the side members are frequently straight both in plan and elevation, but in cars they are nearly always upswept at the rear as shown, in order to clear the rear axle, and they are generally arranged to be closer together at the front than at the rear, either by inclining them as at A or by curving them as at B.   This is done to enable a wide steering lock, and consequently a small turning circle, to be obtained.   The side members are braced by a number of cross members C which may be of channel section as shown or tubular.

At the front and rear " dumb irons " D and brackets E are fitted to which the springs are connected, while brackets F are provided to support the running boards; these brackets are often connected together by a cross member.   Other brackets for supporting the engine, gear box, brake shafts, etc., are provided where necessary. As far as possible the rivets securing these brackets are arranged in the web of the channel section and not in the flanges, because the

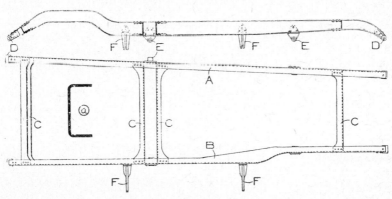

Fig. 32-1

Fig. 32-2

members have to act as beams, and the greatest stresses will be in the flanges which would be weakened by drilling. Bolts and nuts are sometimes used instead of rivets in the construction of frames as they are not so apt to work loose and are more easily replaced.

The tendency to-day is to make frames as rigid as possible. To this end frames are now stiffened with elaborate cross-bracing. Box section frame members, as in Fig. 32-2, are also much used, this section being much stiffer torsionally than the open channel section. When independent suspension is used for the wheels the frame usually has to be made stiffer than when axles are used, this is particularly so at the front end. With the ordinary springing system using four springs, one at each corner, the frame must twist whenever one wheel rises above the others. This twisting can be avoided by pivoting the front axle on a fore and aft pivot, but when this is done the stability of the vehicle is somewhat reduced.

32.2 Sub-frames

In the majority of cars and lorries the various components such as the engine, the gear box, etc., are bolted or carried directly on the main frame members or on cross members of the frame. Sometimes, however, the engine and gear box are carried on a sub-frame of simple construction and this sub-frame is supported by the main frame, usually at three points. The object of this arrangement is to isolate, as far as is possible, these components from the effects of twisting and flexing of the main frame. With a similar object, when the engine and gear box are carried directly on the main frame, they are often attached at three points only. With proper three-point support for a component it would be impossible to distort or stress that component however the relative positions of the supports might vary due to deflections of the frame. The supports would involve the use of ball and socket joints and the arrangement is rarely carried out fully.

Rubber connections are used between the engine gear box unit and the frame in most cars and in many lorries, but usually not in order to allow for distortion of the frame but to prevent or reduce the transmission of vibrations. For the same reason the body is also mounted on rubber blocks on the frame.

Backbone frames are used to a considerable extent by Continental designers, the general shape of these being as indicated in Figs. 32-3 and 32-4. The former is used with the single arm parallel type of

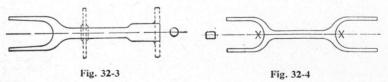

Fig. 32-3   Fig. 32-4

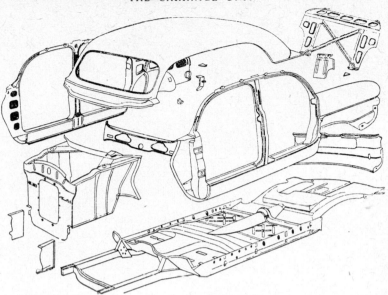

Fig. 32-5

suspension and with the transmissions shown in Figs. 33-14 and 33-16. The forked front end of the frame accommodates the engine gear box unit and the driving shaft passes down the inside of the central tubular portion of the frame. Brackets as indicated by the dotted lines are used to support the body. In the Tatra cars and lorries the forked front end is omitted, the tubular portion being bolted up to the back of the gear box. The arms of the front wheel suspensions are then pivoted directly on the casing of the engine gear box unit. The frame shown in Fig. 32-4 differs from that just described chiefly in that the central portion is rectangular in section and that it is built up of two channel section pressings welded together along the edges of the channels along the line XX. This type of frame has been used with conventional axles as well as with independent suspension.

There is a growing tendency to eliminate the frame, the body being so constructed that it has sufficient strength and stiffness to carry the loads normally taken by the frame. This is not difficult with pressed steel saloon bodies. An example is the Ford " Consul " and " Zephyr " body shown in Figs. 32-5 and 32-6.

32.3 One-piece Frames

Frames are sometimes built on an entirely different plan from that described above, being formed out of one or more large steel pressings welded together, but frames of this type are rare.

Fig. 32-6

32.4 Springs

The suspension springs used on motor cars and lorries are of five kinds, (*a*) laminated or leaf springs; (*b*) coil springs; (*c*) volute springs; (*d*) torsion bar springs and (*e*) rubber springs.

The leaf spring consists of a number of laminations or leaves of gradually decreasing length, piled on top of each other. In theory such a spring is based on a simple single-leaf spring of diamond shape as shown in Fig. 32-7.

If such a spring is cut into strips as indicated, and if the strips, except the centre one, are taken in pairs, a number of leaves of gradually decreasing length and with tapering ends will be obtained. If these leaves are now piled together, with the longest at the top and the shortest at the bottom, an ordinary laminated spring will be obtained. If the lozenge-shaped plate were used as a spring the stress induced in the surface fibres would be the same at every point in the length of the spring. If the shape departed from the lozenge shape some parts of the spring would be more heavily stressed than others, and the spring would be unduly heavy. The laminated spring based on the lozenge-shaped plate is thus the most economical leaf spring, and other things being equal will be the lightest.

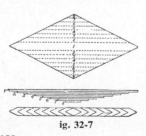

ig. 32-7

The laminated spring obtained from the lozenge-shaped plate will act in a similar manner to that plate except for one important difference. The plates of the laminated spring will have to slide over each other when the spring flexes, and since it is not possible to eliminate friction, the latter will modify the action. From one point of view this friction is advantageous, but from another point of view it is a drawback. Since the friction tends to oppose the motion of the leaves upon each other it tends to prevent the spring from flexing, and, in fact, it renders the spring rigid for small forces; if the friction were very great the spring would not be much good as a spring at all.

On the other hand, if the simple lozenge-shaped plate is held at the ends and deflected at the centre, and then released suddenly, it will vibrate about its normal position, and the vibration will continue for a long time because there is no friction to dissipate the energy of the vibration as heat. The laminated spring under similar conditions would have its vibration " damped out " more or less rapidly and would only make two or three oscillations. In a motor car this is desirable, so that when springs having only slight self-damping properties are used for the suspension, special " damping " arrangements have to be provided. However, even when freely lubricated there is always considerable friction in a laminated spring, and unless the lubrication is attended to the friction will vary and will give variable results. Designers therefore try to reduce the friction to the minimum, and then introduce additional friction when it is required by external devices called " dampers." Some of these are such that no resistance is offered to upward motions of the spring, but additional friction is introduced against downward motion, thus the spring is not deadened against small shocks while at the same time the necessary damping is obtained.

Springs in which the shorter leaves are symmetrically disposed above and below the main leaf and having their ends coupled together are used and springs consisting of a single leaf whose thickness varies from the ends to the middle are coming into use.

32.5 Dampers

As mentioned above, these are devices that introduce resistance to the motion of the springs and road wheels so as to damp out vibrations that might otherwise persist for several complete oscillations and so discomfort the passengers. The resistance of modern dampers is obtained by causing a fluid to pass at high speeds through small holes so that energy is absorbed by the fluid because of its viscosity; this absorbed energy appears, of course, as heat in the fluid. At one time dampers that made use of the " solid " friction that occurs between bodies that are pressed together were used but these have become obsolete. One advantage of the fluid type is that the resistance depends on the square of the speed at which the fluid is forced through the orifices so that for slow movements of the axles or wheels the damper introduces very little resistance but for rapid movements the resistance becomes large.

Three constructional forms of damper are in common use, they are the single lever type shown in Fig. 32-8, the double lever type indicated in Fig. 32-9 and the direct-acting or telescopic type shown in Fig. 32-10. The first type lends itself to incorporation as part of the linkage of an independent wheel suspension and the example

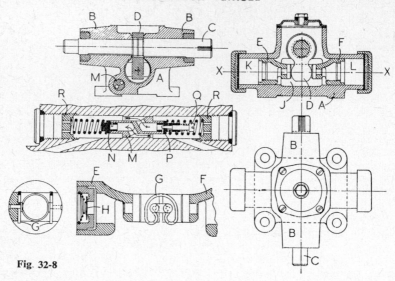

Fig. 32-8

shown, which is a Girling design, is arranged for such use. It consists of a body casting A which is bolted to the frame, and which has two integral bosses BB that provide bearings for the shaft C. The latter has fixed to its ends the inner ends of a wishbone member which forms the upper arm of a double arm type of suspension (see Section 33.5) and so is rotated by the rise and fall of the road wheel. At its centre the shaft C has a lever D splined to it and the end of this lever lies between the pistons E and F. Hardened pads are provided for the lever to bear against and the pistons are held together against the lever by circlip springs G. The pistons are a sliding fit in the bores K and L and are fitted with spring-loaded disc valves H (see enlarged section of pistons). These valves permit fluid to flow freely from the reservoir space J into the bores K and L but prevent any flow in the reverse direction. They thus ensure the bores being kept full of fluid. The bores K and L are connected by an external passage in which is situated a valve assembly M; this is shown separately to an enlarged scale. The central part M is a tight fit in the passage and is fitted with spring-loaded valves N and P which close the passage when in the positions shown. Supposing the piston F to be moved to the right by the lever D then fluid is forced through the right-hand passage leading to the valve M, lifts the valve N and passes through the small slot in the latter into the passage leading to the left-hand bore K. Similarly when the piston E moves to the left the valve P

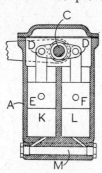

Fig. 32-9

is lifted to allow the fluid to pass L to the bore. The pressures that must be set up in order to lift the valves N and P can be regulated by means of the nuts RR. The pressure that is set up subsequent to the lifting of either of the valves depends on the square of the speed at which the pistons move. For very slow movements the valves N and P are not lifted at all, the fluid passing from side to side through a small orifice provided in the valve P and adjustable by means of the screw Q.

The double lever type indicated in Fig. 32-9 is essentially the same as that just described but the bores K and L are now side by side and the levers DD are connected to the pistons E and F by connecting links. The passage of the fluid from K to L and back is again through a valve assembly that is often situated between the bores in the space M.

The telescopic type shown in Fig. 32-10 consists of a cylinder A to which is welded a head B. The latter is screwed into the outer tube C to which is welded a pressed steel cap and eye D by means of which the cylinder A is secured to the axle or wheel assembly. A piston E slides inside the cylinder A and is secured to the piston rod F which at its upper end has an eye welded to it by which it is attached to the frame of the vehicle. The part of the piston rod that is outside the cylinder is protected by a cover that is welded to the

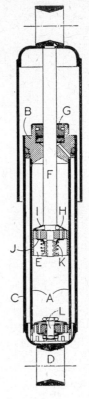

Fig. 32-10

fixing eye. A gland G prevents leakage where the piston rod passes through the head B; any fluid scraped off by the gland packing passes down a drain hole to the reservoir space between the cylinder A and the outer tube C. At the bottom of the cylinder A is a foot-valve assembly L. The piston E has two concentric rings of holes drilled through it, the outer ring is covered by a disc valve H which is held down by a star-shaped disc spring I while the inner ring is covered by the disc valve J which is held up by the coil spring K. The foot-valve assembly is similar to the piston assembly except that the lower disc valve covering the inner ring of holes is held up by a disc spring instead of by a coil spring.

Both ends of the cylinder A are completely filled with fluid and the reservoir space between A and C is half filled. If the eye D is moved upwards then fluid must be displaced from the bottom to the top side of the piston E. This fluid will pass through the outer ring of holes by lifting the valve H against the spring I. But since the increase in the volume of the upper end of the cylinder is less (by the volume of the piston rod that enters the cylinder) than the

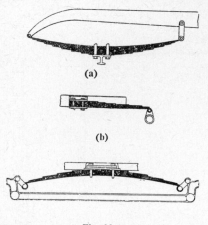

(a)

(b)

Fig. 32-11

decrease in volume of the lower end fluid will also be displaced through the inner ring of holes in the foot valve and the level of the fluid in the reservoir space will rise. The pressures set up will depend on the sizes of the passage opened by the valves in the piston and foot valve, and, of course, on the square of the speed at which the cylinder is moved upwards. For downwards motion of the cylinder, fluid will be displaced from the upper end of the cylinder to the lower end through the inner ring of holes in the piston and the valve J will be forced off its seating, but because of the volume of the piston rod that leaves the cylinder, fluid will also be drawn into the lower end of the cylinder from the reservoir space through the outer ring of holes in the foot valve.

32.6 Types of Laminated Spring

A laminated spring can be used in several ways and the different forms have acquired different names. The commonest form is the *semi-elliptic* shown in Fig. 32-11 (*a*) in which the spring is coupled at its ends to the frame and at its middle to the axle; the shortest leaf must then be at the bottom. A *full-cantilever* spring is pivoted at its centre and connected at its front end to the frame while its rear end is either pivoted or shackled to the axle, depending on whether the spring is called upon to transmit any thrust. The short leaves of a cantilever spring are at the top. The *quarter-elliptic spring* is half a semi-elliptic spring and is arranged as in Fig. 32-11 (*b*).

The names semi- and quarter-elliptic arise from the fact that two semi-elliptic springs used together, as at one time they were, resemble an ellipse.

The springs are sometimes arranged transversely across the car instead of parallel to the centre line. A transverse spring for a front axle is shown in Fig. 32-11 (*c*); it is bolted rigidly to the frame at its centre and shackled to the axle at each end.

Considering first the front axle, this, almost universally, is attached to the frame solely by the springs which have to drag it along against the resistance of the road. With semi-elliptic springs, which are by far the commonest, the springs are usually pivoted on a pin, fixed in the frame, at their front ends and are shackled to the frame at the rear ends. A few makers, however, pivot them at their rear ends and shackle them at the front. This

is done to reduce the
effect of the axle move-
ment on the steering.
When the front axle
moves up and down it
does so approximately
in a circle whose centre
is the pivot of the
spring. If this is at the

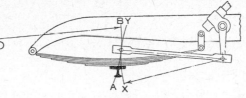

Fig. 32-12

front of the spring, the path of the axle is approximately the circle
AB (Fig. 32-12). Now the side steering rod which connects the
steering arm of the stub axle to the drop arm of the steering box has
to pivot about the ball joint of the drop arm, that is, about a point
which is some distance behind the axle. The forward end of the
side rod therefore moves in a circle such as XY, taking with it the
end of the steering arm of the stub axle. The latter, however, wants
to move in the path AB, and since this does not coincide with the
circle XY, the stub axle is turned slightly about the swivel pin axis
and the steering is affected. When the springs are pivoted at the
rear end the centres of the two paths are fairly close together and
the paths AB and XY more or less coincide, so that the steering is
unaffected by the motion of the axle.

In modern lorries, however, the engine and driver's seat are
placed much farther forward, relative to the front wheels, than they
used to be and the steering box and drop arm thus lie in front of
the axle so that the latter will be pivoted at the front and shackled
at the rear. Cars now usually have independent suspensions at
the front and the arrangement of the steering linkage for these is
considered later on. The same principle applies, however, that is,
the ends of the steering arm and the drag link should be made to
move in the same arc.

32.7 Action of the Springs

The way in which the springs shield the body from shocks can
only be indicated here in a very elementary way by considering
their action in two simple cases. First, when a wheel meets a
sudden rise, and secondly, when it meets a sudden step down.
In the first case the wheel, even when shod with a resilient tyre,
has to follow the contour of the road more or less exactly and therefore must rise rapidly. It is therefore accelerated upward with
a very high acceleration, and this means that a very large force
must act between it and the road. If there were no springs the
body and the passengers would experience similar accelerations
and would be subject to very heavy forces or shocks. With springs,
however, when the wheel moves upwards the body at first does not
move and the spring is merely compressed. The force which the
spring exerts is therefore increased and this increase acts upon the
body and accelerates it upwards. However, since the increase in
the spring force, even when the spring is considerably compressed,

655

is comparatively small, the acceleration of the body will be comparatively small and therefore the forces or shocks experienced by the body will be comparatively small also.

Secondly, on a step down; the action is as follows: When the wheel runs off the step the force acting between it and the road is suddenly removed. The force acting between the spring and the wheel, however, remains, and the wheel is accelerated downwards with a moderately large acceleration and (provided the step is not very deep) reaches the lower level almost before the body has started to move. However, since the wheel has moved downwards the compression of the spring has decreased, and the force of the spring which acts upwards on the body has decreased, but only comparatively little. The body therefore is accelerated downwards, but since the force which is acting (that is, the decrease in the spring force) is comparatively small, the acceleration is comparatively small also, whereas if there had been no springs the acceleration would have been that of gravity.

In each case when the step up or down has been passed, if the wheel does not rebound off the ground, the resulting motion becomes a simple vibration of the body on the springs, and the accelerations are comparatively low. These vibrations are damped out comparatively rapidly by the friction in the springs or in the rebound dampers.

32.8 Laminated Spring Details

The longest or master leaf of a laminated spring is usually coiled round at the ends to form eyes to embrace the shackle or anchorage pins, but sometimes the eye is forged solid with the leaf, and occasionally special arrangements are used. The spring eyes are usually bushed with bronze bushes. In the springs of lorries and often in cars, especially when the Hotchkiss drive is used, the second leaf also partly embraces the eye of the master leaf as a safeguard against the breakage of the latter. The leaves are bolted together at the centre, usually by a single bolt which passes through the centre of the leaves. The spring as a unit (in the case of semi-elliptic springs) is bolted to the spring seat by four bolts and a cap piece or by two U-shaped stirrups. Wood or fibre packing pieces are often interposed between the spring and the spring seat and cap piece, and the head of the bolt which bolts the leaves together often fits in a recess formed in the spring seat. To position the eaves sideways various arrangements are used. The leaves are sometimes made with " pips " or projections on their upper surfaces which project into corresponding recesses formed in the under

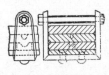

Fig. 32-13

sides of the leaves as shown in Fig. 32-13. Sometimes a rib is rolled the whole length of the leaf on one side and a corresponding groove on the other side. Often only clips as shown in the figure are used. These clips also serve another purpose. When through any cause the wheel and body move far

Fig. 32-14

Fig. 32-15

apart, the spring force acting on the wheel becomes an upward one instead of a downward one. If there were no clips, this upward force would have to be supplied solely by the master leaf, and this might cause fracture.

The clips, however, distribute the load over all the leaves and thus prevent excessive loading of the master leaf on rebounds. For a similar purpose short " rebound " leaves are sometimes fitted on top of the master leaf of semi-elliptic springs.

There is a patented form of spring in which the master leaf is in the middle with the other leaves arranged symmetrically above and below. The ends of corresponding leaves above and below are connected by clips so that all the leaves act whichever way the spring is deflected, upwards or downwards.

Laminated springs require a certain amount of attention if they are not to give trouble. They should be kept externally clean, and at intervals should be lubricated by jacking up the *frame* until the wheel is off the ground so that the leaves can be opened up and oil or grease inserted. The spring clips must, of course, be removed to allow of this.

The lubrication of the shackle pins should also be attended to very carefully as a great deal of motion occurs at those points, and the loads are considerable. If lubrication is neglected wear will be rapid. It is sometimes advisable to jack the frame up when lubricating the shackle pins, so that the load comes on the side of the pin opposite to the normal; this gives the grease or oil gun a chance to clean out the old grease or oil thoroughly.

An alternative to the shackle, having the advantage of providing greater bearing areas, is shown in Fig. 32-14. The ends of the master leaves of the spring are free to slide in a slot formed in a cylindrical member A which is free to turn in the housing B.

Rubber shackles are sometimes used; in one type a rubber fabric link is used, being bolted at its ends to the frame and the spring leaft respectively. A modern type, made by Metalastik Company, is shown in Fig. 32-15.

Rubber bushes are almost universal for the spring eye connections of laminated springs and at the pivot points of the arms of independent suspensions, their great advantage being that no lubrication is required and that they rarely wear out.

The bolts that secure the springs to their seats should also be inspected occasionally as they are liable to stretch, when the spring would become loose on its seat and the consequences might be serious. In the case of front springs and axles it is by no means uncommon, especially in lorries, for an extra heavy shock to shift the axle back along the springs, and this should be looked out for and corrected after such shocks.

It should be noted that specially " heat-treated " bolts are sometimes used instead of ordinary ones. The former have numerous advantages and their use will probably become fairly general. They must not, however, be replaced by ordinary bolts or a serious accident may easily occur.

32.9 Coil Springs

These are used chiefly with independent suspensions, which are considered later. Coil springs are sometimes used with conventional axles, however, and then special arrangements must be made to position the axles relative to the frame and to deal with the driving and braking torque reactions. Methods of doing this have been dealt with in Section 25.9.

32.10 Torsion Springs

A rod or tube acting in torsion may be used as a spring, the action being essentially the same as that which occurs in a coil spring. Such torsion springs are generally used with independent suspension. Thus when a parallel type of suspension is used the arm (or one of the arms in a double arm type) that carries the road wheel is secured to one end of the torsion rod, which is arranged parallel to the frame member with its axis coincident with the axis about which the arm pivots; the other end of the torsion spring is anchored to the frame. When a perpendicular type of suspension is used the arrangement is similar except that the axis of the torsion spring is placed across the frame. The latter arrangement is sometimes a little difficult to fit in as the torsion members get in the way of the engine unit. Torsion springs are no better than coil springs so far as their action is concerned, but they provide a very neat and compact design.

32.11 Rubber Springs

Under suitable conditions rubber is very satisfactory as a spring material and rubber springs have been used experimentally for vehicles for many years. Its use is now becoming more common. Usually the rubber is arranged to be stressed in shear as it withstands this kind of stress better than either tension or compression although compression rubber springs have been and are used successfully. One convenient arrangement consists of a disc of rubber that is bonded to metal plates at either side, one disc is then fixed to the frame and the other to an arm that is coupled to the axle, if one is used, or which forms part of an independent suspension linkage. Movement of the road wheel turns one disc

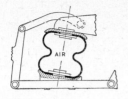 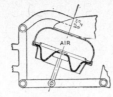 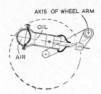

Fig. 32-16

relative to the other and twists the rubber. The cross section of the rubber disc is made trapezoidal in order to keep the stress throughout the rubber fairly uniform. In another convenient arrangement the rubber is in the form of a cylinder bonded on its outside to a metal tube and at its inside to a shaft. The tube is fixed in a bracket in the frame and the shaft carries levers at its end, or ends, by which it is coupled to the road wheel assembly. Again when the road wheel rises or falls the rubber is twisted.

32.12 Air Springs

A volume of air enclosed in a cylinder fitted with a piston or enclosed in a flexible bellows can be used as a spring as in Fig. 32-16. Under the normal load the air is compressed to a definite pressure and subsequent motion of the piston either increases or decreases the pressure and consequently increases or decreases the force acting on the piston. If this force is plotted against the piston travel, a curve similar to the compression curve of an indicator card will be obtained, and it should be clear that the rate at which the force varies with the piston travel becomes greater as the air pressure increases. Thus the " rate " of an air spring is variable, unlike that of a laminated or a coil spring in which equal increments of force correspond to equal increments of deflection. This variable rate is an advantage, as a low rate can be obtained for the normal riding position while keeping the total rise and fall of the axles within reasonable limits.

The use of air springs is becoming common. In double wishbone type suspensions a rubber bellows, circular in section and having two convolutions, is much used and generally merely replaces the coil spring of the conventional design. Alternatively, a metal air container in the form of an inverted drum is fixed to the frame and a " piston " is attached to the lower wish-bone. The piston is considerably smaller than the drum and the seal is provided by a flexible diaphragm which is secured at its outer circumference to the lip of the drum and at its centre to the piston.

Similar arrangements are used for the rear suspensions of cars and light lorries. Coaches and heavy lorries employ elongated bellows (Fig. 32–17) which are approximately rectangular in plan but with semi-circular ends and again having,

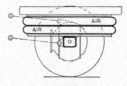

Fig. 32-17

659

usually, two convolutions. These are placed directly between seatings, which are integral with the axle casing and seatings which are fixed to the frame. Radius rods are used to deal with the torques and thrusts as described earlier in Chapter 25.

32.13   Adjustable and Self-adjusting Suspensions

Suspension systems using laminated, coil and torsion-bar springs are sometimes provided with adjusting devices so that the " trim," or general level, of the vehicle can be maintained despite wide variations in the distribution of the load as between the front and back axles. Such adjusting points are, in fact, usually provided for the initial adjustment of torsion-bar springs, because it is very easy to arrange to turn the anchorage end of a torsion-bar to adjust the trim of the vehicle and because small variations in the torsion-bars can make relatively large changes to the trim of the vehicle. Vehicles in which these adjustments can be made " from the driver's seat " are now being produced. The torsion-bar anchorages are coupled by gearing of very low ratio to electric motors so that they can be rotated by switching on the motor. By providing connections between the body and axles or wheels, which will operate the switches, the adjustments could be made automatic but this has not, so far, been done. When air springs are used, however, it is becoming common practice to make the adjustment automatic, and two methods of doing this will now be described.

The system shown in Fig. 32-18 is called a " constant mass " system because the mass, or weight, of air enclosed in the space A, which acts as the spring, is constant. The space O between the floating piston P and the axle piston b is filled with oil and, in normal functioning of the suspension, the oil O moves up and down with the pistons b and P, and the air is correspondingly compressed or extended. The adjustment for varying body loads is controlled by the valve V. Supposing the load to be increased so that the assembly C, which is fixed to the body, moves downwards, then the valve V will open the port D and oil from the pump E will pass into the space O. The piston P and assembly C, together with the body, will therefore move upwards, and this will continue until the

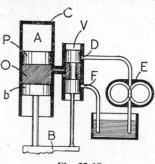

Fig. 32-18

port D closes again. Similarly, if the body load decreases the valve will open the port F and oil will escape from the space O until the valve closes the port F again. Thus the " height " of the suspension can be kept constant. This self-adjusting action is not required when the motions between the body and the axle are due to irregularities of the road and the action is therefore made relatively sluggish, so that it does not have time to act for rapidly occurring

motions. The system shown in Fig.
32-19 is called a "constant volume"
system because the volume of air enclosed
in the space A is maintained constant.
To do this, air has to be pumped into or
out of the space, and so the mass of air
which forms the spring is variable. Again,
if the body load is supposed to increase,
the valve V will open the port D and air
will pass from the reservoir E via the passage F into the space A, and the "height"
of the suspension will be restored. The
reservoir is kept charged by an air supply
which enters through the non-return valve
R. Springs S are now shown in the connection between the axle B and the valve

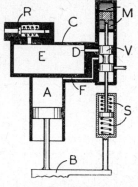

Fig. 32-19

V, and the latter is provided with a "dash-pot" or damper M
(filled with oil). This prevents rapid motions of the valve but will
not impede slow ones. Thus rapid motions of the axle B will
merely affect the springs S, and the self-adjusting action will be
confined to changes of suspension height brought about by variations in the body load. This spring and dash-pot arrangement
can, of course, be equally well used with the previous system.

32.14 Interconnected Suspension Systems

In a four-wheeled vehicle the suspensions of the front and back
axles or wheels are usually quite independent of each other, but
sometimes they are connected together and then the suspension
system is said to be "interconnected," "compensated" or "equalized." The basic principle involved is shown in Fig. 32-20, where
a lever C connects the front and back springs. If the body D is
assumed to move up and down so that it remains parallel to the
ground, the lever has no effect, and the natural frequency of a
vibration of this nature (which is commonly referred to as
"bounce") would be the same as if no lever were used and would
depend chiefly on the stiffness of the springs A. But if the body is
assumed to vibrate about the axis O, the frequency of this type of
vibration (known as "pitch") will depend chiefly on the stiffness
of the springs B
and, by making
these relatively soft
in comparison
with the springs A,
the natural fre-
quency in "pitch"
can be made very
low while keeping

Fig. 32-20

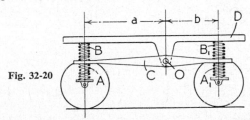

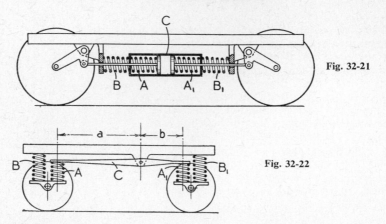

Fig. 32-21

Fig. 32-22

the natural frequency in " bounce " reasonably high. This is the chief claim made for interconnected suspensions.

An equivalent arrangement which is more easily carried out in practice and which is used by the Citroën Company in some of their vehicles is shown in Fig. 32-21.

An alternative arrangement is shown in Fig. 32-22, where the springs B are placed between the body and the axles, and only the springs A are coupled by the lever C. This produces the same kind of effect as the previous arrangement, but the bounce frequency now depends chiefly on the stiffness of the springs B, and the pitch frequency on that of the springs A. A suspension system using this principle has been used, with torsion bar springs, by the Packhard company.

An article on the theory of interconnected suspension systems will be found in the *Automobile Engineer*, Vol. 47, No. 1.

32.15 Interconnected Air and Liquid Suspensions

The interconnection of air springs is a simple matter provided that the actual spring units are of a suitable type. It is essential that they should give an increase in spring force with upward motion of the road wheel *even though the air pressure in the unit remains constant*. This will be seen from the diagrams in Fig. 32-23 (*a*) and (*b*). In the first the air spring units are shown as simple cylinders such that the effective area of the piston or diaphragm on which the pressure acts remains constant as the wheel rises or falls relative to the body of the vehicle. Thus, assuming that both air spring units are of the same size, it follows that the pressures in them when they are interconnected will be equal as also will be the forces P exerted by them. The resultant vertical load will thus be $2P = W$ acting at the mid-point between the wheels. The centre of gravity of the body must therefore always lie at that mid-point in order to obtain equilibrium and this is obviously impossible. Any slight shift of the C.G. would result in one air unit moving up to its extreme upward position and the other to its lowest.

In diagram (b), however, the air units are shown such that the

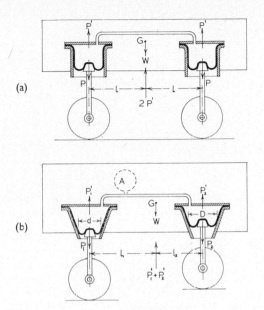

Fig. 32-23

effective area of the diaphragms increases as the road wheels move upward. Thus the effective area of the left-hand unit in the position shown is approximately $\pi d^2/4$ and that of the right-hand unit is $\pi D^2/4$ and so since the air pressure in the units is the same the force P_2 will be greater than P_1. The system will now be stable since any shift of the C.G. will cause one air unit to " move up," thus increasing the force it exerts, while the other unit will " move down," thus reducing its force, and equilibrium will be reached when the resultant of these unequal forces acts along the same line as the weight of the body.

The argument is equally valid if the areas of the units are unequal, the C.G. being no longer at the mid-point.

A system as shown at (b) would be effective if it were filled with liquid instead of air but would give a very stiff, or hard, suspension because liquids are only slightly compressible. The effective stiffness of the system can, however, be adjusted to a suitable value by making some part of the system elastic. This is indicated in the diagram where A represents a flexible container or reservoir whose volume can change considerably with changes of internal pressure. Alternatively, the reservoir can be rigid but fitted with a

663

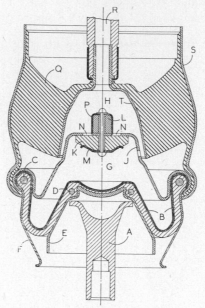

Fig. 32-24

spring-loaded piston or diaphragm or could contain compressible material.

By putting suitable valves in the piping connecting the units of an interconnected fluid system sufficient damping can be obtained to eliminate the necessity for separate dampers.

32.16 The B.M.C. Hydrolastic Suspension Systems

In these the elastic element is rubber acting in compression and shear and the interconnection is by fluid, with which the systems are filled. The general form of the construction is shown in Fig. 32-24, which shows a front-wheel unit for one of the B.M.C. " Mini " vehicles. It is used in an approximately vertical position but in the B.M.C. 1800 a similar unit is used in a horizontal position with its axis transverse to the centre line of the vehicle and for the rear-wheel units the position is again approximately horizontal but parallel to the centre line. The stem A is attached to a rod which bears at its lower end on the upper link of a double wishbone suspension at a point fairly close to the pivot of the wishbone so that the stem motion is only about one-fifth of the wheel movement. The wheel load is supported by the pressure acting on the upper surface of the diaphragm B. This is made of two rubber materials, one providing the required strength and the other the necessary seal for the liquid; it is reinforced by steel beads C and D. A piston member E in conjunction with a skirt F provides support

664

for the diaphragm and helps to give the required spring characteristic. The fluid in the chamber G can at all times pass into the chamber H through a bleed hole provided in the member J which separates the chambers. A damper valve assembly K, L also provides additional passages. Thus the rubber flap valve K which is loaded by the spring M will open downwards when the pressure in H rises sufficiently above that in G, thus allowing fluid to pass through the holes N. The similar valve L, which is at right angles to K, will let fluid pass from G to H. These valves are kept from rotating out of position by fingers integral with the springs M and P which are bent down (as is seen in the case of P) so as to engage the holes N. The fluid in the chamber H acts on the under-side of the rubber element Q and through the hose R is transmitted to the other wheel unit on the same side of the car. The rubber Q is bonded on the outside to the canister S which is fixed to the body structure and at its inside to the pot member T. The skirt F, diaphragm B, member J and the canister S are all secured by rolling over the edges of the metal components as shown.

32.17 Chassis Lubrication

The methods of lubricating the major components of the motor vehicle, the engine, gear box and back axle, have been described; it remains to deal with the minor components and points that must be lubricated. Such points as the joints in the controls and brake linkages may be lubricated in a very simple manner by providing them with oil holes through which oil can, from time to time, be introduced. However, in these minor bearings the clearances are generally liberal, and oil cannot always be maintained within the bearing; grease can then be employed instead of oil. For the more important points such as the brake cross-shaft bearings, shackle-pins and spring pivots, swivel-pin bearings, etc., the usual method is to provide nipples to which a grease or oil gun can be connected and grease or oil thereby forced in under pressure. Oil is to be preferred to grease as a lubricant as it will flow to all parts of a bearing when once introduced, whereas grease will not; it is more easily filtered and rendered grit free, and it will sustain equally high pressures as grease and with less friction.

The labour involved in attending to the large number of lubricating points is, however, great. It can be reduced to some extent by grouping nipples together and connecting them by short pipes to the points to be lubricated.

Alternatively all the points may be fed from a centrally placed reservoir provided with a simple plunger pump which forces oil through a piping system to the lubricating points. The plunger may be spring operated so that after being depressed it gradually rises and forces the oil through the pipes, or it may be operated by the vibration of a spring-suspended mass or by the variation in the pressure in the induction manifold. The chief differences between the systems lie in the arrangements determining the oil flow to each point. One method employs restricted orifices formed sometimes by a loose-fitting screwed plug through the clearances of which the oil has to flow or by a pin fitting fairly tightly in a hole, the oil having to flow between the pin and the walls of the hole.

Another type of central lubrication system uses a pump which is driven at a very low speed from some member of the transmission or engine and which feeds oil continuously through a piping system to the various bearings, regulation of the flow being by restricted orifices.

As an example of a modern central lubrication system the Clayton Dewandre " Milomatic " will be described. It is shown in Fig.

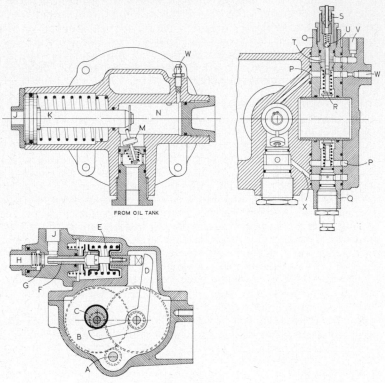

FROM OIL TANK

Fig. 32-25

32-25 and consists essentially of three units: the distributor valve, the intensifier and the delivery valve block. The distributor valve, seen in the lower view, comprises a gear box giving a reduction of 955 to 1 between the input shaft A (which is driven off any convenient part of the transmission, the speedometer drive being frequently used) and the gear wheel B which carries the eccentric C. The latter is thus caused to make one revolution per vehicle mile and it operates the valve plunger F through the bell crank D and spring E. As the plunger is pushed to the left it first makes contact with the disc valve G and thus cuts off the passage from the pipe J to atmosphere which has hitherto been open through the hole in the plunger. The disc valve is then pushed off its seat so that air under pressure can pass from the inlet H, which is connected through a pressure regulating valve to the reservoir of the brake system, to the outlet J which is connected to the inlet J in the upper view. This view shows the intensifier; in the position shown the space N is open, through the valve M, to the oil tank and so is full of oil. When the distributor valve passes air to the inlet J the piston K is forced to the right and immediately releases the valve M which then seals off the inlet from the oil tank. The movement of the piston then raises the pressure in the space N and consequently in the spaces P of the delivery valve block which is shown on the right. This consists of a housing Q which is shown bolted up to the face of the intensifier unit but can be mounted as a separate unit and connected to the intensifier by a pipe. In the housing Q injector units S are mounted radially and each one is coupled by a pipe to a chassis point requiring to be lubricated. The spaces T of the delivery valve block are connected to the oil tank via the passage X or by a separate pipe if the valve block is a separate unit. When the pressure in the spaces P is raised by the action of the intensifier it acts on the area of the plungers R and forces the plungers outward. As soon as the plungers seal off the inlet ports T oil will be forced out through the non-return valves U to the lubrication point. By varying the position of the inlet port the amount of oil delivered per cycle can be varied and three standard positions are available corresponding to deliveries of 0·025, 0·05 and 0·075 cc per cycle. Initially, the system must be filled with oil and so bleeding points are provided as shown at W. Any excess oil can return to the oil tank through the pipe connected to the outlet V. Each valve unit contains 12 injector units and up to six valve units can be operated by one injector unit. The system will continue to operate satisfactorily for all the other lubrication points if one point should become blocked or if the pipe to it should be fractured.

CHAPTER 33

Independent and Dead Axle Suspensions

Principles and designs reviewed

THE term independent suspension is used to describe any arrangement for connecting the road wheels to the frame in which the rise or fall of one wheel has no direct effect on the other wheels. In the ordinary axle arrangement the rise of one wheel causes that wheel and the wheel at the other end of the axle to tilt through an angle whose magnitude depends on the height of the rise and on the track of the wheels. It has been shown that with an axle whose wheels are steered this tilting of the wheels is one cause of wheel wobble or " shimmy "—a vibration of the wheels and stub axles about the swivel pins which may occur at certain speeds, depending on factors which need not here be considered. When independent suspension is used this cause of wheel wobble is eliminated. It is then practicable to use somewhat " softer " springs than with the axle suspension, so that the riding qualities are improved. Also the unsprung parts are less heavy than in axle suspensions and this, too, generally leads to an improvement in the riding qualities. With the advent of front wheel brakes and low pressure tyres, considerable trouble was sometimes experienced from wheel wobble and there was thus a strong incentive to the use of independent suspensions. The result is that now, although wheel wobble is not a serious trouble with axle suspensions, independent suspensions are almost universal at the front of passenger vehicles and are not uncommon at the rear and on lorries.

Independent suspensions can be arranged in many different ways and there is no altogether satisfactory system of classifying them. The classification that follows is fairly comprehensive and covers all the most important types. No attempt has been made to indicate all the possible combinations of type of suspension and type and position of spring.

It is perhaps interesting to note that independent suspension is by no means a new conception, having been used as long ago as 1878.

33.1 Single-arm Perpendicular Type

This type, an example of which is shown diagrammatically in Fig. 33-1, is not much used because in comparison with other types it has several drawbacks. It is, however, almost the simplest arrangement possible. The stub axle is pivoted on a king-pin fixed in the end of a single arm A that is pivoted to the frame on an axis XX which is perpendicular to the centre line of the vehicle. A

668

spring connects the arm to the frame and transmits the weight carried by the wheel. If the spring is a coil spring it is commonly arranged as shown but alternative arrangements have been used. If a torsion bar spring is used it will be placed co-axial with XX and one end will be fixed in the boss of the arm while the other end will be fixed to the frame. The length of the torsion bar is then limited to half the width between the arms and this may be inconvenient in the design of the spring. If the stub axle does not turn on the king-pin the motion of any point of the stub axle and wheel when the arm pivots is in a circular arc having XX as axis; the wheel axis, for example, would move in the arc x and the ball end B of the steering arm would move in the arc x_1. In order that the movements of the arm shall not produce steering movements of the wheel the rod connected to B should be pivoted to a lever at some point on the axis XX, this would not be possible with a torsion bar that was co-axial with XX. The chief drawbacks of this type of suspension are, firstly, that the angle θ between the king-pin axis and the ground varies as the arm pivots and so the amount of castor will vary; secondly, that it is not easy to obtain sufficient stiffness against forces acting from the side, that is, perpendicular to the centre line of the car, and thirdly, that when the body and frame of the car tilt under the action of centrifugal force on corners the wheels tilt to exactly the same extent and the resulting changes in the camber angles reduce the cornering power of the tyres. There is, however, no variation of the " semi-track," that is the distance of the contact point of the wheel with the ground from the centre line of the car, in this type of suspension. For an unsteered wheel

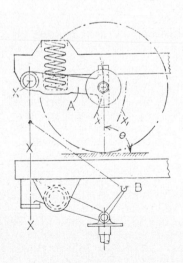

Fig. 33-1

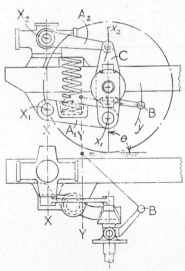

Fig. 33-2

the chief disadvantages of this type are not present and so the arrangement has found more use for rear wheels than for front ones, but, as stated above, it is not greatly used.

33.2 Double-arm Perpendicular Type

This is indicated in Fig. 33-2. There are now two arms A_1 and A_2, both pivoted on axes (X_1 and X_2) that are perpendicular to the centre line of the car. The arms are connected by a member C which carries the king-pin on which the stub axle is pivoted. If the two arms are made exactly the same length and are arranged to be parallel as shown then they will be parallel in all positions and the member C will receive a motion of translation and will not receive any angular motion. The angle θ will not alter as the wheel lifts and thus one of the chief drawbacks of the single-arm type is eliminated. The end B of the steering arm will now move in an arc y whose radius is equal to that of the arcs x_1 and x_2 in which the ends of the arms move. If the rod connected to B is pivoted to a lever at any point on the axis YY of the arc y then the movements of the wheel will have no effects on the steering. In the diagram a coil spring is shown but this type lends itself better to the use of torsion bars than does the single-arm type because the torsion bar for one side can be connected to the upper arm and that of the other side to the lower arm. The diagram also shows what is not uncommon practice, namely, that the hydraulic damper, or " shock-absorber," is made to function as part of the suspension. In this type also, the wheels have to tilt with the body and frame.

33.3 Single-arm Parallel Type

The stub axle is again carried on a king-pin that is fixed in the end of a single arm but the arm is now pivoted to the frame on an axis XX (Fig. 33-3) that is parallel to the centre line of the car. The ball end of the steering arm now moves in a circle concentric with XX and the rod connected to it should be connected to its lever at some point on that axis. The angle θ now varies as the wheel rises and falls and there is an alteration in the semi-track T but these are not serious defects since the side scrubbing action due to the variation in the semi-track can usually be absorbed by the lateral flexibility of the tyre. The variation in the camber angle may be more serious for a steered wheel but the arrangement is used chiefly for unsteered but driven wheels. The drive is easily arranged by making the arm hollow and housing the drive shaft inside it, a universal joint being provided at the pivot axis of the arm. The type lends itself to the use of torsion bar springs as they may be situated alongside the frame members and there is usually plenty of room for them. When coil springs are used they will be placed between seats arranged on the arms and brackets on the frame or body. There is, theoretically, a slight change of castor angle as the wheels lift but this is, practically, quite negligible. Fore and aft

670

stiffness can be obtained by making the arm a " wishbone " as indicated by the dotted lines.

33.4 Double-arm Parallel Type

This is one of the most widely used types and, all factors being considered, is probably the best arrangement. An example, in which a torsion bar spring is indicated, is given in Fig. 33-4. If the arms are made equal in length and are parallel then again the motion of the stub axle carrier C would be one of translation and the camber angle ϕ would not vary as the wheel moved. Usually, however, the upper arm is made shorter than the lower one as shown and in this case there will be some change in the angle ϕ. If the length and disposition of the arms are carefully designed the alteration in the camber angle when the body tilts on a corner can be made to improve the cornering power of the outer wheel which carries the increased load and the total cornering power may thereby be increased. Originally the use of a shorter upper arm was because it was thought desirable to use arms that were as long as possible and the engine got in the way of the upper arms. The end B of the steering arm now moves in a curve that is not circular so that movement of the wheel is bound to have some steering effect; however a centre can usually be found for the connection of the track link to its lever such that the steering effect is negligible. If the end B of the steering arm is made to lie on the axis of the joint between either arm and the member C then its motion will be in a circular arc and the track link connection can be placed on the axis of the arm so that no interference with the steering will result from the wheel movement but this is not usually considered necessary. In the figure a telescopic type of hydraulic damper is shown at S, being connected at its ends to

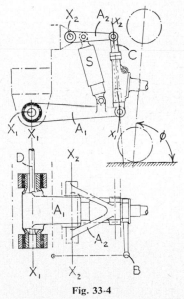

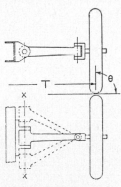

Fig. 33-3   Fig. 33-4

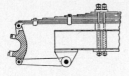

Fig. 33-5

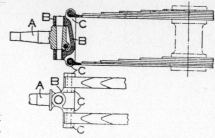

Fig. 33-6

the two arms; this is not a very common arrangement, usually the upper end of the damper is pivoted to the frame.

Two variations of this type of suspension are shown in Figs. 33-5 and 33-6. In the first a laminated spring takes the place of the upper arm while in the latter four laminated springs, two at the top and two at the bottom, replace both arms. The rear suspension of the Triumph Herald is of the double-arm parallel type and a transverse spring is used for the upper link but the lower link is formed by the half-shaft itself. The housing of the wheel bearing at the outer end of the half-shaft (where no universal joint is required) is pivoted to the lower end of a link which at its upper end is pivoted to the spring. A radius rod placed at an angle of about 45° to the centre line of the car provides fore and aft support. A somewhat similar arrangement is used in the E-type Jaguar.

33.5 Broulhiet Arrangement

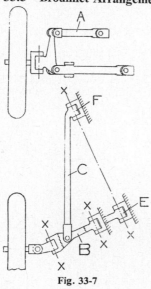

Fig. 33-7

This, which is shown in Fig. 33-7, is a modification of the double-arm parallel, or rather the intermediate, type. A single arm is used at the top and a wishbone- or V-shaped arm at the bottom. The bottom arm is made in two parts, B and C, pinned together. This joint is not, however, a working joint and, as regards the working of the linkage, B and C might be made integral. The axes XX of all the pivots, are parallel to each other but are inclined to the centre line of the car, converging towards the front. The arrangement brings the arm C into a good position for taking the fore and aft forces and also enables that arm to be made longer than in the ordinary double-arm parallel type, and thus enables braking torques to be

672

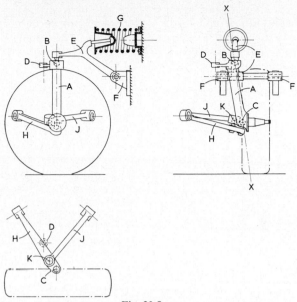

Fig. 33-8

dealt with more easily. Since the pivots E and F are some considerable distance apart it is difficult to keep their axes coincident. To allow for any slight misalignment one or both of the pivots may be made resilient, for example, a Silentbloc bush may be used. Except for misalignment errors the movements of the linkage do not involve any but ordinary pivot action at any of the joints.

33.6 The Rover 2000 Front Suspension

In this, which is shown in the diagram Fig. 33-8, the road wheel is carried on a stub axle which is integral with the tubular member A. This member is supported at the top and bottom on ball and socket joints B and C and so can turn about the axis XX for steering; the steering arm which imparts the motion is seen at D. The ball of the joint B is part of a lever E which is pivoted in rubber bushes carried, at FF, by brackets fixed to the body structure. The lever E is also used to transfer the vertical load carried by the wheel to the spring G and thus to the body. The lower end of the member A the ball of the joint is fixed in the composite wishbone member H, J whose members are pivoted to the body on rubber bushes at their inner ends and are pivoted together by a ball and socket joint K. The latter joint allows for the axes of the members H and J being at an angle to each other. A telescopic damper (not shown) is provided and is coupled at its upper end to the lever E and at its lower end to the body structure.

The advantages claimed for this arrangement are that it facilitates the distribution of the forces on to the body structure and that practically no changes occur in the camber, castor angle and wheel track when the suspension moves up and down.

33.7   Girling Linkage

This also may be regarded as a modification of the double-arm parallel type, a longitudinal arm C (Fig. 33-9) being added to give greater fore and aft rigidity and to deal with braking torques.   The axis of the pivot connecting the arm C to the frame is perpendicular to the centre line of the car.   Since the arm C is bolted rigidly to the stub axle carrier D it tends to make the latter move in the arc XX.   Such a motion involves forward and backwards motion of the outer ends of the transverse arms.   Again, since the ends of the transverse arms move in arcs YY, YY, there is a tendency to make the front end of the arm C move to and fro perpendicular

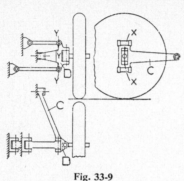

Fig. 33-9

Fig. 33-10

to the centre line of the car.   These motions are conflicting but the conflict can be greatly reduced by tilting the pivots of the transverse arms so that in the side view their axes pass through the pivot point of the arm C, as is indicated in Fig. 33-10.   The paths of the outer ends of the arms are then seen as the lines LL and MM tangential to the arc XX.   However, if ordinary pin and bush pivots were used severe stresses would be set up and would produce great wear. These effects are avoided by using Silentbloc bushes at all the pivot pins.

33.8   The Strut Type

The principle of this is shown in the diagram Fig. 33-11 and the construction in Fig. 33-12.   It is becoming fairly common since it fits in well with the general arrangement of modern cars in which the engine being placed well forward leaves little room for the upper member of other types.   There is a single transverse arm A which is pivoted to the body structure at B and is connected by a ball and socket joint D to the strut C.   The strut comprises also the member E which is free to slide inside C and which is pivoted to the body by the equivalent of a ball and socket joint at F.   Since the motion here is small a rubber joint is usual.   The spring is placed between

674

flanges formed on the members C and E and these members are also used as the damper. Steering is by the rotation of the member C about the axis DF. The fore and aft forces acting on the road wheel are taken by a tie rod or link which is pivoted to the link A near the outer end and to the body structure at the other end, both pivots being usually rubber bushes. In the plan view this tie rod is usually placed at approximately 45 degrees to the centre line of the car, in front of the link A, so that it is in tension. By making

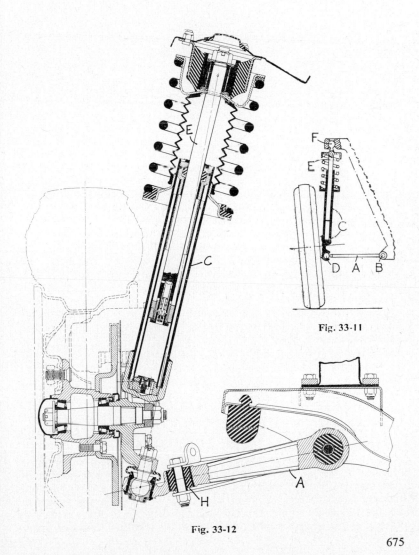

Fig. 33-11

Fig. 33-12

675

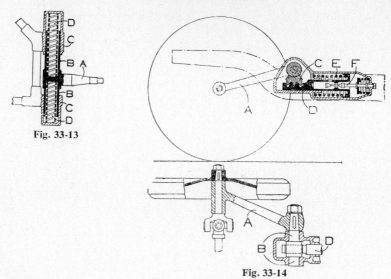

Fig. 33-13

Fig. 33-14

the tie rods for the suspensions at the two sides out of a single rod suitably formed, it can be used as an anti-roll bar so as to stiffen the suspension against rolling motions. The arrangement of the suspension itself gives a relatively high roll axis and it also keeps to the minimum.

An example of the actual construction of a strut type suspension, that used in the Triumph 2000, is shown in Fig. 33-12. To facilitate production the strut is made as a separate member from the stub axle forging to which it is bolted. This also permits the dampers to be replaced, if necessary, without disturbing the wheel assemblies and makes the vertical members the same at each side. At the top the piston rod E is free to turn inside a bush that is fixed to the body structure by a large rubber mounting. The bush provides for the steering motions and the rubber mounting provides the small pivoting freedoms required when the suspension flexes. At the bottom end a wishbone is used consisting of the link A behind which is a second link, or radius rod. The latter is attached to the link A at H and lies at an angle of about 45 degrees to the centre line of the car; the connections at both ends are by rubber bushes.

33.9 Sliding Type

The stub axle member A (Fig. 33-13) can slide up and down in a housing fixed to the frame and can also turn in that housing to enable the wheels to be steered. Coil springs are generally used and may be placed inside the housing as indicated and a rebound damper can also be arranged there. This is the only type in which neither the castor angle, camber angle nor the track of the wheels is altered as the wheels rise or fall. To set against this, however, there

676

is the fact that a sliding joint is more difficult to keep free from shake and slackness than is a pivot.

33.10   Independent Suspensions for Driven Wheels

The arrangements shown in Figs. 33-1 to 33-13 are for undriven wheels; they can easily be adapted for use with driven wheels. An early arrangement of the single-arm perpendicular type which still illustrates current practice is shown in Fig. 33-14, the drive being the De Dion type described in Chapter 18.   The illustration shows how easily a rebound damper can be incorporated as an integral part of the design.   The arm A is fixed to a shaft B pivoted in a casing fixed to the frame.   Integral with the shaft B is a toothed segment C that meshes with the rack of a sliding member D which at its right-hand end is formed into a piston working in the cylinder that is part of the fixed casing.   Between the piston and the casing is a coil spring E through which the weight is transmitted to the road wheel. The cylinder is filled with oil which is displaced, through the small holes shown, from one side of the piston to the other when the piston moves.   A control rod F gradually reduces the opening for the passage of the oil as the piston approaches the end of its stroke, thus increasing the

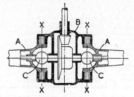

Fig. 33-15 (a)

resistance to the motion.   The passage is completely closed when the piston comes into contact with the auxiliary spring seen at the right.

The " swinging arm " type of suspension which has been much used by Continental designers in rear wheel driven cars and lorries is really an example of the single arm parallel type but adapted to allow for the driving of the road wheels.   Examples are shown in Fig. 33-15 (a) and (b).   In each of these the arms A are tubular and carry the road wheels at their outer ends and the half shafts are carried in bearings in the arms.   In the example at (a) the arms

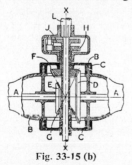

Fig. 33-15 (b)

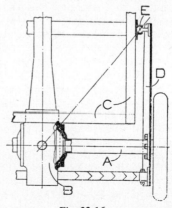

Fig. 33-16

677

Fig. 33-17

are provided with trunnions so that they can pivot about the axes XX in the final drive casing B which is carried by the frame. Universal joints C with their centres placed on the axes XX allow for the swinging of the arms. In (b) the arms A are provided with semi-cylindrical flanges B which fit into similar recesses formed in the final drive casing C. The arms then swing about the central axis XX, this motion being allowed by virtue of the rolling of the bevel wheels D and E about the pinions F and G. The latter are fixed to sleeves which carry the wheels H and J of the spur type differential. The casing of the differential is driven by the shaft L and, in the example, this shaft is extended through the assembly so that another pair of wheels can be driven.

It is somewhat difficult to make the designs described above sufficiently stiff in the fore and aft direction and so radius rods are sometimes provided. These will generally be fixed to the arms at their outer ends and pivoted to the frame at the other ends. The pivots would have to be arranged so that their axes coincided with the axes XX and this is difficult to achieve. In some designs therefore the radius rod was arranged as indicated in Fig. 33-16. This involves making the pivots for the inner ends of the arms spherical and the whole arrangement then really becomes an intermediate single-arm type of suspension.

When a De Dion type of drive is used the intermediate type is very suitable and an example is shown in Fig. 33-17. It is the design used in the Triumph 2000. The single arms are pivoted on rubber bushes carried by a sub-frame which incorporates the final drive

678

casing and which is mounted on the body structure on the four rubber mountings which are clearly visible. The universal joints at the outer ends of the drive shafts are housed inside the ends of the suspension arms and the drive shafts are provided with sliding joints by leaving the inner universal joint forks free to slide on the shafts.

33.11 Steering Linkages for Independent Suspensions

When the front wheels are independently sprung the steering linkage is usually slightly different from the ordinary Ackerman linkage, although the latter has been used, particularly with the sliding type of suspension. A linkage that is suitable for use with the " perpendicular " type of suspension is shown in Fig. 33-18. An Ackerman linkage comprising the two bell-cranks AX and BY pivoted on brackets fixed to the frame and connected by the track rod C is used, but two drag links G and H are provided to connect the ends of the bell-cranks to the steering arms E and F of the stub axles. The joints at E and F and at X and Y must be ball and socket joints or an equivalent and the centres X and Y should be made to coincide, when the road wheels are in the straight ahead position, with the centres about which the stub axles rotate when the springs flex. The wheel motion will not then affect the steering. A linkage commonly used with the " parallel " types of suspension is shown in Fig. 33-19. A and B are the stub axles carried independently by the suspension and OEG is a triangular link pivoted at O to the frame and connected by rods EF and GH to the steering arms of the stub axles. Clearly the links OE, EF and FA constitute an Ackerman linkage for the offside wheel and the links OG, GH and HB form a similar linkage for the nearside wheel. The centres E and G can be placed approximately on the axes about which the stub axles are caused to rotate by the suspension when the wheels rise or fall, and thus again the wheel motion does not affect the steering. The link OEG is operated by the steering wheel, the drop arm of the steering column being arranged to move in a horizontal plane and being connected by a rod to an arm (shown dotted) fixed to the link OEG.

33.12 Roll Axis

When a force acts on a car from the side so as to make the body tilt or roll the motion will be about some line lying in the central

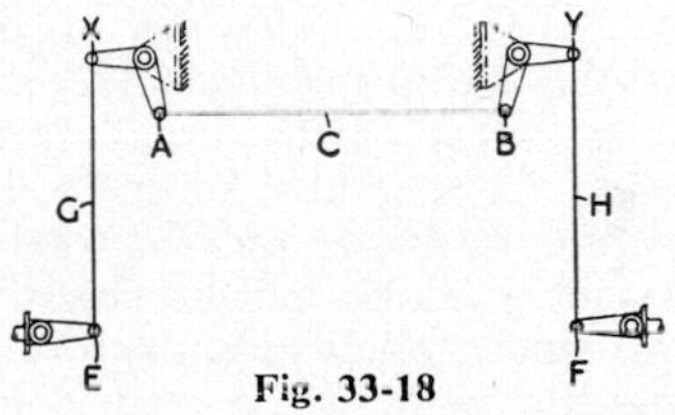

Fig. 33-18

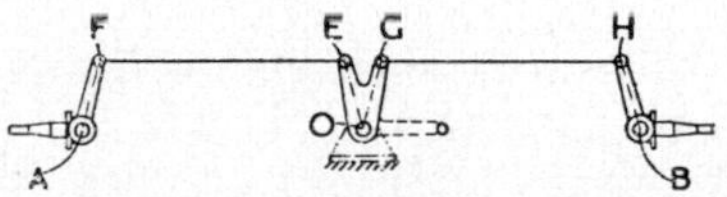

Fig. 33-19

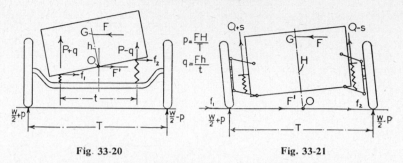

Fig. 33-20   Fig. 33-21

plane of the car; that is, in the vertical plane containing the centre line of the car. This line is called the *roll axis*. Its position depends on the type of suspension fitted at the front and rear. In Fig. 33-20 is shown a front view of a car having an axle and ordinary laminated springs although the latter are merely indicated by zig-zag lines. When no side force acts these springs will be equally compressed and each will exert a force P equal to half the weight carried by the axle. The vertical forces between the wheels and ground will also be equal to P plus half the weight of the axle and wheels. When a side force F acts on the body it sets up forces f_1 and f_2 at the points of connection of the body and springs. The relative magnitude of these forces and the exact position at which they act will always be somewhat uncertain but for present purposes they may be assumed to be equal and to act as shown so that their resultant is a force F^1 equal and opposite to F. These two forces F and F^1 thus constitute a couple of magnitude Fh, h being the perpendicular distance between the forces, which may be assumed to be equal to OG unless the tilt is very large. For equilibrium there must be an equal and opposite couple to balance the couple Fh. This balancing couple is supplied by an increase q in the force exerted by the left-hand spring and by an equal decrease in that exerted by the right-hand one. Because of the increase in the spring force the left-hand spring will be compressed a little more than before and because of the reduction of the force exerted by the right-hand spring its compression will be decreased by the same amount. The body will thus tilt about the point O which is consequently a point on the roll axis. Similarly there will be a corresponding centre O_1 at the rear and the line OO_1 is the roll axis. The change q in the spring force will be equal to Fh/t, t being the *spring base*.

The forces between the wheels and the ground will change by amounts p where $p = FH/T$, T being the wheel track and H the height of the line of action of the force F above the ground. If under the action of the side forces f_1 and f_2, or, more accurately under the reactions of those forces, the springs deflect slightly sideways then the point O would move sideways and the centre of tilt would actually be slightly lower than the point O.

680

Considering now the car with independent suspension as shown in Fig. 33-21, the side force F again sets up a tilting couple and this has to be balanced by an increase in the force exerted by the left-hand spring and a decrease in that exerted by the right-hand spring. If the tilt is not excessive these changes in spring force will be equal so that one force will increase from Q to $Q + s$ and the other will decrease from Q to $Q - s$. The compression of the left-hand spring will be increased by some amount and that of the right-hand spring will be decreased by the same amount. The suspension will thus assume the position shown and the tilt of the body will have been about the point O as centre. Thus O is now a point on the roll axis and the line joining it to the similar centre O_1 at the rear will be the roll axis.

Thus the roll axis for a car having axles at front and back will be some distance above ground level while that having independent suspensions at front and back will have a roll axis lying at ground level. A car having an independent suspension at the front and an axle at the rear will have a roll axis that is inclined, being at ground level at the front and rising to approximately axle level at the rear.

If the roll axis lies at ground level then the overturning couple will be FH and will be greater than the couple producing tilt (Fh) when the roll axis is above ground level and this will tend to make the tilt of the car with independent suspension greater than that of the car with axles.

On the other hand the effective spring base of the car with the independent suspension is T the wheel track and it can be shown that the angle of tilt is approximately proportional to $2q/t^2 = 2Fh/t^2$ for the car with axles and proportional to $2p/T^2 = 2FH/T^2$ for the car with independent suspension and in most cases the latter will be the smaller because the effect of the greater effective spring base will outweigh the effect of the increase in the arm H of the overturning couple.

By making the arms of the suspension such that in the untilted position they are not parallel to each other, the position of the roll centre O can be made to lie below or above the level of the ground as may be desired.

Although the type of independent suspension assumed above was, for convenience, a double-arm parallel type, the same arguments will apply to any independent suspension.

33.13 A Modern Dead-axle System

The De Dion system in which a dead axle was used and the final drive was carried on the frame has been mentioned in Chapter 18 and a modern example of it, which is used on the Rover 2000 car, is shown in Fig. 33-22. The axle member is made in two parts, A_1 and A_2, which are free to slide along and to rotate about the axis XX relatively to each other; the reason for this is given later. This composite axle carries the road wheels whose shafts I rotate

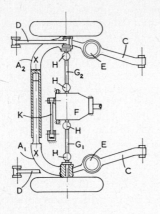

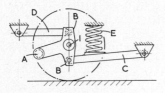

Fig. 33-22

in bearings in the end portions B of the members A and are coupled by the drive shafts G_1 and G_2 to the differential wheel shafts of the final drive assembly F. Universal joints H are provided at the ends of the drive shafts but no provision is made for any sliding freedom. Consideration will show that if both road wheels rise or fall together then the transverse distance between them will change and it is to allow for this that the axle is made in two parts and the sliding freedom along XX is provided. Again, if the road wheels move up or down by different amounts or if one rises while the other falls then the end portions B of the members A will rotate about different angles; the rotational freedom about XX permits this. The members A are thus located sideways by the drive shafts G and sideways thrusts are transmitted to the final drive casing F. The latter has therefore to be effectively fixed sideways to the body structure but in order to minimize the transmission of noise it is carried in rubber mountings and so a radius rod K is provided to take the sideways thrusts. Vertical loads are transmitted from the body to the axle by coil springs E which bear on the links C; these in conjunction with the links D and the ends B of the axle form a Watt's straight line linkage and so the axle will move up and down vertically. The links C and D transmit the driving and braking thrusts to the body but the torque reactions from the final drive and the disc brakes, which are mounted on the differential wheel shafts and are anchored to the final drive casing, are transmitted directly to the body through the rubber mountings of the final drive casing. With the use of a dead axle the changes in camber of the road wheels that occur in many types of independent suspension are eliminated and the use of inboard brakes enables unsprung weight to be reduced. The two part axle construction enables sliding joints in the drive shafts to be eliminated. These sliding joints have been found to cause harshness in the suspension due to the friction set up when sliding occurs whilst heavy torques are being transmitted and with inboard brakes this is often the case.

CHAPTER 34

Six-wheeled Vehicles

Flexible and rigid six-wheelers

IN most countries a limit is set by law to the weight that may be carried on any one axle of a road vehicle; this limit is regulated, presumably, according to the capacity of the roads upon which the vehicles will operate, but other factors than the road also set a limit, for example, the tyres. With unshod steel wheels such as are used on traction engines the permissible load can be increased considerably by increasing the width of the wheel, but with rubber tyred wheels this is not so practicable. The use of twin pneumatic tyres enables the load to be approximately doubled, but this solution of the problem has many drawbacks. The great width of the wheels necessitates the use of a comparatively narrow frame and somewhat hampers the coach builder; stones get wedged between the tyres causing damage; it is difficult to change the inner tyre and the load is not always equally distributed between the tyres. These drawbacks to the twin-tyred wheel have led to the adoption of the alternative method of carrying heavier loads, which is by using more than two axles.

Since the use of three axles is primarily to enable heavier loads to be carried, while keeping the load per axle within definite limits, the arrangement used must be such that the load carried will be properly distributed between the axles, however uneven the road may be. This at once rules out the possibility of simply adding axles having independent springing; since if one of those axles stood on a hump it would carry more than its proper proportion of the total load.

There are two quite different solutions of the problem, and six-wheelers can be divided into two classes accordingly—

(1) " Flexible " or " articulated " vehicles.
(2) " Rigid " vehicles.

Vehicles of the first class consist of a three- or four-wheeled tractor unit having, usually, a short wheelbase, and a two-wheeled trailer, which may be permanently or detachably connected to it. The connection between the two units to provide for road inequalities must consist of a ball and socket joint or its equivalent. The trailer wheels are almost always merely weight carriers and not driving wheels, owing to the difficulty of arranging a satisfactory drive to them. They are usually carried on a simple axle, no provision being made for steering them. The trailer then " cuts-in " when the vehicle is cornering, and manœuvring in reverse requires some skill. Sometimes, however, the trailer wheels are carried by

683

an axle fixed to a turntable and arranged to steer so that the trailer wheels follow in the tracks of the tractor wheels, thus overcoming the " cutting-in " difficulty, which, however, is not a serious disadvantage so that steering trailers are not much used.

This type of six-wheeler cannot operate on very uneven ground, firstly, because it is not practicable to provide for sufficient relative movement between the two units to ensure constant weight distribution; secondly, because such vehicles are somewhat unstable when turning on sloping ground and thirdly, because of insufficient adhesion between the ground and the driving wheels to which nothing is added by the addition of the trailer wheels. This type of vehicle will therefore not be further dealt with.

34.1   The Rigid Six-wheeler

This type of vehicle has been intensively developed during the last twenty years and many different arrangements have been evolved both as regards their suspension and transmission systems. The earliest vehicles consisted essentially of a four-wheeled lorry with the addition of a third axle placed behind and as close as possible to the existing rear axle. The third axle was sometimes merely a weight-carrying dead axle and sometimes a live driving axle. This type of vehicle is still widely used, but other types have been developed.

34.2   Suspensions for Rigid Six-wheelers

Considering first the suspension systems, Fig. 34-1 shows four simple arrangements; in (a) the loads carried by the axles are equalized by connecting the adjacent ends of the springs to a balance beam A pivoted at its centre to the frame. As shown the springs are pivoted at their other ends to the frame and are used to take the torque reactions and driving thrust, but when torque-thrust members are provided for the axles shackles would be fitted. The balance beam cannot be made very long without making the distance between the axle centres rather large, which is undesirable because of steering considerations, and this results

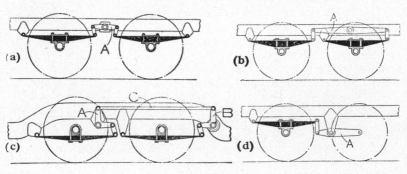

Fig. 34-1

in either excessive angular movement of the lever or undue
limitation of axle movement.
The difficulty is avoided in (b)
where the lever is connected to
the rear ends of the springs,
and the arrangement at (c) overcomes the difficulty as regards
the centre distance of the axles.
In this latter arrangement the
springs are connected by bell-
crank levers A and B and the

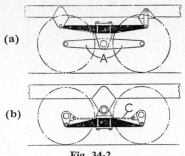

Fig. 34-2

rod C. A variation of (b) is to
connect the lever A to the outer ends of the springs and a variation
of (c) is to connect the adjacent ends of the springs to the bell-
cranks. The centre distance between the axles can be reduced by
using the arrangement (a), but with the rear spring connected to
the front end of the lever and the front spring connected to the
rear of the lever; as the ends of the springs then overlap one has
to be placed above the other, and one is usually placed on the top
of the axle casing, the other being underslung. In (d) a single
spring is used and the rear wheels are carried on the ends of levers A,
no rear axle being used. The rear wheels are then not driven but
are merely weight carriers. For equality of loading the lever arms
must be unequal. In Fig. 34-2 (a) a single spring is again used
and a rigid lever A is pivoted to that spring at its centre and to
the axles at its ends. The single spring has now to carry the
total weight supported by the two axles. The same principle is
used in the Scammell design described later. At (b) is shown a
commonly used arrangement, a single laminated spring being
pivoted at its centre to a bracket fixed to the frame and at its ends

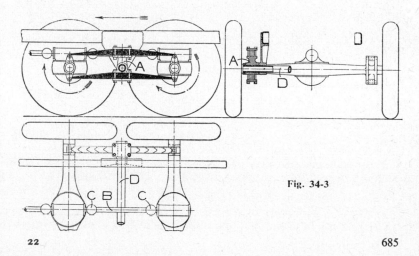

Fig. 34-3

to the axles. When the spring is required to take the driving and braking torque reactions it becomes somewhat difficult to obtain a satisfactory connection between the spring and the axle casings. This is achieved in one design by providing the spring with an extra leaf (as shown dotted), which is separately pivoted to the axle casings. This difficulty is avoided in the arrangement shown in Fig. 34-3 by using two springs secured rigidly to a trunnion block A at their centres and pivoted to the axle casings at their ends. The trunnion block is free to pivot on the end of a cross member of the frame. The design shown in Fig. 34-4 is used by Messrs. Thornycroft. Two springs are again used, but each is separately pivoted at its centre on a pin carried by a bracket fixed to the frame. Lastly, Fig. 34-5 shows the design used by Messrs. Krupps on some of their lorries. Coil springs are used, placed as shown between the upper arms of bell-crank levers which are pivoted to the frame. The other arms of the bell-cranks are connected to arms carrying the road wheels, independent suspensions of the type shown in Fig. 33-3, being used. Rubber bushes are used for the latter connection to accommodate the discrepancy between the paths traced out by the connected points when the wheels rise or fall.

All the above arrangements will equalize the loads carried by the middle and rear wheels when the vehicle to which they are fitted is motionless, but this equality may be destroyed as soon as the wheels are driven or braked, and a driving or braking torque

Fig. 34-4   Fig. 34-5

reaction is set up. To maintain equality during driving or braking the system adopted for dealing with the torque reactions must satisfy certain conditions which will be considered later. However, the resulting inequality when it does occur is seldom of any great importance in vehicles operating on good or moderately good roads, but in vehicles operating on bad ground any serious inequality of loading may render the vehicle useless, and for such vehicles special attention must be given to the arrangements for dealing with the driving and braking torque reactions.

With any of the above systems the rise of the frame when one axle goes over a bump is only half the height of that bump, as shown in Fig. 34-6. The shocks transmitted to the frame and to the road are consequently less than in a four-wheeled vehicle, but two shocks are experienced for each bump instead of only one.

34.3 Transmissions of Six-wheelers

The most important of these are shown in Fig. 34-7. That at (a) is probably the simplest and most widely used, the employment

686

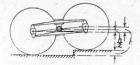

Fig. 34-6

of worm-driven axles enabling the worm shaft of the middle axle to be extended through the back of the axle casing and coupled by an intermediate shaft to the rear axle. The intermediate shaft must be provided with two universal joints (indicated by circles) and a sliding joint S as shown. An overhead worm gives large road clearances and is used for cross-country vehicles, whereas an underhung worm gives a low body position and is used for buses and coaches. The use of bevel driven axles is not so simple, as the diagrams (*b*) and (*c*) will show. In (*b*) a second pinion is mounted at the back of the middle axle in order to drive the intermediate

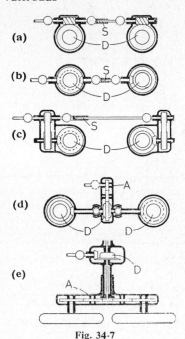

Fig. 34-7

shaft, and it will be seen that the crown wheel of the rear axle has to be mounted on the offside of the pinion in order to make the wheels of the two axles rotate in the same directions. The driving torque for both middle and rear axles is transmitted through the pinion and crown wheel of the middle axle, and the design of those gears is made more difficult. For a given distance between the axles this drive results in the shortest distance between the centres of the universal joints on the intermediate shaft, and thus for a given relative movement of the axles in the greatest angularity of those joints. In (*c*) the drive shaft is mounted above the axles, the drive being carried down to the bevel pinion shafts by chains or gears. By using similar axles turned back to back as shown, the length of the intermediate shaft is increased and the angularity of the universal joints is decreased. This arrangement was evolved and is used by the F.W.D. Company. At (*d*) is shown an American design. The casing A is fixed to the frame and the drive is taken through a train of gears to the bottom shaft, the ends of which are coupled by universal joints to the bevel pinion shafts of the axles. The latter are provided with torque thrust tubes which are anchored to the casing A by ball and socket connections surrounding the universal joints; sliding joints are consequently unnecessary. The length of the torque thrust tubes cannot be made very great without making the centre distance between the axles large, and consequently the

687

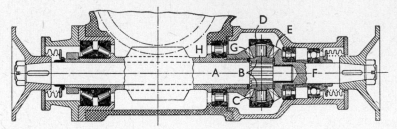

Fig. 34-8: A.E.C. third differential

angles at which the universal joints may have to work may be rather large. Constant velocity type joints are used but even so it is questionable whether this transmission could be used successfully on a cross-country vehicle. For vehicles operating on good roads it should be very satisfactory, and for such vehicles the use of a third differential to divide the torque equally between the two axles is desirable and is very easily provided for as shown. A third differential can be arranged if required when transmission (*a*) is used and an example, the design of the Associated Equipment Company, is shown in Fig. 34-8. The shaft A is coupled by a universal joint to the propeller shaft coming from the gear box and carries the four-armed spider B on splines at its right-hand end. On the arms of this spider the differential pinions C are free to turn and are kept in place by the ring D, the inside of which is made spherical to fit the spherical ends of the pinions. The ring D is itself kept in place by the overlapping portions of the teeth of the differential wheel E. The latter is made integral with its shaft F, which is coupled by a universal joint to the intermediate shaft going to the third axle. The other differential wheel G is splined to the hollow worm shaft H. The transmission evolved for the Scammell six-wheeler is shown in Fig. 34-7 (*e*), a single reduction bevel driven axle being shown, but the double reduction axle shown in Fig. 26-4 can be used equally well. The drive to the road wheels is through a train of gears housed in the lever casing A. It is very difficult to arrange a third differential to divide the drive equally in this transmission, but since it is intended for cross-country work this is not of importance. A similar suspension to the Scammell has been used by the Saurer Company, who used a shaft drive in place of the train of gears used in the Scammell, thus a bevel pinion was mounted on the end of the axle shaft and meshed with two bevel wheels mounted on longitudinal shafts housed in the lever casing; at their outer ends these shafts carried other bevel wheels that meshed with bevel wheels fixed to the road wheel shafts. Fig. 34-9 shows a transmission that has been used in America and on the Continent. Two separate propeller shafts are used, one driving the middle axle and the other the rear axle. The drive coming from the gear box is divided between the two propeller shafts in a " transfer " case A fixed to the frame and a third differential (the principle of whose construction is the same as that of the A.E.C. design shown in Fig. 34-8) is sometimes provided. To enable the rear axle propeller shaft to clear the middle axle casing it is provided with an intermediate bearing B fixed to the frame. An alternative to this is to carry this intermediate bearing on the casing of the middle axle. Offset final drive axles must be used and it is difficult to provide for any great relative movement of the axles. The system is consequently used only for vehicles operating on roads. The use of worm-driven axles facilitates the design somewhat. A German Büssing chassis that used this transmission employed torque thrust tubes to take the driving and braking reactions.

34.4 Laffly Six-wheeler

The main features of this vehicle are shown in Fig. 34-10. The engine and clutch unit is coupled to the gear box unit A which is actually two gear boxes in tandem, one being a four-speed and reverse box and the other a two-speed box, so that eight forward ratios are available. The box also houses a differential and gears to transfer the drive to side shafts, this part being somewhat similar in arrangement to that in Fig. 34-9. The shafts B and C couple the gear box side shafts to layshafts D and E carried in bearings in the front axle, which is a rigid axle connected to the frame by laminated

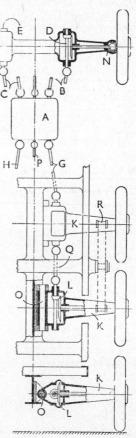

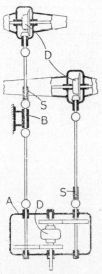

Fig. 34-9

Fig. 34-10: Laffly six-wheeler

springs in the usual way. Ordinary stub axles are used and universal joints N permit the steering of the wheels. The rear wheels are independently sprung, being carried on arms K pivoted at their inner ends on pins O carried by brackets fixed to a central frame member. Bevel gears L transfer the drive from the road wheel shafts to layshafts similar to D and E. These layshafts are coupled by the intermediate shafts Q. The layshafts of the middle axle arms are connected by shafts G and H to the side shafts of the gear box. The shafts G, H and Q have universal joints at each end and a sliding joint at one end, and these joints accommodate the up and down motions of the arms K. Since the layshafts are situated close to the axes of the pivots O the angularity of the universal joints is never very great. Longitudinal laminated springs R pivoted on trunnions on the frame at their centres and coupled to the arms K at their ends transfer the weight to the road wheels.

The Tatra and the Lorraine transmission shown in Fig. 33-17 can obviously be used for six-wheeled vehicles, as was pointed out in the description of that transmission. When the De Dion type of drive is used the transmission can be arranged on the lines of those shown in Fig. 34-7 (*a*) and (*b*), but since the final drive casings will be carried on the frame the joints shown in the intermediate shafts may be eliminated.

34.5   A Scammell Design

The general arrangement of the rear bogie transmission system of the Scammell " Constructor " chassis, which is designed for " off-the-road " use, is shown in Fig. 34-11. The axles A and B are

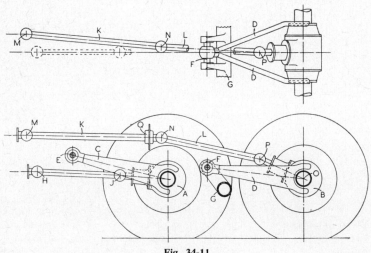

Fig. 34-11

each provided with a torque-thrust member, C and D respectively. These members are connected by ball joints to cross members of the frame and transmit the driving and braking efforts and torque reactions. The drive to the axle A is through a conventional propeller shaft with universal joints, H and J, at the ends. The shaft is provided with axial sliding freedom. The centre E, about

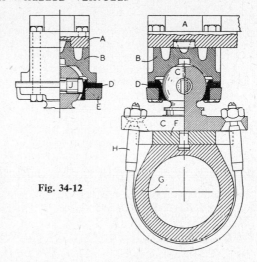

Fig. 34-12

which the axle pivots, is placed relatively to the joints H and J, so that the angles between the propeller shaft and the transfer gear box shaft and between the propeller shaft and the bevel pinion shaft of the axle are always maintained approximately equal in magnitude so that a constant velocity drive is obtained on the lines of those used in front-wheel drives and described in Section 24.4. The axle B is driven by a propeller shaft L through an intermediate propeller shaft K, which is coupled to a shaft of the transfer gear box and which is supported in a flexibly mounted bearing Q at its right-hand end. The centre F is again placed in relation to the joints N and P so that a constant-velocity drive is obtained.

The axles are positioned sideways by Panhard rods. Flat leaf springs are employed, and these are pivoted to the frame at their centres. As the springs play no part in the positioning of the axles, the connections between them and the axles are designed to avoid any constraint of the axles and any undue distortion of the springs. They are shown in Fig. 34-12. The master leaf of the spring has a cup member B bolted to its end, and the spherical part of a pedestal member C fits into this cup, being retained by a collar D, made in two parts, and a cover E. The member C is free to slide on a hardened steel plate F, which is mounted on the axle casing G. The member C is prevented from rotating about a vertical axis by a pin J, whose ends engage slots formed in the collar D. A flexible wire stirrup H prevents separation of the assembly during rebounds of the axle.

34.6 Torque Reaction in Rigid Six-wheelers

Referring to Fig. 34-3, when torque reactions are exerted on the axle casings as indicated by the arrows they will tend to turn the whole unit consisting of the two axles, the springs and the trunnion

691

blocks about the cross member on which the trunnion blocks are free to pivot; this tendency has to be balanced by an increase of load between the rear wheels and the ground and an equal decrease of load between the middle wheels and the ground. Calling the torque reactions t_1 and t_2 and denoting the distance between the axles by l then the magnitude of this alteration in load is given by

$Q = \dfrac{t_1 + t_2}{l}$. In cross-country vehicles fitted with auxiliary gear

boxes giving very low ratios for emergency purposes, it is possible for this alteration Q to become equal to the normal load carried by each axle so that the middle axle would be carrying zero load and would be about to lift off the ground, while the rear axle would be carrying twice the normal load. Under these conditions the rear wheels will probably sink into the ground if the latter is at all soft or sandy and the vehicle will be stalled. The same result will occur with any suspension that deals with the torque reactions in the manner indicated. During braking the reverse of the above action will occur, the middle axle load increasing and the rear axle load decreasing. The arrangement shown in Fig. 34-4 avoids the trouble, the torque reactions being transferred to the frame of the vehicle by means of horizontal forces acting in the springs as shown and which have no effect on the balance of the vertical forces, that is, the loads, acting at the axles. When this arrangement, which was evolved by Messrs. Thornycroft, is used, the total torque reaction $t_1 + t_2$ is balanced by a decrease q in the load carried by the front axle and an equal increase in the load transmitted through the spring trunnions at the rear. This latter increase however will be shared equally by the middle and rear axles, whose loads will remain equal. The

alteration q is given by $q = \dfrac{t_1 + t_2}{L}$ where L is the mean wheelbase

of the whole vehicle (that is, the distance between the spring trunnions and the front axle), and since L is much greater than l the alteration q will be much smaller than Q. The same result is achieved in the War Department design shown in Fig. 34-13. The springs are bolted rigidly to the trunnion blocks D, which are pivoted on the ends of the frame cross member E, but at their outer ends the springs are pivoted to boxes A which are mounted on spherical members C which are free to slide outwards along the axle tubes for a reason that will appear later. Torque rods B, connected at one end to the axle casings and at the other end to the frame, are now used to transmit the torque and brake reactions to the frame. Comparing this arrangement with the Thornycroft it will be seen that the torque rods B are acting as the upper spring in Fig. 34-4 and the two springs in Fig. 34-13 are acting as the lower spring in Fig. 34-4. As the torque reactions are transferred to the frame by horizontal forces, the equilibrium of the vertical forces is unaltered, and this design gives the same results as the Thornycroft. Torque rods, arranged as in the W.D. suspension,

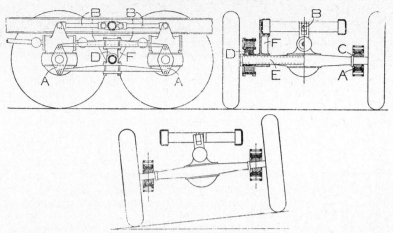

Fig. 34-13: W.D. type suspension

are used by some makers in conjunction with the single spring suspension shown in Fig. 34-2 (*b*). When the suspensions of Fig. 34-1 are used with the springs secured rigidly to the axle casing at the centre and pivoted to the frame at one end so that they take both the torque reactions and thrusts, it can easily be shown that the equality of wheel loading is upset by the torque reactions and also by the couple due to the driving thrust being exerted at axle level and resisted at the level of the spring eyes, the alteration being however that the load on the middle axle increases and that on the rear axle decreases when the vehicle is driven forwards, the opposite action occurring during braking. When each axle is provided with a torque thrust tube then the equality of loading will depend on whether the torque reactions of the two axles are equal or unequal. In the Scammell design, Fig. 34-7 (*e*), equality of loading can only be obtained if the gear ratio between the drive shafts and the road wheels is unity and if those members revolve in the same direction. Actually the gear ratio is a little greater than 2 to 1, so that torque reaction does produce some alteration in wheel loading. Brake torques will also produce an alteration which may be much greater than that due to the driving torque. Experience has shown, however, that these alterations do not affect the performance of the Scammell design, which is outstanding amongst cross-country vehicles.

34.7   Spring Stresses in Rigid Six-wheelers

The suspension systems of six-wheelers must be considered from another point of view than that of weight distribution, namely, the effect of axle or wheel movements on the springs themselves. When the springs are rigidly bolted or are pivoted by pins to the axle and are connected to the frame by pin joints, then clearly when the axles assume angular positions relatively to the frame, as indicated in

693

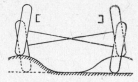

Fig. 34-14

Fig. 34-14, the springs will be twisted. While this twisting is unimportant in vehicles operating on roads where the axle movements will be comparatively small, it is very serious in cross-country vehicles, and if permitted would lead to fracture of the springs. It is avoided in the War Department design by the use of the ball members C (Fig. 34-13), which allow the axles to tilt without producing any corresponding tilt of the boxes A. Twist of the springs is avoided in the suspension shown in Fig. 34-4 (*b*) by using the connection shown in Fig. 34-15, which is self-explanatory. A design, used by the Kirkstall Forge Company, which relieves the springs of longitudinal twisting and of side forces is shown in Fig. 34-16. It comprises a ball and socket joint, the ball of which is capable of sliding along the pin on which it is mounted. Hardened steel pads prevent damage to the joint when unduly large movements occur.

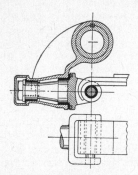

Fig. 34-15

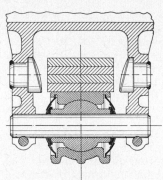

Fig. 34-16

In the Thornycroft design the same result is achieved by using gimbals A (Fig. 34-17), pivoted to the axle casings on trunnions whose axes are fore and aft. The spring ends are pin-jointed to the gimbals. This gives the same freedom as in the War Department design while permitting the torque reactions to be transmitted through the springs to the frame. There is another action which must be avoided however. When the axle tilts, the horizontal distance between the points of connection of the springs becomes smaller, while the horizontal distance between the points of connection of the springs and frame remains unaltered. There is consequently a side bending action which in cross-country vehicles would be serious. It is avoided in the W.D. design by leaving the balls C free to slide outwards along the axle tubes and in the Thornycroft design by leaving the springs free to slide inwards along their central pivots and outwards along the pins connecting them to the gimbals. To avoid bending and twisting of the torque rods them-

694

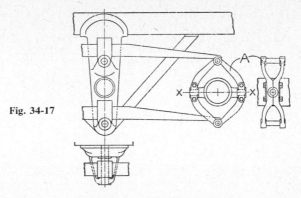

Fig. 34-17

selves they are sometimes connected to the axle and frame by ball and socket joints, but sometimes universal joints are used. In the latter case the rods must be made in two portions free to turn relatively about their longitudinal axis, the joint being made capable of transmitting tension or compression. Some freedom from twisting of the springs is obtained by using swivelling boxes between the spring eyes and the frame brackets or shackles, but while these are satisfactory for vehicles operating on roads it is doubtful whether they can cope with the large movements experienced in cross country work.

34.8 Scammell Articulated Trailer

It has been seen that in the Scammell " Constructor " chassis the springs have been relieved of all stresses, except those due to the weight of the body. In the four-wheeled trailer portion of one of their articulated vehicles, Messrs. Scammell have used the springs to take the braking forces and, in conjunction with torque rods, the brake torque reactions, but the springs are relieved of the sideways forces by transverse radius rods. Undesirable stresses are minimized by employing the connections shown in Fig. 34-18 between the axles and the springs. The end of the spring is provided with a ball A fitting in a socket B which is made in two parts for assembly and which is free to slide sideways, that is parallel to the axle, in the housing C. The latter is bolted to the bracket D of the axle. Lubricating nipples are provided at E. This arrangement enables the springs to take longitudinal and vertical forces, but relieves them of other actions.

The general arrangement of the suspension is shown in Fig. 34-19. The springs B are bolted to seats, which are pivoted on pins C

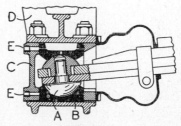

Fig. 34-18

695

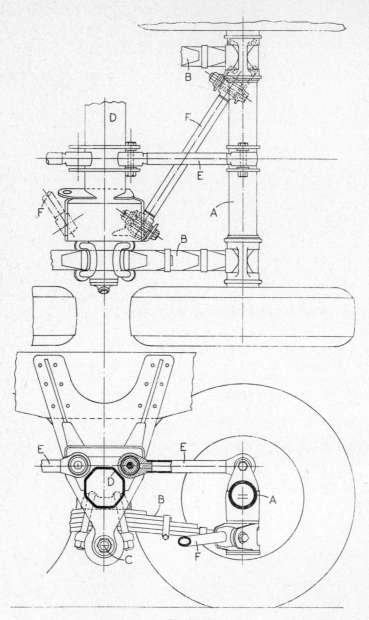

Fig. 34-19

carried by brackets. These brackets are secured to the frame members of the trailer and are braced by the cross member D. The braking forces and torque reactions are transferred to the frame by longitudinal forces in the springs B and torque-rods E, and side forces are taken by the transverse radius rods F, which are pivoted at one end to the axles and at the other end to the spring-pivot brackets. Both the rods E and F are provided with rubber bushes at the pivots, and these accommodate the very small difference in the motion of the axle due to the flexing of the springs and that due to the constraint of the radius rod; they also relieve the rods E of undesirable bending stresses.

Index

#8

THE

FREE LIBRARY

OF

PHILADELPHIA

 PRINTED IN U.S.A.